SEATTLE PUBLIC LIBRARY
FIC KIPLING 010114
Kipling, Rudyard, 000
A Kipling pageant by] Ru 2396984
0000104109913
NO LONGER PROPERTY OF
SEATTLE PUBLIC LIBRARY
D0428552

A KIPLING PAGEANT

BOOKS BY RUDYARD KIPLING

A Book of Words
Actions and Reactions
Brushwood Boy, The
Captains Courageous
Collected Dog Stories
Collected Verse
Complete Stalky & Co., The
Day's Work, The
Debits and Credits
Departmental Ditties and Ballads and Barrack-Room Ballads
Diversity of Creatures, A
Eyes of Asia, The
Five Nations, The
France at War
From Sea to Sea
His Apologies
Humorous Tales of Rudyard Kipling, The
Kipling Pageant, A
If
Independence
Irish Guards in the Great War, The
Jungle Book, The
Jungle Book, The: *Special Illustrated Edition*
Jungle Book, Second
Just So Song Book
Just So Stories
Kim
Kipling Reader
Kipling Birthday Book, The
Land and Sea Tales
Letters of Travel
Life's Handicap: *Being Stories of Mine Own People*
Light That Failed, The
Limits and Renewals
Many Inventions
Naulahka, The (*With Wolcott Balestier*)
Plain Tales from the Hills
Puck of Pook's Hill
Rewards and Fairies
Rudyard Kipling's Inclusive Verse, 1885–1932
Seven Seas, The
Soldiers Stories
Soldiers Three, The Story of the Gadsbys, and In Black and White
Songs for Youth
Songs from Books
Stalky & Co.
Supplication of the Black Aberdeen
They
"Thy Servant A Dog"
Traffics and Discoveries
Two Jungle Books, The
Under the Deodars, The Phantom 'Rickshaw, and Wee Willie Winkie
Years Between, The

A KIPLING PAGEANT

Rudyard Kipling

Doubleday, Doran & Company, Inc.

GARDEN CITY 1935 NEW YORK

PRINTED AT THE *Country Life Press*, GARDEN CITY, N. Y., U. S. A.

FIRST EDITION

FOREWORD TO THE PUBLISHER;

BEING

THE INSTRUCTIONS TO THE NAKHODA, THE CAPTAIN, OF THIS SHIP

1935

In the Name of God, the Compassionate, the Merciful!

IN THOSE DAYS when neither thy Father's beard nor mine needed the *henna* (dyeing) I gave thy Father commission to sell, on my account, my goods in bulk or single to the Western ports of this world. For that trade we built and equipped a little sailing-ship which we both loved. And her venture was felicitous.

Begins now, after very many tides, a voyage for thee, his son, in a ship laden with pieces and patterns and portions and *naqshas* (samples) of my wares, both new and old, as those have issued from beneath my hands during the procession of fifty years. Whereof, through forty and five, thy Father and I ran our Western trade together—ship and cargo—tack for tack.

This new ship here, is fitted according to the reported increase of knowledge among mankind. Namely, she is cumbered, end to end, with bells and trumpets and clocks and wires which, it has been told to me, can call Voices out of the air or the waters to con the ship while her crew sleep. But sleep *thou* lightly, O Nakhoda! It has not yet been told to me that the Sea has ceased to be the Sea.

She has no sail but only engines which jig up and down, and must needs be anointed with oils as though they were dancing-girls. (In the old days, a sailing-ship was as a beloved wife, whereon, with a rope's-end, one wrought miracles.)

Thou knowest all the Ports to which this ship is consigned, as well as that Western Sea whose waves surge like hills and smite like hammers. Thou knowest too, the People of that land to be kindly and well-wishing and, in time of sickness—as *I* know—of a good-will beyond comparison.

But it has reached me that, at this hour, they have somewhat scattered their inheritance. For they believed that it would endure and increase, and when it did not so, they mourned as though earth underfoot were dissolving in dust. This, to my mind, comes about because their country has, till now, driven before following winds, which is always hard steering. But, this time, she has gybed and, the big boom having gone over, many things have fallen (from aloft). It will pass.

They have, since my sojourn among them, afflicted themselves with Voices out of the air which they suffer to call and command them even when they are in the bath. But, through custom and use, this affliction has become unto them a necessity of which, if they be deprived but one hour, they languish; esteeming themselves to be forgotten by mankind. This arises from the vast magnitude of their land; the inhabitants striving to fortify themselves, by noise, against its emptiness. We will add ourselves to those noises and assist to divert (the People).

They have many women; and much talk concerning them, in which women bear loud part. This custom is new since my time. I doubt O Nakhoda, that our ship carries many goods likely to please (such persons). In respect to women-folk, it is well written:—

"Who, having found a Ruby, will tell (where he found it?)
Or who, having bought red glass with (his) blood, will tell
(how he was cheated?)"

It is in my mind—but weigh it well in thine when thou art there—that our best trade will be among the children of those who were faithful to the toys that I devised for them long ago. (And it may be that Allah prepares for us yet a third crop of that sowing!)

Well said the Prince's foster-mother, in the delectable tale of Azil and Azara:—"Lend me thy babe for three years, and hear him call me 'Mother' through thirty."

Therefore, spare no pains. If any ask:—"Where is that clay Tiger, or that painted Beast, or other some small gay image that I handled when I was a child?", make most clear that this my ship is only a ship of samples, and carefully tell them the very places, in the very streets, of the very towns, where stand the very shops where they may buy perpetual abundance of my wares. Engrave this on thy mind!

As to the running-talk of the trade, thou knowest that it is the buyer who buys and *not* the seller. I have seen good trade lost because the seller, almost, as it were, berated, for their slow-mindedness, men who, but for being too much urged to buy, would have bought. Or else he sickened them by too loud praise of the goods. My ship is a *jahaz* (a ship) and not a *jihad* (a holy war). Remember the saying:—"No ship so powerful as a modest eye." Bear all our business, then, softly—softly. Thus:—If any overhauling my goods pronounce such and such of them to be worthless—agree. (He who has gold in his girdle may be robbed, but he can not be wrong.) If he press the matter, tell him how, long ago, I repented me that I had ever fabricated them, and that I went on pilgrimage to Mecca to cleanse the sin. But, if any other pronounce these very same goods to be excellent above the pearls of Oman, agree—agree. If he press the matter, tell him how I myself have always reckoned them the chiefest of my artifices. Thus, out of thy mouth and testimony, both those men will esteem themselves to be perspicacious and—Flattery digs down the wall where the (noise of the) spade warns the watchman.

Allah forbid that thou shouldst lie for none or small advantage; but Truth is as sand-ballast in the hold. Stow it where it cannot choke the bilges.

As to those idlers and sitters along the wharves who leap aboard to feel and to finger, and to fret, and unwrap, and rattle and split open and smell at my goods, that they may tell the world how such a carpet should have been stretched on the loom, or Queen-turquoise set and steadied in the lac, or the gold wire worked into a fringe—agree—agree—agree! Fill them cool pipes under the awnings, and let them run out the cables of their tongues to the clinch. Never was sailor or trader yet who could not instruct his fellow!

And—last—I have left the sole choice of the number and the natures of the samples upon *thy* head. It is long since I had house or hearth in thy land, and markets, even when they are watched, shift like shoals. Nor would I resemble that Crow who said to the Tiger:—"*All* my children are equally beauteous and equally young." Therefore, I have abstained from adding or subtracting in the manifests. Also, it is most certain that if I myself had chosen the samples, many men would have cried out:—"Why did not this Uncle of Owls include in his manifest such and such packets or bales?" Then would they have pursued me with their maledictions and their animadversions and their revisements.

But *thou,* O Nakhoda, art young and wide-shouldered, and on thee will be the strain of that rope and the burden of that loquacity and the multitude of those letters. May it be to thee a refreshment and a delight and a most pleasurable exercise!

This is to end my Hukmnameh—Bill of Instructions—to thee, son of my Friend, thy Father. Strike them all down into the hold of Remembrance and cover them with the tight hatches of Fidelity!

Lest there should be any loose ropes or knots that may slip, I send you in a *murasla* (envelope) apart those very instructions which I delivered to your Father concerning our first venture together in that little sailing-ship which we loved. What is not in the one will be in the other:—

TO THE NAKHODA OR SKIPPER OF THIS VENTURE

A LETTER OR BILL OF INSTRUCTION FROM THE OWNER

1897

In the name of God the Compassionate, the Merciful!

This, O *Nakhoda,* is a new voyage, nothing at all like those which you have already taken to Aden or Muscat, or even to Macassar and the islands where we can count upon the monsoons. Therefore consider the matter carefully. I have given you a new compass, with new rigging masts, sails, and other gear suitable to the *buggalow,* and these cannot be picked up for the asking at Sewree or on Sion Bunder. The cargo is all in new mats, stowed like by like, to be reached more easily; and I have painted her before and behind, and I have put a new plank deck in place of the old bamboo one, and the tiller-ropes are new as well. This is at my risk, and the returns must be prepared with zeal and a single heart. Many men of the seas have told me lies, secretly selling anchors and cables and ascribing the loss to the waves, sharks, and sea-fairies. That was long ago, O *Nakhoda,* and now I do not believe all the stories that come up from the beaches.

The road is West and by South from England, where she will not touch, for the cargo is all for the Western ports, and these, if Allah please, you will find upon the other side of the sea. It is cold water, heavy with fog, and ships go up and down in their hundreds bellowing. Avoid these, for they are of iron and suddenly divide wooden vessels. None the less I have carried many cargoes across, and in lighter craft than the *buggalow.*

The men of those ports—I have lived among them, and Allah, whose name be exalted, has augmented my understanding—come down to trade early in the day, and their hours are longer than we use in the East. Do not, then, sleep in the forenoon or sling a hammock under the stern-awnings; neither unroll the sleeping-mats at sundown.

On Bhao Malung we pray before the voyage; at the Jakaria Musjid we give thanks when the voyage is over, but during the voyage we must trade.

In trading it is to be remembered that there be many who can immediately discern the bad from the good. Do not seek to overwhelm such men with market-talk, or else we two are shamed. Say nothing: let them choose; and throw a sail over certain bales of lesser worth.

Yet there be others who, stamping on the deck and talking loud, infallibly choose the worst. To these it is lawful to sell beads, brass rods, and coarse cloths, since it is written: "The blind pay for him who hath eyes."

And there is a third muster, very cunning in the outside of things and full of words as the foresail of wind. Take these to the lower hold and show them that I do not altogether sell toys or looking-glasses.

Remember, too, that many of the cloths are double-and treble-figured, giving a new pattern in a shift of light. Some are best seen in full sun, others under a lamp, and a few are only good to be used in dark places where they were made. The women should know this.

When, however, the little children come down to the beaches hide away that which is uncomely; let down the gang-plank with the railing on either hand; and spare nothing of the painted clay figures, the talking apes, the dancing bears, the coloured lights, or the sweetmeats to give them pleasure. Thus they will first plague their parents to buy, and later—

for a child's memory is very long—will bring down their own babes when we return. But have a care that they do not wander unchecked through all the holds or sully themselves in the bilges.

But the chief part of our business lies with men who are wearied at the end of the day. It is for the sake of these men that I have laded the *buggalow.* Seek these, O *Nakhoda,* before all others—at the end of the day, as I have said, and in whatever dress (I have put many dresses aboard) may make them look up. Then, little by little, entice them away from their houses and their occupations till they come aboard the *buggalow.* And whether they descend into the run and read the private marks I have put upon the bales, or whether they lie upon the deck in the moonlight pricing the small-arms and *krises;* whether they stare a little and go overside again; or whether they take passage in the *buggalow* for a far voyage, you are the servant of these men, O *Nakhoda,* and the *buggalow* is theirs so long as they please. For though I am only a trader with no ware upon which there is not an open price, I do not forget how, when I was wearied at the end of the day, certain great captains sold me for a little silver that which I could not now find in any market. Pay, then, that debt to these men who are my brothers. (They will not bring their womenfolk aboard, so the talk may be trimmed with a slack sheet.)

The chances of the sea are many and come on all. If ye spy any struggling in broken water or on hen-coops that roll over and over, do not consider the voyage, but go to him, and, with the tackle I have put aboard for such use, work as Allah allows to his comfort. I have myself been many times extricated from calamity by ships whose very names and *Nakhodas* were unknown to me.

Answer questions as to the sun, moon, and stars openly, according to the custom of the sea; for we find our way thereon only by the Lights of God the refuge of terminations which are common to all. It is not needed to show strangers our charts, for these be of man's making, and each must prick his own for himself.

Do not press her overmuch in a following wind, nor think that one good slant will serve without change to land. And I have met long-lasting calms.

I know that all chance-found wreckage is the free gift of Allah to him who finds it, but still I say let not my *buggalow* be first in this work. It is not auspicious to use stray-gathered gear; and who knows but in the very next port may wait the lawful owner and an open shame?

For the rest, her place in port is sideways to the quay, with all hatches clear; and your place, O *Nakhoda,* is upon her after-deck by the gangway, to receive those coming aboard, to make my salaams to friends who remember me when I traded there, to open out the bales, to tempt new men to buy, to give no credit, and to keep a strict account of all.

On the black water it must be as it is ordained, but in my estimation she is well found.

Get ready now, and take her out when the wind serves, remembering this one thing sure in all uncertainty; as it is written:—

Oh true believer, his destiny none can escape: And safe are we against all that is not predestined!

R. K.

CONTENTS

PAGE

From A Book of Words

From Inclusive Verse (1885–1932)

PAGE

A KIPLING PAGEANT

TO THE TRUE ROMANCE
1893

THY face is far from this our war,
Our call and counter-cry,
I shall not find Thee quick and kind,
Nor know Thee till I die.
Enough for me in dreams to see
And touch Thy garments' hem:
Thy feet have trod so near to God
I may not follow them!

Through wantonness if men profess
They weary of Thy parts,
E'en let them die at blasphemy
And perish with their arts;
But we that love, but we that prove
Thine excellence august,
While we adore, discover more
Thee perfect, wise, and just.

Since spoken word Man's Spirit stirred
Beyond his belly-need,
What is is Thine of fair design
In Thought and Craft and Deed.
Each stroke aright of toil and fight,
That was and that shall be,
And hope too high, wherefore we die,
Has birth and worth in Thee.

Who holds by Thee hath Heaven in fee
  To gild his dross thereby,
And knowledge sure that he endure
  A child until he die—
For to make plain that man's disdain
  Is but new Beauty's birth—
For to possess in singleness
  The joy of all the earth.

As Thou didst teach all lovers speech,
  And Life all mystery,
So shalt Thou rule by every school
  Till life and longing die,
Who wast or yet the Lights were set,
  A whisper in the Void,
Who shalt be sung through planets young
  When this is clean destroyed.

Beyond the bounds our staring rounds,
  Across the pressing dark,
The children wise of outer skies
  Look hitherward and mark
A light that shifts, a glare that drifts,
  Rekindling thus and thus—
Not all forlorn, for Thou hast borne
  Strange tales to them of us.

Time hath no tide but must abide
  The servant of Thy will;
Tide hath no time, for to Thy rhyme
  The ranging stars stand still—
Regent of spheres that lock our fears
  Our hopes invisible,
Oh 'twas certes at Thy decrees
  We fashioned Heaven and Hell!

Pure Wisdom hath no certain path
  That lacks thy morning-eyne,

And Captains bold by Thee controlled
Most like to Gods design.
Thou art the Voice to kingly boys
To lift them through the fight,
And Comfortress of Unsuccess,
To give the Dead good-night.

A veil to draw 'twixt God His Law
And Man's infirmity,
A shadow kind to dumb and blind
The shambles where we die;
A rule to trick th' arithmetic,
Too base, of leaguing odds—
The spur of trust, the curb of lust,
Thou handmaid of the Gods!

O Charity, all patiently
Abiding wrack and scaith!
O Faith, that meets ten thousand cheats
Yet drops no jot of faith!
Devil and brute Thou dost transmute
To higher, lordlier show,
Who art in sooth that lovely Truth
The careless angels know!

Thy face is far from this our war,
Our call and counter-cry,
I may not find Thee quick and kind,
Nor know Thee till I die.

Yet may I look with heart unshook
On blow brought home or missed—
Yet may I hear with equal ear
The clarions down the List;
Yet set my lance above mischance
And ride the barriere—
Oh, hit or miss, how little 'tis,
My Lady is not there!

LISPETH
1886

Look, you have cast out Love! What Gods are these
You bid me please?
The Three in One, the One in Three? Not so!
To my own Gods I go.
It may be they shall give me greater ease
Than your cold Christ and tangled Trinities.

—THE CONVERT

SHE was the daughter of Sonoo, a Hill-man of the Himalayas, and Jadéh his wife. One year their maize failed, and two bears spent the night in their only opium poppy-field just above the Sutlej Valley on the Kotgarh side; so, next season, they turned Christian, and brought their baby to the Mission to be baptized. The Kotgarh Chaplain christened her Elizabeth, and "Lispeth" is the Hill or *pahari* pronunciation.

Later, cholera came into the Kotgarh Valley and carried off Sonoo and Jadéh, and Lispeth became half servant, half companion, to the wife of the then Chaplain of Kotgarh. This was after the reign of the Moravian missionaries in that place, but before Kotgarh had quite forgotten her title of "Mistress of the Northern Hills."

Whether Christianity improved Lispeth, or whether the gods of her own people would have done as much for her under any circumstances, I do not know; but she grew very lovely. When a Hill-girl grows lovely, she is worth travelling fifty miles over bad ground to look upon. Lispeth had a Greek face—one of those faces people paint so often, and see so seldom. She was of a pale, ivory colour, and, for her race, extremely tall. Also, she possessed eyes that were wonderful; and, had she not been dressed in the abominable print-cloths affected by Missions, you would, meeting her on the hillside unexpectedly, have thought her the original Diana of the Romans going out to slay.

Lispeth took to Christianity readily, and did not abandon it when she reached womanhood, as do some Hill-girls. Her own people hated her because she had, they said, become a white woman and washed herself daily; and the Chaplain's wife did not know what to do with her. One cannot ask a stately goddess, five foot ten in her shoes, to clean plates and dishes. She played with the Chaplain's children and took classes in the Sunday School, and read all the books in the house, and grew more and more beautiful, like the Princess in fairy tales. The Chaplain's wife said that the girl ought to take service in Simla as a nurse or something "genteel." But Lispeth did not want to take service. She was very happy where she was.

When travellers—there were not many in those years—came in to Kotgarh, Lispeth used to lock herself into her own room for fear they might take her away to Simla, or out into the unknown world.

One day, a few months after she was seventeen years old, Lispeth went out for a walk. She did not walk in the manner of English ladies—a mile and a half out, with a carriage-ride back again. She covered between twenty and thirty miles in her little constitutionals, all about and about, between Kotgarh and Narkunda. This time she came back at full dusk, stepping down the breakneck descent into Kotgarh with something heavy in her arms. The Chaplain's wife was dozing in the drawing-room when Lispeth came in breathing heavily and very exhausted with her burden. Lispeth put it down on the sofa, and said simply, "This is my husband. I found him on the Bagi Road. He has hurt himself. We will nurse him, and when he is well, your husband shall marry him to me."

This was the first mention Lispeth had ever made of her matrimonial views, and the Chaplain's wife shrieked with horror. However, the man on the sofa needed attention first. He was a young Englishman, and his head had been cut to the bone by something jagged. Lispeth said she had found him down the hillside, and had brought him in. He was breathing queerly and was unconscious.

He was put to bed and tended by the Chaplain, who knew something of medicine; and Lispeth waited outside the door in case she could be useful. She explained to the Chaplain that this was the man she meant to marry; and the Chaplain and his wife lectured her severely on the impropriety of her conduct. Lispeth listened quietly, and repeated her first proposition. It takes a great deal of Christianity to wipe out uncivilized Eastern instincts, such as falling in love at first sight. Lispeth, having found the man she worshipped, did not see why she should keep silent as to her choice. She had no intention of being sent away, either. She was going to nurse that Englishman until he was well enough to marry her. This was her programme.

After a fortnight of slight fever and inflammation, the Englishman recovered coherence and thanked the Chaplain and his wife, and Lispeth—especially Lispeth—for their kindness. He was a traveller in the East, he said—they never talked about "globe-trotters" in those days, when the P. & O. fleet was young and small—and had come from Dehra Dun to hunt for plants and butterflies among the Simla hills. No one at Simla, therefore, knew anything about him. He fancied that he must have fallen over the cliff while reaching out for a fern on a rotten tree-trunk, and that his coolies must have stolen his baggage and fled. He thought he would go back to Simla when he was a little stronger. He desired no more mountaineering.

He made small haste to go away, and recovered his strength slowly. Lispeth objected to being advised either by the Chaplain or his wife; therefore the latter spoke to the Englishman, and told him how matters stood in Lispeth's heart. He laughed a good deal, and said it was very pretty and romantic, but, as he was engaged to a girl at Home, he fancied that nothing would happen. Certainly he would behave with discretion. He did that. Still he found it very pleasant to talk to Lispeth, and walk with Lispeth and say nice things to her, and call her pet names, while he was getting strong enough to go away. It meant nothing at all to him, and everything in the world to Lispeth. She was very happy while the fortnight lasted, because she had found a man to love.

Being a savage by birth, she took no trouble to hide her feelings, and the Englishman was amused. When he went away, Lispeth walked with him up the Hill as far as Narkunda, very troubled and very miserable. The Chaplain's wife, being a good Christian and disliking anything in the shape of fuss or scandal,—Lispeth was beyond her management entirely,—had told the Englishman to tell Lispeth that he was coming back to marry her. "She is but a child you know, and, I fear, at heart a heathen," said the Chaplain's wife. So all the twelve miles up the Hill the Englishman, with his arm round Lispeth's waist, was assuring the girl that he would come back and marry her; and Lispeth made him promise over and over again. She wept on the Narkunda Ridge till he had passed out of sight along the Muttiani path.

Then she dried her tears and went in to Kotgarh again, and said to the Chaplain's wife, "He will come back and marry me. He has gone to his own people to tell them so." And the Chaplain's wife soothed Lispeth and said, "He will come back." At the end of two months, Lispeth grew impatient, and was told that the Englishman had gone over the seas to England. She knew where England was, because she had read little geography primers; but, of course, she had no conception of the nature of the sea, being a Hill-girl. There was an old puzzle-map of the World in the house. Lispeth had played with it when she was a child. She unearthed it again, and put it together of evenings, and cried to herself, and tried to imagine where her Englishman was. As she had no ideas of distance or steamboats, her notions were somewhat wild. It would not have made the least difference had she been perfectly correct; for the Englishman had no intention of coming back to marry a Hill-girl. He forgot all about her by the time he was butterfly-hunting in Assam. He wrote a book on the East afterwards. Lispeth's name did not appear there.

At the end of three months, Lispeth made daily pilgrimage

to Narkunda to see if her Englishman was coming along the road. It gave her comfort, and the Chaplain's wife finding her happier thought that she was getting over her "barbarous and most indelicate folly." A little later, the walks ceased to help Lispeth and her temper grew very bad. The Chaplain's wife thought this a profitable time to let her know the real state of affairs—that the Englishman had only promised his love to keep her quiet—that he had never meant anything, and that it was wrong and improper of Lispeth to think of marriage with an Englishman, who was of a superior clay, besides being promised in marriage to a girl of his own people. Lispeth said that all this was clearly impossible because he had said he loved her, and the Chaplain's wife had, with her own lips, asserted that the Englishman was coming back.

"How can what he and you said be untrue?" asked Lispeth.

"We said it as an excuse to keep you quiet, child," said the Chaplain's wife.

"Then you have lied to me," said Lispeth, "you and he?"

The Chaplain's wife bowed her head, and said nothing. Lispeth was silent, too, for a little time; then she went out down the valley, and returned in the dress of a Hill-girl—infamously dirty, but without the nose-stud and ear-rings. She had her hair braided into the long pigtail, helped out with black thread, that Hill-women wear.

"I am going back to my own people," said she. "You have killed Lispeth. There is only left old Jadéh's daughter—the daughter of a *pahari* and the servant of *Tarka Devi*. You are all liars, you English."

By the time that the Chaplain's wife had recovered from the shock of the announcement that Lispeth had 'verted to her mother's gods, the girl had gone; and she never came back.

She took to her own unclean people savagely, as if to make up the arrears of the life she had stepped out of; and, in a little time, she married a woodcutter who beat her after the manner of *paharis,* and her beauty faded soon.

"There is no law whereby you can account for the vagaries of the heathen," said the Chaplain's wife, "and I believe that Lispeth was always at heart an infidel." Seeing she had been taken into the Church of England at the mature age of five weeks, this statement does not do credit to the Chaplain's wife.

Lispeth was a very old woman when she died. She had always a perfect command of English, and when she was sufficiently drunk, could sometimes be induced to tell the story of her first love-affair.

It was hard then to realize that the bleared, wrinkled creature, exactly like a wisp of charred rag, could ever have been "Lispeth of the Kotgarh Mission."

IN THE HOUSE OF SUDDHOO
1886

A stone's throw out on either hand
From that well-ordered road we tread,
And all the world is wild and strange:
Churel *and ghoul and* Djinn *and sprite*
Shall bear us company to-night,
For we have reached the Oldest Land
Wherein the Powers of Darkness range.

—FROM THE DUSK TO THE DAWN

THE house of Suddhoo, near the Taksali Gate, is two-storied, with four carved windows of old brown wood, and a flat roof. You may recognize it by five red hand-prints arranged like the Five of Diamonds on the whitewash between the upper windows. Bhagwan Dass the grocer and a man who says he gets his living by seal-cutting live in the lower story with a troop of wives, servants, friends, and retainers. The two upper rooms used to be occupied by Janoo and Azizun and a little black-and-tan terrier that was stolen from an Englishman's house and given to Janoo by a soldier. To-day, only Janoo lives in the upper rooms. Suddhoo sleeps on the roof generally, except when he sleeps in the street. He used to go to Peshawar in the cold weather to visit his son who sells curiosities near the Edwardes' Gate, and then he slept under a real mud roof. Suddhoo is a great friend of mine, because his cousin had a son who secured, thanks to my recommendation, the post of head-messenger to a big firm in the Station. Suddhoo says that God will make me a Lieutenant-Governor one of these days. I dare say his prophecy will come true. He is very, very old, with white hair and no teeth worth showing, and he has outlived his wits—outlived nearly everything except his fondness for his son at Peshawar. Janoo and Azizun are Kashmiris, Ladies of the City, and theirs was an ancient and more or less honourable profession; but Azizun has since married a medical student from the North-West and has settled down to a most respectable life somewhere near Bareilly. Bhagwan Dass is an extortionate and an adulterator. He is very rich. The man who is supposed to get his living by seal-cutting pretends to be very poor. This lets you know as much as is necessary of the four principal tenants in the house of Suddhoo. Then there is Me of course; but I am only the chorus that comes in at the end to explain things. So I do not count.

Suddhoo was not clever. The man who pretended to cut seals was the cleverest of them all—Bhagwan Dass only knew how to lie—except Janoo. She was also beautiful, but that was her own affair.

Suddhoo's son at Peshawar was attacked by pleurisy, and old Suddhoo was troubled. The seal-cutter man heard of Suddhoo's anxiety and made capital out of it. He was abreast of the times. He got a friend in Peshawar to telegraph daily accounts of the son's health. And here the story begins.

Suddhoo's cousin's son told me, one evening, that Suddhoo wanted to see me; that he was too old and feeble to come personally, and that I should be conferring an everlasting honour on the House of Suddhoo if I went to him. I went; but I think, seeing how well off Suddhoo was then, that he might have sent something better than an *ekka,* which jolted fearfully, to haul out a future Lieutenant-Governor to the City on a muggy April evening. The *ekka* did not run quickly. It was full dark when we pulled up opposite the door of Ranjit Singh's Tomb near the main gate of the Fort. Here was Suddhoo, and he said that, by reason of my condescension, it was absolutely certain that I should become a Lieutenant-Governor while my hair was yet black. Then we talked about the weather and the state of my health, and the wheat crops, for fifteen minutes, in the Huzuri Bagh under the stars.

Suddhoo came to the point at last. He said that Janoo had told him that there was an order of the *Sirkar* against magic, because it was feared that magic might one day kill the Empress of India. I didn't know anything about the state of the law; but I fancied that something interesting was going to happen. I said that so far from magic being discouraged by the Government it was highly commended. The greatest officials of the State practised it themselves. (If the Financial Statement isn't magic, I don't know what is.) Then, to encourage him further, I said that, if there was any *jadoo* afoot, I had not the least objection to giving it my countenance and sanction, and to seeing that it was clean *jadoo*—white magic, as distinguished from the unclean *jadoo* which kills folk. It took a long time before Suddhoo admitted that this was just what he had asked me to come for. Then he told me, in jerks and quavers, that the man who said he cut seals was a sorcerer of the cleanest kind; that every day he gave Suddhoo news of the sick son in Peshawar more quickly than the lightning could fly, and that this news was always corroborated by the letters. Further, that he had told Suddhoo how a great danger was threatening his son, which could be removed by clean *jadoo;* and, of course, heavy payment. I saw exactly how the land lay, and told Suddhoo that I also understood a little *jadoo* in the Western line, and would go to his house to see that everything was done decently and in order. We set off together; and on the way Suddhoo told me that he had already paid the seal-cutter between one hundred and two hundred rupees, and the *jadoo* of that night would cost two hundred more. This was cheap, he said, considering the greatness of his son's danger; but I do not think he meant it.

The lights were all cloaked in the front of the house when we came. I could hear awful noises from behind the seal-cutter's shop-front, as though some one were groaning his soul out. Suddhoo shook all over, and while we groped our way upstairs told me that the *jadoo* had begun. Janoo and Azizun met us at the stair-head, and told us that the *jadoo*-work would take place in their rooms, because there was more space there. Janoo is a lady of a freethinking turn of mind. She whispered that the *jadoo* was an invention to get money out of Suddhoo, and that the seal-cutter would go to a hot place when he died. Suddhoo was nearly crying with fear and old age. He walked up and down the room in the half-light, repeating his son's name over and over again, and asking Azizun if the seal-cutter should not make a reduction in the case of his own landlord. Janoo pulled me over to the shadow in the recess of the carved bow-windows. The boards were up and the rooms were only lit by one tiny oil-lamp. There was no chance of my being seen if I stayed still.

Presently, the groans below ceased, and we heard steps on the staircase. That was the seal-cutter. He stopped outside the door as the terrier barked and Azizun fumbled at the chain, and he told Suddhoo to blow out the lamp. This left the place in jet darkness, except for the red glow from the two *huqas* that belonged to Janoo and Azizun. The seal-cutter came in, and I heard Suddhoo throw himself down on the floor and groan. Azizun caught her breath, and Janoo backed on to one of the beds with a shudder. There was a clink of something metallic, and then shot up a pale blue-green flame near the ground. The light was just enough to show Azizun, pressed against one corner of the room with the terrier between her knees; Janoo with her hands clasped, leaning forward as she sat on the bed; Suddhoo, face down, quivering, and the seal-cutter.

I hope I may never see another man like that seal-cutter. He was stripped to the waist, with a wreath of white jasmine as thick as my wrist round his forehead, a salmon-coloured loin-cloth round his middle, and a steel bangle on each ankle. This was not awe-inspiring. It was the face of the man that turned me cold. It was blue-gray, in the first place. In the second, the eyes were rolled back till you could only see the whites of them; and, in the third, the face was the face of a demon—a ghoul—anything you please except of the sleek, oily old ruffian who sat in the daytime over his turning-lathe downstairs. He was lying on his stomach with his arms turned and crossed behind him, as if he had been thrown down pinioned. His head and neck were the only parts of him off the floor. They were nearly at right angles to the body, like the head of a cobra at spring. It was ghastly. In the centre of the room, on the bare earth floor, stood a big, deep, brass basin, with a pale blue-green light floating in the centre like a night-light. Round that basin the man on the floor wriggled himself three times. How he did it I do not know. I could see the muscles ripple along his spine and fall smooth again; but I could not see any other motion. The head seemed the only thing alive about him, except that slow curl and uncurl of the labouring back-muscles. Janoo from the bed was breathing seventy to the minute; Azizun held her hands before her eyes; and old Suddhoo, fingering at the dirt that had got into his white beard, was crying to himself. The horror of it was that the creeping, crawly thing made no sound—only crawled! And, remember, this lasted for ten minutes, while the terrier whined, and Azizun shuddered, and Janoo gasped, and Suddhoo cried.

I felt the hair lift at the back of my head, and my heart thump like a thermantidote paddle. Luckily, the seal-cutter betrayed himself by his most impressive trick and made me calm again. After he had finished that unspeakable triple crawl, he stretched his head away from the floor as high as he could, and sent out a jet of fire from his nostrils. Now I knew how fire-spouting is done—I can do it myself—so I felt at ease. The business was a fraud. If he had only kept to that crawl without trying to raise the effect, goodness knows what I might not have thought. Both the girls shrieked at the jet of fire and the head dropped, chin-down on the floor, with a thud; the whole body lying then like a corpse with its arms trussed. There was a pause of five full minutes after this, and the blue-green flame died down. Janoo stooped to settle one of her anklets, while Azizun turned her face to the wall and took the terrier in her arms. Suddhoo put out an arm mechanically to Janoo's *huqa,* and she slid it across the floor with her foot. Directly above the body and on the wall, were a couple of flaming portraits, in stamped-paper frames, of the Queen and the Prince of Wales. They looked down on the performance, and to my thinking, seemed to heighten the grotesqueness of it all.

Just when the silence was getting unendurable, the body turned over and rolled away from the basin to the side of the room, where it lay stomach-up. There was a faint "plop" from the basin—exactly like the noise a fish makes when it takes a fly—and the green light in the centre revived.

I looked at the basin, and saw, bobbing in the water, the dried, shrivelled, black head of a native baby—open eyes, open mouth, and shaved scalp. It was worse, being so very sudden, than the crawling exhibition. We had no time to say anything before it began to speak.

Read Poe's account of the voice that came from the mesmerized dying man, and you will realize less than one-half of the horror of that head's voice.

There was an interval of a second or two between each word, and a sort of "ring, ring, ring," in the note of the voice, like the timbre of a bell. It pealed slowly, as if talking to itself, for several minutes before I got rid of my cold sweat. Then the blessed solution struck me. I looked at the body lying near the doorway, and saw, just where the hollow of the throat joins on the shoulders, a muscle that had nothing to do with any man's regular breathing twitching away steadily. The whole thing was a careful reproduction of the Egyptian teraphin that one reads about sometimes; and the voice was as clever and as appalling a piece of ventriloquism as one could wish to hear. All this time the head was "lip-lip-lapping" against the side of the basin, and speaking. It told Suddhoo, on his face again whining, of his son's illness and of the state of the illness up to the evening of that very night. I always shall respect the seal-cutter for keeping so faithfully to the time of the Peshawar telegrams. It went on to say that skilled doctors were night and day watching over the man's life; and that he would eventually recover if the fee to the potent sorcerer, whose servant was the head in the basin, were doubled.

Here the mistake from the artistic point of view came in. To ask for twice your stipulated fee in a voice that Lazarus might have used when he rose from the dead, is absurd. Janoo, who is really a woman of masculine intellect, saw this as quickly as I did. I heard her say *"Asli nahin! Fareib!"* scornfully under her breath; and just as she said so, the light in the basin died out, the head stopped talking, and we heard the room door creak on its hinges. Then Janoo struck a match, lit the lamp, and we saw that head, basin, and seal-cutter were gone. Suddhoo was wringing his hands and explaining to any one who cared to listen, that, if his chance of eternal salvation depended on it, he could not raise another two hundred rupees. Azizun was nearly in hysterics in the corner, while Janoo sat down composedly on one of the beds to discuss the probabilities of the whole thing being a *bunao,* or "make-up."

I explained as much as I knew of the seal-cutter's way of *jadoo;* but her argument was much more simple—"The magic that is always demanding gifts is no true magic," said she. "My mother told me that the only potent love-spells are those which are told you for love. This seal-cutter man is a liar and a devil. I dare not tell, do anything, or get anything done, because I am in debt to Bhagwan Dass the *bunnia* for two gold rings and a heavy anklet. I must get my food from his shop. The seal-cutter is the friend of Bhagwan Dass, and he would poison my food. A fool's *jadoo* has been going on for ten days, and has cost Suddhoo many rupees each night. The seal-cutter used black hens and lemons and *mantras* before. He never showed us anything like this till to-night. Azizun is a fool, and will be a *purdah-nashin* soon. Suddhoo has lost his strength and his wits. See now! I had hoped to get from Suddhoo many rupees while he lived, and many more after his death; and behold, he is spending everything on that offspring of a devil and a she-ass, the seal-cutter!"

Here I said, "But what induced Suddhoo to drag me into

the business? Of course I can speak to the seal-cutter, and he shall refund. The whole thing is child's talk—shame—and senseless."

"Suddhoo *is* an old child," said Janoo. "He has lived on the roofs these seventy years and is as senseless as a milch-goat. He brought you here to assure himself that he was not breaking any law of the *Sirkar,* whose salt he ate many years ago. He worships the dust off the feet of the seal-cutter, and that cow-devourer has forbidden him to go and see his son. What does Suddhoo know of your laws or the lightning-post? I have to watch his money going day by day to that lying beast below."

Janoo stamped her foot on the floor and nearly cried with vexation; while Suddhoo was whimpering under a blanket in the corner, and Azizun was trying to guide the pipe-stem to his foolish old mouth.

• • • • • • •

Now, the case stands thus. Unthinkingly, I have laid myself open to the charge of aiding and abetting the seal-cutter in obtaining money under false pretences, which is forbidden by Section 420 of the Indian Penal Code. I am helpless in the matter for these reasons. I cannot inform the Police. What witnesses would support my statements? Janoo refuses flatly, and Azizun is a veiled woman somewhere near Bareilly—lost in this big India of ours. I dare not again take the law into my own hands, and speak to the seal-cutter; for certain am I that, not only would Suddhoo disbelieve me, but this step would end in the poisoning of Janoo, who is bound hand and foot by her debt to the *bunnia.* Suddhoo is an old dotard; and whenever we meet mumbles my idiotic joke that the *Sirkar* rather patronizes the Black Art than otherwise. His son is well now; but Suddhoo is completely under the influence of the seal-cutter, by whose advice he regulates the affairs of his life. Janoo watches daily the money that she hoped to wheedle out of Suddhoo taken by the seal-cutter, and becomes daily more furious and sullen.

She will never tell, because she dare not, but, unless something happens to prevent her, I am afraid that the seal-cutter will die of cholera—the white arsenic kind—about the middle of May. And thus I shall be privy to a murder in the House of Suddhoo.

THE THREE MUSKETEERS
1887

An' when the war began, we chased the bold Afghan,
An' we made the bloomin' Ghazi for to flee, boys O!
An' we marched into Kabul, an' we tuk the Balar 'Issar
An' we taught 'em to respec' the British Soldier.

—BARRACK ROOM BALLAD

MULVANEY, Ortheris, and Learoyd are Privates in B Company of a Line Regiment, and personal friends of mine. Collectively I think, but am not certain, they are the worst men in the regiment so far as genial blackguardism goes.

They told me this story, in the Umballa Refreshment Room while we were waiting for an up-train. I supplied the beer. The tale was cheap at a gallon and a half.

All men know Lord Benira Trig. He is a Duke, or an Earl, or something unofficial; also a Peer; also a Globe-trotter. On all three counts, as Ortheris says, "'e didn't deserve no consideration." He was out in India for three months collecting materials for a book on "Our Eastern Impedimenta," and quartering himself upon everybody, like a Cossack in evening-dress.

His particular vice—because he was a Radical, men said—was having garrisons turned out for his inspection. He would then dine with the Officer Commanding, and insult him, across the Mess table, about the appearance of the troops. That was Benira's way.

He turned out troops once too often. He came to Helanthami Cantonment on a Tuesday. He wished to go shopping in the bazars on Wednesday, and he "desired" the troops to be turned out on a Thursday. *On—a—Thursday.* The Officer Commanding could not well refuse; for Benira was a Lord. There was an indignation-meeting of subalterns in the Mess Room, to call the Colonel pet names.

"But the rale dimonstrashin," said Mulvaney, "was in B Comp'ny barrack; we three headin' it."

Mulvaney climbed on to the refreshment-bar, settled himself comfortably by the beer, and went on, "Whin the row was at ut's foinest an' B Comp'ny was fur goin' out to murther this man Thrigg on the p'rade-groun', Learoyd here takes up his helmut an' sez,—fwhat was ut ye said?"

"Ah said," said Learoyd, "gie us t' brass. Tak' oop a subscripshun, lads, for to put off t' p'rade, an' if t' p'rade's not put off, ah'll gie t' brass back agean. Thot's wot ah said. All B Coomp'ny knawed me. Ah took oop a big subscripshun—fower rupees eight annas 'twas—an' ah went oot to turn t' job over. Mulvaney an' Orth'ris coom with me."

"We three raises the Divil in couples gin'rally," explained Mulvaney.

Here Ortheris interrupted. "'Ave you read the papers?" said he.

"Sometimes," I said.

"We 'ad read the papers, an' we put hup a faked decoity, a —a sedukshun."

"*Ab*dukshin, ye cockney," said Mulvaney.

"*Ab*dukshun or *se*dukshun—no great odds. Any'ow, we arranged to taik an' put Mister Benhira out o' the way till Thursday was hover, or 'e too busy to rux 'isself about p'raids. *Hi* was the man wot said, 'We'll make a few rupees off o' the business.' "

"We hild a Council av War," continued Mulvaney, "walkin' roun' by the Artill'ry Lines. I was Prisidint, Learoyd was Minister av Finance, an' little Orth'ris here was——"

"A bloomin' Bismarck! *Hi* made the 'ole show pay."

"This interferin' bit av a Benira man," said Mulvaney,

"did the thrick for us himself; for, on me sowl, we hadn't a notion av what was to come afther the next minut. He was shoppin' in the bazar on fut. 'Twas dhrawin' dusk thin, an' we stud watchin' the little man hoppin' in an' out av the shops, thryin' to injuce the naygurs to *mallum* his *bat*. Prisintly, he sthrols up, his arrums full av thruck, an' he sez in a consiquinshal way, shticking out his little belly, 'Me good men,' sez he, 'have ye seen the Kernel's b'roosh?'—'B'roosh?' sez Learoyd. 'There's no b'roosh here—nobbut a *hekka.'*—'Fwhat's that?' sez Thrigg. Learoyd shows him wan down the sthreet, an' he sez, 'How thruly Orientil! I will ride on a *hekka.'* I saw thin that our Rigimintal Saint was for givin' Thrigg over to us neck an' brisket. I purshued a *hekka,* an' I sez to the dhriver-divil, I sez, 'Ye black limb, there's a *Sahib* comin' for this *hekka*. He wants to go *jildi* to the Padsahi Jhil'—'twas about tu moiles away—'to shoot snipe—*chirria*. You dhrive *Jehannum ke marfik, mallum*—like Hell? 'Tis no manner av use *bukkin'* to the *Sahib,* bekaze he doesn't *samjao* your talk. Av he *bolos* anything, just you *choop* and *chel*. *Dekker?* Go *arsty* for the first *arder*-mile from cantonmints. Thin *chel, Shaitan ke marfik,* an the *chooper* you *choops* an' the *jildier* you *cheels* the better *kooshy* will that *Sahib* be; an' here's a rupee for ye?'

"The *hekka*-man knew there was somethin' out av the common in the air. He grinned an' sez, *'Bote achee!* I goin' damn fast.' I prayed that the Kernel's b'roosh wudn't arrive till me darlin' Benira by the grace av God was undher weigh. The little man puts his thruck into the *hekka* an' scuttles in like a fat guinea-pig; niver offerin' us the price av a dhrink for our services in helpin' him home. 'He's off to the Padsahi *jhil,'* sez I to the others."

Ortheris took up the tale—

"Jist then, little Buldoo kim up, 'oo was the son of one of the Artillery grooms—'e would 'av made a 'evinly newspaper-boy in London, bein' sharp an' fly to all manner o' games. 'E 'ad bin watchin' us puttin' Mister Benhira into 'is temporary baroush, an' 'e sez, 'What *'ave* you been a doin' of, *Sahibs?'* sez 'e. Learoyd 'e caught 'im by the ear an' 'e sez—"

"Ah says," went on Learoyd, " 'Young mon, that mon's gooin' to have t' goons out o' Thursday—to-morrow—an' thot's more work for you, young mon. Now, sitha, tak' a *tat* an' a *lookri,* an' ride tha domdest to t' Padsahi Jhil. Cotch thot there *hekka,* and tell t' driver iv your lingo thot you've coom to tak' his place. T' *Sahib* doesn't speak t' *bat,* an' he's a little mon. Drive t' *hekka* into t' Padsahi Jhil into t' watter. Leave t' *Sahib* theer an' roon hoam; an' here's a rupee for tha.' "

Then Mulvaney and Ortheris spoke together in alternate fragments: Mulvaney leading [you must pick out the two speakers as best you can]:—"He was a knowin' little divil was Bhuldoo,—'e sez *bote achee* an' cuts—wid a wink in his oi—but *Hi* sez there's money to be made—an' I wanted to see the ind av the campaign—so *Hi* says we'll double hout to the Padsahi Jhil—an' save the little man from bein' dacoited by the murtherin' Bhuldoo—an' turn hup like reskooers in a Vic'oria Melodrama—so we doubled for the *jhil,* an' prisintly there was the divil av a hurroosh behind us an' three bhoys on grasscuts' ponies come by, poundin' along for the dear life —s'elp me Bob, hif Buldoo 'adn't raised a rig'lar *harmy* of decoits—to do the job in shtile. An' we ran, an' they ran, shplittin' with laughin', till we gets near the *jhil*—and 'ears sounds of distress floatin' molloncolly on the hevenin' hair." [Ortheris was growing poetical under the influence of the beer. The duet recommenced: Mulvaney leading again.]

"Thin we heard Bhuldoo, the dacoit, shoutin' to the *hekka* man, an' wan of the young divils brought his stick down on the top av the *hekka*-cover, an' Benira Thrigg inside howled 'Murther an' Death.' Buldoo takes the reins and dhrives like mad for the *jhil,* havin' dishpersed the *hekka*-dhriver—'oo cum up to us an' 'e sez, sez 'e, 'That *Sahib's* nigh mad with funk! Wot devil's work 'ave you led me into?'—'Hall right,' sez we, 'you catch that there pony an' come along. This *Sahib's* been decoited, an' we're going to resky 'im!' Says the driver, 'Decoits! Wot decoits? That's Buldoo the *budmash*'—'Bhuldoo be shot!' sez we. ' 'Tis a woild dissolute Pathan frum the hills. There's about eight av thim coercin' the *Sahib.* You remimber that an' you'll get another rupee!' Thin we heard the *whop-whop-whop* av the *hekka* turnin' over, an' a splash av water an' the voice av Benira Thrigg callin' upon God to forgive his sins—an' Buldoo an' 'is friends squotterin' in the water like boys in the Serpentine."

Here the Three Musketeers retired simultaneously into the beer.

"Well? What came next?" said I.

"Fwhat nex'?" answered Mulvaney, wiping his mouth. "Wud ye let three bould sodger-bhoys lave the ornamint av the House av Lords to be dhrowned an' dacoited in a *jhil?* We formed line av quarther-column an' we discinded upon the inimy. For the better part av ten minutes you could not hear yerself spake. The *tattoo* was screamin' in chune wid Benira Thrigg an' Bhuldoo's army, an' the shticks was whistlin' roun' the *hekka,* an' Orth'ris was beatin' the *hekka*-cover wid his fistes, an' Learoyd yellin', 'Look out for their knives!' an' me cuttin' into the dark, right an' lef', dishpersin' arrmy corps av Pathans. Holy Mother av Moses! 'twas more disp'rit than Ahmid Kheyl wid Maiwund thrown in. Afther a while Bhuldoo an' his bhoys flees. Have ye iver seen a rale live Lord thryin' to hide his nobility undher a fut an' a half av brown swamp-wather? 'Tis the livin' image av a water-carrier's goatskin wid the shivers. It tuk toime to pershuade me frind Benira he was not disimbowilled: an' more toime to get out the *hekka.* The dhriver come up afther the battle, swearin' he tuk a hand in repulsin' the inimy. Benira was sick wid the fear. We escorted him back, very slow, to cantonmints, for that an' the chill to soak into him. It suk! Glory be to the Rigimintil Saint, but it suk to the marrow av Lord Benira Thrigg!"

Here Ortheris, slowly, with immense pride—" 'E sez, 'You har my noble preservers,' sez 'e. 'You har a *h*onour to the British Harmy,' sez 'e. With that 'e describes the hawful band of dacoits wot set on 'im. There was about forty of 'em an' 'e was hoverpowered by numbers, so 'e was; but 'e never lorst 'is presence of mind, so 'e didn't. 'E guv the *hekka*-driver five rupees for 'is noble assistance, an' 'e said 'e would see to us after 'e 'ad spoken to the Kernul. For we was a *h*onour to the Regiment, we was."

"An' we three," said Mulvaney, with a seraphic smile, "have dhrawn the par-ti-cu-lar attinshin av Bobs Bahadur more than wanst. But he's a rale good little man is Bobs. Go on, Orth'ris, my son."

"Then we leaves 'im at the Kernul's 'ouse, werry sick, an' we cuts hover to B Comp'ny barrick an' we sez we 'ave saved Benira from a bloody doom, an' the chances was agin there bein' p'raid on Thursday. About ten minutes later come three envelicks, one for each of us. S'elp me Bob, if the old bloke 'adn't guv us a fiver apiece—sixty-four rupees in the bazar! On Thursday 'e was in 'orspital recoverin' from 'is sanguinary encounter with a gang of Pathans, an' B Comp'ny was drinkin' 'emselves into Clink by squads. So there never was no Thursday p'raid. But the Kernul, when 'e 'eard of our gallant conduct, 'e sez, 'Hi know there's been some devilry somewheres,' sez 'e, 'but I can't bring it 'ome to you three.' "

"An' my privit imprisshin is," said Mulvaney, getting off the bar and turning his glass upside down, "that, av they had known they wudn't have brought ut home. 'Tis flyin' in the face, firstly av Nature, secon' av the Rig'lations, an' third the will av Terence Mulvaney, to hold p'rades av Thursdays."

"Good, ma son!" said Learoyd; "but, young mon, what's t' notebook for?"

"Let be," said Mulvaney; "this time next month we're in the *Sherapis*. 'Tis immortial fame the gentleman's goin' to give us. But kape it dhark till we're out av the range av me little frind Bobs Bahadur."

And I have obeyed Mulvaney's order.

THE MADNESS OF PRIVATE ORTHERIS
1888

Oh! Where would I be when my froat was dry?
Oh! Where would I be when the bullets fly?
Oh! Where would I be when I come to die?
Why,
Somewheres anigh my chum.
If 'e's liquor 'e'll give me some,
If I'm dyin' 'e'll 'old my 'ead,
An' 'e'll write 'em 'Ome when I'm dead.—
Gawd send us a trusty chum!

—BARRACK-ROOM BALLAD

MY FRIENDS Mulvaney and Ortheris had gone on a shooting-expedition for one day. Learoyd was still in hospital, recovering from fever picked up in Burma. They sent me an invitation to join them, and were genuinely pained when I brought beer—almost enough beer to satisfy two Privates of the Line . . . and Me.

" 'Twasn't for that we bid you welkim, Sorr," said Mulvaney, sulkily. " 'Twas for the pleasure av your comp'ny."

Ortheris came to the rescue with—"Well, 'e won't be none the worse for bringin' liquor with 'im. We ain't a file o' Dooks. We're bloomin' Tommies, ye cantankris Hirishman; an' 'eres your very good 'ealth!"

We shot all the forenoon, and killed two pariah-dogs, four green parrots, sitting, one kite by the burning-ghaut, one snake flying, one mud-turtle, and eight crows. Game was plentiful. Then we sat down to tiffin—"Bull-mate an' bran-bread," Mulvaney called it—by the side of the river, and took pot shots at the crocodiles in the intervals of cutting up the food with our only pocket-knife. Then we drank up all the beer, and threw the bottles into the water and fired at them. After that, we eased belts and stretched ourselves on the warm sand and smoked. We were too lazy to continue shooting.

Ortheris heaved a big sigh, as he lay on his stomach with his head between his fists. Then he swore quietly into the blue sky.

"Fwhat's that for?" said Mulvaney. "Have ye not drunk enough?"

"Tott'nim Court Road, an' a gal I fancied there. Wot's the good of sodgerin'?"

"Orth'ris, me son," said Mulvaney, hastily, "'tis more than likely you've got throuble in your inside wid the beer. I feel that way mesilf whin my liver gets rusty."

Ortheris went on slowly, not heeding the interruption—

"I'm a Tommy—a bloomin', eight-anna, dog-stealin' Tommy, with a number instead of a decent name. Wot's the good o' me? If I 'ad a stayed at 'Ome, I might a married that gal and a kep' a little shorp in the 'Ammersmith 'Igh.—'S. Orth'ris, Prac-ti-cal Taxi-der-mist.' With a stuff' fox, like they 'as in the Haylesbury Dairies, in the winder, an' a little case of blue and yaller glass-heyes, an' a little wife to call 'shorp!' 'shorp!' when the door-bell rung. As it *his,* I'm on'y a Tommy—a Bloomin', Gawd-forsaken, Beer-swillin' Tommy. 'Rest on your harms—*'versed.* Stan' at—*hease; 'Shun.* 'Verse—*harms.* Right an' lef'—*tarrn.* Slow—*march.* 'Alt—*front.* Rest on your harms—*'versed.* With blank-cartridge—*load.*' An' that's the end o' me." He was quoting fragments from Funeral Parties' Orders.

"Stop ut!" shouted Mulvaney. "Whin you've fired into nothin' as often as me, over a better man than yoursilf, you will not make a mock av thim orders. 'Tis worse than whistlin' the *Dead March* in barricks. An' you full as a tick, an' the sun cool, an' all an' all! I take shame for you. You're no better than a Pagin—you an' your firin' parties an' your glass-eyes. Won't *you* stop ut, Sorr?"

What could I do? Could I tell Ortheris anything that he did not know of the pleasures of his life? I was not a Chaplain nor a Subaltern, and Ortheris had a right to speak as he thought fit.

"Let him run, Mulvaney," I said. "It's the beer."

"No! 'Tisn't the beer," said Mulvaney. "I know fwhat's comin'. He's tuk this way now an' agin, an' it's bad—it's bad—for I'm fond av the bhoy."

Indeed, Mulvaney seemed needlessly anxious; but I knew that he looked after Ortheris in a fatherly way.

"Let me talk, let me talk," said Ortheris, dreamily. "D'you stop your parrit screamin' of a 'ot day, when the cage is a-cookin' 'is pore little pink toes orf, Mulvaney?"

"Pink toes! D'ye mane to say you've pink toes undher your bullswools, ye blandanderin',"—Mulvaney gathered himself together for a terrific denunciation—"school-misthress! Pink toes! How much Bass wid the label did that ravin' child dhrink?"

"'Tain't Bass," said Ortheris. "It's a bitterer beer nor that. It's 'ome-sickness!"

"Hark to him! An' he goin' Home in the *Sherapis* in the inside av four months!"

"I don't care. It's all one to me. 'Ow d'you know I ain't 'fraid o' dyin' 'for I gets my discharge paipers?" He recommenced, in a sing-song voice, the Orders.

I had never seen this side of Ortheris' character before, but evidently Mulvaney had, and attached serious importance to it. While Ortheris babbled, with his head on his arms, Mulvaney whispered to me—

"He's always tuk this way whin he's been checked overmuch by the childher they make Sarjints nowadays. That an' havin' nothin' to do. I can't make ut out anyways."

"Well, what does it matter? Let him talk himself through."

Ortheris began singing a parody of "The Ramrod Corps," full of cheerful allusions to battle, murder, and sudden death. He looked out across the river as he sang: and his face was quite strange to me. Mulvaney caught me by the elbow to insure attention.

"Matther? It matthers everything! 'Tis some sort av fit that's on him. I've seen ut. 'Twill hould him all this night, an' in the middle av it he'll get out av his cot an' go rakin' in the rack for his 'coutremints. Thin he'll come over to me an' say, 'I'm goin' to Bombay. Answer for me in the mornin'.' Thin me an' him will fight as we've done before—him to go an' me to hould him—an' so we'll both come on the books for disturbin' in barricks. I've belted him, an' I've bruk his head, an' I've talked to him, but 'tis no manner av use whin the fit's on him. He's as good a bhoy as ever stepped whin his mind's clear. I know fwhat's comin', though, this night in barricks. Lord send he doesn't loose on me whin I rise to knock him down. 'Tis that that's in my mind day an' night."

This put the case in a much less pleasant light, and fully accounted for Mulvaney's anxiety. He seemed to be trying to coax Ortheris out of the fit; for he shouted down the bank where the boy was lying—

"Listen now, you wid the 'pore pink toes' an' the glass-eyes! Did you shwim the Irriwaddy at night, behin' me, as a bhoy shud; or were you hidin' under a bed, as you was at Ahmid Kheyl?"

This was at once a gross insult and a direct lie, and Mulvaney meant it to bring on a fight. But Ortheris seemed shut up in some sort of a trance. He answered slowly, without a sign of irritation, in the same cadenced voice as he had used for his firing-party orders—

"*Hi* swum the Irriwaddy in the night, as you know, for to take the town of Lungtungpen, nakid an' without fear. *Hand* where I was at Ahmed Kheyl you know, and four bloomin' Pathans know too. But that was summat to do, an' I didn't think o' dyin'. Now I'm sick to go 'Ome—go 'Ome—go 'Ome! No, I ain't mammysick, because my uncle brung me up, but I'm sick for London again; sick for the sounds of 'er, an' the sights of 'er, and the stinks of 'er; orange-peel and hasphalte an' gas comin' in over Vaux'all Bridge. Sick for the rail goin' down to Box 'Ill, with your gal on your knee an' a new clay pipe in your face. That, an' the Stran' lights where you knows ev'ry one, an' the Copper that takes you up is a old friend that tuk you up before, when you was a little, smitchy boy lying loose 'tween the Temple an' the Dark Harches. No bloomin' guard-mountin', no bloomin' rotten-stone, nor khaki, an' yourself your own master with a gal to take an' see the

Humaners practisin' a-hookin' dead corpses out of the Serpentine o' Sundays. An' I lef' all that for to serve the Widder beyond the seas, where there ain't no women and there ain't no liquor worth 'avin', and there ain't nothin' to see, nor do, nor say, nor feel, nor think. Lord love you, Stanley Orth'ris, but you're a bigger bloomin' fool than the rest o' the reg'ment and Mulvaney wired together! There's the Widder sittin' at 'Ome with a gold crown on 'er 'ead; and 'ere am Hi, Stanley Orth'ris, the Widder's property, a rottin' FOOL!"

His voice rose at the end of the sentence, and he wound up with a six-shot Anglo-Vernacular oath. Mulvaney said nothing, but looked at me as if he expected that I could bring peace to poor Ortheris' troubled brain.

I remembered once at Rawal Pindi having seen a man, nearly mad with drink, sobered by being made a fool of. Some regiments may know what I mean. I hoped that we might slake off Ortheris in the same way, though he was perfectly sober. So I said—

"What's the use of grousing there, speaking against The Widow?"

"I didn't!" said Ortheris. "S'elp me, Gawd, I never said a word agin 'er, an' I wouldn't—not if I was to desert this minute!"

Here was my opening. "Well, you meant to, anyhow. What's the use of cracking-on for nothing? Would you slip it now if you got the chance?"

"On'y try me!" said Ortheris, jumping to his feet as if he had been stung.

Mulvaney jumped too. "Fwhat are you going to do?" said he.

"Help Ortheris down to Bombay or Karachi, whichever he likes. You can report that he separated from you before tiffin, and left his gun on the bank here!"

"I'm to report that—am I?" said Mulvaney, slowly. "Very well. If Orth'ris manes to desert now, and will desert now, an' you, Sorr, who have been a frind to me an' to him, will help him to ut, I, Terence Mulvaney, on my oath which I've never bruk yet, will report as you say. But——" here he stepped up to Ortheris, and shook the stock of the fowling-piece in his face—"your fistes help you, Stanley Orth'ris, if ever I come across you agin!"

"I don't care!" said Ortheris. "I'm sick o' this dorg's life. Give me a chanst. Don't play with me. Le' me go!"

"Strip," said I, "and change with me, and then I'll tell you what to do."

I hoped that the absurdity of this would check Ortheris; but he had kicked off his ammunition-boots and got rid of his tunic almost before I had loosed my shirt-collar. Mulvaney gripped me by the arm—

"The fit's on him: the fit's workin' on him still! By my Honour and Sowl, we shall be accessiry to a desartion yet. Only, twenty-eight days, as you say, Sorr, or fifty-six, but think o' the shame—the black shame to him an' me!" I had never seen Mulvaney so excited.

But Ortheris was quite calm, and, as soon as he had exchanged clothes with me, and I stood up a Private of the Line, he said shortly, "Now! Come on. What nex'? D'ye mean fair. What must I do to get out o' this 'ere a-Hell?"

I told him that, if he would wait for two or three hours near the river, I would ride into the Station and come back with one hundred rupees. He would, with that money in his pocket, walk to the nearest side-station on the line, about five miles away, and would there take a first-class ticket for Karachi. Knowing that he had no money on him when he went out shooting, his regiment would not immediately wire to the seaports, but would hunt for him in the native villages near the river. Further, no one would think of seeking a deserter in a first-class carriage. At Karachi, he was to buy white clothes and ship, if he could, on a cargo-steamer.

Here he broke in. If I helped him to Karachi, he would arrange all the rest. Then I ordered him to wait where he was until it was dark enough for me to ride into the Station without my dress being noticed. Now God in His Wisdom has made the heart of the British Soldier, who is very often an unlicked ruffian, as soft as the heart of a little child, in order that he may believe in and follow his officers into tight and nasty places. He does not so readily come to believe in a "civilian," but, when he does, he believes implicitly and like a dog. I had had the honour of the friendship of Private Ortheris, at intervals, for more than three years, and we had dealt with each other as man by man. Consequently, he considered that all my words were true, and not spoken lightly.

Mulvaney and I left him in the high grass near the river-bank, and went away, still keeping to the high grass, towards my horse. The shirt scratched me horribly.

We waited nearly two hours for the dusk to fall and allow me to ride off. We spoke of Ortheris in whispers, and strained our ears to catch any sound from the spot where we had left him. But we heard nothing except the wind in the plume-grass.

"I've bruk his head," said Mulvaney, earnestly, "time an' agin. I've nearly kilt him wid the belt, an' *yet* I can't knock thim fits out av his soft head. No! An' he's not soft, for he's reasonable an' likely by natur'. Fwhat is ut? Is ut his breedin' which is nothin', or his edukashin which he niver got? You that think ye know things, answer me that."

But I found no answer. I was wondering how long Ortheris, in the bank of the river, would hold out, and whether I should be forced to help him to desert, as I had given my word.

Just as the dusk shut down and, with a very heavy heart, I was beginning to saddle up my horse, we heard wild shouts from the river.

The devils had departed from Private Stanley Ortheris, No. 22639, B Company. The loneliness, the dusk, and the waiting had driven them out as I had hoped. We set off at the double and found him plunging about wildly through the grass, with his coat off—my coat off, I mean. He was calling for us like a madman.

When we reached him he was dripping with perspiration, and trembling like a startled horse. We had great difficulty in soothing him. He complained that he was in civilian kit, and wanted to tear my clothes off his body. I ordered him to strip, and we made a second exchange as quickly as possible.

The rasp of his own "grayback" shirt and the squeak of his boots seemed to bring him to himself. He put his hands before his eyes and said—

"Wot was it? I ain't mad, I ain't sunstrook, an' I've bin an' done an' said, and bin an' gone an' done . . . *Wot* 'ave I bin an' done?"

"Fwhat have you done?" said Mulvaney. "You've dishgraced yourself—though that's no matter. You've dishgraced B Comp'ny, an', worst av all, you've dishgraced *Me!* Me that taught you how for to walk abroad like a man—whin you was a dhirty little, fish-backed little, whimperin' little recruity. As you are now, Stanley Orth'ris!"

Ortheris said nothing for a while. Then he unslung his belt, heavy with the badges of half a dozen regiments that his own had lain with, and handed it over to Mulvaney.

"I'm too little for to mill you, Mulvaney," said he, "an' you've strook me before; but you can take an' cut me in two with this 'ere if you like."

Mulvaney turned to me.

"Lave me to talk to him, Sorr," said Mulvaney.

I left, and on my way home thought a good deal over Ortheris in particular, and my friend Private Thomas Atkins, whom I love, in general.

But I could not come to any conclusion of any kind whatever.

PRIVATE LEAROYD'S STORY
1888

And he told a tale.—CHRONICLES OF GAUTAMA BUDDHA

FAR from the haunts of Company Officers who insist upon kit-inspections, far from keen-nosed Sergeants who sniff the pipe stuffed into the bedding-roll, two miles from the tumult of the barracks, lies the Trap. It is an old dry well, shadowed by a twisted *pipal* tree and fenced with high grass. Here, in the years gone by, did Private Ortheris establish his depôt and menagerie for such possessions, dead and living, as could not safely be introduced to the barrack-room. Here were gathered Houdin pullets, and fox-terriers of undoubted pedigree and more than doubtful ownership, for Ortheris was an inveterate poacher and pre-eminent among a regiment of neat-handed dog-stealers.

Never again will the long lazy evenings return wherein Ortheris, whistling softly, moved surgeon-wise among the captives of his craft at the bottom of the well; when Learoyd sat in the niche, giving sage counsel on the management of "tykes," and Mulvaney, from the crook of the overhanging *pipal,* waved his enormous boots in benediction above our heads, delighting us with tales of Love and War, and strange experiences of cities and men.

Ortheris—landed at last in the "little stuff bird-shop" for which your soul longed; Learoyd—back again in the smoky, stone-ribbed North, amid the clang of the Bradford looms; Mulvaney—grizzled, tender, and very wise Ulysses, sweltering on the earthwork of a Central India line—judge if I have forgotten old days in the Trap!

Orth'ris, as allus thinks he knaws more than other foaks, said she wasn't a real laady, but nobbut a Hewrasian. I don't gainsay as her culler was a bit doosky, like. But she *was* a laady. Why, she rode iv a carriage, an' good 'osses, too, an' her 'air was that oiled as you could see your faice in it, an' she wore dimond rings an' a goold chain, an' silk an' satin dresses as mun 'a' cost a deal, for it isn't a cheap shop as keeps enough o' one pattern to fit a figure like hers. Her name was Mrs. DeSussa, an' t' waay I coom to be acquainted wi' her was along of our Colonel's Laady's dog Rip.

I've seen a vast o' dogs, but Rip was t' prettiest picter of a cliver fox-tarrier 'at iver I set eyes on. He could do owt you like but speeak, an' t' Colonel's Laady set more store by him than if he hed been a Christian. She hed bairns of her awn, but they was i' England, and Rip seemed to get all t' coodlin' and pettin' as belonged to a bairn by good right.

But Rip were a bit on a rover, an' hed a habit o' breakin' out o' barricks like, and trottin' round t' plaice as if he were t' Cantonment Magistrate coom round inspectin'. The Colonel leathers him once or twice, but Rip didn't care an' kept on gooin' his rounds, wi' his taail a-waggin' as if he were flag-signallin' to t' world at large 'at he was "gettin' on nicely, thank yo', and how's yo' sen?" An' then t' Colonel, as was noa sort of a hand wi' a dog, tees him oop. A real clipper of a dog, an' it's noa wonder yon laady, Mrs. DeSussa, should tek a fancy tiv him. Theer's one o' t' Ten Commandments says yo' maun't cuvvet your neebor's ox nor his jackass, but it doesn't say nowt about his tarrier dogs, an' happen thot's t' reason why Mrs. DeSussa cuvveted Rip, tho' she went to church reg'lar along wi' her husband who was so mich darker 'at if he hedn't such a good coaat tiv his back yo' might ha' called him a black man and nut tell a lee nawther. They said he addled his brass i' jute, an' he'd a rare lot on it.

Well, you seen, when they teed Rip up, t' poor awd lad didn't enjoy very good 'elth. So t' Colonel's Laady sends for me as 'ad a naame for bein' knowledgeable about a dog, an' axes what's ailin' wi' him.

"Why," says I, "he's getten t' mopes, an' what he wants is

his libbaty an' coompany like t' rest on us, wal happen a rat or two 'ud liven him oop. It's low, mum," says I, "is rats, but it's t' nature of a dog; an soa's cuttin' round an' meetin' another dog or two an' passin' t' time o' day, an' hevvin' a bit of a turn-up wi' him like a Christian."

So she says *her* dog maunt niver fight an' noa Christians iver fought.

"Then what's a soldier for?" says I; an' I explains to her t' contrairy qualities of a dog, 'at, when yo' coom to think on't, is one o' t' curusest things as is. For they larn to behave theirsens like gentlemen born, fit for t' fost o' coompany—they tell me t' Widdy herself is fond of a good dog and knaws one when she sees it as well as onny body: then on t' other hand a-tewin' round after cats an' gettin' mixed oop i' all manners o' blackguardly street-rows, an' killin' rats, an' fightin' like divils.

T' Colonel's Laady says:—"Well, Learoyd, I doan't agree wi' you, but you're right in a way o' speeakin', an' I should like yo' to tek Rip out a-walkin' wi' you sometimes; but yo' maun't let him fight, nor chase cats, nor do nowt 'orrid": an them was her very wods.

Soa Rip an' me goes out a-walkin' o' evenin's, he bein' a dog as did credit tiv a man, an' I catches a lot o' rats an we hed a bit of a match on in an awd dry swimmin'-bath at back o' t' cantonments, an' it was none so long afore he was as bright as a button again. He hed a way o' flyin' at them big yaller pariah dogs as if he was a harrow offan a bow, an' though his weight were nowt, he tuk 'em so suddint-like they rolled over like skittles in a halley, an' when they coot he stretched after 'em as if he were rabbit-runnin'. Saame with cats when he cud get t' cat agaate o' runnin'.

One evenin', him an' me was trespassin' ovver a compound wall after one of them mongooses 'at he'd started, an' we was busy grubbin' round a prickle-bush, an' when we looks up there was Mrs. DeSussa wi' a parasel ovver her shoulder, a-watchin' us. "Oh my!" she sings out; "there's that lovelee dog! Would he let me stroke him, Mister Soldier?"

"Ay, he would, mum," sez I, "for he's fond o' laady's

coompany. Coom here, Rip, an' speeak to this kind laady." An' Rip, seein' 'at t' mongoose hed getten clean awaay, cooms up like t' gentleman he was, nivver a hauporth shy or okkord.

"Oh, you beautiful—you prettee dog!" she says, clippin' an' chantin' her speech in a way them sooart has o' their awn; "I would like a dog like you. You are so verree lovelee—so awfullee prettee," an' all thot sort o' talk, 'at a dog o' sense mebbe thinks nowt on, tho' he bides it by reason o' his breedin'.

An' then I meks him joomp ovver my swagger-cane, an' shek hands, an' beg, an' lie dead, an' a lot o' them tricks as laadies teeaches dogs, though I doan't haud with it mysen, for it's makin' a fool o' a good dog to do such like.

An' at lung length it cooms out 'at she'd been thrawin' sheep's eyes, as t' sayin' is, at Rip for many a day. Yo' see, her childer was grown up, an' she'd nowt mich to do, an' were allus fond of a dog. Soa she axes me if I'd tek somethin' to dhrink. An' we goes into t' drawn-room wheer her husband was a-settin'. They meks a gurt fuss ovver t' dog an' I has a bottle o' aale, an' he gave me a handful o' cigars.

Soa I coomed away, but t' awd lass sings out—"Oh, Mister Soldier, please coom again and bring that prettee dog."

I didn't let on to t' Colonel's Laady about Mrs. DeSussa, and Rip, he says nowt nawther; an' I gooes again, an' ivry time there was a good dhrink an' a handful o' good smooaks. An' I telled t' awd lass a heeap more about Rip than I'd ever heeared; how he tuk t' fost prize at Lunnon dog-show and cost thotty-three pounds fower shillin' from t' man as bred him; 'at his own brother was t' propputty o' t' Prince o' Wailes, an' 'at he had a pedigree as long as a Dook's. An' she lapped it all oop an' were niver tired o' admirin' him. But when t' awed lass took to givin' me money an' I seed 'at she were gettin' fair fond about t' dog, I began to suspicion summat. Onny body may give a soldier t' price of a pint in a friendly way an' theer's no 'arm done, but when it cooms to five rupees slipt into your hand, sly like, why, it's what t' 'lectioneerin' fellows calls bribery an' corruption. Specially when Mrs. DeSussa threwed hints how t' cold weather would soon be ovver an' she was goin' to Munsooree Pahar an' we was goin' to Rawalpindi, an' she would niver see Rip any more onless somebody she knowed on would be kind tiv her.

Soa I tells Mulvaney an' Ortheris all t' taale thro', beginnin' to end.

"'Tis larceny that wicked ould laady manes," says t' Irishman, "'tis felony she is sejuicin' ye into, my frind Learoyd, but I'll purtect your innocince. I'll save ye from the wicked wiles av that wealthy ould woman, an' I'll go wid ye this evenin' and spake to her the wurrds av truth an' honesty. But Jock," says he, waggin' his heead, "'twas not like ye to kape all that good dhrink an' thim fine cigars to yerself, while Orth'ris here an' me have been prowlin' round wid throats as dry as lime-kilns, and nothin' to smoke but Canteen plug. 'Twas a dhirty thrick to play on a comrade, for why should you, Learoyd, be balancin' yourself on the butt av a satin chair, as if Terence Mulvaney was not the aquil av anybody who thrades in jute!"

"Let alone me," sticks in Orth'ris, "but that's like life. Them wot's really fitted to decorate society get no show while a blunderin' Yorkshireman like you——"

"Nay," says I, "it's none o' t' blunderin' Yorkshireman she wants; it's Rip. He's the gentleman this journey."

Soa t' next day, Mulvaney an' Rip an' me goes to Mrs. DeSussa's, an' t' Irishman bein' a strainger she wor a bit shy at fost. But you've heeard Mulvaney talk, an' yo' may believe as he fairly bewitched t' awd lass wal she let out 'at she wanted to tek Rip away wi' her to Munsooree Pahar. Then Mulvaney changes his tune an' axes her solemn-like if she'd thought o' t' consequences o' gettin' two poor but honest soldiers sent t' Andamning Islands. Mrs. DeSussa began to cry, so Mulvaney turns round oppen t' other tack and smooths her down, allowin' 'at Rip ud be a vast better off in t' Hills than down i' Bengal, and 'twas a pity he shouldn't go wheer he was so well beliked. And soa he went on, backin' an' fillin' an' workin' up t' awd lass wal she felt as if her life warn't worth nowt if she didn't hev t' dog.

Then all of a suddint he says:—"But ye *shall* have him, marm, for I've a feelin' heart, not like this could-blooded

Yorkshireman; but 'twill cost ye not a penny less than three hundher rupees."

"Don't yo' believe him, mum," says I; "t' Colonel's Laady wouldn't tek five hundred for him."

"Who said she would?" says Mulvaney; "it's not buyin' him I mane, but for the sake o' this kind, good laady, I'll do what I never dreamt to do in my life. I'll stale him!"

"Don't say steal," says Mrs. DeSussa; "he shall have the happiest home. Dogs often get lost, you know, and then they stray, an' he likes me and I like him as I niver liked a dog yet, an' I *must* hev him. If I got him at t' last minute I could carry him off to Munsooree Pahar and nobody would niver knaw."

Now an' again Mulvaney looked acrost at me, an' though I could mak nowt o' what he was after, I concluded to take his leead.

"Well, mum," I says, "I never thowt to coom down to dog-steealin', but if my comrade sees how it could be done to oblige a laady like yo'sen, I'm nut t' man to hod back, tho' it's a bad business I'm thinkin', an' three hundred rupees is a poor set-off again t' chance of them Damning Islands as Mulvaney talks on."

"I'll mek it three fifty," says Mrs. DeSussa; "only let me hev t' dog!"

So we let her persuade us, an' she teks Rip's measure theer an' then, an' sent to Hamilton's to order a silver collar again t' time when he was to be her awn, which was to be t' day she set off for Munsooree Pahar.

"Sitha, Mulvaney," says I, when we was outside, "you're niver goin' to let her hev Rip!"

"An' would ye disappoint a poor old woman?" says he; "she shall have *a* Rip."

"An' wheer's he to come through?" says I.

"Learoyd, my man," he sings out, "you're a pretty man av your inches an' a good comrade, but your head is made av duff. Isn't our friend Orth'ris a Taxidermist, an' a rale artist wid his nimble white fingers? An' what's a Taxidermist but a man who can thrate shkins? Do ye mind the white dog that belongs to the Canteen Sargint, bad cess to him—he that's lost half his time an' snarlin' the rest? He shall be lost for *good* now; an' do ye mind that he's the very spit in shape an' size av the Colonel's, barrin' that his tail is an inch too long, an' he has none av the colour that divarsifies the rale Rip, an' his timper is that av his masther an' worse. But fwhat is an inch on a dog's tail? An' fwhat to a professional like Orth'ris is a few ringstraked shpots av black, brown, an' white? Nothin' at all, at all."

Then we meets Orth'ris, an' that little man, bein' sharp as a needle, seed his way through t' business in a minute. An' he went to work a-practisin' 'air-dyes the very next day, beginnin' on some white rabbits he had, an' then he drored all Rip's markin's on t' back of a white Commissariat bullock, so as to get his 'and in an' be sure of his colours; shadin' off brown into black as nateral as life. If Rip *hed* a fault it was too mich markin', but it was straingely reg'lar an' Orth'ris settled himself to make a fost-rate job on it when he got haud o' t' Canteen Sargint's dog. Theer niver was sich a dog as thot for bad timper, an' it did nut get no better when his tail hed to be fettled an inch an' a half shorter. But they may talk o' theer Royal Academies as they like. *I* niver seed a bit o' animal paintin' to beat t' copy as Orth'ris made of Rip's marks, wal t' picter itself was snarlin' all t' time an' tryin' to get at Rip standin' theer to be copied as good as goold.

Orth'ris allus hed as mich conceit on himsen as would lift a balloon, an' he wor so pleeased wi' his sham Rip he wor for tekking him to Mrs. DeSussa before she went away. But Mulvaney an' me stopped thot, knowin' Orth'ris's work, though niver so cliver, was nobut skin-deep.

An' at last Mrs. DeSussa fixed t' day for startin' to Munsooree Pahar. We was to tek Rip to t' stayshun i' a basket an' hand him ovver just when they was ready to start, an' then she'd give us t' brass—as was agreed upon.

An' my wod! It were high time she were off, for them 'airdyes upon t' cur's back took a vast of paintin' to keep t' reet culler, tho' Orth'ris spent a matter o' seven rupees six annas i' t' best drooggist shops i' Calcutta.

An' t' Canteen Sargint was lookin' for 'is dog everywheer; an', wi' bein' tied up, t' beast's timper got waur nor ever.

It wor i' t' evenin' when t' train started thro' Howrah, an' we 'elped Mrs. DeSussa wi' about sixty boxes, an' then we gave her t' basket. Orth'ris, for pride av his work, axed us to let him coom along wi' us, an' he couldn't help liftin' t' lid an' showin' t' cur as he lay coiled oop.

"Oh!" says t' awd lass; "the beautee! How sweet he looks!" An' just then t' beauty snarled an' showed his teeth, so Mulvaney shuts down t' lid and says: "Ye'll be careful, marm, whin ye tek him out. He's disaccustomed to travelling by t' railway, an' he'll be sure to want his rale mistress an' his friend Learoyd, so ye'll make allowance for his feelings at fost."

She would do all thot an' more for the dear, good Rip, an' she would nut oppen t' basket till they were miles away, for fear anybody should recognize him, an' we were real good and kind soldier-men, we were, an' she honds me a bundle o' notes, an' then cooms up a few of her relations an' friends to say good-by—not more than seventy-five there wasn't—an' we cuts away.

What coom to t' three hundred and fifty rupees? Thot's what I can scarcelins tell yo', but we melted it—we melted it. It was share an' share alike, for Mulvaney said: "If Learoyd got hold of Mrs. DeSussa first, sure 'twas I that remimbered the Sargint's dog just in the nick av time, an' Orth'ris was the artist av janius that made a work av art out av that ugly piece av ill-nature. Yet, by way av a thank-offerin' that I was not led into felony by that wicked 'ould woman, I'll send a thrifle to Father Victor for the poor people he's always beggin' for."

But me an' Orth'ris, he bein' Cockney an' I bein' pretty far north, did nut see it i' t' saame way. We'd getten t' brass, an' we meaned to keep it. An' soa we did—for a short time.

Noa, noa, we niver heered a wod more o' t' awd lass. Our rig'mint went to Pindi, an' t' Canteen Sargint he got himself another tyke insteead o' t' one 'at got lost so reg'lar, an' was lost for good at last.

ON THE CITY WALL
1888

Then she let them down by a cord through the window; for her house was upon the town-wall, and she dwelt upon the wall.—JOSHUA II. 15

LALUN is a member of the most ancient profession in the world. Lilith was her very-great-grandmamma, and that was before the days of Eve as every one knows. In the West, people say rude things about Lalun's profession, and write lectures about it, and distribute the lectures to young persons in order that Morality may be preserved. In the East where the profession is hereditary, descending from mother to daughter, nobody writes lectures or takes any notice; and that is a distinct proof of the inability of the East to manage its own affairs.

Lalun's real husband, for even ladies of Lalun's profession in the East must have husbands, was a big jujube-tree. Her Mamma, who had married a fig-tree, spent ten thousand rupees on Lalun's wedding, which was blessed by forty-seven clergymen of Mamma's church, and distributed five thousand rupees in charity to the poor. And that was the custom of the land. The advantages of having a jujube-tree for a husband are obvious. You cannot hurt his feelings, and he looks imposing.

Lalun's husband stood on the plain outside the City walls, and Lalun's house was upon the east wall facing the river. If you fell from the broad window-seat you dropped thirty feet sheer into the City Ditch. But if you stayed where you should and looked forth, you saw all the cattle of the City being driven down to water, the students of the Government College playing cricket, the high grass and trees that fringed the river-bank, the great sand bars that ribbed the river, the red tombs of dead Emperors beyond the river, and very far away through the blue heat-haze, a glint of the snows of the Himalayas.

Wali Dad used to lie in the window-seat for hours at a time watching this view. He was a young Muhammadan who was suffering acutely from education of the English variety and knew it. His father had sent him to a Mission-school to get wisdom, and Wali Dad had absorbed more than ever his father or the Missionaries intended he should. When his father died, Wali Dad was independent and spent two years experimenting with the creeds of the Earth and reading books that are of no use to anybody.

After he had made an unsuccessful attempt to enter the Roman Catholic Church and the Presbyterian fold at the same time (the Missionaries found him out and called him names, but they did not understand his trouble), he discovered Lalun on the City wall and became the most constant of her few admirers. He possessed a head that English artists at home would rave over and paint amid impossible surroundings—a face that female novelists would use with delight through nine hundred pages. In reality he was only a clean-bred young Muhammadan, with pencilled eyebrows, small-cut nostrils, little feet and hands, and a very tired look in his eyes. By virtue of his twenty-two years he had grown a neat black beard which he stroked with pride and kept delicately scented. His life seemed to be divided between borrowing books from me and making love to Lalun in the window-seat. He composed songs about her, and some of the songs are sung to this day in the City from the Street of the Mutton-Butchers to the Copper-Smiths' ward.

One song, the prettiest of all, says that the beauty of Lalun was so great that it troubled the hearts of the British Government and caused them to lose their peace of mind. That is the way the song is sung in the streets; but, if you examine it carefully and know the key to the explanation, you will find that there are three puns in it—on "beauty," "heart," and "peace of mind,"—so that it runs: "By the subtlety of Lalun the administration of the Government was troubled and it lost such and such a man." When Wali Dad sings that song his eyes glow like hot coals, and Lalun leans back among the cushions and throws bunches of jasmine-buds at Wali Dad.

But first it is necessary to explain something about the Supreme Government which is above all and below all and behind all. Gentlemen come from England, spend a few weeks in India, walk round this great Sphinx of the Plains, and write books upon its ways and its works, denouncing or praising it as their own ignorance prompts. Consequently all the world knows how the Supreme Government conducts itself. But no one, not even the Supreme Government, knows everything about the administration of the Empire. Year by year England sends out fresh drafts for the first fighting-line, which is officially called the Indian Civil Service. These die, or kill themselves by overwork, or are worried to death or broken in health and hope in order that the land may be protected from death and sickness, famine and war, and may eventually become capable of standing alone. It will never stand alone, but the idea is a pretty one, and men are willing to die for it, and yearly the work of pushing and coaxing and scolding and petting the country into good living goes forward. If an advance be made all credit is given to the native, while the Englishmen stand back and wipe their foreheads. If a failure occurs the Englishmen step forward and take the blame. Overmuch tenderness of this kind has bred a strong belief among many natives that the native is capable of administering the country, and many devout Englishmen believe this also, because the theory is stated in beautiful English with all the latest political colour.

There be other men who, though uneducated, see visions and dream dreams, and they, too, hope to administer the country in their own way—that is to say, with a garnish of Red Sauce. Such men must exist among two hundred million people, and, if they are not attended to, may cause trouble and even break the great idol called *Pax Britannic,* which, as the newspapers say, lives between Peshawur and Cape Comorin. Were the Day of Doom to dawn to-morrow, you would find the Supreme Government "taking measures to allay popular excitement" and putting guards upon the graveyards that the Dead might troop forth orderly. The youngest Civilian would arrest Gabriel on his own responsibility if the Archangel could not produce a Deputy Commissioner's permission to "make music or other noises" as the license says.

Whence it is easy to see that mere men of the flesh who would create a tumult must fare badly at the hands of the Supreme Government. And they do. There is no outward sign of excitement; there is no confusion; there is no knowledge. When due and sufficient reasons have been given, weighed and approved, the machinery moves forward, and the dreamer of dreams and the seer of visions is gone from his friends and following. He enjoys the hospitality of Government; there is no restriction upon his movements within certain limits; but he must not confer any more with his brother dreamers. Once in every six months the Supreme Government assures itself that he is well and takes formal acknowledgment of his existence. No one protests against this detention, because the few people who know about it are in deadly fear of seeming to know him; and never a single newspaper "takes up his case" or organizes demonstrations on his behalf, because the newspapers of India have got behind that lying proverb which says the Pen is mightier than the Sword, and can walk delicately.

So now you know as much as you ought about Wali Dad, the educational mixture, and the Supreme Government.

Lalun has not yet been described. She would need, so Wali Dad says, a thousand pens of gold and ink scented with musk. She has been variously compared to the Moon, the Dil Sagar Lake, a spotted quail, a gazelle, the Sun on the Desert of Kutch, the Dawn, the Stars, and the young bamboo. These comparisons imply that she is beautiful exceedingly according to the native standards, which are practically the same as those of the West. Her eyes are black and her hair is black, and her eyebrows are black as leeches; her mouth is tiny and says witty things; her hands are tiny and have saved much money; her feet are tiny and have trodden on the naked hearts of many men. But, as Wali Dad sings: "Lalun *is* Lalun, and when you have said that you have only come to the Beginnings of Knowledge."

The little house on the City wall was just big enough to hold Lalun, and her maid, and a pussy-cat with a silver collar. A big pink and blue cut-glass chandelier hung from the ceiling of the reception room. A petty Nawab had given Lalun the horror, and she kept it for politeness' sake. The floor of the room was of polished chunam, white as curds. A latticed window of carved wood was set in one wall; there was a profusion of squabby pluffy cushions and fat carpets everywhere, and Lalun's silver *huqa,* studded with turquoises, had a special little carpet all to its shining self. Wali Dad was nearly as permanent a fixture as the chandelier. As I have said, he lay in the window-seat and meditated on Life and Death and Lalun—specially Lalun. The feet of the young men of the City tended to her doorways and then—retired, for Lalun was a particular maiden, slow of speech, reserved of mind, and not in the least inclined to orgies which were nearly certain to end in strife. "If I am of no value, I am unworthy of this honour," said Lalun. "If I am of value, they are unworthy of Me." And that was a crooked sentence.

In the long hot nights of latter April and May all the City seemed to assemble in Lalun's little white room to smoke and to talk. Shiahs of the grimmest and most uncompromising persuasion; Sufis who had lost all belief in the Prophet and retained but little in God; wandering Hindu priests passing southward on their way to the Central India fairs and other affairs; Pundits in black gowns, with spectacles on their noses and undigested wisdom in their insides; bearded headmen of the wards; Sikhs with all the details of the latest ecclesiastical scandal in the Golden Temple; red-eyed priests from beyond the Border, looking like trapped wolves and talking like ravens; M. A.'s of the University, very superior and very voluble—all these people and more also you might find in the white room. Wali Dad lay in the window-seat and listened to the talk.

"It is Lalun's *salon,*" said Wali Dad to me, "and it is electic—is not that the word? Outside of a Freemason's Lodge I have never seen such gatherings. *There* I dined once with a Jew—a Yahoudi!" He spat into the City Ditch with apologies for allowing national feelings to overcome him. "Though I have lost every belief in the world," said he, "and try to be proud of my losing, I cannot help hating a Jew. Lalun admits no Jews here."

"But what in the world do all these men do?" I asked.

"The curse of our country," said Wali Dad. "They talk. It is like the Athenians—always hearing and telling some new thing. Ask the Pearl and she will show you how much she knows of the news of the City and the Province. Lalun knows everything."

"Lalun," I said at random—she was talking to a gentleman of the Kurd persuasion who had come in from God-knows-where—"when does the 175th Regiment go to Agra?"

"It does not go at all," said Lalun, without turning her head. "They have ordered the 118th to go in its stead. That Regiment goes to Lucknow in three months, unless they give a fresh order."

"That is so," said Wali Dad without a shade of doubt. "Can you, with your telegrams and your newspapers, do better? Always hearing and telling some new thing," he went on. "My friend, has your God ever smitten a European nation for gossiping in the bazars? India has gossiped for centuries—always standing in the bazars until the soldiers go by. Therefore—you are here to-day instead of starving in your own country, and I am not a Muhammadan—I am a Product—a Demnition Product. That also I owe to you and yours: that I cannot make an end to my sentence without quoting from your authors." He pulled at the *huqa* and mourned, half feelingly, half in earnest, for the shattered hopes of his youth. Wali Dad was always mourning over something or other—the country of which he despaired, or the creed in which he had lost faith, or the life of the English which he could by no means understand.

Lalun never mourned. She played little songs on the *sitar*, and to hear her sing, *"O Peacock, cry again,"* was always a fresh pleasure. She knew all the songs that have ever been sung, from the war-songs of the South that make the old men angry with the young men and the young men angry with the State, to the love-songs of the North where the swords whinny-whicker like angry kites in the pauses between the kisses, and the Passes fill with armed men, and the Lover is torn from his Beloved and cries, *Ai, Ai, Ai!* evermore. She knew how to make up tobacco for the *huqa* so that it smelt like the Gates of Paradise and wafted you gently through them. She could embroider strange things in gold and silver, and dance softly with the moonlight when it came in at the window. Also she knew the hearts of men, and the heart of the City, and whose wives were faithful and whose untrue, and more of the secrets of the Government Offices than are good to be set down in this place. Nasiban, her maid, said that her jewellery was worth ten thousand pounds, and that, some night, a thief would enter and murder her for its possession; but Lalun said that all the City would tear that thief limb from limb, and that he, whoever he was, knew it.

So she took her *sitar* and sat in the window-seat and sang a song of old days that had been sung by a girl of her profession in an armed camp on the eve of a great battle—the day before the Fords of the Jumna ran red and Sivaji fled fifty miles to Delhi with a Toorkh stallion at his horse's tail and another Lalun on his saddle-bow. It was what men called a Mahratta *laonee,* and it said:—

Their warrior forces Chimajee
Before the Peishwa led,
The Children of the Sun and Fire
Behind him turned and fled.

And the chorus said:—

With them there fought who rides so free
With a sword and turban red,
The warrior-youth who earns his fee
At peril of his head.

"At peril of his head," said Wali Dad in English to me. "Thanks to your Government, all our heads are protected, and with the educational facilities at my command"—his eyes twinkled wickedly—"I might be a distinguished member of the local administration. Perhaps, in time, I might even be a member of a Legislative Council."

"Don't speak English," said Lalun, bending over her *sitar* afresh. The chorus went out from the City wall to the blackened wall of Fort Amara which dominates the City. No man knows the precise extent of Fort Amara. Three kings built it hundreds of years ago, and they say that there are miles of underground rooms beneath its walls. It is peopled with many ghosts, a detachment of Garrison Artillery and a Company of Infantry. In its prime it held ten thousand men and filled its ditches with corpses.

"At peril of his head," sang Lalun again and again.

A head moved on one of the Ramparts—the gray head of an old man—and a voice, rough as shark-skin on a sword-hilt, sent back the last line of the chorus and broke into a song that I could not understand, though Lalun and Wali Dad listened intently.

"What is it?" I asked. "Who is it?"

"A consistent man," said Wali Dad. "He fought you in '46, when he was a warrior-youth; refought you in '57, and he tried to fight you in '71, but you had learned the trick of blowing men from guns too well. Now he is old; but he would still fight if he could."

"Is he a Wahabi, then? Why should he answer to a Mahratta *laonee* if he be Wahabi—or Sikh?" said I.

"I do not know," said Wali Dad. "He has lost, perhaps, his religion. Perhaps he wishes to be a King. Perhaps he is a King. I do not know his name."

"That is a lie, Wali Dad. If you know his career you must know his name."

"That is quite true. I belong to a nation of liars. I would rather not tell you his name. Think for yourself."

Lalun finished her song, pointed to the Fort, and said simply: "Khem Singh."

"Hm," said Wali Dad. "If the Pearl chooses to tell you the Pearl is a fool."

I translated to Lalun, who laughed. "I choose to tell what I choose to tell. They kept Khem Singh in Burma," said she. "They kept him there for many years until his mind was changed in him. So great was the kindness of the Government. Finding this, they sent him back to his own country that he might look upon it before he died. He is an old man, but when he looks upon this country his memory will come. Moreover, there be many who remember him."

"He is an Interesting Survival," said Wali Dad, pulling at the *huqa*. "He returns to a country now full of educational and political reform, but, as the Pearl says, there are many who remember him. He was once a great man. There will never be any more great men in India. They will all, when they are boys, go whoring after strange gods, and they will become citizens—'fellow-citizens'—'illustrious fellow-citizens.' What is it that the native papers call them?"

Wali Dad seemed to be in a very bad temper. Lalun looked out of the window and smiled into the dust-haze. I went away thinking about Khem Singh who had once made history with a thousand followers, and would have been a princeling but for the power of the Supreme Government aforesaid.

The Senior Captain Commanding Fort Amara was away on leave, but the Subaltern, his Deputy, had drifted down to he Club, where I found him and enquired of him whether it was really true that a political prisoner had been added to he attractions of the Fort. The Subaltern explained at great ength, for this was the first time that he had held Command of the Fort, and his glory lay heavy upon him.

"Yes," said he, "a man was sent in to me about a week ago rom down the line—a thorough gentleman whoever he is. Of ourse I did all I could for him. He had his two servants and ome silver cooking-pots, and he looked for all the world like a ative officer. I called him Subadar Sahib; just as well to be n the safe side, y'know. 'Look here, Subadar Sahib,' I said, you're handed over to my authority, and I'm supposed to uard you. Now I don't want to make your life hard, but you must make things easy for me. All the Fort is at your disposal, from the flagstaff to the dry ditch, and I shall be happy to entertain you in any way I can, but you mustn't take advantage of it. Give me your word that you won't try to escape, Subadar Sahib, and I'll give you my word that you shall have no heavy guard put over you.' I thought the best way of getting at him was by going at him straight, y'know; and it was, by Jove! The old man gave me his word, and moved about the Fort as contented as a sick crow. He's a rummy chap—always asking to be told where he is and what the buildings about him are. I had to sign a slip of blue paper when he turned up, acknowledging receipt of his body and all that, and I'm responsible, y'know, that he doesn't get away. Queer thing, though, looking after a Johnnie old enough to be your grandfather isn't it? Come to the Fort one of these days and see him?"

For reasons which will appear, I never went to the Fort while Khem Singh was then within its walls. I knew him only as a gray head seen from Lalun's window—a gray head and a harsh voice. But natives told me that, day by day, as he looked upon the fair lands round Amara, his memory came back to him and, with it, the old hatred against the Government that had been nearly effaced in far-off Burma. So he raged up and down the West face of the Fort from morning till noon and from evening till the night, devising vain things in his heart, and croaking war-songs when Lalun sang on the City wall. As he grew more acquainted with the Subaltern he unburdened his old heart of some of the passions that had withered it. "Sahib," he used to say, tapping his stick against the parapet, "when I was a young man I was one of twenty thousand horsemen who came out of the City and rode round the plain here. Sahib, I was the leader of a hundred, then of a thousand, then of five thousand, and now!"—he pointed to his two servants. "But from the beginning to to-day I would cut the throats of all the Sahibs in the land if I could. Hold me fast, Sahib, lest I get away and return to those who would follow me. I forgot them when I was in Burma, but now that I am in my own country again, I remember everything."

"Do you remember that you have given me your Honour not to make your tendance a hard matter?" said the Subaltern.

"Yes, to you, only to you, Sahib," said Khem Singh. "To you because you are of a pleasant countenance. If my turn comes again, Sahib, I will not hang you nor cut your throat."

"Thank you," said the Subaltern gravely, as he looked along the line of guns that could pound the City to powder in half an hour. "Let us go into our own quarters, Khem Singh. Come and talk with me after dinner."

Khem Singh would sit on his own cushion at the Subaltern's feet, drinking heavy, scented anise-seed brandy in great gulps, and telling strange stories of Fort Amara, which had been a palace in the old days, of Begums and Ranees tortured to death—aye, in the very vaulted chamber that now served as a Mess-room; would tell stories of Sobraon that made the Subaltern's cheeks flush and tingle with pride of race, and of the Kuka rising from which so much was expected and the foreknowledge of which was shared by a hundred thousand souls. But he never told tales of '57 because, as he said, he was the Subaltern's guest, and '57 is a year that no man, Black or White, cares to speak of. Once only, when the anise-seed brandy had slightly affected his head, he said: "Sahib, speaking now of a matter which lay between Sobraon and the affair of the Kukas, it was ever a wonder to us that you stayed your hand at all, and that, having stayed it, you did not make the land one prison. Now I hear from without that you do great honour to all men of our country and by your own hands are destroying the Terror of your Name which is your strong rock and defence. This is a foolish thing. Will oil and water mix? Now in '57——"

"I was not born then, Subadar Sahib," said the Subaltern, and Khem Singh reeled to his quarters.

The Subaltern would tell me of these conversations at the Club, and my desire to see Khem Singh increased. But Wali Dad, sitting in the window-seat of the house on the City wall, said that it would be a cruel thing to do, and Lalun pretended that I preferred the society of a grizzled old Sikh to hers.

"Here is tobacco, here is talk, here are many friends and all the news of the City, and, above all, here is myself. I will tell you stories and sing you songs, and Wali Dad will talk his English nonsense in your ears. Is that worse than watching the caged animal yonder? Go to-morrow, then, if you must, but to-day such and such an one will be here, and he will speak of wonderful things."

It happened that To-morrow never came, and the warm heat of the latter Rains gave place to the chill of early October almost before I was aware of the flight of the year. The Captain commanding the Fort returned from leave and took over charge of Khem Singh according to the laws of seniority. The Captain was not a nice man. He called all natives "niggers," which, besides being extreme bad form, shows gross ignorance.

"What's the use of telling off two Tommies to watch tha old nigger?" said he.

"I fancy it soothes his vanity," said the Subaltern. "Th men are ordered to keep well out of his way, but he take them as a tribute to his importance, poor old wretch."

"I won't have Line men taken off regular guards in thi way. Put on a couple of Native Infantry."

"Sikhs?" said the Subaltern, lifting his eyebrows.

"Sikhs, Pathans, Dogras—they're all alike, these blac vermin," and the Captain talked to Khem Singh in a manne which hurt that old gentleman's feelings. Fifteen years before when he had been caught for the second time, every on looked upon him as a sort of tiger. He liked being regarde in this light. But he forgot that the world goes forward i fifteen years, and many Subalterns are promoted to Ca taincies.

"The Captain-pig is in charge of the Fort?" said Kher Singh to his native guard every morning. And the nativ guard said: "Yes, Subadar Sahib," in deference to his ag and his air of distinction; but they did not know who he wa

In those days the gathering in Lalun's little white roo was always large and talked more than before.

"The Greeks," said Wali Dad who had been borrowin

my books, "the inhabitants of the city of Athens, where they were always hearing and telling some new thing, rigorously secluded their women—who were fools. Hence the glorious institution of the heterodox women—is it not?—who were amusing and *not* fools. All the Greek philosophers delighted in their company. Tell me, my friend, how it goes now in Greece and the other places upon the Continent of Europe. Are your women-folk also fools?"

"Wali Dad," I said, "you never speak to us about your women-folk and we never speak about ours to you. That is the bar between us."

"Yes," said Wali Dad, "it is curious to think that our common meeting-place should be here, in the house of a common—how do you call *her?*" He pointed with the pipe-mouth to Lalun.

"Lalun is nothing but Lalun," I said, and that was perfectly true. "But if you took your place in the world, Wali Dad, and gave up dreaming dreams——"

"I might wear an English coat and trouser. I might be a leading Muhammadan pleader. I might be received even at the Commissioner's tennis-parties where the English stand on one side and the natives on the other, in order to promote social intercourse throughout the Empire. Heart's Heart," said he to Lalun quickly, "the Sahib says that I ought to quit you."

"The Sahib is always talking stupid talk," returned Lalun with a laugh. "In this house I am a Queen and thou art a King. The Sahib"—she put her arms above her head and thought for a moment—"the Sahib shall be our Vizier—thine and mine, Wali Dad—because he has said that thou shouldst leave me."

Wali Dad laughed immoderately, and I laughed too. "Be it so," said he. "My friend, are you willing to take this lucrative Government appointment? Lalun, what shall his pay be?"

But Lalun began to sing, and for the rest of the time there was no hope of getting a sensible answer from her or Wali Dad. When the one stopped, the other began to quote Persian poetry with a triple pun in every other line. Some of it was not strictly proper, but it was all very funny, and it only came to an end when a fat person in black, with gold *pince-nez,* sent up his name to Lalun, and Wali Dad dragged me into the twinkling night to walk in a big rose-garden and talk heresies about Religion and Governments and a man's career in life.

The Mohurrum, the great mourning-festival of the Muhammadans, was close at hand, and the things that Wali Dad said about religious fanaticism would have secured his expulsion from the loosest-thinking Muslim sect. There were the rose-bushes round us, the stars above us, and from every quarter of the City came the boom of the big Mohurrum drums. You must know that the City is divided in fairly equal proportions between the Hindus and the Musalmans, and where both creeds belong to the fighting races, a big religious festival gives ample chance for trouble. When they can—that is to say when the authorities are weak enough to allow it—the Hindus do their best to arrange some minor feast-day of their own in time to clash with the period of general mourning for the martyrs Hasan and Hussain, the heroes of the Mohurrum. Gilt and painted paper presentations of their tombs are borne with shouting and wailing, music, torches, and yells, through the principal thoroughfares of the City, which fakements are called *tazias*. Their passage is rigorously laid down beforehand by the Police, and detachments of Police accompany each *tazia,* lest the Hindus should throw bricks at it and the peace of the Queen and the heads of Her loyal subjects should thereby be broken. Mohurrum time in a "fighting" town means anxiety to all the officials, because, if a riot breaks out, the officials and not the rioters are held responsible. The former must foresee everything, and while not making their precautions ridiculously elaborate, must see that they are at least adequate.

"Listen to the drums!" said Wali Dad. "That is the heart of the people—empty and making much noise. How, think you, will the Mohurrum go this year? *I* think that there will be trouble."

He turned down a side-street and left me alone with the stars and a sleepy Police patrol. Then I went to bed and dreamed that Wali Dad had sacked the City and I was made Vizier, with Lalun's silver *huqa* for mark of office.

All day the Mohurrum drums beat in the City, and all day deputations of tearful Hindu gentlemen besieged the Deputy Commissioner with assurances that they would be murdered ere next dawning by the Muhammadans. "Which," said the Deputy Commissioner, in confidence to the Head of Police, "is a pretty fair indication that the Hindus are going to make 'emselves unpleasant. I think we can arrange a little surprise for them. I have given the heads of both Creeds fair warning. If they choose to disregard it, so much the worse for them."

There was a large gathering in Lalun's house that night, but of men that I had never seen before, if I except the fat gentleman in black with the gold *pince-nez*. Wali Dad lay in the window-seat, more bitterly scornful of his Faith and its manifestations than I had ever known him. Lalun's maid was very busy cutting up and mixing tobacco for the guests. We could hear the thunder of the drums as the processions accompanying each *tazia* marched to the central gathering-place in the plain outside the City, preparatory to their triumphant re-entry and circuit within the walls. All the streets seemed ablaze with torches, and only Fort Amara was black and silent.

When the noise of the drums ceased, no one in the white room spoke for a time. "The first *tazia* has moved off," said Wali Dad, looking to the plain.

"That is very early," said the man with the *pince-nez*.

"It is only half-past eight." The company rose and departed.

"Some of them were men from Ladakh," said Lalun, when the last had gone. "They brought me brick-tea such as the Russians sell, and a tea-urn from Peshawur. Show me, now, how the English *Memsahibs* make tea."

The brick-tea was abominable. When it was finished Wali Dad suggested going into the streets. "I am nearly sure that there will be trouble to-night," he said. "All the City thinks so, and *Vox Populi* is *Vox Dei,* as the Babus say. Now I tell you that at the corner of the Padshahi Gate you will find my horse all this night if you want to go about and to see things. It is a most disgraceful exhibition. Where is the pleasure of saying *'Ya Hasan, Ya Hussain,'* twenty thousand times in a night?"

All the processions—there were two and twenty of them—were now well within the City walls. The drums were beating afresh, the crowd were howling *"Ya Hasan! Ya Hussain!"* and beating their breasts, the brass bands were playing their loudest, and at every corner where space allowed, Muhammadan preachers were telling the lamentable story of the death of the Martyrs. It was impossible to move except with the crowd, for the streets were not more than twenty feet wide. In the Hindu quarters the shutters of all the shops were up and cross-barred. As the first *tazia,* a gorgeous erection ten feet high, was borne aloft on the shoulders of a score of stout men into the semi-darkness of the Gully of the Horsemen, a brickbat crashed through its talc and tinsel sides.

"Into thy hands, O Lord?" murmured Wali Dad profanely, as a yell went up from behind, and a native officer of Police jammed his horse through the crowd. Another brickbat followed, and the *tazia* staggered and swayed where it had stopped.

"Go on! In the name of the *Sirkar,* go forward!" shouted the Policeman; but there was an ugly cracking and splintering of shutters, and the crowd halted, with oaths and growlings, before the house whence the brick-bat had been thrown.

Then, without any warning, broke the storm—not only in the Gully of the Horsemen, but in half a dozen other places. The *tazias* rocked like ships at sea, the long pole-torches dipped and rose round them while the men shouted: "The Hindus are dishonouring the *tazias!* Strike! Strike! Into their temples for the faith!" The six or eight Policemen with each *tazia* drew their batons, and struck as long as they could in the hope of forcing the mob forward, but they were overpowered, and as contingents of Hindus poured into the streets, the fight became general. Half a mile away where the *tazias* were yet untouched the drums and the shrieks of *"Ya Hasan! Ya Hussain!"* continued, but not for long. The priests at the corners of the streets knocked the legs from the bedsteads that supported their pulpits and smote for the Faith, while stones fell from the silent houses upon friend and foe, and the packed streets bellowed: *"Din! Din! Din!"* A *tazia* caught fire, and was dropped for a flaming barrier between Hindu and Musalman at the corner of the Gully. Then the crowd surged forward, and Wali Dad drew me close to the stone pillar of a well.

"It was intended from the beginning!" he shouted in my ear, with more heat than blank unbelief should be guilty of. "The bricks were carried up to the houses beforehand. These swine of Hindus! We shall be gutting kine in their temples to-night!"

Tazia after *tazia,* some burning, others torn to pieces, hurried past us and the mob with them, howling, shrieking, and striking at the house doors in their flight. At last we saw the reason of the rush. Hugonin, the Assistant District Superintendent of Police, a boy of twenty, had got together thirty constables and was forcing the crowd through the streets. His old gray Police-horse showed no sign of uneasiness as it was spurred breast-on into the crowd, and the long dog-whip with which he had armed himself was never still.

"They know we haven't enough Police to hold 'em," he cried as he passed me, mopping a cut on his face. "They *know* we haven't! Aren't any of the men from the Club coming down to help? Get on, you sons of burnt fathers!" The dog-whip cracked across the writhing backs, and the constables smote afresh with baton and gun-butt. With these passed the lights and the shouting, and Wali Dad began to swear under his breath. From Fort Amara shot up a single rocket; then two side by side. It was the signal for troops.

Petitt, the Deputy Commissioner, covered with dust and sweat, but calm and gently smiling, cantered up the clean-swept street in rear of the main body of the rioters. "No one killed yet," he shouted. "I'll keep 'em on the run till dawn! Don't let 'em halt, Hugonin! Trot 'em about till the troops come."

The science of the defence lay solely in keeping the mob on the move. If they had breathing-space they would halt and fire a house, and then the work of restoring order would be more difficult, to say the least of it. Flames have the same effect on a crowd as blood has on a wild beast.

Word had reached the Club and men in evening-dress were beginning to show themselves and lend a hand in heading off and breaking up the shouting masses with stirrup-leathers, whips, or chance-found staves. They were not very often attacked, for the rioters had sense enough to know that the death of a European would not mean one hanging but many, and possibly the appearance of the thrice-dreaded Artillery. The clamour in the City redoubled. The Hindus had descended into the streets in real earnest and ere long the mob returned. It was a strange sight. There were no *tazias*—only their riven platforms—and there were no Police. Here and there a City dignitary, Hindu or Muhammadan, was vainly imploring his co-religionists to keep quiet and behave themselves—advice for which his white beard was pulled. Then a native officer of Police, unhorsed but still using his spurs with effect, would be borne along, warning all the crowd of the danger of insulting the Government. Everywhere men struck aimlessly with sticks, grasping each other by the throat, howling and foaming with rage, or beat with their bare hands on the doors of the houses.

"It is a lucky thing that they are fighting with natural weapons," I said to Wali Dad, "else we should have half the City killed."

I turned as I spoke and looked at his face. His nostrils were distended, his eyes were fixed, and he was smiting himself softly on the breast. The crowd poured by with renewed riot—a gang of Musalmans hard-pressed by some hundred Hindu fanatics. Wali Dad left my side with an oath, and shouting: *"Ya Hasan! Ya Hussain!"* plunged into the thick of the fight where I lost sight of him.

I fled by a side alley to the Padshahi Gate where I found Wali Dad's house, and thence rode to the Fort. Once outside the City wall, the tumult sank to a dull roar, very impressive under the stars and reflecting great credit on the fifty thousand angry able-bodied men who were making it. The troops who, at the Deputy Commissioner's instance, had been ordered to rendezvous quietly near the fort, showed no signs of being impressed. Two companies of Native Infantry, a squadron of Native Cavalry and a company of British Infantry were kicking their heels in the shadow of the East face, waiting for orders to march in. I am sorry to say that they were all pleased, unholily pleased, at the chance of what they called "a little fun." The senior officers, to be sure, grumbled at having been kept out of bed, and the English troops pretended to be sulky, but there was joy in the hearts of all the subalterns, and whispers ran up and down the line: "No ball-cartridge—what a beastly shame!" "D'you think the beggars will really stand up to us?" " 'Hope I shall meet my money-lender there. I owe him more than I can afford." "Oh, they won't let us even unsheathe swords." "Hurrah! Up goes the fourth rocket. Fall in, there!"

The Garrison Artillery, who to the last cherished a wild hope that they might be allowed to bombard the City at a hundred yards' range, lined the parapet above the East gateway and cheered themselves hoarse as the British Infantry doubled along the road to the Main Gate of the City. The Cavalry cantered on to the Padshahi Gate, and the Native Infantry marched slowly to the Gate of the Butchers. The surprise was intended to be of a distinctly unpleasant nature, and to come on top of the defeat of the Police who had been just able to keep the Muhammadans from firing the houses of a few leading Hindus. The bulk of the riot lay in the north and north-west wards. The east and south-east were by this time dark and silent, and I rode hastily to Lalun's house for I wished to tell her to send some one in search of Wali Dad. The house was unlighted, but the door was open, and I climbed upstairs in the darkness. One small lamp in the white room showed Lalun and her maid leaning half out of the window, breathing heavily and evidently pulling at something that refused to come.

"Thou art late—very late," gasped Lalun without turning her head. "Help us now, O Fool, if thou hast not spent thy strength howling among the *tazias*. Pull! Nasiban and I can do no more! O Sahib, is it you? The Hindus have been hunting an old Muhammadan round the Ditch with clubs. If they find him again they will kill him. Help us to pull him up."

I put my hands to the long red silk waist-cloth that was hanging out of the window, and we three pulled and pulled with all the strength at our command. There was something very heavy at the end, and it swore in an unknown tongue as it kicked against the City wall.

"Pull, oh, pull!" said Lalun at the last. A pair of brown hands grasped the window-sill and a venerable Muhammadan tumbled upon the floor, very much out of breath. His jaws were tied up, his turban had fallen over one eye, and he was dusty and angry.

Lalun hid her face in her hands for an instant and said something about Wali Dad that I could not catch.

Then, to my extreme gratification, she threw her arms round my neck and murmured pretty things. I was in no haste to stop her; and Nasiban, being a handmaiden of tact, turned to the big jewel-chest that stands in the corner of the white room and rummaged among the contents. The Muhammadan sat on the floor and glared.

"One service more, Sahib, since thou hast come so opportunely," said Lalun. "Wilt thou"—it is very nice to be thou-ed by Lalun—"take this old man across the City—the troops are everywhere, and they might hurt him for he is old—to the Kumharsen Gate? There I think he may find a carriage to take him to his house. He is a friend of mine, and thou art—more than a friend—therefore I ask this."

Nasiban bent over the old man, tucked something into his belt, and I raised him up, and led him into the streets. In crossing from the east to the west of the City there was no chance of avoiding the troops and the crowd. Long before I reached the Gully of the Horsemen I heard the shouts of the

British Infantry crying cheeringly: "Hutt, ye beggars! Hutt, ye devils! Get along! Go forward, there!" Then followed the ringing of rifle-butts and shrieks of pain. The troops were banging the bare toes of the mob with their gun-butts—for not a bayonet had been fixed. My companion mumbled and jabbered as we walked on until we were carried back by the crowd and had to force our way to the troops. I caught him by the wrist and felt a bangle there—the iron bangle of the Sikhs—but I had no suspicions, for Lalun had only ten minutes before put her arms round me. Thrice we were carried back by the crowd, and when we made our way past the British Infantry it was to meet the Sikh Cavalry driving another mob before them with the butts of their lances.

"What are these dogs?" said the old man.

"Sikhs of the Cavalry, Father," I said, and we edged our way up the line of horses two abreast and found the Deputy Commissioner, his helmet smashed on his head, surrounded by a knot of men who had come down from the Club as amateur constables and had helped the Police mightily.

"We'll keep 'em on the run till dawn," said Petitt. "Who's your villainous friend?"

I had only time to say: "The Protection of the *Sirkar!*" when a fresh crowd flying before the Native Infantry carried us a hundred yards nearer to the Kumharsen Gate, and Petitt was swept away like a shadow.

"I do not know—I cannot see—this is all new to me!" moaned my companion. "How many troops are there in the City?"

"Perhaps five hundred," I said.

"A lakh of men beaten by five hundred—and Sikhs among them! Surely, surely, I am an old man, but—the Kumharsen Gate is new. Who pulled down the stone lions? Where is the conduit? Sahib, I am a very old man, and, alas, I—I cannot stand." He dropped in the shadow of the Kumharsen Gate where there was no disturbance. A fat gentleman wearing gold *pince-nez* came out of the darkness.

"You are most kind to my old friend," he said suavely. "He is a landholder of Akala. He should not be in a big City when there is religious excitement. But I have a carriage here. You are quite truly kind. Will you help me to put him into the carriage? It is very late."

We bundled the old man into a hired victoria that stood close to the gate, and I turned back to the house on the City wall. The troops were driving the people to and fro, while the Police shouted, "To your houses! Get to your houses!" and the dog-whip of the Assistant District Superintendent cracked remorselessly. Terror-stricken *bunnias* clung to the stirrups of the cavalry, crying that their houses had been robbed (which was a lie), and the burly Sikh horsemen patted them on the shoulder, and bade them return to those houses lest a worse thing should happen. Parties of five or six British soldiers, joining arms, swept down the side-gullies, their rifles on their backs, stamping, with shouting and song, upon the toes of Hindu and Musalman. Never was religious enthusiasm more systematically squashed; and never were poor breakers of the peace more utterly weary and footsore. They were routed out of holes and corners, from behind well-pillars and byres, and bidden to go to their houses. If they had no houses to go to, so much the worse for their toes.

On returning to Lalun's door I stumbled over a man at the threshold. He was sobbing hysterically and his arms flapped like the wings of a goose. It was Wali Dad, Agnostic and Unbeliever, shoeless, turbanless, and frothing at the mouth, the flesh on his chest bruised and bleeding from the vehemence with which he had smitten himself. A broken torch-handle lay by his side, and his quivering lips murmured, *"Ya Hasan! Ya Hussain!"* as I stooped over him. I pushed him a few steps up the staircase, threw a pebble at Lalun's City window and hurried home.

Most of the streets were very still, and the cold wind that comes before the dawn whistled down them. In the centre of the Square of the Mosque a man was bending over a corpse. The skull had been smashed in by gun-butt or bamboo-stave.

"It is expedient that one man should die for the people," said Petitt grimly, raising the shapeless head. "These brutes were beginning to show their teeth too much."

And from afar we could hear the soldiers singing "Two Lovely Black Eyes," as they drove the remnant of the rioters within doors.

. . . .

Of course you can guess what happened? I was not so clever. When the news went abroad that Khem Singh had escaped from the Fort, I did not, since I was then living this story, not writing it, connect myself, or Lalun, or the fat gentleman with the gold *pince-nez,* with his disappearance. Nor did it strike me that Wali Dad was the man who should have convoyed him across the City, or that Lalun's arms round my neck were put there to hide the money that Nasiban gave to Khem Singh, and that Lalun had used me and my white face as even a better safeguard than Wali Dad who proved himself so untrustworthy. All that I knew at the time was that, when Fort Amara was taken up with the riots, Khem Singh profited by the confusion to get away, and that his two Sikh guards also escaped.

But later on I received full enlightenment; and so did Khem Singh. He fled to those who knew him in the old days, but many of them were dead and more were changed, and all knew something of the Wrath of the Government. He went to the young men, but the glamour of his name had passed away, and they were entering native regiments of Government offices, and Khem Singh could give them neither pension, decorations, nor influence—nothing but a glorious death with their backs to the mouth of a gun. He wrote letters and made promises, and the letters fell into bad hands, and a wholly insignificant subordinate officer of Police tracked them down and gained promotion thereby. Moreover, Khem Singh was old, and anise-seed brandy was scarce, and he had left his silver cooking-pots in Fort Amara with his nice warm bedding, and the gentleman with the gold *pince-nez* was told by those who had employed him that Khem Singh as a popular leader was not worth the money paid.

"Great is the mercy of these fools of English!" said Khem Singh when the situation was put before him. "I will go back to Fort Amara of my own free will and gain honour. Give me good clothes to return in."

So, at his own time, Khem Singh knocked at the wicket-gate of the Fort and walked to the Captain and the Subaltern, who were nearly gray-headed on account of correspondence that daily arrived from Simla marked "Private."

"I have come back, Captain Sahib," said Khem Singh. "Put no more guards over me. It is no good out yonder."

A week later I saw him for the first time to my knowledge, and he made as though there were an understanding between us.

"It was well done, Sahib," said he, "and greatly I admired your astuteness in thus boldly facing the troops when I, whom they would have doubtless torn to pieces, was with you. Now there is a man in Fort Ooltagarh whom a bold man could with ease help to escape. This is the position of the Fort as I draw it on the sand——"

But I was thinking how I had become Lalun's Vizier after all.

THE MAN WHO WOULD BE KING
1888

Brother to a Prince and fellow to a beggar if he be found worthy.

THE Law, as quoted, lays down a fair conduct of life, and one not easy to follow. I have been fellow to a beggar again and again under circumstances which prevented either of us finding out whether the other was worthy. I have still to be brother to a Prince, though I once came near to kinship with what might have been a veritable King and was promised the reversion of a Kingdom—army, law-courts, revenue and policy all complete. But, to-day, I greatly fear that my King is dead, and if I want a crown I must go hunt it for myself.

The beginning of everything was in a railway train upon the road to Mhow from Ajmir. There had been a Deficit in the Budget, which necessitated travelling, not Second-class, which is only half as dear as First-class, but by Intermediate, which is very awful indeed. There are no cushions in the Intermediate class, and the population are either Intermediate, which is Eurasian, or native, which for a long night journey is nasty, or Loafer, which is amusing though intoxicated. Intermediates do not buy from refreshment-rooms. They carry their food in bundles and pots, and buy sweets from the native sweetmeat-sellers, and drink the roadside water. That is why in hot weather Intermediates are taken out of the carriages dead, and in all weathers are most properly looked down upon.

My particular Intermediate happened to be empty till I reached Nasirabad, when a big black-browed gentleman in shirt-sleeves entered, and, following the custom of Intermediates, passed the time of day. He was a wanderer and a vagabond like myself, but with an educated taste for whiskey. He told tales of things he had seen and done, of out-of-the-way corners of the Empire into which he had penetrated, and of adventures in which he risked his life for a few days' food.

"If India was filled with men like you and me, not knowing more than the crows where they'd get their next day's rations, it isn't seventy millions of revenue the land would be paying—it's seven hundred millions," said he; and as I looked at his mouth and chin I was disposed to agree with him.

We talked politics—the politics of Loaferdom that sees things from the underside where the lath and plaster is not smoothed off—and we talked postal arrangements because my friend wanted to send a telegram back from the next station to Ajmir, the turning-off place from the Bombay to the Mhow line as you travel westward. My friend had no money beyond eight annas which he wanted for dinner, and I had no money at all, owing to the hitch in the Budget before mentioned. Further, I was going into a wilderness where, though I should resume touch with the Treasury, there were no telegraph offices. I was, therefore, unable to help him in any way.

"We might threaten a Station-master, and make him send a wire on tick," said my friend, "but that'd mean enquiries for you and for me, and *I*'ve got my hands full these days. Did you say you were travelling back along this line, within any days?"

"Within ten," I said.

"Can't you make it eight?" said he. "Mine is rather urgent business."

"I can send your telegram within ten days if that will serve you," I said.

"I couldn't trust the wire to fetch him now I think of it. It's this way. He leaves Delhi on the 23rd for Bombay. That means he'll be running through Ajmir about the night of the 23rd."

"But I'm going into the Indian Desert," I explained.

"Well *and* good," said he. "You'll be changing at Marwar Junction to get into Jodhpore territory—you must do that—

and he'll be coming through Marwar Junction in the early morning of the 24th by the Bombay Mail. Can you be at Marwar Junction on that time? 'Twon't be inconveniencing you because I know that there's precious few pickings to be got out of these Central India States—even though you pretend to be correspondent of the *Backwoodsman*."

"Have you ever tried that trick?" I asked.

"Again and again, but the Residents find you out, and then you get escorted to the Border before you've time to get your knife into them. But about my friend here. I *must* give him a word o' mouth to tell him what's come to me or else he won't know where to go. I would take it more than kind of you if you was to come out of Central India in time to catch him at Marwar Junction, and say to him: 'He has gone South for the week.' He'll know what that means. He's a big man with a red beard, and a great swell he is. You'll find him sleeping like a gentleman with all his luggage round him in a Second-class apartment. But don't you be afraid. Slip down the window and say: 'He has gone South for the week,' and he'll tumble. It's only cutting your time of stay in those parts by two days. I ask you as a stranger—going to the West," he said with emphasis.

"Where have *you* come from?" said I.

"From the East," said he, "and I am hoping that you will give him the message on the Square—for the sake of my Mother as well as your own."

Englishmen are not usually softened by appeals to the memory of their mothers; but for certain reasons, which will be fully apparent, I saw fit to agree.

"It's more than a little matter," said he, "and that's why I asked you to do it—and now I know that I can depend on you doing it. A Second-class carriage at Marwar Junction, and a red-haired man asleep in it. You'll be sure to remember. I get out at the next station, and I must hold on there till he comes or sends me what I want."

"I'll give the message if I catch him," I said, "and for the sake of your Mother as well as mine I'll give you a word of advice. Don't try to run the Central India States just now as the correspondent of the *Backwoodsman*. There's a real one knocking about here, and it might lead to trouble."

"Thank you," said he simply, "and when will the swine be gone? I can't starve because he's ruining my work. I wanted to get hold of the Degumber Rajah down here about his father's widow, and give him a jump."

"What did he do to his father's widow, then?"

"Filled her up with red pepper and slippered her to death as she hung from a beam. I found that out myself and I'm the only man that would dare going into the State to get hush-money for it. They'll try to poison me, same as they did in Chortumna when I went on the loot there. But you'll give the man at Marwar Junction my message?"

He got out at a little roadside station, and I reflected, I had heard, more than once, of men personating correspondents of newspapers and bleeding small Native States with threats of exposure, but I had never met any of the caste before. They lead a hard life, and generally die with great suddenness. The Native States have a wholesome horror of English newspapers, which may throw light on their peculiar methods of government, and do their best to choke correspondents with champagne, or drive them out of their mind with four-in-hand barouches. They do not understand that nobody cares a straw for the internal administration of Native States so long as oppression and crime are kept within decent limits, and the ruler is not drugged, drunk, or diseased from one end of the year to the other. They are the dark places of the earth, full of unimaginable cruelty, touching the Railway and the Telegraph on one side, and, on the other, the days of Harun-al-Raschid. When I left the train I did business with divers Kings, and in eight days passed through many changes of life. Sometimes I wore dress-clothes and consorted with Princes and Politicals, drinking from crystal and eating from silver. Sometimes I lay out upon the ground and devoured what I could get, from a plate made of leaves, and drank the running water, and slept under the same rug as my servant. It was all in the day's work.

Then I headed for the Great Indian Desert upon the proper

date, as I had promised, and the night Mail set me down at Marwar Junction, where a funny little, happy-go-lucky, native-managed railway runs to Jodhpore. The Bombay Mail from Delhi makes a short halt at Marwar. She arrived as I got in, and I had just time to hurry to her platform and go down the carriages. There was only one Second-class on the train. I slipped the window and looked down upon a flaming red beard, half covered by a railway rug. That was my man, fast asleep, and I dug him gently in the ribs. He woke with a grunt and I saw his face in the light of the lamps. It was a great and shining face.

"Tickets again?" said he.

"No," said I. "I am to tell you that he is gone South for the week. He has gone South for the week!"

The train had begun to move out. The red man rubbed his eyes. "He has gone South for the week," he repeated. "Now that's just like his impidence. Did he say that I was to give you anything? 'Cause I won't."

"He didn't," I said and dropped away, and watched the red lights die out in the dark. It was horribly cold because the wind was blowing off the sands. I climbed into my own train—not an Intermediate carriage this time—and went to sleep.

If the man with the beard had given me a rupee I should have kept it as a memento of a rather curious affair. But the consciousness of having done my duty was my only reward.

Later on I reflected that two gentlemen like my friends could not do any good if they foregathered and personated correspondents of newspapers, and might, if they blackmailed one of the little rat-trap states of Central India or Southern Rajputana, get themselves into serious difficulties. I therefore took some trouble to describe them as accurately as I could remember to people who would be interested in deporting them: and succeeded, so I was later informed, in having them headed back from the Degumber borders.

Then I became respectable, and returned to an Office where there were no Kings and no incidents outside the daily manufacture of a newspaper. A newspaper office seems to attract every conceivable sort of person, to the prejudice of discipline. Zenana-mission ladies arrive, and beg that the Editor will instantly abandon all his duties to describe a Christian prize-giving in a back-slum of a perfectly inaccessible village; Colonels who have been overpassed for command sit down and sketch the outline of a series of ten, twelve, or twenty-four leading articles on Seniority *versus* Selection; missionaries wish to know why they have not been permitted to escape from their regular vehicles of abuse and swear at a brother-missionary under special patronage of the editorial We; stranded theatrical companies troop up to explain that they cannot pay for their advertisements, but on their return from New Zealand or Tahiti will do so with interest; inventors of patent punkah-pulling machines, carriage couplings and unbreakable swords and axle-trees call with specifications in their pockets and hours at their disposal; tea-companies enter and elaborate their prospectuses with the office pens; secretaries of ball-committees clamour to have the glories of their last dance more fully described; strange ladies rustle in and say: "I want a hundred lady's cards printed *at once,* please," which is manifestly part of an Editor's duty; and every dissolute ruffian that ever tramped the Grand Trunk Road makes it his business to ask for employment as a proof-reader. And, all the time, the telephone-bell is ringing madly, and Kings are being killed on the Continent, and Empires are saying—"You're another," and Mister Gladstone is calling down brimstone upon the British Dominions, and the little black copy-boys are whining, *"kaa-pi chay-ha-yeh"* (copy wanted) like tired bees, and most of the paper is as blank as Modred's shield.

But that is the amusing part of the year. There are six other months when none ever come to call, and the thermometer walks inch by inch up to the top of the glass, and the office is darkened to just above reading-light, and the press-machines are red-hot to touch, and nobody writes anything but accounts of amusements in the Hill-stations or obituary notices. Then the telephone becomes a tinkling terror, because it tells you of the sudden deaths of men and women that you knew intimately, and the prickly heat covers you with a garment, and you sit down and write: "A slight increase of sickness is reported from the Khuda Janta Khan District. The outbreak is purely sporadic in its nature, and, thanks to the energetic efforts of the District authorities, is now almost at an end. It is, however, with deep regret we record the death," etc.

Then the sickness really breaks out, and the less recording and reporting the better for the peace of the subscribers. But the Empires and the Kings continue to divert themselves as selfishly as before, and the Foreman thinks that a daily paper really ought to come out once in twenty-four hours, and all the people at the Hill-stations in the middle of their amusements say: "Good gracious! Why can't the paper be sparkling? I'm sure there's plenty going on up here."

That is the dark half of the moon, and, as the advertisements say, "must be experienced to be appreciated."

It was in that season, and a remarkably evil season, that the paper began running the last issue of the week on Saturday night, which is to say Sunday morning, after the custom of a London paper. This was a great convenience, for immediately after the paper was put to bed, the dawn would lower the thermometer from 96° to almost 84° for half an hour, and in that chill—you have no idea how cold is 84° on the grass until you begin to pray for it—a very tired man could get off to sleep ere the heat roused him.

One Saturday night it was my pleasant duty to put the paper to bed alone. A King or courtier or a courtesan or a Community was going to die or get a new Constitution, or do something that was important on the other side of the world, and the paper was to be held open till the latest possible minute in order to catch the telegram.

It was a pitchy black night, as stifling as a June night can be, and the *loo,* the red-hot wind from the westward, was booming among the tinder-dry trees and pretending that the rain was on its heels. Now and again a spot of almost boiling water would fall on the dust with the flop of a frog, but all our weary world knew that was only pretence. It was a shade cooler in the press-room than the office, so I sat there, while the type ticked and clicked, and the night-jars hooted at the windows, and the all but naked compositors wiped the sweat from their foreheads, and called for water. The thing that was keeping us back, whatever it was, would not come off, though the *loo* dropped and the last type was set, and the whole round earth stood still in the choking heat, with its finger on its lip, to wait the event. I drowsed, and wondered whether the telegraph was a blessing, and whether this dying man, or struggling people, might be aware of the inconvenience the delay was causing. There was no special reason beyond the heat and worry to make tension, but, as the clock-hands crept up to three o'clock and the machines spun their fly-wheels two and three times to see that all was in order, before I said the word that would set them off, I could have shrieked aloud.

Then the roar and rattle of the wheels shivered the quiet into little bits. I rose to go away, but two men in white clothes stood in front of me. The first one said: "It's him!" The second said: "So it is!" And they both laughed almost as loudly as the machinery roared, and mopped their foreheads. "We seed there was a light burning across the road and we were sleeping in that ditch there for coolness, and I said to my friend here, The office is open. Let's come along and speak to him as turned us back from the Degumber State," said the smaller of the two. He was the man I had met in the Mhow train, and his fellow was the red-bearded man of Marwar Junction. There was no mistaking the eyebrows of the one or the beard of the other.

I was not pleased, because I wished to go to sleep, not to squabble with loafers. "What do you want?" I asked.

"Half an hour's talk with you, cool and comfortable, in the office," said the red-bearded man. "We'd *like* some drink—the Contrack doesn't begin yet, Peachey, so you needn't look—but what we really want is advice. We don't want money. We ask you as a favour, because we found out you did us a bad turn about Degumber State."

I led from the press-room to the stifling office with the maps on the walls, and the red-haired man rubbed his hands. "That's something like," said he. "This was the proper shop to come to. Now, Sir, let me introduce to you Brother Peachey Carnehan, that's him, and Brother Daniel Dravot, that is *me,* and the less said about our professions the better, for we have been most things in our time. Soldier, sailor, compositor, photographer, proof-reader, street-preacher, and correspondents of the *Backwoodsman* when we thought the paper wanted one. Carnehan is sober, and so am I. Look at us first, and see that's sure. It will save you cutting into my talk. We'll take one of your cigars apiece, and you shall see us light up."

I watched the test. The men were absolutely sober, so I gave them each a tepid whiskey and soda.

"Well *and* good," said Carnehan of the eyebrows, wiping the froth from his moustache. "Let me talk now, Dan. We have been all over India, mostly on foot. We have been boiler-fitters, engine-drivers, petty contractors, and all that, and we have decided that India isn't big enough for such as us."

They certainly were too big for the office. Dravot's beard seemed to fill half the room and Carnehan's shoulders the other half, as they sat on the big table. Carnehan continued: "The country isn't half worked out because they that governs it won't let you touch it. They spend all their blessed time in governing it, and you can't lift a spade, nor chip a rock, nor look for oil, nor anything like that without all the Government saying—'Leave it alone, and let us govern.' Therefore, such *as* it is, we will let it alone, and go away to some other place where a man isn't crowded and can come to his own. We are not little men, and there is nothing that we are afraid of except Drink, and we have signed a Contrack on that. *Therefore,* we are going away to be Kings."

"Kings in our own right," muttered Dravot.

"Yes, of course," I said. "You've been tramping in the sun, and it's a very warm night, and hadn't you better sleep over the notion? Come to-morrow."

"Neither drunk nor sunstruck," said Dravot. "We have slept over the notion half a year, and require to see Books and Atlases, and we have decided that there is only one place now in the world that two strong men can Sar-a-*whack*. They call it Kafiristan. By my reckoning it's the top right-hand corner of Afghanistan, not more than three hundred miles from Peshawar. They have two-and-thirty heathen idols there, and we'll be the thirty-third and fourth. It's a mountaineous country, and the women of those parts are very beautiful."

"But that is provided against in the Contrack," said Carnehan. "Neither Woman nor Liqu-or, Daniel."

"And that's all we know, except that no one has gone there, and they fight, and in any place where they fight a man who knows how to drill men can always be a King. We shall go to those parts and say to any King we find—'D'you want to vanquish your foes?' and we will show him how to drill men; for that we know better than anything else. Then we will subvert that King and seize his Throne and establish a Dy-nasty."

"You'll be cut to pieces before you're fifty miles across the Border," I said. "You have to travel through Afghanistan to get to that country. It's one mass of mountains and peaks and glaciers, and no Englishman has been through it. The people are utter brutes, and even if you reached them you couldn't do anything."

"That's more like," said Carnehan. "If you could think us a little more mad we would be more pleased. We have come to you to know about this country, to read a book about it, and to be shown maps. We want you to tell us that we are fools and to show us your books." He turned to the bookcases.

"Are you at all in earnest?" I said.

"A little," said Dravot sweetly. "As big a map as you have got, even if it's all blank where Kafiristan is, and any books you've got. We can read, though we aren't very educated."

I uncased the big thirty-two-miles-to-the-inch map of India, and two smaller Frontier maps, hauled down volume INF-KAN of the *Encyclopædia Britannica,* and the men consulted them.

"See here!" said Dravot, his thumb on the map. "Up to Jagdallak, Peachey and me know the road. We was there with Roberts' Army. We'll have to turn off to the right at Jagdallak through Laghmann territory. Then we get among the hills—fourteen thousand feet—fifteen thousand—it will be cold work there, but it don't look very far on the map."

I handed him Wood on the *Sources of the Oxus*. Carnehan was deep in the *Encyclopædia*.

"They're a mixed lot," said Dravot reflectively; "and it won't help us to know the names of their tribes. The more tribes the more they'll fight, and the better for us. From Jagdallak to Ashang. H'mm!"

"But all the information about the country is as sketchy and inaccurate as can be," I protested. "No one knows anything about it really. Here's the file of the *United Services' Institute*. Read what Bellew says."

"Blow Bellew!" said Carnehan. "Dan, they're a stinkin' lot of heathens, but this book here says they think they're related to us English."

I smoked while the men pored over *Raverty, Wood,* the maps, and the *Encyclopædia*.

"There is no use your waiting," said Dravot politely. "It's about four o'clock now. We'll go before six o'clock if you want to sleep, and we won't steal any of the papers. Don't you sit up. We're two harmless lunatics, and if you come to-morrow evening down to the Serai we'll say good-bye to you."

"You *are* two fools," I answered. "You'll be turned back at the Frontier or cut up the minute you set foot in Afghanistan. Do you want any money or a recommendation down-country? I can help you to the chance of work next week."

"Next week we shall be hard at work ourselves, thank you," said Dravot. "It isn't so easy being a King as it looks. When we've got our Kingdom in going order we'll let you know, and you can come up and help us to govern it."

"Would two lunatics make a Contrack like that?" said Carnehan, with subdued pride, showing me a greasy half-sheet of notepaper on which was written the following. I copied it, then and there, as a curiosity—

This Contract between me and you persuing witnesseth in the name of God—Amen and so forth.

(*One*) *That me and you will settle this matter together;* i.e., *to be Kings of Kafiristan.*

(*Two*) *That you and me will not, while this matter is being settled, look at any Liquor, nor any Woman black, white, or brown, so as to get mixed up with one or the other harmful.*

(*Three*) *That we conduct ourselves with Dignity and Discretion, and if one of us gets into trouble the other will stay by him.*

Signed by you and me this day.
Peachey Taliaferro Carnehan.
Daniel Dravot.
Both Gentlemen at Large.

"There was no need for the last article," said Carnehan, blushing modestly; "but it looks regular. Now you know the sort of men that loafers are—we *are* loafers, Dan, until we get out of India—and *do* you think that we would sign a Contrack like that unless we was in earnest? We have kept away from the two things that make life worth having."

"You won't enjoy your lives much longer if you are going to try this idiotic adventure. Don't set the office on fire," I said, "and go away before nine o'clock."

I left them still poring over the maps and making notes on the back of the "Contrack." "Be sure to come down to the Serai to-morrow," were their parting words.

The Kumharsen Serai is the great four-square sink of humanity where the strings of camels and horses from the North load and unload. All the nationalities of Central Asia may be found there, and most of the folk of India proper. Balkh and Bokhara there meet Bengal and Bombay, and try to draw eye-teeth. You can buy ponies, turquoises, Persian pussy-cats, saddle-bags, fat-tailed sheep and musk in the Kumharsen Serai, and get many strange things for nothing. In the afternoon I went down to see whether my friends intended to keep their word or were lying there drunk.

A priest attired in fragments of ribbons and rags stalked up to me, gravely twisting a child's paper whirligig. Behind him was his servant bending under the load of a crate of mud toys. The two were loading up two camels, and the inhabitants of the Serai watched them with shrieks of laughter.

"The priest is mad," said a horse-dealer to me. "He is going up to Kabul to sell toys to the Amir. He will either be raised to honour or have his head cut off. He came in here this morning and has been behaving madly ever since."

"The witless are under the protection of God," stammered a flat-cheeked Usbeg in broken Hindi. "They foretell future events."

"Would they could have foretold that my caravan would have been cut up by the Shinwaris almost within shadow of the Pass!" grunted the Eusufzai agent of a Rajputana trading-house whose goods had been diverted into the hands of other robbers just across the Border, and whose misfortunes were the laughing-stock of the bazar. "Ohé, priest, whence come you and whither do you go?"

"From Roum have I come," shouted the priest, waving his whirligig; "from Roum, blown by the breath of a hundred devils across the sea! O thieves, robbers, liars, the blessing of Pir Khan on pigs, dogs, and perjurers! Who will take the Protected of God to the North to sell charms that are never still to the Amir? The camels shall not gall, the sons shall not fall sick, and the wives shall remain faithful while they are away, of the men who give me place in their caravan. Who will assist me to slipper the King of the Roos with a golden slipper with a silver heel? The protection of Pir Khan be upon his labours!" He spread out the skirts of his gaberdine and pirouetted between the lines of tethered horses.

"There starts a caravan from Peshawar to Kabul in twenty days, *Huzrut,*" said the Eusufzai trader. "My camels go therewith. Do thou also go and bring us good-luck."

"I will go even now!" shouted the priest. "I will depart upon my winged camels, and be at Peshawar in a day! Ho! Hazar Mir Khan," he yelled to his servant, "drive out the camels, but let me first mount my own."

He leaped on the back of his beast as it knelt, and, turning round to me, cried: "Come thou also, Sahib, a little along the road, and I will sell thee a charm—an amulet that shall make thee King of Kafiristan."

Then the light broke upon me, and I followed the two camels out of the Serai till we reached open road and the priest halted.

"What d'you think o' that?" said he in English. "Carnehan can't talk their patter, so I've made him my servant. He makes a handsome servant. 'Tisn't for nothing that I've been knocking about the country for fourteen years. Didn't I do that talk neat? We'll hitch on to a caravan at Peshawar till we get to Jagdallak, and then we'll see if we can get donkeys for our camels, and strike into Kafiristan. Whirligigs for the Amir, O Lor! Put your hand under the camel-bags and tell me what you feel."

I felt the butt of a Martini, and another and another.

"Twenty of 'em," said Dravot placidly. "Twenty of 'em and ammunition to correspond, under the whirligigs and the mud dolls."

"Heaven help you if you are caught with those things!" I said. "A Martini is worth her weight in silver among the Pathans."

"Fifteen hundred rupees of capital—very rupee we could beg, borrow, or steal—are invested on these two camels," said Dravot. "We won't get caught. We're going through the Khaiber with a regular caravan. Who'd touch a poor mad priest?"

"Have you got everything you want?" I asked, overcome with astonishment.

"Not yet, but we shall soon. Give us a memento of your kindness, *Brother*. You did me a service, yesterday, and that time in Marwar. Half my Kingdom shall you have, as the saying is." I slipped a small charm compass from my watch chain and handed it up to the priest.

"Good-bye," said Dravot, giving me hand cautiously. "It's the last time we'll shake hands with an Englishman these many days. Shake hands with him, Carnehan," he cried, as the second camel passed me.

Carnehan leaned down and shook hands. Then the camels passed away along the dusty road, and I was left alone to wonder. My eye could detect no failure in the disguises. The scene in the Serai proved that they were complete to the native mind. There was just the chance, therefore, that Carnehan and Dravot would be able to wander through Afghanistan without detection. But, beyond, they would find death—certain and awful death.

Ten days later a native correspondent giving me the news of the day from Peshawar, wound up his letter with: "There has been much laughter here on account of a certain mad priest who is going in his estimation to sell petty gauds and insignificant trinkets which he ascribes as great charms to H.H. the Amir of Bokhara. He passed through Peshawar and associated himself to the Second Summer caravan that goes to Kabul. The merchants are pleased because through superstition they imagine that such mad fellows bring good-fortune."

The two, then, were beyond the Border. I would have prayed for them, but, that night, a real King died in Europe, and demanded an obituary notice.

. . . .

The wheel of the world swings through the same phases again and again. Summer passed and winter thereafter, and came and passed again. The daily paper continued and I with it, and upon the third summer there fell a hot night, a night-issue, and a strained waiting for something to be telegraphed from the other side of the world, exactly as had happened before. A few great men had died in the past two years, the machines worked with more clatter, and some of the trees in the Office garden were a few feet taller. But that was all the difference.

I passed over to the press-room, and went through just such a scene as I have already described. The nervous tension was stronger than it had been two years before, and I felt the heat more acutely. At three o'clock I cried, "Print off," and turned to go, when there crept to my chair what was left of a man. He was bent into a circle, his head was sunk between his shoulders, and he moved his feet one over the other like a bear. I could hardly see whether he walked or crawled—this rag-wrapped, whining cripple who addressed me by name, crying that he was come back. "Can you give me a drink?" he whimpered. "For the Lord's sake, give me a drink!"

I went back to the office, the man following with groans of pain, and I turned up the lamp.

"Don't you know me?" he gasped, dropping into a chair, and he turned his drawn face, surmounted by a shock of gray hair, to the light.

I looked at him intently. Once before had I seen eyebrows that met over the nose in an inch-broad black band, but for the life of me I could not tell where.

"I don't know you," I said, handing him the whiskey. "What can I do for you?"

He took a gulp of the spirit raw, and shivered in spite of the suffocating heat.

"I've come back," he repeated; "and I was the King of Kafiristan—me and Dravot—crowned Kings we was! In this office we settled it—you setting there and giving us the books. I am Peachey—Peachey Taliaferro Carnehan, and you've been setting here ever since—O Lord!"

I was more than a little astonished, and expressed my feelings accordingly.

"It's true," said Carnehan, with a dry cackle, nursing his feet, which were wrapped in rags. "True as gospel. Kings we were, with crowns upon our heads—me and Dravot—poor Dan—oh, poor, poor Dan, that would never take advice, not though I begged of him!"

"Take the whiskey," I said, "and take your own time. Tell me all you can recollect of everything from beginning to end. You got across the border on your camels, Dravot dressed as a mad priest and you his servant. Do you remember that?"

"I ain't mad—yet, but I shall be that way soon. Of course I remember. Keep looking at me, or maybe my words will go all to pieces. Keep looking at me in my eyes and don't say anything."

I leaned forward and looked into his face as steadily as I could. He dropped one hand upon the table and I grasped it by the wrist. It was twisted like a bird's claw, and upon the back was a ragged, red, diamond-shaped scar.

"No, don't look there. Look at *me,*" said Carnehan. "That comes afterwards, but for the Lord's sake don't distrack me. We left with that caravan, me and Dravot playing all sorts of antics to amuse the people we were with. Dravot used to make us laugh in the evenings when all the people was cooking their dinners—cooking their dinners, and . . . what did they do then? They lit little fires with sparks that went into Dravot's beard, and we all laughed—fit to die. Little red fires they was, going into Dravot's big red beard—so funny." His eyes left mine and he smiled foolishly.

"You went as far as Jagdallak with that caravan," I said at a venture, "after you had lit those fires. To Jagdallak, where you turned off to try to get into Kafiristan."

"No, we didn't neither. What are you talking about? We turned off before Jagdallak, because we heard the roads was good. But they wasn't good enough for our two camels—mine and Dravot's. When we left the caravan, Dravot took off all his clothes and mine too, and said we would he heathen, because the Kafirs didn't allow Mohammedans to talk to them. So we dressed betwixt and between, and such a sight as Daniel Dravot I never saw yet nor expect to see again. He burned half his beard, and slung a sheep-skin over his shoulder, and shaved his head into patterns. He shaved mine, too, and made me wear outrageous things to look like a heathen. That was in a most mountaineous country, and our camels couldn't go along any more because of the mountains.

They were tall and black, and coming home I saw them fight like wild goats—there are lots of goats in Kafiristan. And these mountains, they never keep still, no more than the goats. Always fighting they are, and don't let you sleep at night."

"Take some more whisky," I said very slowly. "What did you and Daniel Dravot do when the camels could go no further because of the rough roads that led into Kafiristan?"

"What did which do? There was a party called Peachey Taliaferro Carnehan that was with Dravot. Shall I tell you about him? He died out there in the cold. Slap from the bridge fell old Peachey, turning and twisting in the air like a penny whirligig that you can sell to the Amir.—No; they was two for three ha'pence, those whirligigs, or I am much mistaken and woeful sore. . . . And then these camels were no use, and Peachey said to Dravot—'For the Lord's sake let's get out of this before our heads are chopped off,' and with that they killed the camels all among the mountains, not having anything in particular to eat, but first they took off the boxes with the guns and the ammunition, till two men came along driving four mules. Dravot up and dances in front of them, singing—'Sell me four mules.' Says the first man—'If you are rich enough to buy, you are rich enough to rob;' but before ever he could put his hand to his knife, Dravot breaks his neck over his knee, and the other party runs away. So Carnehan loaded the mules with the rifles that was taken off the camels, and together we starts forward into those bitter cold mountaineous parts, and never a road broader than the back of your hand."

He paused for a moment, while I asked him if he could remember the nature of the country through which he had journeyed.

"I am telling you as straight as I can, but my head isn't as good as it might be. They drove nails through it to make me hear better how Dravot died. The country was mountaineous and the mules were most contrary, and the inhabitants were dispersed and solitary. They went up and up, and down and down, and that other party, Carnehan, was imploring of Dravot not to sing and whistle so loud, for fear of bringing down the tremenjus avalanches. But Dravot says that if a King couldn't sing it wasn't worth being King, and whacked the mules over the rump, and never took no heed for ten cold days. We came to a big level valley all among the mountains, and the mules were near dead, so we killed them, not having anything in special for them or us to eat. We sat upon the boxes, and played odd and even with the cartridges that was jolted out.

"Then ten men with bows and arrows ran down that valley, chasing twenty men with bows and arrows, and the row was tremenjus. They was fair men—fairer than you or me—with yellow hair and remarkable well built. Says Dravot, unpacking the guns—'This is the beginning of the business. We'll fight for the ten men,' and with that he fires two rifles at the twenty men, and drops one of them at two hundred yards from the rock where he was sitting. The other men began to run, but Carnehan and Dravot sits on the boxes picking them off at all ranges, up and down the valley. Then we goes up to the ten men that had run across the snow too, and they fires a footy little arrow at us. Dravot he shoots above their heads and they all falls down flat. Then he walks over them and kicks them, and then he lifts them up and shakes hands all round to make them friendly like. He calls them and gives them the boxes to carry, and waves his hand for all the world as though he was King already. They takes the boxes and him across the valley and up the hill into a pine wood on the top, where there was half a dozen big stone idols. Dravot he goes to the biggest—a fellow they call Imbra—and lays a rifle and a cartridge at his feet, rubbing his nose respectful with his own nose, patting him on the head, and saluting in front of it. He turns round to the men and nods his head, and says—'That's all right. I'm in the know too, and all these old jim-jams are my friends.' Then he opens his mouth and points down it, and when the first man brings him food, he says—'No;' and when the second man brings him food he says—'No;' but when one of the old priests and the boss of the village brings him food, he says

—'Yes;' very haughty, and eats it slow. That was how we came to our first village, without any trouble, just as though we had tumbled from the skies. But we tumbled from one of those damned rope-bridges, you see and—you couldn't expect a man to laugh much after that?"

"Take some more whisky and go on," I said. "That was the first village you came into. How did you get to be King?"

"I wasn't King," said Carnehan. "Dravot he was the King, and a handsome man he looked with the gold crown on his head and all. Him and the other party stayed in that village, and every morning Dravot sat by the side of old Imbra, and the people came and worshipped. That was Dravot's order. Then a lot of men came into the valley, and Carnehan Dravot picks them off with the rifles before they knew where they was, and runs down into the valley and up again the other side and finds another village, same as the first one, and the people all falls down flat on their faces, and Dravot says—'Now what is the trouble between you two villages?' and the people points to a woman, as fair as you or me, that was carried off, and Dravot takes her back to the first village and counts up the dead—eight there was. For each dead man Dravot pours a little milk on the ground and waves his arms like a whirligig and 'That's all right,' says he. Then he and Carnehan takes the big boss of each village by the arm and walks them down into the valley, and shows them how to scratch a line with a spear right down the valley, and gives each a sod of turf from both sides of the line. Then all the people comes down and shouts like the devil and all, and Dravot says—'Go and dig the land, and be fruitful and multiply,' which they did, though they didn't understand. Then we asks the names of things in their lingo—bread and water and fire and idols and such, and Dravot leads the priest of each village up to the idol, and says he must sit there and judge the people, and if anything goes wrong he is to be shot.

"Next week they was all turning up the land in the valley as quiet as bees and much prettier, and the priests heard all the complaints and told Dravot in dumb show what it was about. 'That's just the beginning,' says Dravot. 'They think we're Gods.' He and Carnehan picks out twenty good men and shows them how to click off a rifle, and form fours, and advance in line, and they was very pleased to do so, and clever to see the hang of it. Then he takes out his pipe and his baccy-pounch and leaves one at one village, and one at the other, and off we two goes to see what was to be done in the next valley. That was all rock, and there was a little village there, and Carnehan says—'Send 'em to the old valley to plant,' and takes 'em there and gives 'em some land that wasn't took before. They were a poor lot, and we blooded 'em with a kid before letting 'em into the new Kingdom. That was to impress the people, and then they settled down quiet, and Carnehan went back to Dravot who had got into another valley, all snow and ice and most mountaineous. There was no people there and the Army got afraid, so Dravot shoots one of them, and goes on till he finds some people in a village, and the Army explains that unless the people wants to be killed they had better not shoot their little matchlocks; for they had matchlocks. We makes friends with the priest and I stays there alone with two of the Army, teaching the men how to drill, and a thundering big Chief comes across the snow with kettle-drums and horns twanging, because he heard there was a new God kicking about. Carnehan sights for the brown of the men half a mile across the snow and wings one of them. Then he sends a message to the Chief that, unless he wished to be killed, he must come and shake hands with me and leave his arms behind. The Chief comes alone first, and Carnehan shakes hands with him and whirls his arms about, same as Dravot used, and very much surprised that Chief was, and strokes my eyebrows. Then Carnehan goes alone to the Chief, and asks him in dumb show if he had an enemy he hated. 'I have,' says the Chief. So Carnehan weeds out the pick of the men, and sets the two of the Army to show them drill and at the end of two weeks the men can manœuvre about as well as Volunteers. So he marches with the Chief to a great big plain on the top of a mountain, and the Chief's men rushes into a village and takes it; we three Martinis firing into the brown of the enemy. So we took that village too, and I gives the Chief a rag from my coat and says 'Occupy till I come;' which was scriptural. By way of a reminder, when me and the Army was eighteen hundred yards away, I drops a bullet near him standing on the snow, and all the people falls flat on their faces. Then I sends a letter to Dravot wherever he be by land or by sea."

At the risk of throwing the creature out of train I interrupted—"How could you write a letter up yonder?"

"The letter?—Oh!—The letter! Keep looking at me between the eyes, please. It was a string-talk letter, that we'd learned the way of it from a blind beggar in the Punjab."

I remember that there had once come to the office a blind man with a knotted twig and a piece of string which he wound round the twig according to some cipher of his own. He could, after the lapse of days or hours, repeat the sentence which he had reeled up. He had reduced the alphabet to eleven primitive sounds; and tried to teach me his method, but I could not understand.

"I sent that letter to Dravot," said Carnehan; "and told him to come back because this Kingdom was growing too big for me to handle, and then I struck for the first valley, to see how the priests were working. They called the village we took along with the Chief, Bashkai, and the first village we took, Er-Heb. The priests at Er-Heb was doing all right, but they had a lot of pending cases about land to show me, and some men from another village had been firing arrows at night. I went out and looked for that village, and fired four rounds at it from a thousand yards. That used all the cartridges I cared to spend, and I waited for Dravot, who had been away two or three months, and I kept my people quiet.

"One morning I heard the devil's own noise of drums and horns, and Dan Dravot marches down the hill with his Army and a tail of hundreds of men, and, which was the most amazing, a great gold crown on his head. 'My Gord, Carnehan,' says Daniel, 'this is a tremenjus business, and we've got the whole country as far as it's worth having. I am the son of Alexander by Queen Semiramis, and you're my younger brother and a God too! It's the biggest thing we've ever seen. I've been marching and fighting for six weeks with the Army, and every footy little village for fifty miles has come in rejoiceful; and more than that, I've got the key of the whole show, as you'll see, and I've got a crown for you! I told 'em to make two of 'em at a place called Shu, where the gold lies in the rock like suet in mutton. Gold I've seen, and turquoise I've kicked out of the cliffs, and there's garnets in the sands of the river, and here's a chunk of amber that a man brought me. Call up all the priests and, here, take your crown.'

"One of the men opens a black hair bag, and I slips the crown on. It was too small and too heavy, but I wore it for the glory. Hammered gold it was—five pound weight, like a hoop of a barrel.

" 'Peachey,' says Dravot, 'we don't want to fight no more. The Craft's the trick so help me!' and he brings forward that same Chief that I left at Bashkai—Billy Fish we called him afterwards, because he was so like Billy Fish that drove the big tank-engine at Mach on the Bolan in the old days. 'Shake hands with him,' says Dravot, and I shook hands and nearly dropped, for Billy Fish gave me the Grip. I said nothing, but tried him with the Fellow Craft Grip. He answers, all right, and I tried the Master's Grip, but that was a slip. 'A Fellow Craft he is;' I says to Dan. 'Does he know the word?'—'He does,' says Dan, 'and all the priests know. It's a miracle. The Chiefs and the priests can work a Fellow Craft Lodge in a way that's very like ours, and they've cut the marks on the rocks, but they don't know the Third Degree, and they've come to find out. It's Gord's Truth. I've known these long years that the Afghans knew up to the Fellow Craft Degree, but this is a miracle. A God and a Grand-Master of the Craft am I, and a Lodge in the Third Degree I will open, and we'll raise the head priests and the Chiefs of the villages.'

" 'It's against all the law,' I says, 'holding a Lodge without warrant from any one; and you know we never held office in any Lodge.'

" 'It's a master-stroke o' policy,' says Dravot. 'It means running the country as easy as a four-wheeled bogie on a down grade. We can't stop to enquire now, or they'll turn against us. I've forty Chiefs at my heel, and passed and raised according to their merit they shall be. Billet these men on his villages, and see that we run up a Lodge of some kind. The temple of Imbra will do for the Lodge-room. The women must make aprons as you show them. I'll hold a levee of Chiefs to-night and Lodge to-morrow.'

"I was fair run off my legs, but I wasn't such a fool as not to see what a pull this Craft business gave us. I showed the priests' families how to make aprons of the degrees, but for Dravot's apron the blue border and marks was made of turquoise lumps on white hide, not cloth. We took a great square stone in the temple for the Master's chair, and little stones for the officers' chairs, and painted the black pavement with white squares, and did what we could to make things regular.

"At the levee which was held that night on the hillside with big bonfires, Dravot gives out that him and me were Gods and sons of Alexander, and Past Grand Masters in the Craft, and was come to make Kafiristan a country where every man should eat in peace and drink in quiet, and specially obey us. Then the Chiefs come round to shake hands, and they were so hairy and white and fair it was just shaking hands with old friends. We gave them names according as they was like men we had known in India—Billy Fish, Holly Dilworth, Pikky Kergan, that was Bazar-master when I was at Mhow, and so on, and so on.

"*The* most amazing miracles was at Lodge next night. One of the old priests was watching us continuous, and I felt uneasy, for I knew we'd have to fudge the Ritual, and I didn't know what the men knew. The old priest was a stranger come in from beyond the village of Bashkai. The minute Dravot puts on the Master's apron that the girls had made for him, the priest fetches a whoop and a howl, and tries to overturn the stone that Dravot was sitting on. 'It's all up now,' I says. 'That comes of meddling with the Craft without warrant!'

Dravot never winked an eye, not when ten priests took and tilted over the Grand-Master's chair—which was to say the stone of Imbra. The priest begins rubbing the bottom end of it to clear away the black dirt, and presently he shows all the other priests the Master's Mark, same as was on Dravot's apron, cut into the stone. Not even the priests of the temple of Imbra knew it was there. The old chap falls flat on his face at Dravot's feet and kisses 'em. 'Luck again,' says Dravot, across the Lodge to me, 'they say it's the missing Mark that no one could understand the why of. We're more than safe now.' Then he bangs the butt of his gun for a gavel and says: 'By virtue of the authority vested in me by my own right hand and the help of Peachey, I declare myself Grand-Master of all Freemasonry in Kafiristan in this the Mother Lodge o' the country, and King of Kafiristan equally with Peachey!' At that he puts on his crown and I puts on mine—I was doing Senior Warden—and we opens the Lodge in most ample form. It was a amazing miracle! The priests moved in Lodge through the first two degrees almost without telling, as if the memory was coming back to them. After that, Peachey and Dravot raised such as was worthy—high priests and Chiefs of far-off villages. Billy Fish was the first, and I can tell you we scared the soul out of him. It was not in any way according to Ritual, but it served our turn. We didn't raise more than ten of the biggest men, because we didn't want to make the Degree common. And they was clamouring to be raised.

"'In another six months,' says Dravot, 'we'll hold another Communication, and see how you are working.' Then he asks them about their villages, and learns that they was fighting one against the other, and were sick and tired of it. And when they wasn't doing that they was fighting with the Mohammedans. 'You can fight those when they come into our country,' says Dravot. 'Tell off every tenth man of your tribes for a Frontier guard, and send two hundred at a time to this valley to be drilled. Nobody is going to be shot or speared any more so long as he does well, and I know that you won't cheat me, because you're white people—sons of

Alexander—and not like common, black Mohammedans. You are *my* people, and by God,' says he, running off into English at the end—'I'll make a damned fine Nation of you, or I'll die in the making!'

"I can't tell all we did for the next six months, because Dravot did a lot I couldn't see the hang of, and he learned their lingo in a way I never could. My work was to help the people plough, and now and again go out with some of the Army and see what the other villages were doing, and make 'em throw rope-bridges across the ravines which cut up the country horrid. Dravot was very kind to me, but when he walked up and down in the pine wood pulling that bloody red beard of his with both fists I knew he was thinking plans I could not advise about, and I just waited for orders.

"But Dravot never showed me disrespect before the people. They were afraid of me and the Army, but they loved Dan. He was the best of friends with the priests and the Chiefs; but any one could come across the hills with a complaint, and Dravot would hear him out fair, and call four priests together and say what was to be done. He used to call in Billy Fish from Bashkai, and Pikky Kergan from Shu, and an old Chief we called Kafuzelum—it was like enough to his real name—and hold councils with 'em when there was any fighting to be done in small villages. That was his Council of War, and the four priests of Bashkai, Shu, Khawak, and Madora was his Privy Council. Between the lot of 'em they sent me, with forty men and twenty rifles, and sixty men carrying turquoises, into the Ghorband country to buy those hand-made Martini rifles, that come out of the Amir's workshops at Kabul, from one of the Amir's Herati regiments that would have sold the very teeth out of their mouths for turquoises.

"I stayed in Ghorband a month, and gave the Governor there the pick of my baskets for hush-money, and bribed the Colonel of the regiment some more, and, between the two and the tribes-people, we got more than a hundred hand-made Martinis, a hundred good Kohat Jezails that'll throw to six hundred yards, and forty manloads of very bad ammunition for the rifles. I came back with what I had, and distributed 'em among the men that the Chiefs sent in to me to drill. Dravot was too busy to attend to those things, but the old Army that we first made helped me, and we turned out five hundred men that could drill, and two hundred that knew how to hold arms pretty straight. Even those cork-screwed, hand-made guns was a miracle to them. Dravot talked big about powder-shops and factories, walking up and down in the pine wood when the winter was coming on.

"'I won't make a Nation,' says he. 'I'll make an Empire! These men aren't niggers; they're English! Look at their eyes—look at their mouths. Look at the way they stand up. They sit on chairs in their own houses. They're the Lost Tribes, or something like it, and they've grown to be English. I'll take a census in the spring if the priests don't get frightened. There must be a fair two million of 'em in these hills. The villages are full o' little children. Two million people—two hundred and fifty thousand fighting men—and all English! They only want the rifles and a little drilling. Two hundred and fifty thousand men, ready to cut in on Russia's right flank when she tries for India! Peachey, man,' he says, chewing his beard in great hunks, 'we shall be Emperors—Emperors of the Earth! Rajah Brooke will be a suckling to us. I'll treat with the Viceroy on equal terms. I'll ask him to send me twelve picked English—twelve that I know of—to help us govern a bit. There's Mackray, Sergeant-pensioner at Segowli—many's the good dinner he's given me, and his wife a pair of trousers. There's Donkin, the Warder of Tounghoo Jail; there's hundreds that I could lay my hand on if I was in India. The Viceroy shall do it for me, I'll send a man through in the spring for those men, and I'll write for a dispensation from the Grand Lodge for what I've done as Grand-Master. That—and all the Sniders that'll be thrown out when the native troops in India take up the Martini. They'll be worn smooth, but they'll do for fighting in these hills. Twelve English, a hundred thousand Sniders run through the Amir's country in driblets—I'd be content with twenty thousand in one year—and we'd be an Empire. When everything was shipshape, I'd hand over the crown—this crown I'm wearing now—to Queen Victoria on my knees, and she'd say: "Rise up, Sir Daniel Dravot." Oh, it's big! It's big, I tell you! But there's so much to be done in every place—Bashkai, Khawak, Shu, and everywhere else.'

"'What is it?" I says. 'There are no more men coming in to be drilled this autumn. Look at those fat, black clouds. They're bringing the snow.'

"'It isn't that,' says Daniel, putting his hand very hard on my shoulder; 'and I don't wish to say anything that's against you, for no other living man would have followed me and made me what I am as you have done. You're a first-class Commander-in-Chief, and the people know you; but—it's a big country, and somehow you can't help me, Peachey, in the way I want to be helped.'

"'Go to your blasted priests, then!' I said, and I was sorry when I made that remark, but it did hurt me sore to find Daniel talking so superior when I'd drilled all the men, and done all he told me.

"'Don't let's quarrel, Peachey,' says Daniel without cursing. 'You're a King too, and the half of this Kingdom is yours; but can't you see, Peachey, we want cleverer men than us now—three or four of 'em, that we can scatter about for our Deputies. It's a hugeous great State, and I can't always tell the right thing to do, and I haven't time for all I want to do, and here's the winter coming on and all.' He put half his beard into his mouth, all red like the gold of his crown.

"'I'm sorry, Daniel,' says I. 'I've done all I could. I've drilled the men and shown the people how to stack their oats better; and I've brought in those tin-ware rifles from Ghorband—but I know what you're driving at. I take it Kings always feel oppressed that way.'

"'There's another thing too,' says Dravot, walking up and down. 'The winter's coming and these people won't be giving much trouble, and if they do we can't move about. I want a wife.'

"'For Gord's sake leave the women alone!' I says. 'We've

both got all the work we can, though I *am* a fool. Remember the Contrack, and keep clear o' women.'

"'The Contrack only lasted till such time as we was Kings; and Kings we have been these months past,' says Dravot, weighing his crown in his hand. 'You go get a wife too, Peachey—a nice, strappin', plump girl that'll keep you warm in the winter. They're prettier than English girls, and we can take the pick of 'em. Boil 'em once or twice in hot water, and they'll come out like chicken and ham.'

"'Don't tempt me!' I says. 'I will not have any dealings with a woman not till we are a dam' side more settled than we are now. I've been doing the work o' two men, and you've been doing the work o' three. Let's lie off a bit, and see if we can get some better tobacco from Afghan country and run in some good liquor; but no women.'

"'Who's talking o' *women?*' says Dravot. 'I said *wife*—a queen to breed a King's son for the King. A Queen out of the strongest tribe, that'll make them your blood-brothers, and that'll lie by your side and tell you all the people thinks about you and their own affairs. That's what I want.'

"'Do you remember that Bengali women I kept at Mogul Serai when I was a platea-layer?' says I. 'A fat lot o' good she was to me. She taught me the lingo and one or two other things; but what happened? She ran away with the Station Master's servant and half my month's pay. Then she turned up at Dadur Junction in tow of a half-caste, and had the impidence to say I was her husband—all among the drivers in the running-shed too!'

"'We've done with that,' says Dravot, 'these women are whiter than you or me, and a Queen I will have for the winter months.'

"'For the last time o' asking, Dan, do *not,*' I says. 'It'll only bring us harm. The Bible says that Kings ain't to waste their strength on women, 'specially when they've got a new raw Kingdom to work over.'

"'For the last time of answering I will,' said Dravot, and he went away through the pine-trees looking like a big red devil, the sun being on his crown and beard and all.

"But getting a wife was not as easy as Dan thought. He put it before the Council, and there was no answer till Billy Fish said he'd better ask the girls. Dravot damned them all round. 'What's wrong with me?' he shouts, standing by the idol Imbra. 'Am I a dog or am I not enough of a man for your wenches? Haven't I put the shadow of my hand over this country? Who stopped the last Afghan raid?' It was me really, but Dravot was too angry to remember. 'Who bought your guns? Who repaired the bridges? Who's the Grand-Master of the sign cut in the stone?' says he, and he thumped his hand on the block that he used to sit on in Lodge, and at Council, which opened like Lodge always. Billy Fish said nothing and no more did the others. 'Keep your hair on, Dan,' said I; 'and ask the girls. That's how it's done at Home, and these people are quite English.'

" 'The marriage of the King is a matter of State,' says Dan, in a white-hot rage, for he could feel, I hope, that he was going against his better mind. He walked out of the Council-room, and the others sat still, looking at the ground.

" 'Billy Fish,' says I to the Chief of Bashkai, 'what's the difficulty here? A straight answer to a true friend.'

" 'You know,' says Billy Fish. 'How should a man tell you who knows everything? How can daughters of men marry Gods or Devils? It's not proper.'

"I remembered something like that in the Bible; but if, after seeing us as long as they had, they still believed we were Gods, it wasn't for me to undeceive them.

" 'A God can do anything,' says I. 'If the King is fond of a girl he'll not let her die.'—'She'll have to,' said Billy Fish. 'There are all sorts of Gods and Devils in these mountains, and now and again a girl marries one of them and isn't seen any more. Besides, you two know the Mark cut in the stone. Only the Gods know that. We thought you were men till you showed the sign of the Master.'

"I wished then that we had explained about the loss of the genuine secrets of a Master-Mason at the first go-off; but I said nothing. All that night there was a blowing of horns in a little dark temple half-way down the hill, and I heard a girl crying fit to die. One of the priests told us that she was being prepared to marry the King.

" 'I'll have no nonsense of that kind,' says Dan. 'I don't want to interfere with your customs, but I'll take my own wife.'—'The girl's a little bit afraid,' says the priest. 'She thinks she's going to die, and they are a-heartening of her up down in the temple.'

" 'Hearten her very tender, then,' says Dravot, 'or I'll hearten you with the butt of a gun so you'll never want to be heartened again.' He licked his lips, did Dan, and stayed up walking about more than half the night, thinking of the wife that he was going to get in the morning. I wasn't by any means comfortable, for I knew that dealings with a woman in foreign parts, though you was a crowned King twenty times over, could not but be risky. I got up very early in the morning while Dravot was asleep, and I saw the priests talking together in whispers, and the Chiefs talking together too, and they looked at me out of the corners of their eyes.

" 'What is up, Fish?' I say to the Bashkai man, who was wrapped up in his furs and looking splendid to behold.

" 'I can't rightly say,' says he; 'but if you can make the King drop all this nonsense about marriage, you'll be doing him and me and yourself a great service.'

" 'That I do believe,' says I. 'But sure, you know, Billy, as well as me, having fought against and for us, that the King and me are nothing more than two of the finest men that God Almighty ever made. Nothing more, I do assure you.'

" 'That may be,' says Billy Fish, 'and yet I should be sorry if it was.' He sinks his head upon his great fur cloak for a minute and thinks. 'King,' says he, 'be you man or God or Devil, I'll stick by you to-day. I have twenty of my men with me, and they will follow me. We'll go to Bashkai until the storm blows over.'

"A little snow had fallen in the night, and everything was white except the greasy fat clouds that blew down and down from the north. Dravot came out with his crown on his head, swinging his arms and stamping his feet, and looking more pleased than Punch.

" 'For the last time, drop it, Dan,' says I in a whisper, 'Billy Fish here says that there will be a row.'

" 'A row among my people!' says Dravot. 'Not much. Peachey, you're a fool not to get a wife too. Where's the girl?' says he with a voice as loud as the braying of a jackass. 'Call up all the Chiefs and priests, and let the Emperor see if his wife suits him.'

"There was no need to call any one. They were all there leaning on their guns and spears round the clearing in the centre of the pine wood. A lot of priests went down to the little temple to bring up the girl, and the horns blew fit to wake the dead. Billy Fish saunters round and gets as close to Daniel as he could, and behind him stood his twenty men with matchlocks. Not a man of them under six feet. I was next to Dravot, and behind me was twenty men of the regular Army. Up comes the girl, and a strapping wench she was, covered with silver and turquoises but white as death, and looking back every minute at the priests.

" 'She'll do,' said Dan, looking her over. 'What's to be afraid of, lass? Come and kiss me.' He puts his arm round her. She shuts her eyes, gives a bit of a squeak, and down goes her face in the side of Dan's flaming red beard.

" 'The slut's bitten me!' says he, clapping his hand to his neck, and, sure enough, his hand was red with blood. Billy Fish and two of his matchlock-men catches hold of Dan by the shoulders and drags him into the Bashkai lot, while the priests howls in their lingo,—'Neither God nor Devil but a man!' I was all taken aback, for a priest cut at me in front, and the Army began firing into the Bashkai men.

" 'God A'mighty!' says Dan. 'What is the meaning o' this?'

" 'Come back! Come away!' says Billy Fish. 'Ruin and Mutiny is the matter. We'll break for Bashkai if we can.'

"I tried to give some sort of orders to my men—the men o' the regular Army—but it was no use, so I fired into the brown of 'em with an English Martini and drilled three beggars in a line. The valley was full of shouting, howling creatures, and every soul was shrieking, 'Not a God nor a Devil but only a man!' The Bashkai troops stuck to Billy Fish all they were worth, but their matchlocks wasn't half as good as the Kabul breech-loaders, and four of them dropped. Dan was bellowing like a bull, for he was very wrathy; and Billy Fish had a hard job to prevent him running out at the crowd.

" 'We can't stand,' says Billy Fish. 'Make a run for it down the valley! The whole place is against us.' The matchlock-men ran, and we went down the valley in spite of Dravot. He was swearing horrible and crying out he was a King. The priests rolled great stones on us, and the regular Army fired hard, and there wasn't more than six men, not counting Dan, Billy Fish, and Me, that came down to the bottom of the valley alive.

"Then they stopped firing and the horns in the temple blew again. 'Come away—for Gord's sake come away!' says Billy Fish. 'They'll send runners out to all the villages before ever we get to Bashkai. I can protect you there, but I can't do anything now.'

"My own notion is that Dan began to go mad in his head from that hour. He stared up and down like a stuck pig. Then he was all for walking back alone and killing the priests with his bare hands; which he could have done. 'An Emperor am I,' says Daniel, 'and next year I shall be a Knight of the Queen.'

" 'All right, Dan,' says I; 'but come along now while there's time.'

" 'It's your fault,' says he, 'for not looking after your Army better. There was mutiny in the midst, and you didn't know—you damned engine-driving, plate-laying, missionary's-pass-hunting hound!' He sat upon a rock and called me every foul name he could lay tongue to. I was too heart-sick to care, though it was all his foolishness that brought the smash.

" 'I'm sorry, Dan,' says I, 'but there's no accounting for natives. This business is our Fifty-seven. Maybe we'll make something out of it yet, when we've got to Bashkai.'

" 'Let's get to Bashkai, then,' says Dan, 'and, by God, when I come back here again I'll sweep the valley so there isn't a bug in a blanket left!'

"We walked all that day, and all that night Dan was stumping up and down on the snow, chewing his beard and muttering to himself.

" 'There's no hope o' getting clear,' said Billy Fish. 'The priests will have sent runners to the villages to say that you are only men. Why didn't you stick on as Gods till things was more settled? I'm a dead man,' says Billy Fish, and he throws himself down on the snow and begins to pray to his Gods.

"Next morning we was in a cruel bad country—all up and down, no level ground at all, and no food either. The six Bashkai men looked at Billy Fish hungry-way as if they wanted to ask something, but they said never a word. At noon we came to the top of a flat mountain all covered with snow, and when we climbed up into it, behold, there was an Army in position waiting in the middle!

" 'The runners have been very quick,' says Billy Fish, with a little bit of a laugh. 'They are waiting for us.'

"Three or four men began to fire from the enemy's side, and a chance shot took Daniel in the calf of the leg. That brought him to his senses. He looks across the snow at the Army, and sees the rifles that we had brought into the country.

" 'We're done for,' says he. 'They are Englishmen, these people,—and it's my blasted nonsense that has brought you to this. Get back, Billy Fish, and take your men away; you've done what you could, and now cut for it. Carnehan,' says he, 'shake hands with me and go along with Billy. Maybe they won't kill you. I'll go and meet 'em alone. It's me that did it. Me, the King!'

" 'Go!' says I. 'Go to Hell, Dan. I'm with you here. Billy Fish, you clear out, and we two will meet those folk.'

" 'I'm a Chief,' says Billy Fish, quite quiet. 'I stay with you. My men can go.'

"The Bashkai fellows didn't wait for a second word but ran off, and Dan and Me and Billy Fish walked across to where the drums were drumming and the horns were horning. It was cold—awful cold. I've got that cold in the back of my head now. There's a lump of it there."

The punkah-coolies had gone to sleep. Two kerosene lamps

were blazing in the office, and the perspiration poured down my face and splashed on the blotter as I leaned forward. Carnehan was shivering, and I feared that his mind might go. I wiped my face, took a fresh grip of the piteously mangled hands, and said, "What happened after that?"

The momentary shift of my eyes had broken the clear current.

"What was you pleased to say?" whined Carnehan. "They took them without any sound. Not a little whisper all along the snow, not though the King knocked down the first man that set hand on him—not though old Peachey fired his last cartridge into the brown of 'em. Not a single solitary sound did those swines make. They just closed up tight, and I tell you their furs stunk. There was a man called Billy Fish, a good friend of us all, and they cut his throat, Sir, then and there, like a pig; and the King kicks up the bloody snow and says: 'We've had a dashed fine run for our money. What's coming next?' But Peachey, Peachy Taliaferro, I tell you, Sir, in confidence as betwixt two friends, he lost his head, Sir. No, he didn't neither. The King lost his head, so he did, all along o' one of those cunning rope-bridges. Kindly let me have the paper-cutter, Sir. It tilted this way. They marched him a mile across that snow to a rope-bridge over a ravine with a river at the bottom. You may have seen such. They prodded him behind like an ox. 'Damn your eyes!' says the King. 'D'you suppose I can't die like a gentleman?' He turns to Peachey —Peachey that was crying like a child. 'I've brought you to this, Peachey,' says he. 'Brought you out of your happy life to be killed in Kafiristan where you was late Commander-in-Chief of the Emperor's forces. Say you forgive me, Peachey.'—'I do,' says Peachey. 'Fully and freely do I forgive you, Dan.'—'Shake hands, Peachey,' says he. 'I'm going now.' Out he goes, looking neither right nor left, and when he was plumb in the middle of those dizzy dancing ropes,—'Cut, you beggars,' he shouts, and they cut, and old Dan fell, turning round and round and round, twenty thousand miles, for he took half an hour to fall till he struck the water, and I could see his body caught on a rock with the gold crown close beside.

"But do you know what they did to Peachey between two pine-trees? They crucified him, Sir, as Peachey's hands will show. They used wooden pegs for his hands and his feet; and he didn't die. He hung there and screamed, and they took him down next day, and said it was a miracle that he wasn't dead. They took him down—poor old Peachey that hadn't done them any harm—that hadn't done them any——"

He rocked to and fro and wept bitterly, wiping his eyes with the back of his scarred hands and moaning like a child for some ten minutes.

"They was cruel enough to feed him up in the temple, because they said he was more of a God than old Daniel that was a man. Then they turned him out on the snow, and told him to go home, and Peachey came home in about a year, begging along the roads quite safe; for Daniel Dravot he walked before and said: 'Come along, Peachey. It's a big thing we're doing.' The mountains they danced at night, and the mountains they tried to fall on Peachey's head, but Dan he held up his hand, and Peachey came along bent double. He never let go of Dan's hand, and he never let go of Dan's head. They gave it to him as a present in the temple, to remind him not to come again, and though the crown was pure gold, and Peachey was starving, never would Peachey sell the same. You knew Dravot, Sir! You knew Right Worshipful Brother Dravot! Look at him now!"

He fumbled in the mass of rags round his bent waist; brought out a black horsehair bag embroidered with silver thread; and shook therefrom on to my table—the dried, withered head of Daniel Dravot! The morning sun that had long been paling the lamps struck the red beard and blind sunken eyes; struck, too, a heavy circlet of gold studded with raw turquoises, that Carnehan placed tenderly on the battered temples.

"You be'old now," said Carnehan, "the Emperor in his 'abit as he lived—the King of Kafiristan with his crown upon his head. Poor old Daniel that was a monarch once!"

I shuddered, for, in spite of defacements manifold, I recognized the head of the man of Marwar Junction. Carnehan rose to go. I attempted to stop him. He was not fit to walk abroad. "Let me take away the whiskey, and give me a little money," he gasped. "I was a King once. I'll go to the Deputy Commissioner and ask to set in the Poorhouse till I get my health. No, thank you, I can't wait till you get a carriage for me. I've urgent private affairs—in the south—at Marwar."

He shambled out of the office and departed in the direction of the Deputy Commissioner's house. That day at noon I had occasion to go down the blinding hot Mall, and I saw a crooked man crawling along the white dust of the roadside, his hat in his hand, quavering dolorously after the fashion of street-singers at Home. There was not a soul in sight, and he was out of all possible earshot of the houses. And he sang through his nose, turning his head from right to left:—

"The Son of Man goes forth to war,
A golden crown to gain;
His blood-red banner streams afar—
Who follows in his train?"

I waited to hear no more, but put the poor wretch into my carriage and drove him off to the nearest missionary for eventual transfer to the Asylum. He repeated the hymn twice while he was with me whom he did not in the least recognize, and I left him singing it to the missionary.

Two days later I enquired after his welfare of the Superintendent of the Asylum.

"He was admitted suffering from sun-stroke. He died early yesterday morning," said the Superintendent. "Is it true that he was half an hour bare-headed in the sun at midday?"

"Yes," said I, "but do you happen to know if he had anything upon him by any chance when he died?"

"Not to my knowledge," said the Superintendent.

And there the matter rests.

THE DRUMS OF THE FORE AND AFT
1888

IN THE Army List they still stand as "The Fore and Fit Princess Hohenzollern-Sigmaringen-Anspach's Merther-Tydfilshire Own Royal Loyal Light Infantry, Regimental District 329 A," but the Army through all its barracks and canteens knows them now as the "Fore and Aft." They may in time do something that shall make their new title honourable, but at present they are bitterly ashamed, and the man who calls them "Fore and Aft" does so at the risk of the head which is on his shoulders.

Two words breathed into the stables of a certain Cavalry Regiment will bring the men out into the streets with belts and mops and bad language; but a whisper of "Fore and Aft" will bring out this regiment with rifles.

Their one excuse is that they came again and did their best to finish the job in style. But for a time all their world knows that they were openly beaten, whipped, dumb-cowed, shaking and afraid. The men know it; their officers know it; the Horse Guards know it, and when the next war comes the enemy will know it also. There are two or three regiments of the Line that have a black mark against their names which they will then wipe out; and it will be excessively inconvenient for the troops upon whom they do their wiping.

The courage of the British soldier is officially supposed to be above proof, and, as a general rule, it is so. The exceptions are decently shovelled out of sight, only to be referred to in the freshest of unguarded talk that occasionally swamps a Mess-table at midnight. Then one hears strange and horrible stories of men not following their officers, of orders being given by those who had no right to give them, and of disgrace that, but for the standing luck of the British Army, might have ended in brilliant disaster. These are unpleasant stories to listen to, and the Messes tell them under their breath, sitting by the big wood fires, and the young officer bows his head and thinks to himself, please God, his men shall never behave unhandily.

The British soldier is not altogether to be blamed for occasional lapses; but this verdict he should not know. A moderately intelligent General will waste six months in mastering the craft of the particular war that he may be waging; a Colonel may utterly misunderstand the capacity of his regiment for three months after it has taken the field, and even a Company Commander may err and be deceived as to the temper and temperament of his own handful: wherefore the soldier, and the soldier of to-day more particularly, should not be blamed for falling back. He should be shot or hanged afterwards—to encourage the others; but he should not be vilified in newspapers, for that is want of tact and waste of space.

He has, let us say, been in the service of the Empress for, perhaps, four years. He will leave in another two years. He has no inherited morals, and four years are not sufficient to drive toughness into his fibre, or to teach him how holy a thing is his Regiment. He wants to drink, he wants to enjoy himself—in India he wants to save money—and he does not in the least like getting hurt. He has received just sufficient education to make him understand half the purport of the orders he receives, and to speculate on the nature of clean, incised and shattering wounds. Thus, if he is told to deploy under fire preparatory to an attack, he knows that he runs a very great risk of being killed while he is deploying, and suspects that he is being thrown away to gain ten minutes' time. He may either deploy with desperate swiftness, or he may shuffle, or bunch, or break, according to the discipline under which he has lain for four years.

Armed with imperfect knowledge, cursed with the rudiments of an imagination, hampered by the intense selfishness of the lower classes, and unsupported by any regimental associations, this young man is suddenly introduced to an enemy who in eastern lands is always ugly, generally tall and hairy, and frequently noisy. If he looks to the right and the left and sees old soldiers—men of twelve years' service, who, he knows, know what they are about—taking a charge, rush, or demonstration without embarrassment, he is consoled and applies his shoulder to the butt of his rifle with a stout heart. His peace is the greater if he hears a senior, who has taught him his soldiering and broken his head on occasion, whispering: "They'll shout and carry on like this for five minutes. Then they'll rush in, and then we've got 'em by the short hairs!"

But, on the other hand, if he sees only men of his own term of service, turning white and playing with their triggers and saying: "What the Hell's up now?" while the Company Commanders are sweating into their sword-hilts and shouting: "Front-rank, fix bayonets. Steady there—steady! Sight for three hundred—no, for five! Lie down all! Steady! Front-rank kneel!" and so forth, he becomes unhappy, and grows acutely miserable when he hears a comrade turn over with the rattle of fire-irons falling into the fender, and the grunt of a pole-axed ox. If he can be moved about a little and allowed to watch the effect of his own fire on the enemy he feels merrier, and may be then worked up to the blind passion of fighting, which is, contrary to general belief, controlled by a chilly Devil and shakes men like ague. If he is not moved about, and begins to feel cold at the pit of the stomach, and in that crisis is badly mauled and hears orders that were never given, he will break, and he will break badly, and of all things under the light of the Sun there is nothing more terrible than a broken British regiment. When the worst comes to the worst and the panic is really epidemic, the men must be e'en let go, and the Company Commanders had better escape to the enemy and stay there for safety's sake. If they can be made to come again they are not pleasant men to meet; because they will not break twice.

About thirty years from this date, when we have succeeded in half-educating everything that wears trousers, our Army will be a beautifully unreliable machine. It will know too much and it will do too little. Later still, when all men are at the mental level of the officer of to-day, it will sweep the earth. Speaking roughly, you must employ either blackguards or gentlemen, or, best of all, blackguards commanded by gentlemen, to do butcher's work with efficiency and despatch. The ideal soldier should, of course, think for himself—the *Pocket-book* says so. Unfortunately, to attain this virtue, he has to pass through the phase of thinking of himself, and that is misdirected genius. A blackguard may be slow to think for himself, but he is genuinely anxious to kill, and a little punishment teaches him how to guard his own skin and perforate another's. A powerfully prayerful Highland Regiment, officered by rank Presbyterians, is, perhaps, one degree more terrible in action than a hard-bitten thousand of irresponsible Irish ruffians led by most improper young unbelievers. But these things prove the rule—which is that the midway men are not to be trusted alone. They have ideas about the value of life and an upbringing that has not taught them to go on and take the chances. They are carefully unprovided with a backing of comrades who have been shot over, and until that backing is re-introduced, as a great many Regimental Commanders intend it shall be, they are more liable to disgrace themselves than the size of the Empire or the dignity of the Army allows. Their officers are as good as good can be, because their training begins early, and God has arranged that a clean-run youth of the British middle classes shall, in the matter of backbone, brains, and bowels, surpass all other youths. For this reason a child of eighteen will stand up, doing nothing, with a tin sword in his hand and joy in his heart until he is dropped. If he dies, he dies like a gentleman. If he lives, he writes Home that he has been "potted," "sniped," "chipped," or "cut over," and sits down to besiege Government for a wound-gratuity until the next little war breaks out, when he perjures himself before a Medical Board, blarneys his Colonel, burns incense round his Adjutant, and is allowed to go to the Front once more.

Which homily brings me directly to a brace of the most finished little fiends that ever banged drum or tootled fife in the Band of a British Regiment. They ended their sinful career by open and flagrant mutiny and were shot for it. Their names were Jakin and Lew—Piggy Lew—and they were bold, bad drummer-boys, both of them frequently birched by the Drum-Major of the Fore and Aft.

Jakin was a stunted child of fourteen, and Lew was about the same age. When not looked after, they smoked and drank. They swore habitually after the manner of the Barrack-room, which is cold-swearing and comes from between clinched teeth, and they fought religiously once a week. Jakin had sprung from some London gutter and may or may not have passed through Dr. Barnardo's hands ere he arrived at the dignity of drummer-boy. Lew could remember nothing except the Regiment and the delight of listening to the Band from his earliest years. He hid somewhere in his grimy little soul a genuine love for music, and was most mistakenly furnished with the head of a cherub: insomuch that beautiful ladies who watched the Regiment in church were wont to speak of him as a "darling." They never heard his vitriolic comments on their manners and morals, as he walked back to barracks with the Band and matured fresh causes of offence against Jakin.

The other drummer-boys hated both lads on account of their illogical conduct. Jakin might be pounding Lew, or Lew might be rubbing Jakin's head in the dirt, but any attempt at aggression on the part of an outsider was met by the combined forces of Lew and Jakin; and the consequences were painful. The boys were the Ishmaels of the corps, but wealthy Ishmaels, for they sold battles in alternate weeks for the sport of the barracks when they were not pitted against other boys; and thus amassed money.

On this particular day there was dissension in the camp. They had just been convicted afresh of smoking, which is bad for little boys who use plug-tobacco, and Lew's contention was that Jakin had "stunk so orrid bad from keepin' the pipe in pocket," that he and he alone was responsible for the birching they were both tingling under.

"I tell you I 'id the pipe back o' barracks," said Jakin pacifically.

"You're a bloomin' liar," said Lew without heat.

"You're a bloomin' little barstard," said Jakin, strong in the knowledge that his own ancestry was unknown. Now there is one word in the extended vocabulary of Barrack-room abuse that cannot pass without comment. You may call a man a thief and risk nothing. You may even call him a coward without finding more than a boot whiz past your ear, but you must not call a man a bastard unless you are prepared to prove it on his front teeth.

"You might ha' kep' that till I wasn't so sore," said Lew sorrowfully, dodging round Jakin's guard.

"I'll make you sorer," said Jakin genially, and got home on Lew's alabaster forehead. All would have gone well and this story, as the books say, would never have been written, had not his evil fate prompted the Bazar-Sergeant's son, a long, employless man of five-and-twenty, to put in an appearance after the first round. He was eternally in need of money, and knew that the boys had silver.

"Fighting again," said he. "I'll report you to my father, and he'll report you to the Colour-Sergeant."

"What's that to you?" said Jakin with an unpleasant dilation of the nostrils.

"Oh! nothing to *me*. You'll get into trouble, and you've been up too often to afford that."

"What the Hell do you know about what we've done?" asked Lew the Seraph. "*You* aren't in the Army, you lousy, cadging civilian."

He closed in on the man's left flank.

"Jes' 'cause you find two gentlemen settlin' their diff'rences with their fistes you stick in your ugly nose where you aren't wanted. Run 'ome to your 'arf-caste slut of a Ma—or we'll give you what-for," said Jakin.

The man attempted reprisals by knocking the boys' heads together. The scheme would have succeeded had not Jakin punched him vehemently in the stomach, or had Lew refrained from kicking his shins. They fought together, bleeding and breathless, for half an hour, and, after heavy punishment, triumphantly pulled down their opponent as terriers pull down a jackal.

"Now," gasped Jakin, "I'll give you what-for." He proceeded to pound the man's features while Lew stamped on the outlying portions of his anatomy. Chivalry is not a strong point in the composition of the average drummer-boy. He fights, as do his betters, to make his mark.

Ghastly was the ruin that escaped, and awful was the wrath of the Bazar-Sergeant. Awful too was the scene in Orderly-room when the two reprobates appeared to answer the charge of half-murdering a "civilian." The Bazar-Sergeant thirsted for a criminal action, and his son lied. The boys stood to attention while the black clouds of evidence accumulated.

"You little devils are more trouble than the rest of the Regiment put together," said the Colonel angrily. "One might as well admonish thistledown, and I can't well put you in cells or under stoppages. You must be birched again."

"Beg y' pardon, Sir. Can't we say nothin' in our own defence, Sir?" shrilled Jakin.

"Hey! What? Are you going to argue with *me?*" said the Colonel.

"No, Sir," said Lew. "But if a man come to you, Sir, and said he was going to report you, Sir, for 'aving a bit of a turn-up with a friend, Sir, an' wanted to get money out o' *you,* Sir——"

The Orderly-room exploded in a roar of laughter. "Well?" said the Colonel.

"That was what that measly *jarnwar* there did, Sir, and 'e'd 'a' *done* it, Sir, if we 'adn't prevented 'im. We didn't 'it 'im much, Sir. 'E 'adn't no manner o' right to interfere with us, Sir. I don't mind bein' birched by the Drum-Major, Sir, nor yet reported by *any* Corp'ral, but I'm—but I don't think it's fair, Sir, for a civilian to come an' talk over a man in the Army."

A second shout of laughter shook the Orderly-room, but the Colonel was grave.

"What sort of characters have these boys?" he asked of the Regimental Sergeant-Major.

"Accordin' to the Bandmaster, Sir," returned that revered official—the only soul in the Regiment whom the boys feared —"they do everything *but* lie, Sir."

"Is it like we'd go for that man for fun, Sir?" said Lew, pointing to the plaintiff.

"Oh, admonished,—admonished!" said the Colonel testily, and when the boys had gone he read the Bazar-Sergeant's son a ecture on the sin of unprofitable meddling, and gave orders hat the Bandmaster should keep the Drums in better discipline.

"If either of you come to practice again with so much as a cratch on your two ugly little faces," thundered the Bandmaster, "I'll tell the Drum-Major to take the skin off your backs. Understand that, you young devils."

Then he repented of his speech for just the length of time hat Lew, looking like a seraph in red worsted embellishments, took the place of one of the trumpets—in hospital— nd rendered the echo of a battle-piece. Lew certainly was a nusician, and had often in his more exalted moments expressed yearning to master every instrument of the Band.

"There's nothing to prevent your becoming a Bandmaster, Lew," said the Bandmaster, who had composed waltzes of is own, and worked day and night in the interests of the Band.

"What did he say?" demanded Jakin after practice.

"'Said I might be a bloomin' Bandmaster, an' be asked in o 'ave a glass o' sherry-wine on Mess-nights."

"Ho! 'Said you might be a bloomin' non-combatant, did 'e! That's just about wot 'e would say. When I've put in my boy's service—it's a bloomin' shame that doesn't count for pension—I'll take on as a privit. Then I'll be a Lance in a ear—knowin' what I know about the ins and outs o' things. n three years I'll be a bloomin' Sergeant. I won't marry then, ot I! I'll 'old on and learn the orf'cers' ways an' apply for xchange into a reg'ment that doesn't know all about me. Then I'll be a bloomin' orf'cer. Then I'll ask you to 'ave a glass o' sherry-wine, *Mister* Lew, an' you'll bloomin' well 'ave to stay in the hanty-room while the Mess-Sergeant brings it to your dirty 'ands."

"'S'pose I'm going to be a Bandmaster? Not I, quite. I'll be a orf'cer too. There's nothin' like takin' to a thing an' stickin' to it, the Schoolmaster says. The Reg'ment don't go 'ome for another seven years. I'll be a Lance then or near to."

Thus the boys discussed their futures, and conducted themselves piously for a week. That is to say, Lew started a flirtation with the Colour-Sergeant's daughter, aged thirteen—"not," as he explained to Jakin, "with any intention o' matrimony, but by way o' keepin' my 'and in." And the black-haired Cris Delighan enjoyed that flirtation more than previous ones, and the other drummer-boys raged furiously together, and Jakin preached sermons on the dangers of "bein tangled along o' petticoats."

But neither love nor virtue would have held Lew long in the paths of propriety had not the rumour gone abroad that the Regiment was to be sent on active service, to take part in a war which, for the sake of brevity, we will call "The War of the Lost Tribes."

The barracks had the rumour almost before the Mess room, and of all the nine hundred men in barracks, not te had seen a shot fired in anger. The Colonel had, twenty year ago, assisted at a Frontier expedition; one of the Majors ha seen service at the Cape; a confirmed deserter in E Compan had helped to clear streets in Ireland; but that was all. Th Regiment had been put by for many years. The overwhelm ing mass of its rank and file had from three to four years service; the non-commissioned officers were under thirty year old; and men and sergeants alike had forgotten to speak c the stories written in brief upon the Colours—the Ne Colours that had been formally blessed by an Archbisho in England ere the Regiment came away.

They wanted to go to the Front—they were enthusia tically anxious to go—but they had no knowledge of wh war meant, and there was none to tell them. They were a educated regiment, the percentage of school-certificates their ranks was high, and most of the men could do more than read and write. They had been recruited in loyal observance of the territorial idea; but they themselves had no notion of that idea. They were made up of drafts from an over-populated manufacturing district. The system had put flesh and muscle upon their small bones, but it could not put heart into the sons of those who for generations had done overmuch work for over-scanty pay, had sweated in drying-rooms, stooped over looms, coughed among white-lead, and shivered on lime-barges. The men had found food and rest in the Army, and now they were going to fight "niggers"—people who ran away if you shook a stick at them. Wherefore they cheered lustily when the rumour ran, and the shrewd, clerkly non-commissioned officers speculated on the chances of batta and of saving their pay. At Headquarters, men said: "The Fore and Fit have never been under fire within the last generation. Let us, therefore, break them in easily by setting them to guard lines of communication." And this would have been done but for the fact that British Regiments were wanted—badly wanted—at the Front, and there were doubtful Native Regiments that could fill the minor duties. "Brigade 'em with two strong Regiments," said Headquarters. 'They may be knocked about a bit, but they'll learn their usiness before they come through. Nothing like a night-ılarm and a little cutting-up of stragglers to make a Regiment smart in the field. Wait till they've had half a dozen entries' throats cut."

The Colonel wrote with delight that the temper of his men vas excellent, that the Regiment was all that could be wished, nd as sound as a bell. The Majors smiled with a sober joy, nd the subalterns waltzed in pairs down the Mess-room fter dinner, and nearly shot themselves at revolver-practice. But there was consternation in the hearts of Jakin and Lew. Vhat was to be done with the Drums? Would the Band go o the Front? How many of the Drums would accompany ne Regiment?

They took council together, sitting in a tree and smoking. "It's more than a bloomin' toss-up they'll leave us be'ind at the Depôt with the women. You'll like that," said Jakin sarcastically.

"'Cause o' Cris, y' mean? Wot's a woman, or a 'ole bloomin' depôt o' women, 'longside o' the chanst of field-service? You know I'm as keen on goin' as you," said Lew.

"'Wish I was a bloomin' bugler," said Jakin sadly. "They'll take Tom Kidd along, that I can plaster a wall with, an' like as not they won't take us."

"Then let's go an' make Tom Kidd so bloomin' sick 'e can't bugle no more. You 'old 'is 'ands an' I'll kick 'im," said Lew, wriggling on the branch.

"That ain't no good neither. We ain't the sort o' characters to presoon on our rep'tations—they're bad. If they have the Band at the Depôt we don't go, and no error *there*. If they take the Band we may get cast for medical unfitness. Are you medical fit, Piggy?" said Jakin, digging Lew in the ribs with force.

"Yus," said Lew with an oath. "The Doctor says your 'eart's weak through smokin' on an empty stummick. Throw a chest an' I'll try yer."

Jakin threw out his chest, which Lew smote with all his might. Jakin turned very pale, gasped, crowed, screwed up his eyes and said—"That's all right."

"You'll do," said Lew. "I've 'eard o' men dying when you 'it 'em fair on the breastbone."

"Don't bring us no nearer goin', though," said Jakin. "Do you know where we're ordered?"

"Gawd knows, an' 'E won't split on a pal. Somewheres up to the Front to kill Paythans—hairy big beggars that turn you inside out if they get 'old o' you. They say their women are good-looking, too."

"Any loot?" asked the abandoned Jakin.

"Not a bloomin' anna, they say, unless you dig up the ground an' see what the niggers 'ave 'id. They're a poor lot." Jakin stood upright on the branch and gazed across the plain.

"Lew," said he, "there's the Colonel coming. 'Colonel a good old beggar. Let's go an' talk to 'im."

Lew nearly fell out of the tree at the audacity of the suggestion. Like Jakin he feared not God, neither regarded he Man, but there are limits even to the audacity of a drummer-boy, and to speak to a Colonel was——

But Jakin had slid down the trunk and doubled in the direction of the Colonel. That officer was walking wrapped in thought and visions of a C. B.—yes, even a K. C. B., for had he not at command one of the best Regiments of the Line—the Fore and Fit? And he was aware of two small boys charging down upon him. Once before it had been solemnly reported to him that "the Drums were in a state of mutiny," Jakin and Lew being the ringleaders. This looked like an organized conspiracy.

The boys halted at twenty yards, walked to the regulation four paces, and saluted together, each as well set-up as a ramrod and little taller.

The Colonel was in a genial mood; the boys appeared very forlorn and unprotected on the desolate plain, and one of them was handsome.

"Well!" said the Colonel, recognizing them. "Are you going to pull me down in the open? I'm sure I never interfere with you, even though"—he sniffed suspiciously—"you have been smoking."

It was time to strike while the iron was hot. Their hearts beat tumultuously.

"Beg y' pardon, Sir," began Jakin. "The Reg'ment's ordered on active service, Sir?"

"So I believe," said the Colonel courteously.

"Is the Band goin', Sir?" said both together. Then, without pause, "We're goin', Sir, ain't we?"

"You!" said the Colonel stepping back the more fully to take in the two small figures. "You! You'd die in the first march."

"No, we wouldn't, Sir. We can march with the Reg'ment anywheres—p'rade an' anywhere else," said Jakin.

"If Tom Kidd goes 'e'll shut up like a clasp-knife," said Lew. "Tom 'as very-close veins in both 'is legs, Sir."

"Very how much?"

"Very-close veins, Sir. That's why they swells after long p'rade, Sir. If 'e can go, we can go, Sir."

Again the Colonel looked at them long and intently.

"Yes, the Band is going," he said as gravely as though he had been addressing a brother officer. "Have you any parents, either of you two?"

"No, Sir," rejoicingly from Lew and Jakin. "We're both orphans, Sir. There's no one to be considered of on our account, Sir."

"You poor little sprats, and you want to go up to the Front with the Regiment, do you? Why?"

"I've wore the Queen's Uniform for two years," said Jakin. "It's very 'ard, Sir, that a man don't get no recompense for doin' of 'is dooty, Sir."

"An'—an' if I don't go, Sir," interrupted Lew, "the Bandmaster 'e says 'e'll catch an' make a bloo—a blessed musician o' me, Sir. Before I've seen any service, Sir."

The Colonel made no answer for a long time. Then he said quietly: "If you're passed by the Doctor I dare say you can go. I shouldn't smoke if I were you."

The boys saluted and disappeared. The Colonel walked home and told the story to his wife, who nearly cried over it. The Colonel was well pleased. If that was the temper of the children, what would not the men do?

Jakin and Lew entered the boys' barrack-room with great stateliness, and refused to hold any conversation with their comrades for at least ten minutes. Then, bursting with pride, Jakin drawled: "I've bin intervooin' the Colonel. Good old beggar is the Colonel. Says I to 'im 'Colonel,' says I, 'let me go to the Front, along o' the Reg'ment.'—'To the Front you shall go,' says 'e, 'an' I only wish there was more like you among the dirty little devils that bang the bloomin' drums.' Kidd, if you throw your 'courtrements at me for tellin' you the truth to your own advantage, your legs'll swell."

None the less there was a Battle-Royal in the barrack-room, for the boys were consumed with envy and hate, and neither Jakin nor Lew behaved in conciliatory wise.

"I'm goin' out to say adoo to my girl," said Lew, to cap

the climax. "Don't none o' you touch my kit because it's wanted for active service; me bein' specially invited to go by the Colonel."

He strolled forth and whistled in the clump of trees at the back of the Married Quarters till Cris came to him, and, the preliminary kisses being given and taken, Lew began to explain the situation.

"I'm goin' to the Front with the Reg'ment," he said valiantly.

"Piggy, you're a little liar," said Cris, but her heart misgave her, for Lew was not in the habit of lying.

"Liar yourself, Cris," said Lew, slipping an arm round her. "I'm goin'. When the Reg'ment marches out you'll see me with 'em, all galliant and gay. Give us another kiss, Cris, on the strength of it."

"If you'd on'y a-stayed at the Depôt—where you *ought* to ha' bin—you could get as many of 'em as—as you dam please," whimpered Cris, putting up her mouth.

"It's 'ard, Cris. I grant you it's 'ard. But what's a man to do? If I'd a-stayed at the Depôt, you wouldn't think anything of me."

"Like as not, but I'd 'ave you with me, Piggy. An' all the thinkin' in the world isn't like kissin'."

"An' all the kissin' in the world isn't like 'avin' a medal to wear on the front o' your coat."

"*You* won't get no medal."

"Oh yus, I shall though. Me an' Jakin are the only acting-drummers that'll be took along. All the rest is full men, an' we'll get our medals with them."

"They might ha' taken anybody but you, Piggy. You'll get killed—you're so venturesome. Stay with me, Piggy, darlin', down at the Depôt, an' I'll love you true, for ever."

"Ain't you goin' to do that *now,* Cris? You said you was."

"O' course I am, but th' other's more comfortable. Wait till you've growed a bit, Piggy. You aren't no taller than me now."

"I've bin in the Army for two years an' I'm not goin' to get out of a chanst o' seein' service an' don't you try to make me do so. I'll come back, Cris, an' when I take on as a man I'll marry you—marry you when I'm a Lance."

"Promise, Piggy?"

Lew reflected on the future as arranged by Jakin a short time previously, but Cris's mouth was very near to his own.

"I promise, s'elp me, Gawd!" said he.

Cris slid an arm round his neck.

"I won't 'old you back no more, Piggy. Go away an' get your medal, an' I'll make you a new button-bag as nice as I know how," she whispered.

"Put some o' your 'air into it, Cris, an' I'll keep it in my pocket so long's I'm alive."

Then Cris wept anew, and the interview ended. Public feeling among the drummer-boys rose to fever pitch and the lives of Jakin and Lew became unenviable. Not only had they been permitted to enlist two years before the regulation boy's age—fourteen—but, by virtue, it seemed, of their extreme youth, they were allowed to go to the Front—which thing had not happened to acting-drummers within the knowledge of boy. The Band which was to accompany the Regiment had been cut down to the regulation twenty men, the surplus returning to the ranks. Jakin and Lew were attached to the Band as supernumeraries, though they would much have preferred being company buglers.

"'Don't matter much," said Jakin after the medical inspection. "Be thankful that we're 'lowed to go at all. The Doctor 'e said that if we could stand what we took from the Bazar-Sergeant's son we'd stand pretty nigh anything."

"Which we will," said Lew, looking tenderly at the ragged and ill-made housewife that Cris had given him, with a lock of her hair worked into a sprawling "L" upon the cover.

"It was the best I could," she sobbed. "I wouldn't let mother nor the Sergeant's tailor 'elp me. Keep it always, Piggy, an' remember I love you true."

They marched to the railway station, nine hundred and sixty strong, and every soul in cantonments turned out to see them go. The drummers gnashed their teeth at Jakin and Lew marching with the Band, the married women wept upon the platform, and the Regiment cheered its noble self black in the face.

"A nice level lot," said the Colonel to the Second-in-Command as they watched the first four companies entraining.

"Fit to do anything," said the Second-in-Command enthusiastically. "But it seems to me they're a thought too young and tender for the work in hand. It's bitter cold up at the Front now."

"They're sound enough," said the Colonel. "We must take our chance of sick casualties."

So they went northward, ever northward, past droves and droves of camels, armies of camp-followers, and legions of laden mules, the throng thickening day by day, till with a shriek the train pulled up at a hopelessly congested junction where six lines of temporary track accommodated six forty-waggon trains; where whistles blew, Babus sweated and Commissariat officers swore from dawn till far into the night amid the wind-driven chaff of the fodder-bales and the lowing of a thousand steers.

"Hurry up—you're badly wanted at the Front," was the message that greeted the Fore and Aft, and the occupants of the Red Cross carriages told the same tale.

" 'Tisn't so much the bloomin' fightin'," gasped a head-bound trooper of Hussars to a knot of admiring Fore and Afts. " 'Tisn't so much the bloomin' fightin', though there's enough o' that. It's the bloomin' food an' the bloomin' climate. Frost all night 'cept when it hails, and biling sun all day, and the water stinks fit to knock you down. I got my 'ead chipped like a egg; I've got pneumonia too, an' my guts is all out o' order. 'Tain't no bloomin' picnic in those parts, I can tell you."

"Wot are the niggers like?" demanded a private.

"There's some prisoners in that train yonder. Go an' look at 'em. They're the aristocracy o' the country. The common folk are a dashed sight uglier. If you want to know what they fight with, reach under my seat an' pull out the long knife that's there."

They dragged out and beheld for the first time the grim,

bone-handled, triangular Afghan knife. It was almost as long as Lew.

"That's the thing to jint ye," said the trooper feebly. "It can take off a man's arm at the shoulder as easy as slicing butter. I halved the beggar that used that 'un, but there's more of his likes up above. They don't understand thrustin', but they're devils to slice."

The men strolled across the tracks to inspect the Afghan prisoners. They were unlike any "niggers" that the Fore and Aft had ever met—these huge, black-haired, scowling sons of the Beni-Israel. As the men stared the Afghans spat freely and muttered one to another with lowered eyes.

"My eyes! Wot awful swine!" said Jakin, who was in the rear of the procession. "Say, old man, how you got *puckrowed,* eh? *Kiswasti* you wasn't hanged for your ugly face, hey?"

The tallest of the company turned, his leg-irons clanking at the movement, and stared at the boy. "See!" he cried to his fellows in Pushto. "They send children against us. What a people, and what fools!"

"Hya!" said Jakin, nodding his head cheerily. "You go down-country. *Khana* get, *peenikapanee* get—live like a bloomin' Raja *ke marfik.* That's a better *bandobust* than baynit get it in your innards. Good-bye, ole man. Take care o' your beautiful figure-'ed, an' try to look *kushy.*"

The men laughed and fell in for their first march when they began to realize that a soldier's life was not all beer and skittles. They were much impressed with the size and bestial ferocity of the niggers whom they had now learned to call "Paythans," and more with the exceeding discomfort of their own surroundings. Twenty old soldiers in the corps would have taught them how to make themselves moderately snug at night, but they had no old soldiers, and, as the troops on the line of march said, "they lived like pigs." They learned the heart-breaking cussedness of camp-kitchens and camels and the depravity of an E. P. tent and a wither-wrung mule. They studied animalculæ in water, and developed a few cases of dysentery in their study.

At the end of their third march they were disagreeably surprised by the arrival in their camp of a hammered iron slug which, fired from a steady rest at seven hundred yards, flicked out the brains of a private seated by the fire. This robbed them of their peace for a night, and was the beginning of a long-range fire carefully calculated to that end. In the daytime they saw nothing except an unpleasant puff of smoke from a crag above the line of march. At night there were distant spurts of flame and occasional casualties, which set the whole camp blazing into the gloom and, occasionally, into opposite tents. Then they swore vehemently and vowed that this was magnificent but not war.

Indeed it was not. The Regiment could not halt for reprisals against the sharpshooters of the country-side. Its duty was to go forward and make connection with the Scotch and Gurkha troops with which it was brigaded. The Afghans knew this, and knew too, after their first tentative shots, that they were dealing with a raw regiment. Thereafter they devoted themselves to the task of keeping the Fore and Aft on the strain. Not for anything would they have taken equal liberties with a seasoned corps—with the wicked little Gurkhas, whose delight it was to lie out in the open on a dark night and stalk their stalkers—with the terrible, big men dressed in women's clothes, who could be heard praying to their God in the night-watches, and whose peace of mind no amount of "sniping" could shake—or with those vile Sikhs, who marched so ostentatiously unprepared and who dealt out such grim reward to those who tried to profit by that unpreparedness. This white regiment was different—quite different. It slept like a hog, and, like a hog, charged in every direction when it was roused. Its sentries walked with a footfall that could be heard for a quarter of a mile; would fire at anything that moved—even a driven donkey—and when they had once fired, could be scientifically "rushed" and laid out a horror and an offence against the morning sun. Then there were camp-followers who straggled and could be cut up without fear. Their shrieks would disturb the white boys, and the loss of their services would inconvenience them sorely.

Thus, at every march, the hidden enemy became bolder and the regiment writhed and twisted under attacks it could not avenge. The crowning triumph was a sudden night-rush ending in the cutting of many tent-ropes, the collapse of the sodden canvas and a glorious knifing of the men who struggled and kicked below. It was a great deed, neatly carried out, and it shook the already shaken nerves of the Fore and Aft. All the courage that they had been required to exercise up to this point was the "two o'clock in the morning courage," and, so far, they had only succeeded in shooting their comrades and losing their sleep.

Sullen, discontented, cold, savage, sick, with their uniforms dulled and unclean, the Fore and Aft joined their Brigade.

"I hear you had a tough time of it coming up," said the Brigadier. But when he saw the hospital-sheets his face fell.

"This is bad," said he to himself. "They're as rotten as sheep." And aloud to the Colonel—"I'm afraid we can't spare you just yet. We want all we have, else I should have given you ten days to recover in."

The Colonel winced. "On my honour, Sir," he returned, "there is not the least necessity to think of sparing us. My men have been rather mauled and upset without a fair return. They only want to go in somewhere where they can see what's before them."

"Can't say I think much of the Fore and Fit," said the Brigadier in confidence to his Brigade-Major. "They've lost all their soldiering, and, by the trim of them, might have marched through the country from the other side. A more fagged-out set of men I never put eyes on."

"Oh, they'll improve as the work goes on. The parade gloss has been rubbed off a little, but they'll put on field polish before long," said the Brigade-Major. "They've been mauled, and they quite don't understand it."

They did not. All the hitting was on one side, and it was cruelly hard hitting with accessories that made them sick. There was also the real sickness that laid hold of a strong man and dragged him howling to the grave. Worst of all, their officers knew just as little of the country as the men themselves, and looked as if they did. The Fore and Aft were in a thoroughly unsatisfactory condition, but they believed that all would be well if they could once get a fair go-in at the enemy. Pot-shots up and down the valleys were unsatisfactory, and the bayonet never seemed to get a chance. Perhaps it was as well, for a long-limbed Afghan with a knife had a reach of eight feet, and could carry away lead that would disable three Englishmen.

The Fore and Aft would like some rifle-practice at the enemy—all seven hundred rifles blazing together. That wish showed the mood of the men.

The Gurkhas walked into their camp, and in broken, Barrack-room English strove to fraternize with them; offered them pipes of tobacco and stood them treat at the canteen. But the Fore and Aft, not knowing much of the nature of the Gurkhas, treated them as they would treat any other "niggers," and the little men in green trotted back to their firm friends the Highlanders, and with many grins confided to them: "That dam white regiment no dam use. Sulky—ugh! Dirty—ugh! Hya, any tot for Johnny?" Whereat the Highlanders smote the Gurkhas as to the head, and told them not to vilify a British Regiment, and the Gurkhas grinned cavernously, for the Highlanders were their elder brothers and entitled to the privileges of kinship. The common soldier who touches a Gurkha is more than likely to have his head sliced open.

Three days later the Brigadier arranged a battle according to the rules of war and the peculiarity of the Afghan temperament. The enemy were massing in inconvenient strength among the hills, and the moving of many green standards warned him that the tribes were "up" in aid of the Afghan regular troops. A Squadron and a half of Bengal Lancers represented the available Cavalry, and two screw-guns borrowed from a column thirty miles away, the Artillery at the General's disposal.

"If they stand, as I've a very strong notion that they will, I fancy we shall see an infantry fight that will be worth watching," said the Brigadier. "We'll do it in style. Each regiment shall be played into action by its Band, and we'll hold the Cavalry in reserve."

"For *all* the reserve?" somebody asked.

"For all the reserve; because we're going to crumple them up," said the Brigadier, who was an extraordinary Brigadier, and did not believe in the value of a reserve when dealing with Asiatics. Indeed, when you come to think of it, had the British Army consistently waited for reserves in all its little affairs, the boundaries of Our Empire would have stopped at Brighton beach.

That battle was to be a glorious battle.

The three regiments debouching from three separate gorges, after duly crowning the heights above, were to converge from the centre, left, and right upon what we will call the Afghan army, then stationed towards the lower extremity of a flat-bottomed valley. Thus it will be seen that three sides of the valley practically belonged to the English, while the fourth was strictly Afghan property. In the event of defeat the Afghans had the rocky hills to fly to, where the fire from the guerilla tribes in aid would cover their retreat. In the event of victory these same tribes would rush down and lend their weight to the rout of the British.

The screw-guns were to shell the head of each Afghan rush that was made in close formation, and the Cavalry, held in reserve in the right valley, were to gently stimulate the break-up which would follow on the combined attack. The Brigadier, sitting upon a rock overlooking the valley, would watch the battle unrolled at his feet. The Fore and Aft would debouch from the central gorge, the Gurkhas from the left, and the Highlanders from the right, for the reason that the left flank of the enemy seemed as though it required the most hammering. It was not every day that an Afghan force would take ground in the open, and the Brigadier was resolved to make the most of it.

"If we only had a few more men," he said plaintively, "we could surround the creatures and crumple 'em up thoroughly. As it is, I'm afraid we can only cut them up as they run. It's a great pity."

The Fore and Aft had enjoyed unbroken peace for five days, and were beginning, in spite of dysentery, to recover their nerve. But they were not happy, for they did not know the work in hand, and had they known, would not have known how to do it. Throughout those five days in which old soldiers might have taught them the craft of the game, they discussed together their misadventures in the past—how such an one was alive at dawn and dead ere the dusk, and with what shrieks and struggles such another had given up his soul under the Afghan knife. Death was a new and horrible thing to the sons of mechanics who were used to die decently of zymotic disease; and their careful conservation in barracks had done nothing to make them look upon it with less dread.

Very early in the dawn the bugles began to blow, and the Fore and Aft, filled with a misguided enthusiasm, turned out without waiting for a cup of coffee and a biscuit; and were rewarded by being kept under arms in the cold while the other regiments leisurely prepared for the fray. All the world knows that it is ill taking the breeks off a Highlander. It is much iller to try to make him stir unless he is convinced of the necessity for haste.

The Fore and Aft waited, leaning upon their rifles and listening to the protests of their empty stomachs. The Colonel did his best to remedy the default of lining as soon as it was borne in upon him that the affair would not begin at once, and so well did he succeed that the coffee was just ready when—the men moved off, their Band leading. Even then there had been a mistake in time, and the Fore and Aft came out into the valley ten minutes before the proper hour. Their Band wheeled to the right after reaching the open, and retired behind a little rocky knoll still playing while the Regiment went past.

It was not a pleasant sight that opened on the uninstructed view, for the lower end of the valley appeared to be filled by an army in position—real and actual regiments attired in red coats, and—of this there was no doubt—firing Martini-Henri bullets which cut up the ground a hundred yards in front of the leading company. Over that pockmarked ground the Regiment had to pass, and it opened the ball with a general and profound courtesy to the piping pickets; ducking in perfect time, as though it had been brazed on a rod. Being half-capable of thinking for itself, it fired a volley by the simple process of pitching its rifle into its shoulder and pulling the trigger. The bullets may have accounted for some of the watchers on the hillside, but they certainly did not affect the mass of enemy in front, while the noise of the rifles drowned any orders that might have been given.

"Good God!" said the Brigadier, sitting on the rock high above all. "That regiment has spoilt the whole show. Hurry up the others, and let the screw-guns get off."

But the screw-guns, in working round the heights, had stumbled upon a wasp's nest of a small mud fort which they incontinently shelled at eight hundred yards, to the huge discomfort of the occupants, who were unaccustomed to weapons of such devilish precision.

The Fore and Aft continued to go forward but with shortened stride. Where were the other regiments, and why did these niggers use Martinis? They took open order instinctively, lying down and firing at random, rushing a few paces forward and lying down again, according to the regulations. Once in this formation, each man felt himself desperately alone, and edged in towards his fellow for comfort's sake.

Then the crack of his neighbour's rifle at his ear led him to fire as rapidly as he could—again for the sake of the comfort of the noise. The reward was not long delayed. Five volleys plunged the files in banked smoke impenetrable to the eye, and the bullets began to take ground twenty or thirty yards in front of the firers, as the weight of the bayonet dragged down and to the right arms wearied with holding the kick of the leaping Martini. The Company Commanders peered helplessly through the smoke, the more nervous mechanically trying to fan it away with their helmets.

"High and to the left!" bawled a Captain till he was hoarse. "No good! Cease firing, and let it drift away a bit."

Three and four times the bugles shrieked the order, and

when it was obeyed the Fore and Aft looked that their foe should be lying before them in mown swaths of men. A light wind drove the smoke to leeward, and showed the enemy still in position and apparently unaffected. A quarter of a ton of lead had been buried a furlong in front of them, as the ragged earth attested.

That was not demoralizing to the Afghans, who have not European nerves. They were waiting for the mad riot to die down, and were firing quietly into the heart of the smoke. A private of the Fore and Aft spun up his company shrieking with agony, another was kicking the earth and gasping, and a third, ripped through the lower intestines by a jagged bullet, was calling aloud on his comrades to put him out of his pain. These were the casualties, and they were not soothing to hear or see. The smoke cleared to a dull haze.

Then the foe began to shout with a great shouting and a mass—a black mass—detached itself from the main body, and rolled over the ground at horrid speed. It was composed of, perhaps, three hundred men, who would shout and fire and slash if the rush of their fifty comrades who were determined to die carried home. The fifty were Ghazis, half-maddened with drugs and wholly mad with religious fanaticism. When they rushed the British fire ceased, and in the lull the order was given to close ranks and meet them with the bayonet.

Any one who knew the business could have told the Fore and Aft that the only way of dealing with a Ghazi rush is by volleys at long ranges; because a man who means to die, who desires to die, who will gain heaven by dying, must, in nine cases out of ten, kill a man who has a lingering prejudice in favour of life. Where they should have closed and gone forward, the Fore and Aft opened out and skirmished, and where they should have opened out and fired, they closed and waited.

A man dragged from his blankets half awake and unfed is never in a pleasant frame of mind. Nor does his happiness increase when he watches the whites of the eyes of three hundred six-foot fiends upon whose beards the foam is lying, upon whose tongues is a roar of wrath, and whose hands are yard-long knives.

The Fore and Aft heard the Gurkha bugles bringing that regiment forward at the double, while the neighing of the Highland pipes came from the left. They strove to stay where they were, though the bayonets wavered down the line like the oars of a ragged boat. Then they felt body to body the amazing physical strength of their foes; a shriek of pain ended the rush, and the knives fell amid scenes not to be told. The men clubbed together and smote blindly—as often as not at their own fellows. Their front crumpled like paper, and the fifty Ghazis passed on; their backers, now drunk with success, fighting as madly as they.

Then the rear-ranks were bidden to close up, and the subalterns dashed into the stew—alone. For the rear-ranks had heard the clamour in front, the yells and the howls of pain, and had seen the dark stale blood that makes afraid. They were not going to stay. It was the rushing of the camps over again. Let their officers go to Hell, if they chose; they would get away from the knives.

"Come on!" shrieked the subalterns, and their men, cursing them, drew back, each closing into his neighbour and wheeling round.

Charteris and Devlin, subalterns of the last company, faced their death alone in the belief that their men would follow.

"You've killed me, you cowards," sobbed Devlin and dropped, cut from the shoulder-strap to the centre of the chest, and a fresh detachment of his men retreating, always retreating, trampled him under foot as they made for the pass whence they had emerged.

I kissed her in the kitchen, and I kissed her in the hall.
Child'um, child'um, follow me!
Oh Golly, said the cook, is he gwine to kiss us all?
Halla—Halla—Halla—Hallelujah!

The Gurkhas were pouring through the left gorge and over the heights at the double to the invitation of their Regimental

Quick-step. The black rocks were crowned with dark green spiders as the bugles gave tongue jubilantly:—

In the morning! In the morning by *the bright light!*
When Gabriel blows his trumpet in the morning!

The Gurkha rear-companies tripped and blundered over loose stones. The front-files halted for a moment to take stock of the valley and to settle stray boot-laces. Then a happy little sigh of contentment soughed down the ranks, and it was as though the land smiled, for behold there below was the enemy, and it was to meet them that the Gurkhas had doubled so hastily. There was much enemy. There would be amusement. The little men hitched their *kukris* well to hand, and gaped expectantly at their officers as terriers grin ere the stone is cast for them to fetch. The Gurkhas' ground sloped downward to the valley, and they enjoyed a fair view of the proceedings. They sat upon the bowlders to watch, for their officers were not going to waste their wind in assisting to repulse a Ghazi rush more than half a mile away. Let the white men look to their own front.

"Hi! yi!" said the Subadar-Major, who was sweating profusely. "Dam fools yonder, stand close-order! This is no time for close order, it is the time for volleys. Ugh!"

Horrified, amused, and indignant, the Gurkhas beheld the retirement of the Fore and Aft with a running chorus of oaths and commentaries.

"They run! The white men run! Colonel Sahib, may *we* also do a little running?" murmured Runbir Thappa, the Senior Jemadar.

But the Colonel would have none of it. "Let the beggars be cut up a little," said he wrathfully. "'Serves 'em right. They'll be prodded into facing round in a minute." He looked through his field-glasses, and caught the glint of an officer's sword.

"Beating 'em with the flat—damned conscripts! How the Ghazis are walking into them!" said he.

The Fore and Aft, heading back, bore with them their officers. The narrowness of the pass forced the mob into solid formation, and the rear-ranks delivered some sort of a wavering volley. The Ghazis drew off, for they did not know what reserve the gorge might hide. Moreover, it was never wise to chase white men too far. They returned as wolves return to cover, satisfied with the slaughter that they had done, and only stopping to slash at the wounded on the ground. A quarter of a mile had the Fore and Aft retreated, and now, jammed in the pass, was quivering with pain, shaken and demoralized with fear, while the officers, maddened beyond control, smote the men with the hilts and the flats of their swords.

"Get back! Get back, you cowards—you women! Right about face—column of companies, form—you hounds!" shouted the Colonel, and the subalterns swore aloud. But the Regiment wanted to go—to go anywhere out of the range of those merciless knives. It swayed to and fro irresolutely with shouts and outcries, while from the right the Gurkhas dropped volley after volley of cripple-stopper Snider bullets at long range into the mob of the Ghazis returning to their own troops.

The Fore and Aft Band, though protected from direct fire by the rocky knoll under which it had sat down, fled at the first rush. Jakin and Lew would have fled also, but their short legs left them fifty yards in the rear, and by the time the Band had mixed with the Regiment, they were painfully aware that they would have to close in alone and unsupported.

"Get back to that rock," gasped Jakin. "They won't see us there."

And they returned to the scattered instruments of the Band; their hearts nearly bursting their ribs.

"Here's a nice show for *us,*" said Jakin, throwing himself full length on the ground. "A bloomin' fine show for British Infantry! Oh, the devils! They've gone an' left us alone here! Wot'll we do?"

Lew took possession of a cast-off water bottle, which naturally was full of canteen rum, and drank till he coughed again.

"Drink," said he shortly. "They'll come back in a minute or two—you see."

Jakin drank, but there was no sign of the Regiment's return. They could hear a dull clamour from the head of the valley of retreat, and saw the Ghazis slink back, quickening their pace as the Gurkhas fired at them.

"We're all that's left of the Band, an' we'll be cut up as sure as death," said Jakin.

"I'll die game, then," said Lew thickly, fumbling with his tiny drummer's sword. The drink was working on his brain as it was on Jakin's.

"'Old on! I know something better than fightin'," said Jakin, stung by the splendour of a sudden thought due chiefly to rum. "Tip our bloomin' cowards yonder the word to come back. The Paythan beggars are well away. Come on, Lew! We won't get hurt. Take the fife an' give me the drum. The Old Step for all your bloomin' guts are worth! There's a few of our men coming back now. Stand up, ye drunken little defaulter. By your right—quick march!"

He slipped the drum-sling over his shoulder, thrust the fife into Lew's hand, and the two boys marched out of the cover of the rock into the open, making a hideous hash of the first bars of the "British Grenadiers."

As Lew had said, a few of the Fore and Aft were coming back sullenly and shamefacedly under the stimulus of blows and abuse; their red coats shone at the head of the valley, and behind them were wavering bayonets. But between this shattered line and the enemy, who with Afghan suspicion feared that the hasty retreat meant an ambush, and had not moved therefore, lay half a mile of a level ground dotted only by the wounded.

The tune settled into full swing and the boys kept shoulder to shoulder, Jakin banging the drum as one possessed. The one fife made a thin and pitiful squeaking, but the tune carried far, even to the Gurkhas.

"Come on, you dogs!" muttered Jakin to himself. "Are we to play forhever?" Lew was staring straight in front of him and marching more stiffly than ever he had done on parade.

And in bitter mockery of the distant mob, the old tune of the Old Line shrilled and rattled:—

Some talk of Alexander,
And some of Hercules;
Of Hector and Lysander,
And such great names as these!

There was a far-off clapping of hands from the Gurkhas, and a roar from the Highlanders in the distance, but never a shot was fired by British or Afghan. The two little red dots moved forward in the open parallel to the enemy's front.

But of all the world's great heroes
There's none that can compare,
With a tow-row-row-row-row-row,
To the British Grenadier!

The men of the Fore and Aft were gathering thick at the entrance into the plain. The Brigadier on the heights far above was speechless with rage. Still no movement from the enemy. The day stayed to watch the children.

Jakin halted and beat the long roll of the Assembly, while the fife squealed despairingly.

"Right about face! Hold up, Lew, you're drunk," said Jakin. They wheeled and marched back:—

Those heroes of antiquity
Ne'er saw a cannon-ball,
Nor knew the force o' powder,

"Here they come!" said Jakin. "Go on, Lew":—

To scare their foes withal!

The Fore and Aft were pouring out of the valley. What officers had said to men in that time of shame and humiliation will never be known; for neither officers nor men speak of it now.

"They are coming anew!" shouted a priest among the Afghans. "Do not kill the boys! Take them alive, and they shall be of our faith."

But the first volley had been fired, and Lew dropped on his face. Jakin stood for a minute, spun round and collapsed, as the Fore and Aft came forward, the curses of their officers in their ears, and in their hearts the shame of open shame.

Half the men had seen the drummers die, and they made no sign. They did not even shout. They doubled out straight across the plain in open order, and they did not fire.

"This," said the Colonel of Gurkhas, softly, "is the real attack, as it should have been delivered. Come on, my children."

"Ulu-lu-lu-lu!" squealed the Gurkhas, and came down with a joyful clicking of *kukris*—those vicious Gurkha knives.

On the right there was no rush. The Highlanders, cannily commending their souls to God (for it matters as much to a dead man whether he has been shot in a Border scuffle or at Waterloo), opened out and fired according to their custom, hat is to say without heat and without intervals, while the screw-guns, having disposed of the impertinent mud fort aforementioned, dropped shell after shell into the clusters ound the flickering green standards on the heights.

"Charrging is an unfortunate necessity," murmured the Colour-Sergeant of the right company of the Highlanders. 'It makes the men sweer so, but I am thinkin' that it will ome to a charrge if these black devils stand much longer. Stewarrt, man, you're firing into the eye of the sun, and he'll ot take any harm for Government ammuneetion. A foot ower and a great deal slower! What are the English doing? They're very quiet there in the centre. Running again?"

The English were not running. They were hacking and ewing and stabbing, for though one white man is seldom hysically a match for an Afghan in a sheepskin or wadded oat, yet, through the pressure of many white men behind, nd a certain thirst for revenge in his heart, he becomes capable of doing much with both ends of his rifle. The Fore and Aft held their fire till one bullet could drive through five or six men, and the front of the Afghan force gave on the volley. They then selected their men, and slew them with deep gasps and short hacking coughs, and groanings of leather belts against strained bodies, and realized for the first time that an Afghan attacked is far less formidable than an Afghan attacking; which fact old soldiers might have told them.

But they had no old soldiers in their ranks.

The Gurkhas' stall at the bazar was the noisiest, for the men were engaged—to a nasty noise as of beef being cut on the block—with the *kukri,* which they preferred to the bayonet; well knowing how the Afghan hates the half-moon blade.

As the Afghans wavered, the green standards on the mountain moved down to assist them in a last rally. This was unwise. The Lancers chafing in the right gorge had thrice despatched their only subaltern as galloper to report on the progress of affairs. On the third occasion he returned, with a bullet-graze on his knee, swearing strange oaths in Hindustani, and saying that all things were ready. So that Squadron swung round the right of the Highlanders with a wicked whistling of wind in the pennons of its lances, and fell upon the remnant just when, according to all the rules of war, it should have waited for the foe to show more signs of wavering.

But it was a dainty charge, deftly delivered, and it ended by the Cavalry finding itself at the head of the pass by which the Afghans intended to retreat; and down the track that the lances had made streamed two companies of the Highlanders, which was never intended by the Brigadier. The new development was successful. It detached the enemy from his base as a sponge is torn from a rock, and left him ringed about with fire in that pitiless plain. And as a sponge is chased round the bath-tub by the hand of the bather, so were the Afghans chased till they broke into little detachments much more difficult to dispose of than large masses.

"See!" quoth the Brigadier. "Everything has come as

arranged. We've cut their base, and now we'll bucket 'em to pieces."

A direct hammering was all that the Brigadier had dared to hope for, considering the size of the force at his disposal; but men who stand or fall by the errors of their opponents may be forgiven for turning Chance into Design. The bucketing went forward merrily. The Afghan forces were upon the run—the run of wearied wolves who snarl and bite over their shoulders. The red lances dipped by twos and threes, and, with a shriek, uprose the lance-butt, like a spar on a stormy sea, as the trooper cantering forward cleared his point. The Lancers kept between their prey and the steep hills, for all who could were trying to escape from the valley of death. The Highlanders gave the fugitives two hundred yards' law, and then brought them down, gasping and choking ere they could reach the protection of the bowlders above. The Gurkhas followed suit; but the Fore and Aft were killing on their own account, for they had penned a mass of men between their bayonets and a wall of rock, and the flash of the rifles was lighting the wadded coats.

"We cannot hold them, Captain Sahib!" panted a Ressaidar of Lancers. "Let us try the carbine. The lance is good, but it wastes time."

They tried the carbine, and still the enemy melted away—fled up the hills by hundreds when there were only twenty bullets to stop them. On the heights the screw-guns ceased firing—they had run out of ammunition—and the Brigadier groaned, for the musketry fire could not sufficiently smash the retreat. Long before the last volleys were fired, the doolies were out in force looking for the wounded. The battle was over, and, but for want of fresh troops, the Afghans would have been wiped off the earth. As it was they counted their dead by hundreds, and nowhere were the dead thicker than in the track of the Fore and Aft.

But the Regiment did not cheer with the Highlanders, nor did they dance uncouth dances with the Gurkhas among the dead. They looked under their brows at the Colonel as they leaned upon their rifles and panted.

"Get back to camp, you. Haven't you disgraced yourself enough for one day! Go and look to the wounded. It's all you're fit for," said the Colonel. Yet for the past hour the Fore and Aft had been doing all that mortal commander could expect. They had lost heavily because they did not know how to set about their business with proper skill, but they had borne themselves gallantly, and this was their reward.

A young and sprightly Colour-Sergeant, who had begun to imagine himself a hero, offered his water bottle to a Highlander, whose tongue was black with thirst. "I drink with no cowards," answered the youngster huskily, and, turning to a Gurkha, said, "Hya, Johnny! Drink water got it?" The Gurkha grinned and passed his bottle. The Fore and Aft said no word.

They went back to camp when the field of strife had been a little mopped up and made presentable, and the Brigadier, who saw himself a Knight in three months, was the only soul who was complimentary to them. The Colonel was heart-broken, and the officers were savage and sullen.

"Well," said the Brigadier, "they are young troops of course, and it was not unnatural that they should retire in disorder for a bit."

"Oh, my only Aunt Maria!" murmured a junior Staff Officer. "Retire in disorder! It was a bally run!"

"But they came again as we all know," cooed the Brigadier, the Colonel's ashy-white face before him, "and they behaved as well as could possibly be expected. Behaved beautifully, indeed. I was watching them. It's not a matter to take to heart, Colonel. As some German General said of his men, they wanted to be shooted over a little, that was all." To himself he said—"Now they're blooded I can give 'em responsible work. It's as well that they got what they did. 'Teach 'em more than half a dozen rifle flirtations, that will —later—run alone and bite. Poor old Colonel, though."

All that afternoon the heliograph winked and flickered on the hills, striving to tell the good news to a mountain forty miles away. And in the evening there arrived, dusty, sweating, and sore, a misguided Correspondent who had gone out to assist at a trumpery village-burning, and who had read off the message from afar, cursing his luck the while.

"Let's have the details somehow—as full as ever you can, please. It's the first time I've ever been left this campaign," said the Correspondent to the Brigadier, and the Brigadier, nothing loth, told him how an Army of Communication had been crumpled up, destroyed, and all but annihilated by the craft, strategy, wisdom, and foresight of the Brigadier.

But some say, and among these be the Gurkhas who watched on the hillside, that that battle was won by Jakin and Lew, whose little bodies were borne up just in time to fit two gaps at the head of the big ditch-grave for the dead under the heights of Jagai.

THE COURTING OF DINAH SHADD
1899

What did the colonel's lady think?
Nobody never knew.
Somebody asked the sergeant's wife
An' she told 'em true.
When you git to a man in the case
They're like a row o' pins,
For the colonel's lady an' Judy O'Grady
Are sisters under their skins.

—BARRACK-ROOM BALLAD

All day I had followed at the heels of a pursuing army engaged on one of the finest battles that ever camp of exercise beheld. Thirty thousand troops had by the wisdom of the Government of India been turned loose over a few thousand square miles of country to practise in peace what they would never attempt in war. Consequently cavalry charged unshaken infantry at the trot. Infantry captured artillery by frontal attacks delivered in line of quarter columns, and mounted infantry skirmished up to the wheels of an armoured train which carried nothing more deadly than a twenty-five pounder Armstrong, two Nordenfeldts, and a few score volunteers all cased in three-eighths-inch boiler-plate. Yet it was a very lifelike camp. Operations did not cease at sundown; nobody knew the country and nobody spared man or horse. There was unending cavalry scouting and almost unending forced work over broken ground. The Army of the South had finally pierced the centre of the Army of the North, and was pouring through the gap hot-foot to capture a city of strategic importance. Its front extended fanwise, the sticks being represented by regiments strung out along the line of route backwards to the divisional transport columns and all the lumber that trails behind an army on the move. On its right the broken left of the Army of the North was flying in mass, chased by the Southern horse and hammered by the Southern guns till these had been pushed far beyond the limits of their last support. Then the flying sat down to rest, while the elated commandant of the pursuing force telegraphed that he held all in check and observation.

Unluckily he did not observe that three miles to his right flank a flying column of Northern horse with a detachment of Ghoorkhas and British troops had been pushed round, as fast as the failing light allowed, to cut across the entire rear of the Southern Army, to break, as it were, all the ribs of the fan where they converged by striking at the transport, reserve ammunition, and artillery supplies. Their instructions were to go in, avoiding the few scouts who might not have been drawn off by the pursuit, and create sufficient excitement to impress the Southern Army with the wisdom of guarding their own flank and rear before they captured cities. It was a pretty manœuvre, neatly carried out.

Speaking for the second division of the Southern Army, our first intimation of the attack was at twilight, when the artillery were labouring in deep sand, most of the escort were trying to help them out, and the main body of the infantry had gone on. A Noah's Ark of elephants, camels, and the mixed menagerie of an Indian transport-train bubbled and squealed behind the guns when there appeared from nowhere in particular British infantry to the extent of three companies, who sprang to the heads of the gun-horses and brought all to a standstill amid oaths and cheers.

"How's that, umpire?" said the major commanding the attack, and with one voice the drivers and limber gunners answered "Hout!" while the colonel of artillery sputtered.

"All your scouts are charging our main body," said the major. "Your flanks are unprotected for two miles. I think we've broken the back of this division. And listen,—there go the Ghoorkhas!"

A weak fire broke from the rear-guard more than a mile away, and was answered by cheerful howlings. The Ghoorkhas, who should have swung clear of the second division, had stepped on its tail in the dark, but drawing off hastened to reach the next line of attack, which lay almost parallel to us five or six miles away.

Our column swayed and surged irresolutely,—three batteries, the divisional ammunition reserve, the baggage, and a section of the hospital and bearer corps. The commandant ruefully promised to report himself "cut up" to the nearest umpire, and commending his cavalry and all other cavalry to the special care of Eblis, toiled on to resume touch with the rest of the division.

"We'll bivouac here to-night," said the major, "I have a notion that the Ghoorkhas will get caught. They may want us to re-form on. Stand easy till the transport gets away."

A hand caught my beast's bridle and led him out of the choking dust; a larger hand deftly canted me out of the saddle; and two of the hugest hands in the world received me sliding. Pleasant is the lot of the special correspondent who falls into such hands as those of Privates Mulvaney, Ortheris, and Learoyd.

"An' that's all right," said the Irishman calmly. "We thought we'd find you somewheres here by. Is there anything av yours in the transport? Orth'ris 'll fetch ut out."

Ortheris did "fetch ut out," from under the trunk of an elephant, in the shape of a servant and an animal both laden with medical comforts. The little man's eyes sparkled.

"If the brutil an' licentious soldiery av these parts gets sight av the thruck," said Mulvaney, making practised investigations, "they'll loot ev'rything. They're bein' fed on iron-filin's an' dog-biscuit these days, but glory's no compensation for a belly-ache. Praise be, we're here to protect you, sorr. Beer, sausage, bread (soft an' that's a cur'osity), soup in a tin, whisky by the smell av ut, an' fowls! Mother av Moses, but ye take the field like a confectioner! 'Tis scand'lus."

"'Ere's a orficer," said Ortheris significantly. "When the sergent's done lushin' the privit may clean the pot."

I bundled several things into Mulvaney's haversack before the major's hand fell on my shoulder and he said tenderly, "Requisitioned for the Queen's service. Wolseley was quite wrong about special correspondents: they are the soldier's best friends. Come and take pot-luck with us to-night."

And so it happened amid laughter and shoutings that my well-considered commissariat melted away to reappear later at the mess-table, which was a waterproof sheet spread on the ground. The flying column had taken three days' rations with it, and there be few things nastier than government rations—especially when government is experimenting with German toys. Erbsenwurst, tinned beef of surpassing tinniness, compressed vegetables, and meat-biscuits may be nourishing, but what Thomas Atkins needs is bulk in his inside. The major, assisted by his brother officers, purchased goats for the camp and so made the experiment of no effect. Long before the fatigue-party sent to collect brushwood had returned, the men were settled down by their valises, kettles and pots had appeared from the surrounding country and were dangling over fires as the kid and the compressed vegetable bubbled together; there rose a cheerful clinking of mess-tins; outrageous demands for "a little more stuffin' with that there liver-wing;" and gust on gust of chaff as pointed as a bayonet and as delicate as a gun-butt.

"The boys are in a good temper," said the major. "They'll be singing presently. Well, a night like this is enough to keep them happy."

Over our heads burned the wonderful Indian stars, which are not all pricked in on one plane, but, preserving an orderly perspective, draw the eye through the velvet darkness of the void up to the barred doors of heaven itself. The earth was a gray shadow more unreal than the sky. We could hear her breathing lightly in the pauses between the howling of the jackals, the movement of the wind in the tamarisks, and the fitful mutter of musketry-fire leagues away to the left. A native woman from some unseen hut began to sing, the mail-train thundered past on its way to Delhi, and a roosting crow cawed drowsily. Then there was a belt-loosening silence about the fires, and the even breathing of the crowded earth took up the story.

The men, full fed, turned to tobacco and song,—their officers with them. The subaltern is happy who can win the approval of the musical critics in his regiment, and is honoured among the more intricate step-dancers. By him, as by him who plays cricket cleverly, Thomas Atkins will stand in time of need, when he will let a better officer go on alone. The ruined tombs of forgotten Mussulman saints heard the ballad of *Agra Town, The Buffalo Battery, Marching to Kabul, The long, long Indian Day, The Place where the Punkah-coolie died,* and that crashing chorus which announces,

Youth's daring spirit, manhood's fire,
Firm hand and eagle eye,
Must he acquire who would aspire
To see the gray boar die.

To-day, of all those jovial thieves who appropriated my commissariat and lay and laughed round that water-proof sheet, not one remains. They went to camps that were not of exercise and battles without umpires. Burmah, the Soudan, and the frontier,—fever and fight,—took them in their time.

I drifted across to the men's fires in search of Mulvaney, whom I found strategically greasing his feet by the blaze. There is nothing particularly lovely in the sight of a private thus engaged after a long day's march, but when you reflect on the exact proportion of the "might, majesty, dominion; and power" of the British Empire which stands on those feet you take an interest in the proceedings.

"There's a blister, bad luck to ut, on the heel," said Mulvaney. "I can't touch ut. Prick ut out, little man."

Ortheris took out his house-wife, eased the trouble with a needle, stabbed Mulvaney in the calf with the same weapon, and was swiftly kicked into the fire.

"I've bruk the best av my toes over you, ye grinnin' child av disruption," said Mulvaney, sitting cross-legged and nursing his feet; then seeing me, "Oh, ut's you, sorr! Be welkim, an' take that maraudin' scutt's place. Jock, hold him down on the cindhers for a bit."

But Ortheris escaped and went elsewhere, as I took possession of the hollow he had scraped for himself and lined with his greatcoat. Learoyd on the other side of the fire grinned affably and in a minute fell fast asleep.

"There's the height av politeness for you," said Mulvaney, lighting his pipe with a flaming branch. "But Jock's eaten half a box av your sardines at wan gulp, an' I think the tin too. What's the best wid you, sorr, an' how did you happen to be on the losin' side this day whin we captured you?"

"The Army of the South is winning all along the line," I said.

"Then that line's the hangman's rope, savin' your presence. You'll learn to-morrow how we rethreated to dhraw thim on before we made thim trouble, an' that's what a woman does. By the same tokin we'll be attacked before the dawnin' an' ut would be betther not to slip your boots. How do I know that? By the light av pure reason. Here are three companies av us ever so far inside av the enemy's flank an' a crowd av roarin', tarin', squealin' cavalry gone on just to turn out the whole hornet's nest av them. Av course the enemy will pursue, by brigades like as not, an' thin we'll have to run for ut. Mark my words. I am av the opinion av Polonius whin he said, 'Don't fight wid ivry scutt for the pure joy av fightin', but if you do, knock the nose av him first an' frequint.' We ought to ha' gone on an' helped the Ghoorkhas."

"But what do you know about Polonius?" I demanded. This was a new side of Mulvaney's character.

"All that Shakespeare iver wrote an' a dale more that the gallery shouted," said the man of war, carefully lacing his boots. "Did I not tell you av Silver's theatre in Dublin, whin I was younger than I am now an' a patron av the drama? Ould Silver wud never pay actor-man or woman their just dues, an' by consequince his comp'nies was collapsible at the last minut. Thin the bhoys wud clamour to take a part, an' oft as not ould Silver made them pay for the fun. Faith, I've seen Hamlut played wid a new black eye an' the queen as full as a cornucopia. I remimber wanst Hogin that 'listed in the Black Tyrone an' was shot in South Africa, he sejuced ould Silver into givin' him Hamlut's part instid av me that had a fine fancy for rhetoric in those days. Av course I wint into the gallery an' began to fill the pit wid other people's hats, an' I passed the time av day to Hogin walkin' through Denmark like a hamstrung mule wid a pall on his back. 'Hamlut,' sez I, 'there's a hole in your heel. Pull up your shtockin's, Hamlut,' sez I. 'Hamlut, Hamlut, for the love av decincy dhrop that skull an' pull up your shtockin's.' The whole house begun to tell him that. He stopped his soliloquishms mid-between. 'My shtockin's may be comin' down or they may not,' sez he, screwin' his eye into the gallery, for well he knew who I was. 'But afther this performince is over me an' the Ghost 'll trample the tripes out av you, Terence, wid your ass's bray!' An' that's how I come to know about Hamlut. Eyah! Those days, those days! Did you iver have onendin' devilmint an' nothin' to pay for it in your life, sorr?"

"Never, without having to pay," I said.

"That's thrue! 'Tis mane whin you considher on ut; but ut's the same wid horse or fut. A headache if you dhrink, an' a belly-ache if you eat too much, an' a heartache to kape all down. Faith, the beast only gets the colic, an' he's the lucky man."

He dropped his head and stared into the fire, fingering his moustache the while. From the far side of the bivouac the voice of Corbet-Nolan, senior subaltern of B company, uplifted itself in an ancient and much appreciated song of sentiment, the men moaning melodiously behind him.

The north wind blew coldly, she drooped from that hour,
My own little Kathleen, my sweet little Kathleen,
Kathleen, my Kathleen, Kathleen O'Moore!

With forty-five O's in the last word: even at that distance you might have cut the soft South Irish accent with a shovel

"For all we take we must pay, but the price is cruel high," murmured Mulvaney when the chorus had ceased.

"What's the trouble?" I said gently, for I knew that he was a man of an inextinguishable sorrow.

"Hear now," said he. "Ye know what I am now. *I* know what I mint to be at the beginnin' av my service. I've tould you time an' again, an' what I have not Dinah Shadd has. An' what am I? Oh, Mary Mother av Hiven, an ould dhrunken, untrustable baste av a privit that has seen the reg'ment change out from colonel to drummer-boy, not wanst or twice, but scores av times! Ay, scores! An' me not so near gettin' promotion as in the first! An' me livin' on an' kapin' clear av clink, not by my own good conduck, but the kindness av some orf'cer-bhoy young enough to be son to me! Do I not know ut? Can I not tell whin I'm passed over at p'rade, tho' I'm rockin' full av liquor an' ready to fall all in wan piece, such as even a suckin' child might see, bekaze, 'Oh, 'tis only ould Mulvaney!' An' whin I'm let off in ord'ly-room through some thrick of the tongue an' a ready answer an' the ould man's mercy, is ut smilin' I feel whin I fall away an' go back to Dinah Shadd, thryin' to carry ut all off as a joke? Not I! 'Tis hell to me, dumb hell through ut all; an' next time whin the fit comes I will be as bad again. Good cause the reg'ment has to know me for the best soldier in ut. Better cause have I to know mesilf for the worst man. I'm only fit to tache the new drafts what I'll niver learn mesilf; an' I am sure, as tho' I heard ut, that the minut wan av these pink-eyed recruities gets away from my 'Mind ye now,' an' 'Listen to this, Jim, bhoy,'—sure I am that the sergint houlds me up to him for a warnin'. So I tache, as they say at musketry-instruction, by direct and ricochet fire. Lord be good to me, for I have stud some throuble!"

"Lie down and go to sleep," said I, not being able to comfort or advise. "You're the best man in the regiment, and, next to Ortheris, the biggest fool. Lie down and wait till we're attacked. What force will they turn out? Guns, think you?"

"Try that wid your lorrds an' ladies, twistin' an' turnin' the talk, tho' you mint ut well. Ye cud say nothin' to help me, an' yet ye niver knew what cause I had to be what I am."

"Begin at the beginning and go on to the end," I said royally. "But rake up the fire a bit first."

I passed Ortheris's bayonet for a poker.

"That shows how little we know what we do," said Mulvaney, putting it aside. "Fire takes all the heart out av the steel, an' the next time, may be, that our little man is fighting for his life his bradawl 'll break, an' so you'll ha' killed him, manin' no more than to kape yourself warm. 'Tis a recruity's thrick that. Pass the clanin'-rod, sorr."

I snuggled down abased; and after an interval the voice of Mulvaney began.

"Did I iver tell you how Dinah Shadd came to be wife av mine?"

I dissembled a burning anxiety that I had felt for some months—ever since Dinah Shadd, the strong, the patient, and the infinitely tender, had of her own good love and free will washed a shirt for me, moving in a barren land where washing was not.

"I can't remember," I said casually. "Was it before or after you made love to Annie Bragin, and got no satisfaction?"

The story of Annie Bragin is written in another place. It is one of the many less respectable episodes in Mulvaney's chequered career.

"Before—before—long before, was that business av Annie Bragin an' the corp'ril's ghost. Niver woman was the worse for me whin I had married Dinah. There's a time for all things, an' I know how to kape all things in place—barrin' the dhrink, that kapes me in my place wid no hope av comin' to be aught else."

"Begin at the beginning," I insisted. "Mrs. Mulvaney told me that you married her when you were quartered in Krab Bokhar barracks."

"An' the same is a cess-pit," said Mulvaney piously. "She spoke thrue, did Dinah. 'Twas this way. Talkin' av that, have ye iver fallen in love, sorr?"

I preserved the silence of the damned. Mulvaney continued—

"Thin I will assume that ye have not. *I* did. In the days av my youth, as I have more than wanst tould you, I was a man that filled the eye an' delighted the sowl av women. Niver man was hated as I have bin. Niver man was loved as I—no, not within half a day's march av ut! For the first five years av my service, whin I was what I wud give my sowl to be now, I tuk whatever was within my reach an' digested ut—an' that's more than most men can say. Dhrink I tuk, an' ut did me no harm. By the Hollow av Hiven, I cud play wid four women at wanst, an' kape them from findin' out anythin' about the other three, an' smile like a full-blown marigold through ut all. Dick Coulhan, av the battery we'll have down on us to-night, could drive his team no betther than I mine, an' I hild the worser cattle! An' so I lived, an' so I was happy till afther that business wid Annie Bragin—she that turned me off as cool as a meat-safe, an' taught me where I stud in the mind av an honest woman. 'Twas no sweet dose to swallow.

"Afther that I sickened awhile an' tuk thought to my reg'-mental work; conceiting mesilf I wud study an' be a sergint, an' a major-gineral twinty minutes afther that. But on top av my ambitiousness there was an empty place in my sowl, an' me own opinion av mesilf cud not fill ut. Sez I to mesilf, 'Terence, you're a great man an' the best set-up in the reg'mint. Go on an' get promotion.' Sez mesilf to me, 'What for?' Sez I to mesilf, 'For the glory av ut!' Sez mesilf to me, 'Will that fill these two strong arrums av yours, Terence?' 'Go to the devil,' sez I to mesilf. 'Go to the married lines,' sez mesilf to me. ''Tis the same thing,' sez I to mesilf. 'Av you're the same man, ut is,' said mesilf to me; an' wid that I considhered on ut a long while. Did you iver feel that way, sorr?"

I snored gently, knowing that if Mulvaney were uninterrupted he would go on. The clamour from the bivouac fires beat up to the stars, as the rival singers of the companies were pitted against each other.

"So I felt that way an' a bad time ut was. Wanst, bein' a fool, I wint into the married lines more for the sake av spakin' to our ould colour-sergint Shadd than for any thruck wid women-folk. I was a corp'ril then—rejuced aftherwards, but a corp'ril then. I've got a photograft av mesilf to prove ut. 'You'll take a cup av tay wid us?' sez Shadd. 'I will that,' I sez, 'tho' tay is not my divarsion.'

" ' 'Twud be better for you if ut were,' sez ould Mother Shadd, an' she had ought to know, for Shadd, in the ind av his service, dhrank bung-full each night.

"Wid that I tuk off my gloves—there was pipe-clay in thim, so that they stud alone—an' pulled up my chair, lookin' round at the china ornaments an' bits av things in the Shadds' quarters. They were things that belonged to a man, an' no camp-kit here to-day an' dishipated next. 'You're comfortable in this place, sergint,' sez I. ' 'Tis the wife that did ut, boy,' sez he, pointin' the stem av his pipe to ould Mother Shadd, an' she smacked the top av his bald head apon the compliment. 'That manes you want money,' sez she.

"An' thin—an' thin whin the kettle was to be filled, Dinah came in—my Dinah—her sleeves rowled up to the elbow an' her hair in a winkin' glory over her forehead, the big blue eyes beneath twinklin' like stars on a frosty night, an' the tread av her two feet lighter than waste-paper from the colonel's basket in ord'ly-room whin ut's emptied. Bein' but a shlip av a girl she went pink at seein' me, an' I twisted me moustache an' looked at a picture forninst the wall. Niver show a woman that ye care the snap av a finger for her, an' begad she'll come bleatin' to your boot-heels!"

"I suppose that's why you followed Annie Bragin till everybody in the married quarters laughed at you," said I, remembering that unhallowed wooing and casting off the disguise of drowsiness.

"I'm layin' down the gin'ral theory av the attack," said Mulvaney, driving his boot into the dying fire. "If you read the *Soldier's Pocket Book,* which niver any soldier reads, you'll see that there are exceptions. Whin Dinah was out av the door (an' 'twas as tho' the sunlight had shut too)—'Mother av Hiven, sergint,' sez I, 'but is that your daughter?' —'I've believed that way these eighteen years,' sez ould Shadd, his eyes twinklin'; 'but Mrs. Shadd has her own opinion, like iv'ry woman.'—' 'Tis wid yours this time, for a mericle,' sez

Mother Shadd. 'Thin why in the name av fortune did I niver see her before?' sez I. 'Bekaze you've been thrapesin' round wid the married women these three years past. She was a bit av a child till last year, an' she shot up wid the spring,' sez ould Mother Shadd. 'I'll thrapese no more,' sez I. 'D'you mane that?' sez ould Mother Shadd, lookin' at me side-ways like a hen looks at a hawk whin the chickens are runnin' free. 'Try me, an' tell,' sez I. Wid that I pulled on my gloves, dhrank off the tay, an' went out av the house as stiff as at gin'ral p'rade, for well I knew that Dinah Shadd's eyes were in the small av my back out av the scullery window. Faith! that was the only time I mourned I was not a cav'lry-man for the pride av the spurs to jingle.

"I wint out to think, an' I did a powerful lot av thinkin', but ut all came round to that shlip av a girl in the dotted blue dhress, wid the blue eyes an' the sparkil in them. Thin I kept off canteen, an' I kept to the married quarthers, or near by, on the chanst av meetin' Dinah. Did I meet her? Oh, my time past, did I not; wid a lump in my throat as big as my valise an' my heart goin' like a farrier's forge on a Saturday morning? 'Twas 'Good day to ye, Miss Dinah,' an' 'Good day t'you, corp'ril,' for a week or two, and divil a bit further could I get bekaze av the respect I had to that girl that I cud ha' broken betune finger an' thumb."

Here I giggled as I recalled the gigantic figure of Dinah Shadd when she handed me my shirt.

"Ye may laugh," grunted Mulvaney. "But I'm speakin' the trut', an' 'tis you that are in fault. Dinah was a girl that wud ha' taken the imperiousness out av the Duchess av Clonmel in those days. Flower hand, foot av shod air, an' the eyes av the livin' mornin' she had that is my wife to-day—ould Dinah, and niver aught else than Dinah Shadd to me.

"'Twas after three weeks standin' off an' on, an' niver makin' headway excipt through the eyes, that a little drummer-boy grinned in me face whin I had admonished him wid the buckle av my belt for riotin' all over the place. 'An' I'm not the only wan that doesn't kape to barricks,' sez he. I tuk him by the scruff av his neck,—my heart was hung on a hairthrigger those days, you will onderstand—an' 'Out wid ut,' sez I, 'or I'll lave no bone av you unbreakable.'—'Speak to Dempsey,' sez he howlin'. 'Dempsey which?' sez I, 'ye unwashed limb av Satan.'—'Av the Bob-tailed Dhragoons,' sez he. 'He's seen her home from her aunt's house in the civil lines four times this fortnight.'—'Child!' sez I, dhroppin' him, 'your tongue's stronger than your body. Go to your quarters. I'm sorry I dhressed you down.'

"At that I went four ways to wanst huntin' Dempsey. I was mad to think that wid all my airs among women I shud ha' been chated by a basin-faced fool av a cav'lry-man not fit to trust on a trunk. Presintly I found him in our lines—the Bobtails was quartered next us—an' a tallowy, topheavy son av a she-mule he was wid his big brass spurs an' his plastrons on his epigastrons an' all. But he niver flinched a hair.

" 'A word wid you, Dempsey,' sez I. 'You've walked wid Dinah Shadd four times this fortnight gone.'

" 'What's that to you?' sez he. 'I'll walk forty times more, an' forty on top av that, ye shovel-futted clod-breakin' infantry lance-corp'ril.'

"Before I cud gyard he had his gloved fist home on my cheek an' down I went full-sprawl. 'Will that content you?' sez he, blowin' on his knuckles for all the world like a Scots Greys orf'cer. 'Content!' sez I. 'For your own sake, man, take off your spurs, peel your jackut, an' onglove. 'Tis the beginnin' av the overture; stand up!'

"He stud all he know, but he niver peeled his jackut, an' his shoulders had no fair play. I was fightin' for Dinah Shadd an' that cut on my cheek. What hope had he forninst me? 'Stand up,' sez I, time an' again whin he was beginnin' to quarter the ground an' gyard high an' go large. 'This isn't ridin'-school,' I sez. 'O man, stand up an' let me get in at ye.' But whin I saw he wud be runnin' about, I grup his shtock in my left an' his waist-belt in my right an' swung him clear to my right front, head undher, he hammerin' my nose till the wind was knocked out av him on the bare ground. 'Stand up,' sez I, 'or I'll kick your head into your chest!' and I wud ha' done ut too, so ragin' mad I was.

" 'My collar-bone's bruk,' sez he. 'Help me back to lines. I'll walk wid her no more.' So I helped him back."

"And was his collar-bone broken?" I asked, for I fancied that only Learoyd could neatly accomplish that terrible throw.

"He pitched on his left shoulder-point. Ut was. Next day the news was in both barricks, an' whin I met Dinah Shadd wid a cheek on me like all the reg'mintal tailor's samples there was no 'Good mornin', corp'ril,' or aught else. 'An' what have I done, Miss Shadd,' sez I, very bould, plantin' mesilf forninst her, 'that ye should not pass the time of day?'

" 'Ye've half-killed rough-rider Dempsey,' sez she, her dear blue eyes fillin' up.

" 'May be,' sez I. 'Was he a friend av yours that saw ye home four times in the fortnight?'

" 'Yes,' sez she, but her mouth was down at the corners. 'An'—an' what's that to you?' she sez.

" 'Ask Dempsey,' sez I, purtendin' to go away.

" 'Did you fight for me then, ye silly man?' she sez, tho' she knew ut all along.

" 'Who else?' sez I, an' I tuk wan pace to the front.

" 'I wasn't worth ut,' sez she, fingerin' in her apron.

" 'That's for me to say,' sez I. 'Shall I say ut?'

" 'Yes,' sez she in a saint's whisper, an' at that I explained mesilf; and she tould me what ivry man that is a man, an' many that is a woman, hears wanst in his life.

" 'But what made ye cry at startin', Dinah, darlin'?' sez I.

" 'Your—your bloody cheek,' sez she, duckin' her little head down on my sash (I was on duty for the day) an' whimperin' like a sorrowful angil.

"Now a man cud take that two ways. I tuk ut as pleased me best an' my first kiss wid ut. Mother av Innocence! but I kissed her on the tip av the nose an' undher the eye; an' a girl that lets a kiss come tumbleways like that has never been kissed before. Take note av that, sorr. Thin we wint hand in hand to ould Mother Shadd like two little childher, an' she said 'twas no bad thing, an' ould Shadd nodded behind his pipe, an' Dinah ran away to her own room. That day I throd on rollin' clouds. All earth was too small to hould me. Begad, I cud ha' hiked the sun out av the sky for a live coal to my pipe, so magnificent I was. But I tuk recruities at squad-drill instid, an' began wid general battalion advance whin I shud ha' been balance-steppin' them. Eyah! that day! that day!"

A very long pause. "Well?" said I.

"'Twas all wrong," said Mulvaney, with an enormous sigh. "An' I know that ev'ry bit av ut was my own foolishness. That night I tuk maybe the half av three pints—not enough to turn the hair of a man in his natural senses. But I was more than half drunk wid pure joy, an' that canteen beer was so much whisky to me. I can't tell how it came about, but *bekaze* I had no thought for anywan except Dinah, *bekaze* I hadn't slipped her little white arms from my neck five minuts, *bekaze* the breath of her kiss was not gone from my mouth, I must go through the married lines on my way to quarters an' I must stay talkin' to a red-headed Mullingar heifer av a girl, Judy Sheehy, that was daughter to Mother Sheehy, the wife of Nick Sheehy, the canteen-sergint—the Black Curse av Shielygh be on the whole brood that are above groun' this day!

"'An' what are ye houldin' your head that high for, corp'-ril?' sez Judy. 'Come in an' thry a cup av tay,' she sez, standin' in the doorway. Bein' an ontrustable fool, an' thinkin' av anything but tay, I wint.

"'Mother's at canteen,' sez Judy, smoothin' the hair av hers that was like red snakes, an' lookin' at me corner-ways out av her green cats' eyes. 'Ye will not mind, corp'ril?'

"'I can endure,' sez I; ould Mother Sheehy bein' no divarsion av mine, nor her daughter too. Judy fetched the tea things an' put thim on the table, leanin' over me very close to get thim square. I dhrew back, thinkin' av Dinah.

"'Is ut afraid you are av a girl alone?' sez Judy.

"'No,' sez I. 'Why should I be?'

"'That rests wid the girl,' sez Judy, dhrawin' her chair next to mine.

"'Thin there let ut rest,' sez I; an' thinkin' I'd been a trifle onpolite, I sez, 'The tay's not quite sweet enough for my taste.

Put your little finger in the cup, Judy. 'Twill make ut necthar.'

" 'What's necthar?' sez she.

" 'Somethin' very sweet,' sez I; an' for the sinful life av me I cud not help lookin' at her out av the corner av my eye, as I was used to look at a woman.

" 'Go on wid ye, corp'ril,' sez she. 'You're a flirrt.'

" 'On me sowl I'm not,' sez I.

" 'Then you're a cruel handsome man, an' that's worse,' sez she, heaving big sighs an' lookin' crossways.

" 'You know your own mind,' sez I.

" ' 'Twud be better for me if I did not,' she sez.

" 'There's a dale to be said on both sides av that,' sez I, unthinkin'.

" 'Say your own part av ut, then, Terence, darlin',' sez she; 'for begad I'm thinkin' I've said too much or too little for an honest girl,' an' wid that she put her arms round my neck an' kissed me.

" 'There's no more to be said afther that,' sez I, kissin' her back again—Oh the mane scutt that I was, my head ringin' wid Dinah Shadd! How does ut come about, sorr, that when a man has put the comether on wan woman, he's sure bound to put it on another? 'Tis the same thing at musketry. Wan day ivry shot goes wide or into the bank, an' the next, lay high lay low, sight or snap, ye can't get off the bull's-eye for ten shots runnin'."

"That only happens to a man who has had a good deal of experience. He does it without thinking," I replied.

"Thankin' you for the complimint, sorr, ut may be so. But I'm doubtful whether you mint ut for a complimint. Hear now; I sat there wid Judy on my knee tellin' me all manner av nonsinse an' only sayin' 'yes' an' 'no,' when I'd much better ha' kept tongue betune teeth. An' that was not an hour afther I had left Dinah! What I was thinkin' av I cannot say. Presintly, quiet as a cat, ould Mother Sheehy came in velvet-dhrunk. She had her daughter's red hair, but 'twas bald in patches, an' I cud see in her wicked ould face, clear as lightnin', what Judy wud be twenty years to come. I was for jumpin' up, but Judy niver moved.

" 'Terence has promust, mother,' sez she, an' the could sweat bruk out all over me. Ould Mother Sheehy sat down of a heap an' began playin' wid the cups. 'Thin you're a well-matched pair,' she sez very thick. 'For he's the biggest rogue that iver spoiled the queen's shoe-leather' an'——

" 'I'm off, Judy,' sez I. 'Ye should not talk nonsinse to your mother. Get her to bed, girl.'

" 'Nonsinse!' sez the ould woman, prickin' up her ears like a cat an' grippin' the table-edge. ' 'Twill be the most non-sinsical nonsinse for you, ye grinnin' badger, if nonsinse 'tis. Git clear, you. I'm goin' to bed.'

"I ran out into the dhark, my head in a stew an' my heart sick, but I had sinse enough to see that I'd brought ut all on mysilf. 'It's this to pass the time av day to a panjandhrum av hell-cats,' sez I. 'What I've said, an' what I've not said do not matther. Judy an' her dam will hould me for a promust man, an' Dinah will give me the go, an' I desarve ut. I will go an' get dhrunk,' sez I, 'an' forget about ut, for 'tis plain I'm not a marrin' man.'

"On my way to canteen I ran against Lascelles, colour-sergint that was av E Comp'ny, a hard, hard man, wid a tor-ment av a wife. 'You've the head av a drowned man on your shoulders,' sez he; 'an' you're goin' where you'll get a worse wan. Come back,' sez he. 'Let me go,' sez I. 'I've thrown my luck over the wall wid my own hand!'—'Then that's not the way to get ut back again,' sez he. 'Have out wid your throuble, ye fool-bhoy.' An' I tould him how the matther was.

"He sucked in his lower lip. 'You've been thrapped,' sez he. 'Ju Sheehy wud be the betther for a man's name to hers as soon as can. An' ye thought ye'd put the comether on her,—that's the natural vanity of the baste. Terence, you're a big born fool, but you're not bad enough to marry into that com-p'ny. If you said anythin', an' for all your protestations I'm sure ye did—or did not, which is worse,—eat ut all—lie like the father of all lies, but come out av ut free av Judy. Do I not know what ut is to marry a woman that was the very spit an' image av Judy whin she was young? I'm gettin' old an' I've larnt patience, but you, Terence, you'd raise hand on

Judy an' kill her in a year. Never mind if Dinah gives you the go, you've desarved ut; never mind if the whole reg'mint laughs you all day. Get shut av Judy an' her mother. They can't dhrag you to church, but if they do, they'll dhrag you to hell. Go back to your quarters and lie down,' sez he. Thin over his shoulder, 'You *must* ha' done with thim.'

"Next day I wint to see Dinah, but there was no tucker in me as I walked. I knew the throuble wud come soon enough widout any handlin' av mine, an' I dreaded ut sore.

"I heard Judy callin' me, but I hild straight on to the Shadds' quarthers, an' Dinah wud ha' kissed me but I put her back.

"'Whin all's said, darlin',' sez I, 'you can give ut me if ye will, tho' I misdoubt 'twill be so easy to come by then.'

"I had scarce begun to put the explanation into shape before Judy an' her mother came to the door. I think there was a verandah, but I'm forgettin'.

"'Will ye not step in?' sez Dinah, pretty and polite, though the Shadds had no dealin's with the Sheehys. Ould Mother Shadd looked up quick, an' she was the fust to see the throuble; for Dinah was her daughter.

"'I'm pressed for time to-day,' sez Judy as bould as brass; 'an' I've only come for Terence,—my promust man. 'Tis strange to find him here the day afther the day.'

"Dinah looked at me as though I had hit her, an' I answered straight.

"'There was some nonsinse last night at the Sheehys' quarthers, an' Judy's carryin' on the joke, darlin',' sez I.

"'At the Sheehys' quarthers?' sez Dinah very slow, an' Judy cut in wid: 'He was there from nine till ten, Dinah Shadd, an' the betther half av that time I was sittin' on his knee, Dinah Shadd. Ye may look and ye may look an' ye may look me up an' down, but ye won't look away that Terence is my promust man. Terence, darlin', 'tis time for us to be comin' home.'

"Dinah Shadd niver said word to Judy. 'Ye left me at half-past eight,' she sez to me, 'an' I niver thought that ye'd leave me for Judy,—promises or no promises. Go back wid her, you that have to be fetched by a girl! I'm done with you,' sez she, and she ran into her own room, her mother followin'. So I was alone wid those two women and at liberty to spake my sentiments.

"'Judy Sheehy,' sez I, 'if you made a fool av me betune the lights you shall not do ut in the day. I niver promised you words or lines.'

"'You lie,' sez ould Mother Sheehy, 'an' may ut choke you where you stand!' She was far gone in dhrink.

"'An' tho' ut choked me where I stud I'd not change,' sez I. 'Go home, Judy. I take shame for a decent girl like you dhraggin' your mother out bare-headed on this errand. Hear now, and have ut for an answer. I gave my word to Dinah Shadd yesterday, an', more blame to me, I was wid you last night talkin' nonsinse but nothin' more. You've chosen to thry to hould me on ut. I will not be held thereby for anythin' in the world. Is that enough?'

"Judy wint pink all over. 'An' I wish you joy av the perjury,' sez she, duckin' a curtsey. 'You've lost a woman that would ha' wore her hand to the bone for your pleasure; an' 'deed, Terence, ye were not thrapped. . . .' Lascelles must ha' spoken plain to her. 'I am such as Dinah is—'deed I am! Ye've lost a fool av a girl that'll niver look at you again, an' ye've lost what he niver had,—your common honesty. If you manage your men as you manage your love-makin', small wondher they call you the worst corp'ril in the comp'ny. Come away, mother,' sez she.

"But divil a fut would the ould woman budge! 'D'you hould by that?' sez she, peerin' up under her thick gray eyebrows.

"'Ay, an' wud,' sez I, 'tho' Dinah give me the go twinty times. I'll have no thruck with you or yours,' sez I. 'Take your child away, ye shameless woman.'

"'An' am I shameless?' sez she, bringin' her hands up above her head. 'Thin what are you, ye lyin', schamin', weak-kneed, dhirty-souled son av a sutler? Am *I* shameless? Who put the open shame on me an' my child that we shud go beggin' through the lines in the broad daylight for the broken word of a man? Double portion of my shame be on you, Terence Mulvaney, that think yourself so strong! By Mary and the saints, by blood and water an' by ivry sorrow that came into the world since the beginnin', the black blight fall on you and yours, so that you may niver be free from pain for another when ut's not your own! May your heart bleed in your breast drop by drop wid all your friends laughin' at the bleedin'! Strong you think yourself? May your strength be a curse to you to dhrive you into the divil's hands against your own will! Clear-eyed you are? May your eyes see clear ivry step av the dark path you take till the hot cindhers av hell put thim out! May the ragin' dry thirst in my own ould bones go to you that you shall niver pass bottle full nor glass empty. God preserve the light av your onderstandin' to you, my jewel av a bhoy, that ye may niver forget what you mint to be an' do, whin you're wallowin' in the muck! May ye see the betther and follow the worse as long as there's breath in your body; an' may ye die quick in a strange land, watchin' your death before ut takes you, an' onable to stir hand or foot!'

"I heard a scufflin' in the room behind, and thin Dinah Shadd's hand dhropped into mine like a rose-leaf into a muddy road.

"'The half av that I'll take,' sez she, 'an' more too if I can. Go home, ye silly talkin' woman,—go home an' confess.'

"'Come away! Come away!' sez Judy, pullin' her mother by the shawl. ''Twas none av Terence's fault. For the love av Mary stop the talkin'!'

"'An' you!' said ould Mother Sheehy, spinnin' round forninst Dinah. 'Will ye take the half av that man's load? Stand off from him, Dinah Shadd, before he takes you down too—you that look to be a quarther-master-sergeant's wife in five years. You look too high, child. You shall *wash* for the quarther-master-sergeant, whin he plases to give you the job out av charity; but a privit's wife you shall be to the end, an' ivry sorrow of a privit's wife you shall know and niver a joy but wan, that shall go from you like the running tide from a rock. The pain av bearin' you shall know but niver the pleasure av giving the breast; an' you shall put away a man-child into the common ground wid niver a priest to say a prayer over him, an' on that man-child ye shall think ivry day av your life. Think long, Dinah Shadd, for you'll niver have another tho' you pray till your knees are bleedin'. The mothers av childher shall mock you behind your back when you're wringing over the washtub. You shall know what ut is to help a dhrunken husband home an' see him go to the gyard-room. Will that plase you, Dinah Shadd, that won't be seen talkin' to my daughter? You shall talk to worse than Judy before all's over. The sergints' wives shall look down on you contemptuous, daughter av a sergint, an' you shall cover ut all up wid a smiling face when your heart's burstin'. Stand off av him, Dinah Shadd, for I've put the Black Curse of Shielygh upon him an' his own mouth shall make ut good.'

"She pitched forward on her head an' began foamin' at the mouth. Dinah Shadd ran out wid water, an' Judy dhragged the ould woman into the verandah till she sat up.

" 'I'm old an' forlore,' she sez, thremblin' an' cryin', 'and 'tis like I say a dale more than I mane.'

" 'When you're able to walk,—go,' says ould Mother Shadd. 'This house has no place for the likes av you that have cursed my daughter.'

" 'Eyah!' said the ould woman. 'Hard words break no bones, an' Dinah Shadd'll kape the love av her husband till my bones are green corn. Judy darlin', I misremember what I came here for. Can you lend us the bottom av a taycup av tay, Mrs. Shadd?'

"But Judy dhragged her off cryin' as tho' her heart wud break. An' Dinah Shadd an' I, in ten minutes we had forgot ut all."

"Then why do you remember it now?" said I.

"Is ut like I'd forget? Ivry word that wicked ould woman spoke fell thrue in my life aftherwards, an' I cud ha' stud ut all—stud ut all—excipt when my little Shadd was born. That was on the line av march three months afther the regiment was taken with cholera. We were betune Umballa an' Kalka thin, an' I was on picket. Whin I came off duty the women showed me the child, an' ut turned on uts side an' died as I looked. We buried him by the road, an' Father Victor was a day's march behind wid the heavy baggage, so the comp'ny captain read a prayer. An' since then I've been a childless man, an' all else that ould Mother Sheehy put upon me an' Dinah Shadd. What do you think, sorr?"

I thought a good deal, but it seemed better then to reach out for Mulvaney's hand. The demonstration nearly cost me the use of three fingers. Whatever he knows of his weaknesses, Mulvaney is entirely ignorant of his strength.

"But what do you think?" he repeated, as I was straightening out the crushed fingers.

My reply was drowned in yells and outcries from the next fire, where ten men were shouting for "Orth'ris," "Privit Orth'ris," "Mistah Or—ther—ris!" "Deah boy," "Cap'n Orth'ris," "Field-Marshal Orth'ris," "Stanley, you pen'north o' pop, come 'ere to your own comp'ny!" And the cockney, who had been delighting another audience with recondite and Rabelaisian yarns, was shot down among his admirers by the major force.

"You've crumpled my dress-shirt 'orrid," said he, "an' I shan't sing no more to this 'ere bloomin' drawin'-room."

Learoyd, roused by the confusion, uncoiled himself, crept behind Ortheris, and slung him aloft on his shoulders.

"Sing, ye bloomin' hummin' bird!" said he, and Ortheris, beating time on Learoyd's skull, delivered himself, in the raucous voice of the Ratcliffe Highway, of this song:—

My girl she give me the go onst,
When I was a London lad,
An' I went on the drink for a fortnight,
An' then I went to the bad.
The Queen she give me a shillin'
To fight for 'er over the seas;
But Guv'ment built me a fever-trap,
An' Injia give me disease.

CHORUS.

Ho! don't you 'eed what a girl says,
An' don't you go for the beer;

But I was an ass when I was at grass,
An' that is why I'm 'ere.

I fired a shot at a Afghan,
The beggar 'e fired again,
An' I lay on my bed with a 'ole in my 'ed;
An' missed the next campaign!
I up with my gun at a Burman
Who carried a bloomin' dah,
But the cartridge stuck and the bay'nit bruk,
An' all I got was the scar.

CHORUS.

Ho! don't you aim at a Afghan
When you stand on the sky-line clear;
An' don't you go for a Burman
If none o' your friends is near.

I served my time for a corp'ral,
An' wetted my stripes with pop,
For I went on the bend with a intimate friend,
An' finished the night in the "shop."
I served my time for a sergeant;
The colonel 'e sez "No!
The most you'll see is a full C. B."[1]
An' . . . very next night 'twas so.

CHORUS.

Ho! don't you go for a corp'ral
Unless your 'ed is clear;
But I was an ass when I was at grass,
An' that is why I'm 'ere.

[1]Confined to barracks.

I've tasted the luck o' the army
In barrack an' camp an' clink,
An' I lost my tip through the bloomin' trip
Along o' the women an' drink.
I'm down at the heel o' my service
An' when I am laid on the shelf,
My very wust friend from beginning to end
By the blood of a mouse was myself!

CHORUS.

Ho! don't you 'eed what a girl says,
An' don't you go for the beer;
But I was an ass when I was at grass,
An' that is why I'm 'ere.

"Ay, listen to our little man now, singin' an' shoutin' as tho' trouble had niver touched him. D'you remember when he went mad with the home-sickness?" said Mulvaney, recalling a never-to-be-forgotten season when Ortheris waded through the deep waters of affliction and behaved abominably. "But he's talkin' bitter truth, though. Eyah!

"My very worst frind from beginnin' to ind
By the blood av a mouse was mesilf!"

. . . .

When I woke I saw Mulvaney, the night-dew gemming his moustache, leaning on his rifle at picket, lonely as Prometheus on his rock, with I know not what vultures tearing his liver.

THE MAN WHO WAS
1890

The Earth gave up her dead that tide,
Into our camp he came,
And said his say, and went his way,
And left our hearts aflame.

Keep tally—on the gun-butt score
The vengeance we must take,
When God shall bring full reckoning,
For our dead comrade's sake.

—BALLAD

LET it be clearly understood that the Russian is a delightful person till he tucks in his shirt. As an Oriental he is charming. It is only when he insists upon being treated as the most easterly of western peoples instead of the most westerly of easterns that he becomes a racial anomaly extremely difficult to handle. The host never knows which side of his nature is going to turn up next.

Dirkovitch was a Russian—a Russian of the Russians—who appeared to get his bread by serving the Czar as an officer in a Cossack regiment, and corresponding for a Russian newspaper with a name that was never twice alike. He was a handsome young Oriental, fond of wandering through unexplored portions of the earth, and he arrived in India from nowhere in particular. At least no living man could ascertain whether it was by way of Balkh, Badakshan, Chitral, Beluchistan, or Nepaul, or anywhere else. The Indian Government, being in an unusually affable mood, gave orders that he was to be civilly treated and shown everything that was to be seen. So he drifted, talking bad English and worse French, from one city to another, till he foregathered with

Her Majesty's White Hussars in the city of Peshawur, which stands at the mouth of that narrow swordcut in the hills that men call the Khyber Pass. He was undoubtedly an officer, and he was decorated after the manner of the Russians with little enamelled crosses, and he could talk, and (though this has nothing to do with his merits) he had been given up as a hopeless task, or cask, by the Black Tyrone, who individually and collectively, with hot whisky and honey, mulled brandy, and mixed spirits of every kind, had striven in all hospitality to make him drunk. And when the Black Tyrone, who are exclusively Irish, fail to disturb the peace of head of a foreigner—that foreigner is certain to be a superior man.

The White Hussars were as conscientious in choosing their wine as in charging the enemy. All that they possessed, including some wondrous brandy, was placed at the absolute disposition of Dirkovitch, and he enjoyed himself hugely—even more than among the Black Tyrones.

But he remained distressingly European through it all. The White Hussars were "My dear true friends," "Fellow-soldiers glorious," and "Brothers inseparable." He would unburden himself by the hour on the glorious future that awaited the combined arms of England and Russia when their hearts and their territories should run side by side and the great mission of civilizing Asia should begin. That was unsatisfactory, because Asia is not going to be civilized after the methods of the West. There is too much Asia and she is too old. You cannot reform a lady of many lovers, and Asia has been insatiable in her flirtations aforetime. She will never attend Sunday-school or learn to vote save with swords for tickets.

Dirkovitch knew this as well as any one else, but it suited him to talk special-correspondently and to make himself as genial as he could. Now and then he volunteered a little, a very little, information about his own sotnia of Cossacks, left apparently to look after themselves somewhere at the back of beyond. He had done rough work in Central Asia, and had seen rather more help-yourself fighting than most men of his years. But he was careful never to betray his superiority, and more than careful to praise on all occasions the appearance, drill, uniform, and organization of Her Majesty's White Hussars. And indeed they were a regiment to be admired. When Lady Durgan, widow of the late Sir John Durgan, arrived in their station, and after a short time had been proposed to by every single man at mess, she put the public sentiment very neatly when she explained that they were all so nice that unless she could marry them all, including the colonel and some majors already married, she was not going to content herself with one hussar. Wherefore she wedded a little man in a rifle regiment, being by nature contradictious; and the White Hussars were going to wear crape on their arms, but compromised by attending the wedding in full force, and lining the aisle with unutterable reproach. She had jilted them all—from Basset-Holmer the senior captain to little Mildred the junior subaltern, who could have given her four thousand a year and a title.

The only persons who did not share the general regard for the White Hussars were a few thousand gentlemen of Jewish extraction who lived across the border, and answered to the name of Pathan. They had once met the regiment officially and for something less than twenty minutes, but the interview, which was complicated with many casualties, had filled them with prejudice. They even called the White Hussars children of the devil and sons of persons whom it would be perfectly impossible to meet in decent society. Yet they were not above making their aversion fill their money-belts. The regiment possessed carbines—beautiful Martini-Henri carbines that would lob a bullet into an enemy's camp at one thousand yards, and were even handier than the long rifle. Therefore they were coveted all along the border, and since demand inevitably breeds supply, they were supplied at the risk of life and limb for exactly their weight in coined silver—seven and one-half pounds weight of rupees, or sixteen pounds sterling reckoning the rupee at par. They were stolen at night by snaky-haired thieves who crawled on their stomachs under the nose of the sentries; they disappeared mysteriously from locked arm-racks, and in the hot weather, when all the barrack doors and windows were open, they vanished like puffs of their own smoke. The border people desired them for family vendettas and contingencies. But in the long cold nights of the northern Indian winter they were stolen most extensively. The traffic of murder was liveliest among the hills at that season, and prices ruled high. The regimental guards were first doubled and then trebled. A trooper does not much care if he loses a weapon—Government must make it good—but he deeply resents the loss of his sleep. The regiment grew very angry, and one rifle-thief bears the visible marks of their anger upon him to this hour. That incident stopped the burglaries for a time, and the guards were reduced accordingly, and the regiment devoted itself to polo with unexpected results; for it beat by two goals to one that very terrible polo corps the Lushkar Light Horse, though the latter had four ponies apiece for a short hour's fight, as well as a native officer who played like a lambent flame across the ground.

They gave a dinner to celebrate the event. The Lushkar team came, and Dirkovitch came, in the fullest full uniform of a Cossack officer, which is as full as a dressing-gown, and was introduced to the Lushkars, and opened his eyes as he regarded. They were lighter men than the Hussars, and they carried themselves with the swing that is the peculiar right of the Punjab Frontier Force and all Irregular Horse. Like everything else in the Service it has to be learnt, but, unlike many things, it is never forgotten, and remains on the body till death.

The great beam-roofed mess-room of the White Hussars was a sight to be remembered. All the mess plate was out on the long table—the same table that had served up the bodies of five officers after a forgotten fight long and long ago—the dingy, battered standards faced the door of entrance, clumps of winter-roses lay between the silver candlesticks, and the portraits of eminent officers deceased looked down on their successors from between the heads of sambhur, nilghai, markhor, and, pride of all the mess, two grinning snow-leopards that had cost Basset-Holmer four months' leave that he might have spent in England, instead of on the road to Thibet and the daily risk of his life by ledge, snow-slide, and grassy slope.

The servants in spotless white muslin and the crest of their regiments on the brow of their turbans waited behind their masters, who were clad in the scarlet and gold of the White Hussars, and the cream and silver of the Lushkar Light Horse. Dirkovitch's dull green uniform was the only dark spot at the board, but his big onyx eyes made up for it. He was fraternizing effusively with the captain of the Lushkar team, who was wondering how many of Dirkovitch's Cossacks his own dark wiry down-countrymen could account for in a fair charge. But one does not speak of these things openly.

The talk rose higher and higher, and the regimental band played between the courses, as is the immemorial custom, till all tongues ceased for a moment with the removal of the dinner-slips and the first toast of obligation, when an officer rising said, "Mr. Vice, the Queen," and little Mildred from the bottom of the table answered, "The Queen, God bless her," and the big spurs clanked as the big men heaved themselves up and drank the Queen upon whose pay they were falsely supposed to settle their mess-bills. That Sacrament of the Mess never grows old, and never ceases to bring a lump into the throat of the listener wherever he be by sea or by land. Dirkovitch rose with his "brothers glorious," but he could not understand. No one but an officer can tell what the toast means; and the bulk have more sentiment than comprehension. Immediately after the little silence that follows on the ceremony there entered the native officer who had played for the Lushkar team. He could not, of course, eat with the mess, but he came in at dessert, all six feet of him, with the blue and silver turban atop, and the big black boots below. The mess rose joyously as he thrust forward the hilt of his sabre in token of fealty for the colonel of the White Hussars to touch, and dropped into a vacant chair amid shouts of: "*Rung ho,* Hira Singh!" (which being translated means "Go in and win"). "Did I whack you over the knee, old man?" "Ressaidar Sahib, what the devil made you play that kicking pig of a pony in the last ten minutes?" "*Shabash,* Ressaidar Sahib!" Then the voice of the colonel, "The health of Ressaidar Hira Singh!"

After the shouting had died away Hira Singh rose to reply, for he was the cadet of a royal house, the son of a king's son, and knew what was due on these occasions. Thus he spoke in the vernacular:—"Colonel Sahib and officers of this regiment. Much honour have you done me. This will I remember. We came down from afar to play you. But we were beaten." ("No fault of yours, Ressaidar Sahib. Played on our own ground y'know. Your ponies were cramped from the railway. Don't apologize!") "Therefore perhaps we will come again if it be so ordained." ("Hear! Hear! Hear, indeed! Bravo! Hsh!") "Then we will play you afresh" ("Happy to meet you.") "till there are left no feet upon our ponies. Thus far for sport." He dropped one hand on his sword-hilt and his eye wandered to Dirkovitch lolling back in his chair. "But if by the will of God there arises any other game which is not the polo game, then be assured, Colonel Sahib and officers, that we will play it out side by side, though *they,*" again his eye sought Dirkovitch, "though *they* I say have fifty ponies to our one horse." And with a deep-mouthed *Rung ho!* that sounded like a musket-butt on flagstones he sat down amid leaping glasses.

Dirkovitch, who had devoted himself steadily to the brandy —the terrible brandy aforementioned—did not understand, nor did the expurgated translations offered to him at all convey the point. Decidedly Hira Singh's was the speech of the evening, and the clamour might have continued to the dawn had it not been broken by the noise of a shot without that sent every man feeling at his defenceless left side. Then there was a scuffle and a yell of pain.

"Carbine-stealing again!" said the adjutant, calmly sinking back in his chair. "This comes of reducing the guards. I hope the sentries have killed him."

The feet of armed men pounded on the verandah flags, and it was as though something was being dragged.

"Why don't they put him in the cells till the morning?" said the colonel testily. "See if they've damaged him, sergeant."

The mess sergeant fled out into the darkness and returned with two troopers and a corporal, all very much perplexed.

"Caught a man stealin' carbines, sir," said the corporal.

"Leastways 'e was crawlin' towards the barricks, sir, past the main road sentries, an' the sentry 'e sez, sir——"

The limp heap of rags upheld by the three men groaned. Never was seen so destitute and demoralized an Afghan. He was turbanless, shoeless, caked with dirt, and all but dead with rough handling. Hira Singh started slightly at the sound of the man's pain. Dirkovitch took another glass of brandy.

"*What* does the sentry say?" said the colonel.

"Sez 'e speaks English, sir," said the corporal.

"So you brought him into mess instead of handing him over to the sergeant! If he spoke all the Tongues of the Pentecost you've no business——"

Again the bundle groaned and muttered. Little Mildred had risen from his place to inspect. He jumped back as though he had been shot.

"Perhaps it would be better, sir, to send the men away," said he to the colonel, for he was a much privileged subaltern. He put his arms round the ragbound horror as he spoke, and dropped him into a chair. It may not have been explained that the littleness of Mildred lay in his being six feet four and big in proportion. The corporal seeing that an officer was disposed to look after the capture, and that the colonel's eye was beginning to blaze, promptly removed himself and his men. The mess was left alone with the carbine-thief, who laid his head on the table and wept bitterly, hopelessly, and inconsolably, as little children weep.

Hira Singh leapt to his feet. "Colonel Sahib," said he, "that man is no Afghan, for they weep *Ai! Ai!* Nor is he of Hindustan, for they weep *Oh! Ho!* He weeps after the fashion of the white men, who say *Ow! Ow!*"

"Now where the dickens did you get that knowledge, Hira Singh?" said the captain of the Lushkar team.

"Hear him!" said Hira Singh simply, pointing at the crumpled figure that wept as though it would never cease.

"He said, 'My God!' " said little Mildred. "I heard him say it."

The colonel and the mess-room looked at the man in silence. It is a horrible thing to hear a man cry. A woman can sob from the top of her palate, or her lips, or anywhere else, but a man must cry from his diaphragm, and it rends him to pieces.

"Poor devil!" said the colonel, coughing tremendously. "We ought to send him to hospital. He's been manhandled."

Now the adjutant loved his carbines. They were to him as his grandchildren, the men standing in the first place. He grunted rebelliously: "I can understand an Afghan stealing, because he's built that way. But I can't understand his crying. That makes it worse."

The brandy must have affected Dirkovitch, for he lay back in his chair and stared at the ceiling. There was nothing special in the ceiling beyond a shadow as of a huge black coffin. Owing to some peculiarity in the construction of the mess-room this shadow was always thrown when the candles were lighted. It never disturbed the digestion of the White Hussars. They were in fact rather proud of it.

"Is he going to cry all night?" said the colonel, "or are we supposed to sit up with little Mildred's guest until he feels better?"

The man in the chair threw up his head and stared at the mess. "Oh, my God!" he said, and every soul in the mess rose to his feet. Then the Lushkar captain did a deed for which he ought to have been given the Victoria Cross—distinguished gallantry in a fight against overwhelming curiosity. He picked up his team with his eyes as the hostess picks up the ladies at the opportune moment, and pausing only by the colonel's chair to say, "This isn't *our* affair, you know, sir," led them into the verandah and the gardens. Hira Singh was the last to go, and he looked at Dirkovitch. But Dirkovitch had departed into a brandy-paradise of his own. His lips moved without sound and he was studying the coffin on the ceiling.

"White—white all over," said Basset-Holmer, the adjutant. "What a pernicious renegade he must be! I wonder where he came from?"

The colonel shook the man gently by the arm, and "Who are you?" said he.

There was no answer. The man stared round the mess-room and smiled in the colonel's face. Little Mildred, who was always more of a woman than a man till "Boot and saddle" was sounded, repeated the question in a voice that would have drawn confidences from a geyser. The man only smiled. Dirkovitch at the far end of the table slid gently from his chair to the floor. No son of Adam in this present imperfect world can mix the Hussars' champagne with the Hussars' brandy by five and eight glasses of each without remembering the pit whence he was digged and descending thither. The band began to play the tune with which the White Hussars from the date of their formation have concluded all their functions. They would sooner be disbanded than abandon that tune; it is a part of their system. The man straightened himself in his chair and drummed on the table with his fingers.

"I don't see why we should entertain lunatics," said the colonel. "Call a guard and send him off to the cells. We'll look into the business in the morning. Give him a glass of wine first though."

Little Mildred filled a sherry-glass with the brandy and thrust it over to the man. He drank, and the tune rose louder, and he straightened himself yet more. Then he put out his long-taloned hands to a piece of plate opposite and fingered it lovingly. There was a mystery connected with that piece of plate, in the shape of a spring which converted what was a seven-branched candlestick, three springs on each side and one in the middle, into a sort of wheel-spoke candelabrum. He found the spring, pressed it, and laughed weakly. He rose from his chair and inspected a picture on the wall, then moved on to another picture, the mess watching him without a word. When he came to the mantelpiece he shook his head and seemed distressed. A piece of plate representing a mounted hussar in full uniform caught his eye. He pointed to it, and then to the mantelpiece with inquiry in his eyes.

"What is it—Oh what is it?" said little Mildred. Then as a mother might speak to a child, "That is a horse. Yes, a horse."

Very slowly came the answer in a thick, passionless guttural—"Yes, I—have seen. But—where is *the* horse?"

You could have heard the hearts of the mess beating as the men drew back to give the stranger full room in his wanderings. There was no question of calling the guard.

Again he spoke—very slowly, "Where is *our* horse?"

There is but one horse in the White Hussars, and his portrait hangs outside the door of the mess-room. He is the piebald drum-horse, the king of the regimental band, that served the regiment for seven-and-thirty years, and in the end was shot for old age. Half the mess tore the thing down from its place and thrust it into the man's hands. He placed it above the mantelpiece, it clattered on the ledge as his poor hands dropped it, and he staggered towards the bottom of the table, falling into Mildred's chair. Then all the men spoke to one another something after this fashion, "The drum-horse hasn't hung over the mantelpiece since '67." "How does he know?" "Mildred, go and speak to him again." "Colonel, what are you going to do?" "Oh, dry up, and give the poor devil a chance to pull himself together." "It isn't possible anyhow. The man's a lunatic."

Little Mildred stood at the colonel's side talking in his ear. "Will you be good enough to take your seats please, gentlemen!" he said, and the mess dropped into the chairs. Only Dirkovitch's seat, next to little Mildred's, was blank, and little Mildred himself had found Hira Singh's place. The wide-eyed mess-sergeant filled the glasses in deep silence. Once more the colonel rose, but his hand shook and the port spilled on the table as he looked straight at the man in little Mildred's chair and said hoarsely, "Mr. Vice, the Queen." There was a little pause, but the man sprung to his feet and answered without hesitation, "The Queen, God bless her!" and as he emptied the thin glass he snapped the shank between his fingers.

Long and long ago, when the Empress of India was a young woman and there were no unclean ideals in the land, it was the custom of a few messes to drink the Queen's toast in broken glass, to the vast delight of the mess-contractors. The custom is now dead, because there is nothing to break anything for, except now and again the word of a Government, and that has been broken already.

"That settles it," said the colonel, with a gasp. "He's not a sergeant. What in the world is he?"

The entire mess echoed the word, and the volley of questions would have scared any man. It was no wonder that the ragged, filthy invader could only smile and shake his head.

From under the table, calm and smiling, rose Dirkovitch, who had been roused from healthful slumber by feet upon his body. By the side of the man he rose, and the man shrieked and grovelled. It was a horrible sight coming so swiftly upon the pride and glory of the toast that had brought the strayed wits together.

Dirkovitch made no offer to raise him, but little Mildred heaved him up in an instant. It is not good that a gentleman who can answer to the Queen's toast should lie at the feet of a subaltern of Cossacks.

The hasty action tore the wretch's upper clothing nearly to the waist, and his body was seamed with dry black scars. There is only one weapon in the world that cuts: in parallel lines, and it is neither the cane nor the cat. Dirkovitch saw the marks and the pupils of his eyes dilated. Also his face changed. He said something that sounded like *Shto ve takete,* and the man fawning answered, *Chetyre.*

"What's that?" said everybody together.

"His number. That is number four, you know." Dirkovitch spoke very thickly.

"What has a Queen's officer to do with a qualified number?" said the Colonel, and an unpleasant growl ran round the table.

"How can I tell?" said the affable Oriental with a sweet smile. "He is a—how you have it?—escape—run-a-way, from over there." He nodded towards the darkness of the night.

"Speak to him if he'll answer you, and speak to him gently," said little Mildred, settling the man in a chair. It seemed most improper to all present that Dirkovitch should sip brandy as he talked in purring, spitting Russian to the creature who answered so feebly and with such evident dread. But since Dirkovitch appeared to understand no one said a word. All breathed heavily, leaning forward, in the long gaps of the conversation. The next time that they have no engagements on hand the White Hussars intend to go to St. Petersburg in a body to learn Russian.

"He does not know how many years ago," said Dirkovitch, facing the mess, "but he says it was very long ago in a war. I think that there was an accident. He says he was of this glorious and distinguished regiment in the war."

"The rolls! The rolls! Holmer, get the rolls!" said little Mildred, and the adjutant dashed off bare-headed to the orderly-room, where the muster-rolls of the regiment were kept. He returned just in time to hear Dirkovitch conclude, "Therefore, my dear friends, I am most sorry to say there was an accident which would have been reparable if he had apologized to that our colonel, which he had insulted."

Then followed another growl which the colonel tried to beat down. The mess was in no mood just then to weigh insults to Russian colonels.

"He does not remember, but I think that there was an accident, and so he was not exchanged among the prisoners, but he was sent to another place—how do you say?—the country. *So,* he says, he came here. He does not know how he came. Eh? He was at Chepany"—the man caught the word, nodded, and shivered—"at Zhigansk and Irkutsk. I cannot understand how he escaped. He says, too, that he was in the forests for many years, but how many years he has forgotten—that with many things. It was an accident; done because he did not apologize to that our colonel. Ah!"

Instead of echoing Dirkovitch's sigh of regret, it is sad to record that the White Hussars livelily exhibited un-Christian delight and other emotions, hardly restrained by their sense of hospitality. Holmer flung the frayed and yellow regimental rolls on the table, and the men flung themselves at these.

"Steady! Fifty-six—fifty-five—fifty-four," said Holmer. "Here we are. 'Lieutenant Austin Limmason. *Missing.*' That was before Sebastopol. What an infernal shame! Insulted one of their colonels, and was quietly shipped off. Thirty years of his life wiped out."

"But he never apologized. Said he'd see him damned first," chorused the mess.

"Poor chap! I suppose he never had the chance afterwards. How did he come here?" said the colonel.

The dingy heap in the chair could give no answer.

"Do you know who you are?"

It laughed weakly.

"Do you know that you are Limmason—Lieutenant Limmason of the White Hussars?"

Swiftly as a shot came the answer, in a slightly surprised tone, "Yes, I'm Limmason, of course." The light died out in his eyes, and the man collapsed, watching every motion of Dirkovitch with terror. A flight from Siberia may fix a few elementary facts in the mind, but it does not seem to lead to continuity of thought. The man could not explain how, like a homing pigeon, he had found his way to his own old mess again. Of what he had suffered or seen he knew nothing. He cringed before Dirkovitch as instinctively as he had pressed the spring of the candlestick, sought the picture of the drum-horse, and answered to the toast of the Queen. The rest was a blank that the dreaded Russian tongue could only in part remove. His head bowed on his breast, and he giggled and cowered alternately.

The devil that lived in the brandy prompted Dirkovitch at this extremely inopportune moment to make a speech. He rose, swaying slightly, gripped the table-edge, while his eyes glowed like opals, and began:

"Fellow-soldiers glorious—true friends and hospitables. It was an accident, and deplorable—most deplorable." Here he smiled sweetly all round the mess. "But you will think of this little, little thing. So little, is it not? The Czar! Posh! I slap my fingers—I snap my fingers at him. Do I believe in him? No! But in us Slav who has done nothing, *him* I believe. Seventy—how much—millions peoples that have done nothing—not one thing. Posh! Napoleon was an episode." He banged a hand on the table. "Hear you, old peoples, we have done nothing in the world—out here. All our work is to do; and it shall be done, old peoples. Get a-way!" He waved his hand imperiously, and pointed to the man. "You see him. He is not good to see. He was just one little—oh, so little—accident, that no one remembered. Now he is *That!* So will you be, brother-soldiers so brave—so will you be. But you will never come back. You will all go where he is gone, or"—he pointed to the great coffin-shadow on the ceiling, and muttering, "Seventy millions—get a-way, you old peoples," fell asleep.

"Sweet, and to the point," said little Mildred. "What's the use of getting wroth? Let's make this poor devil comfortable."

But that was a matter suddenly and swiftly taken from the loving hands of the White Hussars. The lieutenant had returned only to go away again three days later, when the wail of the Dead March, and the tramp of the squadrons, told the wondering Station, who saw no gap in the mess-table, that an officer of the regiment had resigned his new-found commission.

And Dirkovitch, bland, supple, and always genial, went away too by a night train. Little Mildred and another man saw him off, for he was the guest of the mess, and even had he smitten the colonel with the open hand, the law of that mess allowed no relaxation of hospitality.

"Good-bye, Dirkovitch, and a pleasant journey," said little Mildred.

"Au revoir," said the Russian.

"Indeed! But we thought you were going home?"

"Yes, but I will come again. My dear friends, is that road shut?" He pointed to where the North Star burned over the Khyber Pass.

"By Jove! I forgot. Of course. Happy to meet you, old man, any time you like. Got everything you want? Cheroots, ice, bedding? That's all right. Well, *au revoir,* Dirkovitch."

"Um," said the other man, as the tail-lights of the train grew small. "Of—all—the—unmitigated——!"

Little Mildred answered nothing, but watched the North star and hummed a selection from a recent Simla burlesque that had much delighted the White Hussars. It ran—

I'm sorry for Mister Bluebeard,
I'm sorry to cause him pain;
But a terrible spree there's sure to be
When he comes back again.

WITHOUT BENEFIT OF CLERGY
1890

Before my Spring I garnered Autumn's gain,
Out of her time my field was white with grain,
The year gave up her secrets to my woe.
Forced and deflowered each sick season lay,
In mystery of increase and decay;
I saw the sunset ere men saw the day,
Who am too wise in that I should not know.

—BITTER WATERS

"BUT if it be a girl?"

"Lord of my life, it cannot be. I have prayed for so many nights, and sent gifts to Sheikh Badl's shrine so often, that I know God will give us a son—a man-child that shall grow into a man. Think of this and be glad. My mother shall be his mother till I can take him again, and the mullah of the Pattan mosque shall cast his nativity—God send he be born in an auspicious hour!—and then, and then thou wilt never weary of me, thy slave."

"Since when hast thou been a slave, my queen?"

"Since the beginning—till this mercy came to me. How could I be sure of thy love when I knew that I had been bought with silver?"

"Nay, that was the dowry. I paid it to thy mother."

"And she has buried it, and sits upon it all day long like a hen. What talk is yours of dower! I was bought as though I had been a Lucknow dancing-girl instead of a child."

"Art thou sorry for the sale?"

"I have sorrowed; but to-day I am glad. Thou wilt never cease to love me now?—answer, my king."

"Never—never. No."

"Not even though the *mem-log*—the white women of thy

own blood—love thee? And remember, I have watched them driving in the evening; they are very fair."

"I have seen fire-balloons by the hundred. I have seen the moon, and—then I saw no more fire-balloons."

Ameera clapped her hands and laughed. "Very good talk," she said. Then with an assumption of great stateliness, "It is enough. Thou hast my permission to depart,—if thou wilt."

The man did not move. He was sitting on a low red-lacquered couch in a room furnished only with a blue and white floor-cloth, some rugs, and a very complete collection of native cushions. At his feet sat a woman of sixteen, and she was all but all the world in his eyes. By every rule and law she should have been otherwise, for he was an Englishman, and she a Mussulman's daughter bought two years before from her mother, who, being left without money, would have sold Ameera shrieking to the Prince of Darkness if the price had been sufficient.

It was a contract entered into with a light heart; but even before the girl had reached her bloom she came to fill the greater portion of John Holden's life. For her, and the withered hag her mother, he had taken a little house overlooking the great red-walled city, and found,—when the marigolds had sprung up by the well in the courtyard and Ameera had established herself according to her own ideas of comfort, and her mother had ceased grumbling at the inadequacy of the cooking-places, the distance from the daily market, and at matters of house-keeping in general,—that the house was to him his home. Any one could enter his bachelor's bungalow by day or night, and the life that he led there was an unlovely one. In the house in the city his feet only could pass beyond the outer courtyard to the women's rooms; and when the big wooden gate was bolted behind him he was king in his own territory, with Ameera for queen. And there was going to be added to this kingdom a third person whose arrival Holden felt inclined to resent. It interfered with his perfect happiness. It disarranged the orderly peace of the house that was his own. But Ameera was wild with delight at the thought of it, and her mother not less so. The love of a man, and particularly a white man, was at the best an inconstant affair, but it might, both women argued, be held fast by a baby's hands. "And then," Ameera would always say, "then he will never care for the white *mem-log*. I hate them all—I hate them all."

"He will go back to his own people in time," said the mother; "but by the blessing of God that time is yet afar off."

Holden sat silent on the couch thinking of the future, and his thoughts were not pleasant. The drawbacks of a double life are manifold. The Government, with singular care, had ordered him out of the station for a fortnight on special duty in the place of a man who was watching by the bedside of a sick wife. The verbal notification of the transfer had been edged by a cheerful remark that Holden ought to think himself lucky in being a bachelor and a free man. He came to break the news to Ameera.

"It is not good," she said slowly, "but it is not all bad. There is my mother here, and no harm will come to me—unless indeed I die of pure joy. Go thou to thy work and think no troublesome thoughts. When the days are done I believe . . . nay, I am sure. And—and then I shall lay *him* in thy arms, and thou wilt love me for ever. The train goes to-night, at midnight is it not? Go now, and do not let thy heart be heavy by cause of me. But thou wilt not delay in returning? Thou wilt not stay on the road to talk to the bold white *mem-log*. Come back to me swiftly, my life."

As he left the courtyard to reach his horse that was tethered to the gate-post, Holden spoke to the white-haired old watchman who guarded the house, and bade him under certain contingencies despatch the filled-up telegraph-form that Holden gave him. It was all that could be done, and with the sensations of a man who has attended his own funeral Holden went away by the night mail to his exile. Every hour of the day he dreaded the arrival of the telegram, and every hour of the night he pictured to himself the death of Ameera. In consequence his work for the State was not of first-rate quality, nor was his temper towards his colleagues of the most amiable. The fortnight ended without a sign from his home, and, torn to pieces by his anxieties, Holden returned to be swallowed up for two precious hours by a dinner at the club, wherein he heard, as a man hears in a swoon, voices telling him how execrably he had performed the other man's duties, and how he had endeared himself to all his associates. Then he fled on horseback through the night with his heart in his mouth. There was no answer at first to his blows on the gate, and he had just wheeled his horse round to kick it in when Pir Khan appeared with a lantern and held his stirrup.

"Has aught occurred?" said Holden.

"The news does not come from my mouth, Protector of the Poor, but——" He held out his shaking hand as befitted the bearer of good news who is entitled to a reward.

Holden hurried through the courtyard. A light burned in the upper room. His horse neighed in the gateway, and he heard a shrill little wail that sent all the blood into the apple of his throat. It was a new voice, but it did not prove that Ameera was alive.

"Who is there?" he called up the narrow brick staircase.

There was a cry of delight from Ameera, and then the voice of the mother, tremulous with old age and pride—"We be two women and—the—man—thy—son."

On the threshold of the room Holden stepped on a naked dagger, that was laid there to avert ill-luck, and it broke at the hilt under his impatient heel.

"God is great!" cooed Ameera in the half-light. "Thou hast taken his misfortunes on thy head."

"Ay, but how is it with thee, life of my life? Old woman, how is it with her?"

"She has forgotten her sufferings for joy that the child is born. There is no harm; but speak softly," said the mother.

"It only needed thy presence to make me all well," said Ameera. "My king, thou hast been very long away. What gifts hast thou for me? Ah, ah! It is I that bring gifts this time. Look, my life, look. Was there ever such a babe? Nay, I am too weak even to clear my arm from him."

"Rest then, and do not talk. I am here, *bachari* [little woman]."

"Well said, for there is a bond and a heel-rope [*peecharee*] between us now that nothing can break. Look—canst thou see in this light? He is without spot or blemish. Never was such a man-child. *Ya illah!* he shall be a pundit—no, a trooper of the Queen. And, my life, dost thou love me as well as ever, though I am faint and sick and worn? Answer truly."

"Yea. I love as I have loved, with all my soul. Lie still, pearl, and rest."

"Then do not go. Sit by my side here—so. Mother, the lord of this house needs a cushion. Bring it." There was an almost imperceptible movement on the part of the new life that lay in the hollow of Ameera's arm. "Aho!" she said, her voice breaking with love. "The babe is a champion from his birth. He is kicking me in the side with mighty kicks. Was there ever such a babe! And he is ours to us—thine and mine. Put thy hand on his head, but carefully, for he is very young, and men are unskilled in such matters."

Very cautiously Holden touched with the tips of his fingers the downy head.

"He is of the faith," said Ameera; "for lying here in the night-watches I whispered the call to prayer and the profession of faith into his ears. And it is most marvellous that he was born upon a Friday, as I was born. Be careful of him, my life; but he can almost grip with his hands."

Holden found one helpless little hand that closed feebly on his finger. And the clutch ran through his body till it settled about his heart. Till then his sole thought had been for Ameera. He began to realize that there was some one else in the world, but he could not feel that it was a veritable son with a soul. He sat down to think, and Ameera dozed lightly.

"Get hence, *sahib,*" said her mother under her breath. "It is not good that she should find you here on waking. She must be still."

"I go," said Holden submissively. "Here be rupees. See that my *baba* gets fat and finds all that he needs."

The chink of the silver roused Ameera. "I am his mother, and no hireling," she said weakly. "Shall I look to him more or less for the sake of money? Mother, give it back. I have borne my lord a son."

The deep sleep of weakness came upon her almost before the sentence was completed. Holden went down to the courtyard very softly with his heart at ease. Pir Khan, the old watchman, was chuckling with delight. "This house is now complete," he said, and without further comment thrust into Holden's hands the hilt of a sabre worn many years ago when he, Pir Khan, served the Queen in the police. The bleat of a tethered goat came from the well-kerb.

"There be two," said Pir Khan, "two goats of the best. I bought them, and they cost much money; and since there is no birth-party assembled their flesh will be all mine. Strike craftily, *sahib!* 'Tis an ill-balanced sabre at the best. Wait till they raise their heads from cropping the marigolds."

"And why?" said Holden, bewildered.

"For the birth-sacrifice. What else? Otherwise the child being unguarded from fate may die. The Protector of the Poor knows the fitting words to be said."

Holden had learned them once with little thought that he would ever speak them in earnest. The touch of the cold sabre-hilt in his palm turned suddenly to the clinging grip of the child upstairs—the child that was his own son—and a dread of loss filled him.

"Strike!" said Pir Khan. "Never life came into the world but life was paid for it. See, the goats have raised their heads. Now! With a drawing cut!"

Hardly knowing what he did Holden cut twice as he muttered the Mahomedan prayer that runs: "Almighty! In place of this my son I offer life for life, blood for blood, head for head, bone for bone, hair for hair, skin for skin." The waiting horse snorted and bounded in his pickets at the smell of the raw blood that spirted over Holden's riding-boots.

"Well smitten!" said Pir Khan, wiping the sabre. "A swordsman was lost in thee. Go with a light heart, Heaven-born. I am thy servant, and the servant of thy son. May the Presence live a thousand years and . . . the flesh of the goats is all mine?" Pir Khan drew back richer by a month's pay. Holden swung himself into the saddle and rode off through the low-hanging wood-smoke of the evening. He was full of riotous exultation, alternating with a vast vague tenderness directed towards no particular object, that made him choke as he bent over the neck of his uneasy horse. "I never felt like this in my life," he thought. "I'll go to the club and pull myself together."

A game of pool was beginning, and the room was full of men. Holden entered, eager to get to the light and the company of his fellows, singing at the top of his voice—

In Baltimore a-walking, a lady I did meet!

"Did you?" said the club-secretary from his corner. "Did she happen to tell you that your boots were wringing wet? Great goodness, man, it's blood!"

"Bosh!" said Holden, picking his cue from the rack. "May I cut in? It's dew. I've been riding through high crops. My faith! my boots are in a mess though!

"And if it be a girl she shall wear a wedding-ring,
And if it be a boy he shall fight for his king,
With his dirk, and his cap, and his little jacket blue,
He shall walk the quarter-deck—"

"Yellow on blue—green next player," said the marker monotonously.

"He shall walk the quarter-deck,—Am I green, marker? *He shall walk the quarter-deck,*—eh! that's a bad shot,—*As his daddy used to do!"*

"I don't see that you have anything to crow about," said a zealous junior civilian acidly. "The Government is not exactly pleased with your work when you relieved Sanders."

"Does that mean a wigging from headquarters?" said Holden with an abstracted smile. "I think I can stand it."

The talk beat up round the ever-fresh subject of each man's work, and steadied Holden till it was time to go to his dark empty bungalow, where his butler received him as one who knew all his affairs. Holden remained awake for the greater part of the night, and his dreams were pleasant ones.

2

"How old is he now?"

"*Ya illah!* What a man's question! He is all but six weeks old; and on this night I go up to the housetop with thee, my life, to count the stars. For that is auspicious. And he was born on a Friday under the sign of the Sun, and it has been told to me that he will outlive us both and get wealth. Can we wish for aught better, beloved?"

"There is nothing better. Let us go up to the roof, and thou shalt count the stars—but a few only for the sky is heavy with cloud."

"The winter rains are late, and maybe they come out of season. Come, before all the stars are hid. I have put on my richest jewels."

"Thou hast forgotten the best of all."

"*Ai!* Ours. He comes also. He has never yet seen the skies."

Ameera climbed the narrow staircase that led to the flat roof. The child, placid and unwinking, lay in the hollow of her right arm, gorgeous in silver-fringed muslin with a small skull-cap on his head. Ameera wore all that she valued most. The diamond nose-stud that takes the place of the Western patch in drawing attention to the curve of the nostril, the gold ornament in the centre of the forehead studded with tallow-drop emeralds and flawed rubies, the heavy circlet of beaten gold that was fastened round her neck by the softness of the pure metal, and the chinking curb-patterned silver anklets hanging low over the rosy ankle-bone. She was dressed in jade-green muslin as befitted a daughter of the Faith, and from shoulder to elbow and elbow to wrist ran bracelets of silver tied with floss silk, frail glass bangles slipped over the wrist in proof of the slenderness of the hand, and certain heavy gold bracelets that had no part in her country's ornaments but, since they were Holden's gift and fastened with a cunning European snap, delighted her immensely.

They sat down by the low white parapet of the roof, overlooking the city and its lights.

"They are happy down there," said Ameera. "But I do not

think that they are as happy as we. Nor do I think the white *mem-log* are as happy. And thou?"

"I know they are not."

"How dost thou know?"

"They give their children over to the nurses."

"I have never seen that," said Ameera with a sigh, "nor do I wish to see. *Ahi!*"—she dropped her head on Holden's shoulder,—"I have counted forty stars, and I am tired. Look at the child, love of my life, he is counting too."

The baby was staring with round eyes at the dark of the heavens. Ameera placed him in Holden's arms, and he lay there without a cry.

"What shall we call him among ourselves?" she said. "Look! Art thou ever tired of looking? He carries thy very eyes. But the mouth——"

"Is thine, most dear. Who should know better than I?"

" 'Tis such a feeble mouth. Oh, so small! And yet it holds my heart between its lips. Give him to me now. He has been too long away."

"Nay, let him lie; he has not yet begun to cry."

"When he cries thou wilt give him back—eh? What a man of mankind thou art! If he cried he were only the dearer to me. But, my life, what little name shall we give him?"

The small body lay close to Holden's heart. It was utterly helpless and very soft. He scarcely dared to breathe for fear of crushing it. The caged green parrot that is regarded as a sort of guardian-spirit in most native households moved on its perch and fluttered a drowsy wing.

"There is the answer," said Holden. "Mian Mittu has spoken. He shall be the parrot. When he is ready he will talk mightily and run about. Mian Mittu is the parrot in thy—in the Mussulman tongue, is it not?"

"Why put me so far off?" said Ameera fretfully. "Let it be like unto some English name—but not wholly. For he is mine."

"Then call him Tota, for that is likest English."

"Ay, Tota, and that is still the parrot. Forgive me, my lord, for a minute ago, but in truth he is too little to wear all the weight of Mian Mittu for name. He shall be Tota—our Tota to us. Hearest thou, O small one? Littlest, thou art Tota." She touched the child's cheek, and he waking wailed, and it was necessary to return him to his mother, who soothed him with the wonderful rhyme of *Aré koko, Jaré koko!* which says:

Oh crow! Go crow! Baby's sleeping sound,
And the wild plums grow in the jungle, only a penny a pound.
Only a penny a pound, baba, *only a penny a pound.*

Reassured many times as to the price of those plums, Tota cuddled himself down to sleep. The two sleek, white well-bullocks in the courtyard were steadily chewing the cud of their evening meal; old Pir Khan squatted at the head of Holden's horse, his police sabre across his knees, pulling drowsily at a big water-pipe that croaked like a bull-frog in a pond. Ameera's mother sat spinning in the lower verandah, and the wooden gate was shut and barred. The music of a marriage-procession came to the roof above the gentle hum of the city, and a string of flying-foxes crossed the face of the low moon.

"I have prayed," said Ameera after a long pause, "I have prayed for two things. First, that I may die in thy stead if thy death is demanded, and in the second that I may die in the place of the child. I have prayed to the Prophet and to Beebee Miriam [the Virgin Mary]. Thinkest thou either will hear?"

"From thy lips who would not hear the lightest word?"

"I asked for straight talk, and thou hast given me sweet talk. Will my prayers be heard?"

"How can I say? God is very good."

"Of that I am not sure. Listen now. When I die, or the child dies, what is thy fate? Living, thou wilt return to the bold white *mem-log,* for kind calls to kind."

"Not always."

"With a woman, no; with a man it is otherwise. Thou wilt in this life, later on, go back to thine own folk. That I could almost endure, for I should be dead. But in thy very death thou wilt be taken away to a strange place and a paradise that I do not know."

"Will it be paradise?"

"Surely, for who would harm thee? But we two—I and the child—shall be elsewhere, and we cannot come to thee, nor canst thou come to us. In the old days, before the child was born, I did not think of these things; but now I think of them always. It is very hard talk."

"It will fall as it will fall. To-morrow we do not know, but to-day and love we know well. Surely we are happy now."

"So happy that it were well to make our happiness assured. And thy Beebee Miriam should listen to me; for she is also a woman. But then she would envy me! It is not seemly for men to worship a woman."

Holden laughed aloud at Ameera's little spasm of jealousy. "Is it not seemly? Why didst thou not turn me from worship of thee, then?"

"Thou a worshipper! And of me? My king, for all thy sweet words, well I know that I am thy servant and thy slave, and the dust under thy feet. And I would not have it otherwise. See!"

Before Holden could prevent her she stooped forward and touched his feet; recovering herself with a little laugh she hugged Tota closer to her bosom. Then almost savagely—

"Is it true that the bold white *mem-log* live for three times the length of my life? Is it true that they make their marriages not before they are old women?"

"They marry as do others—when they are women."

"That I know, but they wed when they are twenty-five. Is that true?"

"That is true."

"Ya illah! At twenty-five! Who would of his own will take a wife even of eighteen? She is a woman—aging every hour. Twenty-five! I shall be an old woman at that age, and—— Those *mem-log* remain young for ever. How I hate them!"

"What have they to do with us?"

"I cannot tell. I know only that there may now be alive on this earth a woman ten years older than I who may come to thee and take thy love ten years after I am an old woman, gray-headed, and the nurse of Tota's son. That is unjust and evil. They should die too."

"Now, for all thy years thou art a child, and shalt be picked up and carried down the staircase."

"Tota! Have a care for Tota, my lord! Thou at least art as foolish as any babe!" Ameera tucked Tota out of harm's way in the hollow of her neck, and was carried downstairs laughing in Holden's arms, while Tota opened his eyes and smiled after the manner of the lesser angels.

He was a silent infant, and, almost before Holden could realize that he was in the world, developed into a small gold-coloured little god and unquestioned despot of the house overlooking the city. Those were months of absolute happiness to Holden and Ameera—happiness withdrawn from the world, shut in behind the wooden gate that Pir Khan guarded. By day Holden did his work with an immense pity for such as were not so fortunate as himself, and a sympathy for small children that amazed and amused many mothers at the little station-gatherings. At nightfall he returned to Ameera,—Ameera, full of the wondrous doings of Tota; how he had been seen to clap his hands together and move his fingers with intention and purpose—which was manifestly a miracle—how later, he had of his own initiative crawled out of his low bedstead on to the floor and swayed on both feet for the space of three breaths.

"And they were long breaths, for my heart stood still with delight," said Ameera.

Then Tota took the beasts into his councils—the well-bullocks, the little gray squirrels, the mongoose that lived in a hole near the well, and especially Mian Mittu, the parrot, whose tail he grievously pulled, and Mian Mittu screamed till Ameera and Holden arrived.

"O villain! Child of strength! This to thy brother on the house-top! *Tobah, tobah!* Fie! Fie! But I know a charm to make him wise as Suleiman and Aflatoun [Solomon and Plato]. Now look," said Ameera. She drew from an embroidered bag a handful of almonds. "See! we count seven. In the name of God!"

She placed Mian Mittu, very angry and rumpled, on the top of his cage, and seating herself between the babe and the bird she cracked and peeled an almond less white than her teeth. "This is a true charm, my life, and do not laugh. See! I give the parrot one half and Tota the other." Mian Mittu with careful beak took his share from between Ameera's lips, and she kissed the other half into the mouth of the child, who ate it slowly with wondering eyes. "This I will do each day of seven, and without doubt he who is ours will be a bold speaker and wise. Eh, Tota, what wilt thou be when thou art a man and I am gray-headed?" Tota tucked his fat legs into adorable creases. He could crawl, but he was not going to waste the spring of his youth in idle speech. He wanted Mian Mittu's tail to tweak.

When he was advanced to the dignity of a silver belt—which, with a magic square engraved on silver and hung round his neck, made up the greater part of his clothing—he staggered on a perilous journey down the garden to Pir Khan and proffered him all his jewels in exchange for one little ride on Holden's horse, having seen his mother's mother chaffering with pedlars in the verandah. Pir Khan wept and set the untried feet on his own gray head in sign of fealty, and brought the bold adventurer to his mother's arms, vowing that Tota would be a leader of men ere his beard was grown.

One hot evening, while he sat on the roof between his father and mother watching the never-ending warfare of the kites that the city boys flew, he demanded a kite of his own with Pir Khan to fly it, because he had a fear of dealing with anything larger than himself, and when Holden called him a "spark," he rose to his feet and answered slowly in defence of his new-found individuality, *"Hum' park nahin hai. Hum admi hai* [I am no spark, but a man]."

The protest made Holden choke and devote himself very seriously to a consideration of Tota's future. He need hardly have taken the trouble. The delight of that life was too perfect to endure. Therefore it was taken away as many things are taken away in India—suddenly and without warning. The little lord of the house, as Pir Khan called him, grew sorrowful and complained of pains who had never known the meaning of pain. Ameera, wild with terror, watched him through the night, and in the dawning of the second day the life was shaken out of him by fever—the seasonal autumn fever. It seemed altogether impossible that he could die, and neither Ameera nor Holden at first believed the evidence of the little body on the bedstead. Then Ameera beat her head against the wall and would have flung herself down the well in the garden had Holden not restrained her by main force.

One mercy only was granted to Holden. He rode to his office in broad daylight and found waiting him an unusually heavy mail that demanded concentrated attention and hard work. He was not, however, alive to this kindness of the gods.

3

The first shock of a bullet is no more than a brisk pinch. The wrecked body does not send in its protest to the soul till ten or fifteen seconds later. Holden realized his pain slowly, exactly as he had realized his happiness, and with the same imperious necessity for hiding all trace of it. In the beginning he only felt that there had been a loss, and that Ameera needed comforting, where she sat with her head on her knees shivering as Mian Mittu from the house-top called, *Tota! Tota! Tota!* Later all his world and the daily life of it rose up to hurt him. It was an outrage that any one of the children at the band-stand in the evening should be alive and clamorous, when his own child lay dead. It was more than mere pain when one of them touched him, and stories told by over-fond fathers of their children's latest performances cut him to the quick. He could not declare his pain. He had neither help, comfort, nor sympathy; and Ameera at the end of each weary day would lead him through the hell of self-questioning reproach which is reserved for those who have lost a child and believe that with a little—just a little—more care it might have been saved.

"Perhaps," Ameera would say, "I did not take sufficient heed. Did I, or did I not? The sun on the roof that day when he played so long alone and I was—*ahi!* braiding my hair—it may be that the sun then bred the fever. If I had warned him from the sun he might have lived. But, oh my life, say that I am guiltless! Thou knowest that I loved him as I love thee. Say that there is no blame on me, or I shall die—I shall die!"

"There is no blame,—before God, none. It was written and how could we do aught to save? What has been, has been. Let it go, beloved."

"He was all my heart to me. How can I let the thought go when my arm tells me every night that he is not here? *Ahi! Ahi!* O Tota, come back to me—come back again, and let us be all together as it was before!"

"Peace, peace! For thine own sake, and for mine also, if thou lovest me—rest."

"By this I know thou dost not care; and how shouldst thou? The white men have hearts of stone and souls of iron. Oh, that I had married a man of mine own people—though he beat me—and had never eaten the bread of an alien!"

"Am I an alien—mother of my son?"

"What else—*Sahib?* . . . Oh, forgive me—forgive! The death has driven me mad. Thou art the life of my heart, and the light of my eyes, and the breath of my life, and—and I have put thee from me, though it was but for a moment. If thou goest away, to whom shall I look for help? Do not be angry. Indeed, it was the pain that spoke and not thy slave."

"I know, I know. We be two who were three. The greater need therefore that we should be one."

They were sitting on the roof as of custom. The night was a warm one in early spring, and sheet-lightning was dancing on the horizon to a broken tune played by far-off thunder. Ameera settled herself in Holden's arms.

"The dry earth is lowing like a cow for the rain, and I—I am afraid. It was not like this when we counted the stars. But thou lovest me as much as before, though a bond is taken away? Answer!"

"I love more because a new bond has come out of the sorrow that we have eaten together, and that thou knowest."

"Yea, I knew," said Ameera in a very small whisper. "But it is good to hear thee say so, my life, who art so strong to help. I will be a child no more, but a woman and an aid to thee. Listen! Give me my *sitar* and I will sing bravely."

She took the light silver-studded *sitar* and began a song of the great hero Rajah Rasalu. The hand failed on the strings, the tune halted, checked, and at a low note turned off to the poor little nursery-rhyme about the wicked crow—

And the wild plums grow in the jungle, only a penny a pound.
Only a penny a pound, baba—*only* . . .

Then came the tears, and the piteous rebellion against fate till she slept, moaning a little in her sleep, with the right arm thrown clear of the body as though it protected something that was not there. It was after this night that life became a little easier for Holden. The ever-present pain of loss drove him into his work, and the work repaid him by filling up his mind for nine or ten hours a day. Ameera sat alone in the house and brooded, but grew happier when she understood that Holden was more at ease, according to the custom of women. They touched happiness again, but this time with caution.

"It was because we loved Tota that he died. The jealousy of God was upon us," said Ameera. "I have hung up a large black jar before our window to turn the evil eye from us, and we must make no protestations of delight, but go softly underneath the stars, lest God find us out. Is that not good talk, worthless one?"

She had shifted the accent on the word that means "beloved," in proof of the sincerity of her purpose. But the kiss that followed the new christening was a thing that any deity might have envied. They went about henceforward saying, "It is naught, it is naught;" and hoping that all the Powers heard.

The Powers were busy on other things. They had allowed thirty million people four years of plenty wherein men fed well and the crops were certain, and the birthrate rose year by year; the districts reported a purely agricultural population varying from nine hundred to two thousand to the square mile of the overburdened earth; and the Member for Lower Tooting, wandering about India in pot-hat and frock-coat, talked largely of the benefits of British rule and suggested as the one thing needful the establishment of a duly qualified electoral system and a general bestowal of the franchise. His long-suffering hosts smiled and made him welcome, and when he paused to admire, with pretty picked words, the blossom of the blood-red *dhak*-tree that had flowered untimely for a sign of what was coming, they smiled more than ever.

It was the Deputy Commissioner of Kot-Kumharsen, staying at the club for a day, who lightly told a tale that made Holden's blood run cold as he overheard the end.

"He won't bother any one any more. Never saw a man so astonished in my life. By Jove, I thought he meant to ask a question in the House about it. Fellow-passenger in his ship—dined next him—bowled over by cholera and died in eighteen hours. You needn't laugh, you fellows. The Member for Lower Tooting is awfully angry about it; but he's more scared. I think he's going to take his enlightened self out of India."

"I'd give a good deal if he were knocked over. It might keep a few vestrymen of his kidney to their own parish. But what's this about cholera? It's full early for anything of that kind," said the warden of an unprofitable salt-lick.

"Don't know," said the Deputy Commissioner reflectively. "We've got locusts with us. There's sporadic cholera all along the north—at least we're calling it sporadic for decency's sake. The spring crops are short in five districts, and nobody seems to know where the rains are. It's nearly March now. I don't want to scare anybody, but it seems to me that Nature's going to audit her accounts with a big red pencil this summer."

"Just when I wanted to take leave, too!" said a voice across the room.

"There won't be much leave this year, but there ought to be

a great deal of promotion. I've come in to persuade the Government to put my pet canal on the list of famine-relief works. It's an ill-wind that blows no good. I shall get that canal finished at last."

"Is it the old programme then," said Holden; "famine, fever, and cholera?"

"Oh, no. Only local scarcity and an unusual prevalence of seasonal sickness. You'll find it all in the reports if you live till next year. You're a lucky chap. *You* haven't got a wife to send out of harm's way. The hill-stations ought to be full of women this year."

"I think you're inclined to exaggerate the talk in the *bazars,*" said a young civilian in the Secretariat. "Now I have observed——"

"I daresay you have," said the Deputy Commissioner, "but you've a great deal more to observe, my son. In the meantime, I wish to observe to you——" and he drew him aside to discuss the construction of the canal that was so dear to his heart. Holden went to his bungalow and began to understand that he was not alone in the world, and also that he was afraid for the sake of another,—which is the most soul-satisfying fear known to man.

Two months later, as the Deputy had foretold, Nature began to audit her accounts with a red pencil. On the heels of the spring-reapings came a cry for bread, and the Government, which had decreed that no man should die of want, sent wheat. Then came the cholera from all four quarters of the compass. It struck a pilgrim-gathering of half a million at a sacred shrine. Many died at the feet of their god; the others broke and ran over the face of the land carrying the pestilence with them. It smote a walled city and killed two hundred a day. The people crowded the trains, hanging on to the footboards and squatting on the roofs of the carriages, and the cholera followed them, for at each station they dragged out the dead and the dying. They died by the roadside, and the horses of the Englishmen shied at the corpses in the grass. The rains did not come, and the earth turned to iron lest man should escape death by hiding in her. The English sent their wives away to the hills and went about their work, coming forward as they were bidden to fill the gaps in the fighting-line. Holden, sick with fear of losing his chiefest treasure on earth, had done his best to persuade Ameera to go away with her mother to the Himalayas.

"Why should I go?" said she one evening on the roof. "There is sickness, and people are dying, and all the white *mem-log* have gone."

"All of them?"

"All—unless perhaps there remain some old scald-head who vexes her husband's heart by running risk of death."

"Nay; who stays is my sister, and thou must not abuse her, for I will be a scald-head too. I am glad all the bold *mem-log* are gone."

"Do I speak to a woman or a babe? Go to the hills and I will see to it that thou goest like a queen's daughter. Think, child. In a red-lacquered bullock-cart, veiled and curtained, with brass peacocks upon the pole and red cloth hangings. I will send two orderlies for guard, and——"

"Peace! Thou art the babe in speaking thus. What use are those toys to me? *He* would have patted the bullocks and played with the housings. For his sake, perhaps,—thou hast made me very English—I might have gone. Now, I will not. Let the *mem-log* run."

"Their husbands are sending them, beloved."

"Very good talk. Since when hast thou been my husband to tell me what to do? I have but borne thee a son. Thou art only all the desire of my soul to me. How shall I depart when I know that if evil befall thee by the breadth of so much as my littlest finger-nail—is that not small?—I should be aware of it though I were in paradise. And here, this summer thou mayest die—*ai, janee,* die! and in dying they might call to tend thee a white woman, and she would rob me in the last of thy love!"

"But love is not born in a moment or on a death-bed!"

"What dost thou know of love, stoneheart? She would take thy thanks at least and, by God and the Prophet and Beebee Miriam the mother of thy Prophet, that I will never endure. My lord and my love, let there be no more foolish talk of going away. Where thou art, I am. It is enough." She put an arm round his neck and a hand on his mouth.

There are not many happinesses so complete as those that are snatched under the shadow of the sword. They sat together and laughed, calling each other openly by every pet name that could move the wrath of the gods. The city below them was locked up in its own torments. Sulphur fires blazed in the streets; the conches in the Hindu temples screamed and bellowed, for the gods were inattentive in those days. There was a service in the great Mahomedan shrine, and the call to prayer from the minarets was almost unceasing. They heard the wailing in the houses of the dead, and once the shriek of a mother who had lost a child and was calling for its return. In the gray dawn they saw the dead borne out through the city gates, each litter with its own little knot of mourners. Wherefore they kissed each other and shivered.

It was a red and heavy audit, for the land was very sick and needed a little breathing-space ere the torrent of cheap life should flood it anew. The children of immature fathers and undeveloped mothers made no resistance. They were cowed and sat still, waiting till the sword should be sheathed in November if it were so willed. There were gaps among the English, but the gaps were filled. The work of superintending famine-relief, cholera-sheds, medicine-distribution, and what little sanitation was possible, went forward because it was so ordered.

Holden had been told to keep himself in readiness to move to replace the next man who should fall. There were twelve hours in each day when he could not see Ameera, and she might die in three. He was considering what his pain would be if he could not see her for three months, or if she died out of his sight. He was absolutely certain that her death would be demanded—so certain that when he looked up from the telegram and saw Pir Khan breathless in the doorway, he laughed aloud. "And?" said he,——

"When there is a cry in the night and the spirit flutters into the throat, who has a charm that will restore? Come swiftly, Heaven-born! It is the black cholera."

Holden galloped to his home. The sky was heavy with clouds, for the long-deferred rains were near and the heat was stifling. Ameera's mother met him in the courtyard, whimpering, "She is dying. She is nursing herself into death. She is all but dead. What shall I do, *sahib?*"

Ameera was lying in the room in which Tota had been born. She made no sign when Holden entered, because the human soul is a very lonely thing and, when it is getting ready to go away, hides itself in a misty borderland where the living may not follow. The black cholera does its work quietly and without explanation. Ameera was being thrust out of life as though the Angel of Death had himself put his hand upon her. The quick breathing seemed to show that she was either afraid or in pain, but neither eyes nor mouth gave any answer to Holden's kisses. There was nothing to be said or done, Holden could only wait and suffer. The first drops of the rain began to fall on the roof, and he could hear shouts of joy in the parched city.

The soul came back a little and the lips moved. Holden bent down to listen. "Keep nothing of mine," said Ameera. "Take no hair from my head. *She* would make thee burn it later on. That flame I should feel. Lower! Stoop lower! Remember only that I was thine and bore thee a son. Though thou wed a white woman to-morrow, the pleasure of receiving in thy arms thy first son is taken from thee for ever. Remember me when thy son is born—the one that shall carry thy name before all men. His misfortunes be on my head. I bear witness—I bear witness"—the lips were forming the words on his ear—"that there is no God but—thee, beloved!"

Then she died. Holden sat still, and all thought was taken from him,—till he heard Ameera's mother lift the curtain.

"Is she dead, *sahib?*"

"She is dead."

"Then I will mourn, and afterwards take an inventory of the furniture in this house. For that will be mine. The *sahib* does not mean to resume it? It is so little, so very little, *sahib*, and I am an old woman. I would like to lie softly."

"For the mercy of God be silent a while. Go out and mourn where I cannot hear."

"*Sahib,* she will be buried in four hours."

"I know the custom. I shall go ere she is taken away. That matter is in thy hands. Look to it, that the bed on which—on which she lies——"

"Aha! That beautiful red-lacquered bed. I have long desired——"

"That the bed is left here untouched for my disposal. All else in the house is thine. Hire a cart, take everything, go hence, and before sunrise let there be nothing in this house but that which I have ordered thee to respect."

"I am an old woman. I would stay at least for the days of mourning, and the rains have just broken. Whither shall I go?"

"What is that to me? My order is that there is a going. The house-gear is worth a thousand rupees and my orderly shall bring thee a hundred rupees to-night."

"That is very little. Think of the cart-hire."

"It shall be nothing unless thou goest, and with speed. O woman, get hence and leave me with my dead!"

The mother shuffled down the staircase, and in her anxiety to take stock of the house-fittings forgot to mourn. Holden stayed by Ameera's side and the rain roared on the roof. He could not think connectedly by reason of the noise, though he made many attempts to do so. Then four sheeted ghosts glided dripping into the room and stared at him through their veils. They were the washers of the dead. Holden left the room and went out to his horse. He had come in a dead, stifling calm through ankle-deep dust. He found the courtyard a rain-lashed pond alive with frogs; a torrent of yellow water ran under the gate, and a roaring wind drove the bolts of the rain like buckshot against the mud-walls. Pir Khan was shivering in his little hut by the gate, and the horse was stamping uneasily in the water.

"I have been told the *sahib's* order," said Pir Khan. "It is well. This house is now desolate. I go also, for my monkey-face would be a reminder of that which has been. Concerning the bed, I will bring that to thy house yonder in the morning; but remember, *sahib,* it will be to thee a knife turning in a green wound. I go upon a pilgrimage, and I will take no money. I have grown fat in the protection of the Presence whose sorrow is my sorrow. For the last time I hold his stirrup."

He touched Holden's foot with both hands and the horse sprang out into the road, where the creaking bamboos were whipping the sky and all the frogs were chuckling. Holden could not see for the rain in his face. He put his hands before his eyes and muttered—

"Oh you brute! You utter brute!"

The news of his trouble was already in his bungalow. He read the knowledge in his butler's eyes when Ahmed Khan brought in food, and for the first and last time in his life laid a hand upon his master's shoulder, saying, "Eat, *sahib,* eat. Meat is good against sorrow. I also have known. Moreover the shadows come and go, *sahib;* the shadows come and go. These be curried eggs."

Holden could neither eat nor sleep. The heavens sent down eight inches of rain in that night and washed the earth clean. The waters tore down walls, broke roads, and scoured open the shallow graves on the Mahomedan burying-ground. All next day it rained, and Holden sat still in his house considering his sorrow. On the morning of the third day he received a telegram which said only, "Ricketts, Myndonie. Dying. Holden relieve. Immediate." Then he thought that before he departed he would look at the house wherein he had been master and lord. There was a break in the weather, and the rank earth steamed with vapour.

He found that the rains had torn down the mud pillars of the gateway, and the heavy wooden gate that had guarded his life hung lazily from one hinge. There was grass three inches high in the courtyard; Pir Khan's lodge was empty, and the sodden thatch sagged between the beams. A gray squirrel was in possession of the verandah, as if the house had been untenanted for thirty years instead of three days. Ameera's mother had removed everything except some mildewed matting. The *tick-tick* of the little scorpions as they hurried across the floor was the only sound in the house. Ameera's room and the other one where Tota had lived were heavy with mildew; and the narrow staircase leading to the roof was streaked and stained with rain-borne mud. Holden saw all these things, and came out again to meet in the road Durga Dass, his landlord,—portly, affable, clothed in white muslin, and driving a Cee-spring buggy. He was overlooking his property to see how the roofs stood the stress of the first rains.

"I have heard," said he, "you will not take this place any more, *sahib?*"

"What are you going to do with it?"

"Perhaps I shall let it again."

"Then I will keep it on while I am away."

Durga Dass was silent for some time. "You shall not take it on, *sahib*," he said. "When I was a young man I also——, but to-day I am a member of the Municipality. Ho! Ho! No. When the birds have gone what need to keep the nest? I will have it pulled down—the timber will sell for something always. It shall be pulled down, and the Municipality shall make a road across, as they desire, from the burning-ghat to the city wall, so that no man may say where this house stood."

THE MARK OF THE BEAST
1890

Your Gods and my Gods—do you or I know which are the stronger?

—NATIVE PROVERB

EAST of Suez, some hold, the direct control of Providence ceases; Man being there handed over to the power of the Gods and Devils of Asia, and the Church of England Providence only exercising an occasional and modified supervision in the case of Englishmen.

This theory accounts for some of the more unnecessary horrors of life in India: it may be stretched to explain my story.

My friend Strickland of the Police, who knows as much of natives of India as is good for any man, can bear witness to the facts of the case. Dumoise, our doctor, also saw what Strickland and I saw. The inference which he drew from the evidence was entirely incorrect. He is dead now; he died, in a rather curious manner, which has been elsewhere described.

When Fleete came to India he owned a little money and some land in the Himalayas, near a place called Dharmsala. Both properties had been left him by an uncle, and he came out to finance them. He was a big, heavy, genial, and inoffensive man. His knowledge of natives was, of course, limited, and he complained of the difficulties of the language.

He rode in from his place in the hills to spend New Year in the station, and he stayed with Strickland. On New Year's Eve there was a big dinner at the club, and the night was excusably wet. When men foregather from the uttermost ends of the Empire, they have a right to be riotous. The Frontier had sent down a contingent o' Catch-'em-Alive-O's who had not seen twenty white faces for a year, and were used to ride fifteen miles to dinner at the next Fort at the risk of a Khyberee bullet where their drinks should lie. They profited by their new security, for they tried to play pool with a curled-up hedgehog found in the garden, and one of them carried the marker round the room in his teeth. Half a dozen planters had come in from the south and were talking "horse" to the Biggest Liar in Asia, who was trying to cap all their stories at once. Everybody was there, and there was a general closing up of ranks and taking stock of our losses in dead or disabled that had fallen during the past year. It was a very wet night, and I remember that we sang "Auld Lang Syne" with our feet in the Polo Championship Cup, and our heads among the stars, and swore that we were all dear friends. Then some of us went away and annexed Burma, and some tried to open up the Soudan and were opened up by Fuzzies in that cruel scrub outside Suakim, and some found stars and medals, and some were married, which was bad, and some did other things which were worse, and the others of us stayed in our chains and strove to make money on insufficient experiences.

Fleete began the night with sherry and bitters, drank champagne steadily up to dessert, then raw, rasping Capri with all the strength of whisky, took Benedictine with his coffee, four or five whiskies and sodas to improve his pool strokes, beer and bones at half-past two, winding up with old brandy. Consequently, when he came out, at half-past three in the morning, into fourteen degrees of frost, he was very angry with his horse for coughing, and tried to leapfrog into the saddle. The horse broke away and went to his stables; so Strickland and I formed a Guard of Dishonour to take Fleete home.

Our road lay through the bazaar, close to a little temple of Hanuman, the Monkey-god, who is a leading divinity worthy of respect. All gods have good points, just as have all priests. Personally, I attach much importance to Hanuman, and am kind to his people—the great gray apes of the hills. One never knows when one may want a friend.

There was a light in the temple, and as we passed, we could hear voices of men chanting hymns. In a native temple, the priests rise at all hours of the night to do honour to their god. Before we could stop him, Fleete dashed up the steps, patted two priests on the back, and was gravely grinding the ashes of his cigar-butt into the forehead of the red stone image of Hanuman. Strickland tried to drag him out, but he sat down and said solemnly:

"Shee that? 'Mark of the B—beasht! *I* made it. Ishn't it fine?"

In half a minute the temple was alive and noisy, and Strickland, who knew what came of polluting gods, said that things might occur. He, by virtue of his official position, long residence in the country, and weakness for going among the natives, was known to the priests and he felt unhappy. Fleete sat on the ground and refused to move. He said that "good old Hanuman" made a very soft pillow.

Then, without any warning, a Silver Man came out of a recess behind the image of the god. He was perfectly naked in that bitter, bitter cold, and his body shone like frosted silver, for he was what the Bible calls "a leper as white as snow." Also he had no face, because he was a leper of some years' standing and his disease was heavy upon him. We two stooped to haul Fleete up, and the temple was filling and filling with folk who seemed to spring from the earth, when the Silver Man ran in under our arms, making a noise exactly like the mewing of an otter, caught Fleete round the body and dropped his head on Fleete's breast before we could wrench him away. Then he retired to a corner and sat mewing while the crowd blocked all the doors.

The priests were very angry until the Silver Man touched Fleete. That nuzzling seemed to sober them.

At the end of a few minutes' silence one of the priests came to Strickland and said, in perfect English, "Take your friend away. He has done with Hanuman, but Hanuman has not done with him." The crowd gave room and we carried Fleete into the road.

Strickland was very angry. He said that we might all three have been knifed, and that Fleete should thank his stars that he had escaped without injury.

Fleete thanked no one. He said that he wanted to go to bed. He was gorgeously drunk.

We moved on, Strickland silent and wrathful, until Fleete was taken with violent shivering fits and sweating. He said that the smells of the bazaar were overpowering, and he wondered why slaughter-houses were permitted so near English residences. "Can't you smell the blood?" said Fleete.

We put him to bed at last, just as the dawn was breaking, and Strickland invited me to have another whisky and soda. While we were drinking he talked of the trouble in the temple, and admitted that it baffled him completely. Strickland hates being mystified by natives, because his business in life is to overmatch them with their own weapons. He has not yet succeeded in doing this, but in fifteen or twenty years he will have made some small progress.

"They should have mauled us," he said, "instead of mewing at us. I wonder what they meant. I don't like it one little bit."

I said that the Managing Committee of the temple would in all probability bring a criminal action against us for insulting their religion. There was a section of the Indian Penal Code which exactly met Fleete's offence. Strickland said he only hoped and prayed that they would do this. Before I left I looked into Fleete's room, and saw him lying on his right side, scratching his left breast. Then I went to bed cold, depressed, and unhappy, at seven o'clock in the morning.

At one o'clock I rode over to Strickland's house to inquire after Fleete's head. I imagined that it would be a sore one. Fleete was breakfasting and seemed unwell. His temper was gone, for he was abusing the cook for not supplying him with an underdone chop. A man who can eat raw meat after a wet night is a curiosity. I told Fleete this and he laughed.

"You breed queer mosquitoes in these parts," he said. "I've been bitten to pieces, but only in one place."

"Let's have a look at the bite," said Strickland. "It may have gone down since this morning."

While the chops were being cooked, Fleete opened his shirt and showed us, just over his left breast, a mark, the perfect double of the black rosettes—the five or six irregular blotches arranged in a circle—on a leopard's hide. Strickland looked and said, "It was only pink this morning. It's grown black now."

Fleete ran to a glass.

"By Jove!" he said, "this is nasty. What is it?"

We could not answer. Here the chops came in, all red and juicy, and Fleete bolted three in a most offensive manner. He ate on his right grinders only, and threw his head over his right shoulder as he snapped the meat. When he had finished, it struck him that he had been behaving strangely, for he said apologetically, "I don't think I ever felt so hungry in my life. I've bolted like an ostrich."

After breakfast Strickland said to me, "Don't go. Stay here, and stay for the night."

Seeing that my house was not three miles from Strickland's, this request was absurd. But Strickland insisted, and was going to say something when Fleete interrupted by declaring in a shamefaced way that he felt hungry again. Strickland sent a man to my house to fetch over my bedding and a horse, and we three went down to Strickland's stables to pass the hours until it was time to go out for a ride. The man who has a weakness for horses never wearies of inspecting them; and when two men are killing time in this way they gather knowledge and lies the one from the other.

There were five horses in the stables, and I shall never forget the scene as we tried to look them over. They seemed to have gone mad. They reared and screamed and nearly tore up their pickets; they sweated and shivered and lathered and were distraught with fear. Strickland's horses used to know him as well as his dogs; which made the matter more curious. We left the stable for fear of the brutes throwing themselves in their panic. Then Strickland turned back and called me. The horses were still frightened, but they let us "gentle" and make much of them, and put their heads in our bosoms.

"They aren't afraid of *us,*" said Strickland. "D'you know, I'd give three months' pay if *Outrage* here could talk."

But *Outrage* was dumb, and could only cuddle up to his master and blow out his nostrils, as is the custom of horses when they wish to explain things but can't. Fleete came up when we were in the stalls, and as soon as the horses saw him, their fright broke out afresh. It was all that we could do to escape from the place unkicked. Strickland said, "They don't seem to love you, Fleete."

"Nonsense," said Fleete; "my mare will follow me like a dog." He went to her; she was in a loose-box; but as he slipped the bars she plunged, knocked him down, and broke away into the garden. I laughed, but Strickland was not amused. He took his moustache in both fists and pulled at it till it nearly came out. Fleete, instead of going off to chase his property, yawned, saying that he felt sleepy. He went to the house to lie down, which was a foolish way of spending New Year's Day.

Strickland sat with me in the stables and asked if I had noticed anything peculiar in Fleete's manner. I said that he ate his food like a beast; but that this might have been the result of living alone in the hills out of the reach of society as refined and elevating as ours for instance. Strickland was not amused. I do not think that he listened to me, for his next sentence referred to the mark on Fleete's breast, and I said that it might have been caused by blister-flies, or that it was possibly a birth-mark newly born and now visible for the first time. We both agreed that it was unpleasant to look at, and Strickland found occasion to say that I was a fool.

"I can't tell you what I think now," said he, "because you would call me a madman; but you must stay with me for the next few days, if you can. I want you to watch Fleete, but don't tell me what you think till I have made up my mind."

"But I am dining out to-night," I said.

"So am I," said Strickland, "and so is Fleete. At least if he doesn't change his mind."

We walked about the garden smoking, but saying nothing—because we were friends, and talking spoils good tobacco—till our pipes were out. Then we went to wake up Fleete. He was wide awake and fidgeting about his room.

"I say, I want some more chops," he said. "Can I get them?"

We laughed and said, "Go and change. The ponies will be round in a minute."

"All right," said Fleete. "I'll go when I get the chops—underdone ones, mind."

He seemed to be quite in earnest. It was four o'clock, and we had had breakfast at one; still, for a long time, he demanded those underdone chops. Then he changed into riding clothes and went out into the verandah. His pony—the mare had not been caught—would not let him come near. All three horses were unmanageable—mad with fear—and finally Fleete said that he would stay at home and get something to eat. Strickland and I rode out wondering. As we passed the temple of Hanuman, the Silver Man came out and mewed at us.

"He is not one of the regular priests of the temple," said Strickland. "I think I should peculiarly like to lay my hands on him."

There was no spring in our gallop on the racecourse that

evening. The horses were stale, and moved as though they had been ridden out.

"The fright after breakfast has been too much for them," said Strickland.

That was the only remark he made through the remainder of the ride. Once or twice I think he swore to himself; but that did not count.

We came back in the dark at seven o'clock, and saw that there were no lights in the bungalow. "Careless ruffians my servants are!" said Strickland.

My horse reared at something on the carriage drive, and Fleete stood up under its nose.

"What are you doing, grovelling about the garden?" said Strickland.

But both horses bolted and nearly threw us. We dismounted by the stables and returned to Fleete, who was on his hands and knees under the orange-bushes.

"What the devil's wrong with you?" said Strickland.

"Nothing, nothing in the world," said Fleete, speaking very quickly and thickly. "I've been gardening—botanizing you know. The smell of the earth is delightful. I think I'm going for a walk—a long walk—all night."

Then I saw that there was something excessively out of order somewhere, and I said to Strickland, "I am not dining out."

"Bless you!" said Strickland. "Here, Fleete, get up. You'll catch fever there. Come in to dinner and let's have the lamps lit. We'll all dine at home."

Fleete stood up unwillingly, and said, "No lamps—no lamps. It's much nicer here. Let's dine outside and have some more chops—lots of 'em and underdone—bloody ones with gristle."

Now a December evening in Northern India is bitterly cold, and Fleete's suggestion was that of a maniac.

"Come in," said Strickland sternly. "Come in at once."

Fleete came, and when the lamps were brought, we saw that he was literally plastered with dirt from head to foot. He must have been rolling in the garden. He shrank from the light and went to his room. His eyes were horrible to look at. There was a green light behind them, not in them, if you understand, and the man's lower lip hung down.

Strickland said, "There is going to be trouble—big trouble—to-night. Don't you change your riding-things."

We waited and waited for Fleete's reappearance, and ordered dinner in the meantime. We could hear him moving about his own room, but there was no light there. Presently from the room came the long-drawn howl of a wolf.

People write and talk lightly of blood running cold and hair standing up and things of that kind. Both sensations are too horrible to be trifled with. My heart stopped as though a knife had been driven through it, and Strickland turned as white as the tablecloth.

The howl was repeated, and was answered by another howl far across the fields.

That set the gilded roof on the horror. Strickland dashed into Fleete's room. I followed, and we saw Fleete getting out of the window. He made beast-noises in the back of his throat. He could not answer us when we shouted at him. He spat.

I don't quite remember what followed, but I think that Strickland must have stunned him with the long boot-jack or else I should never have been able to sit on his chest. Fleete could not speak, he could only snarl, and his snarls were those of a wolf, not of a man. The human spirit must have been giving way all day and have died out with the twilight. We were dealing with a beast that had once been Fleete.

The affair was beyond any human and rational experience. I tried to say "Hydrophobia," but the word wouldn't come, because I knew that I was lying.

We bound this beast with leather thongs of the punkah-rope, and tied its thumbs and big toes together, and gagged it with a shoe-horn, which makes a very efficient gag if you know how to arrange it. Then we carried it into the dining-room, and sent a man to Dumoise, the doctor, telling him to come over at once. After we had despatched the messenger and were drawing breath, Strickland said, "It's no good. This isn't any doctor's work." I, also, knew that he spoke the truth.

The beast's head was free, and it threw it about from side to side. Any one entering the room would have believed that we were curing a wolf's pelt. That was the most loathsome accessory of all.

Strickland sat with his chin in the heel of his fist, watching the beast as it wriggled on the ground, but saying nothing. The shirt had been torn open in the scuffle and showed the black rosette mark on the left breast. It stood out like a blister.

In the silence of the watching we heard something without mewing like a she-otter. We both rose to our feet, and, I answer for myself, not Strickland, felt sick—actually and physically sick. We told each other, as did the men in *Pinafore,* that it was the cat.

Dumoise arrived, and I never saw a little man so unprofessionally shocked. He said that it was a heartrending case of hydrophobia, and that nothing could be done. At least any palliative measures would only prolong the agony. The beast was foaming at the mouth. Fleete, as we told Dumoise, had been bitten by dogs once or twice. Any man who keeps half a dozen terriers must expect a nip now and again. Dumoise could offer no help. He could only certify that Fleete was dying of hydrophobia. The beast was then howling, for it had managed to spit out the shoe-horn. Dumoise said that he would be ready to certify to the cause of death, and that the end was certain. He was a good little man, and he offered to remain with us; but Strickland refused the kindness. He did not wish to poison Dumoise's New Year. He would only ask him not to give the real cause of Fleete's death to the public.

So Dumoise left, deeply agitated; and as soon as the noise of the cart-wheels had died away, Strickland told me, in a whisper, his suspicions. They were so wildly improbable that he dared not say them out aloud; and I, who entertained all Strickland's beliefs, was so ashamed of owning to them that I pretended to disbelieve.

"Even if the Silver Man had bewitched Fleete for polluting the image of Hanuman, the punishment could not have fallen so quickly."

As I was whispering this the cry outside the house rose again, and the beast fell into a fresh paroxysm of struggling till we were afraid that the thongs that held it would give way.

"Watch!" said Strickland. "If this happens six times I shall take the law into my own hands. I order you to help me."

He went into his room and came out in a few minutes with the barrels of an old shot-gun, a piece of fishing-line, some thick cord, and his heavy wooden bedstead. I reported that the convulsions had followed the cry by two seconds in each case, and the beast seemed perceptibly weaker.

Strickland muttered, "But he can't take away the life! He can't take away the life!"

I said, though I knew that I was arguing against myself, "It may be a cat. It must be a cat. If the Silver Man is responsible, why does he dare to come here?"

Strickland arranged the wood on the hearth, put the gun-barrels into the glow of the fire, spread the twine on the table and broke a walking stick in two. There was one yard of fishing line, gut, lapped with wire, such as is used for *mahseer*-fishing, and he tied the two ends together in a loop.

Then he said, "How can we catch him? He must be taken alive and unhurt."

I said that we must trust in Providence, and go out softly with polo-sticks into the shrubbery at the front of the house. The man or animal that made the cry was evidently moving round the house as regularly as a night-watchman. We could wait in the bushes till he came by and knock him over.

Strickland accepted this suggestion, and we slipped out from a bath-room window into the front verandah and then across the carriage drive into the bushes.

In the moonlight we could see the leper coming round the corner of the house. He was perfectly naked, and from time to time he mewed and stopped to dance with his shadow. It was an unattractive sight, and thinking of poor Fleete, brought to such degradation by so foul a creature, I put away all my doubts and resolved to help Strickland from the heated gun-barrels to the loop of twine—from the loins to the head and back again—with all tortures that might be needful.

The leper halted in the front porch for a moment and we jumped out on him with the sticks. He was wonderfully strong, and we were afraid that he might escape or be fatally injured before we caught him. We had an idea that lepers were frail creatures, but this proved to be incorrect. Strickland knocked his legs from under him and I put my foot on his neck. He mewed hideously, and even through my riding-boots I could feel that his flesh was not the flesh of a clean man.

He struck at us with his hand and feet-stumps. We looped the lash of a dog-whip round him, under the armpits, and dragged him backwards into the hall and so into the dining-room where the beast lay. There we tied him with trunk-straps. He made no attempt to escape, but mewed.

When we confronted him with the beast the scene was beyond description. The beast doubled backwards into a bow as though he had been poisoned with strychnine, and moaned in the most pitiable fashion. Several other things happened also, but they cannot be put down here.

"I think I was right," said Strickland. "Now we will ask him to cure this case."

But the leper only mewed. Strickland wrapped a towel round his hand and took the gun-barrels out of the fire. I put the half of the broken walking stick through the loop of fishing-line and buckled the leper comfortably to Strickland's bedstead. I understood then how men and women and little children can endure to see a witch burnt alive; for the beast was moaning on the floor, and though the Silver Man had no face, you could see horrible feelings passing through the slab that took its place, exactly as waves of heat play across red-hot iron—gun-barrels for instance.

Strickland shaded his eyes with his hands for a moment and we got to work. This part is not to be printed.

. . . .

The dawn was beginning to break when the leper spoke. His mewings had not been satisfactory up to that point. The beast had fainted from exhaustion and the house was very still. We unstrapped the leper and told him to take away the evil spirit. He crawled to the beast and laid his hand upon the left breast. That was all. Then he fell face down and whined, drawing in his breath as he did so.

We watched the face of the beast, and saw the soul of Fleete coming back into the eyes. Then a sweat broke out on the forehead and the eyes—they were human eyes—closed. We waited for an hour but Fleete still slept. We carried him to his room and bade the leper go, giving him the bedstead, and the sheet on the bedstead to cover his nakedness, the gloves and the towels with which we had touched him, and the whip that had been hooked round his body. He put the sheet about him and went out into the early morning without speaking or mewing.

Strickland wiped his face and sat down. A night-gong, far away in the city, made seven o'clock.

"Exactly four-and-twenty hours!" said Strickland. "And I've done enough to ensure my dismissal from the service, besides permanent quarters in a lunatic asylum. Do you believe that we are awake?"

The red-hot gun-barrel had fallen on the floor and was singeing the carpet. The smell was entirely real.

That morning at eleven we two together went to wake up Fleete. We looked and saw that the black leopard-rosette on his chest had disappeared. He was very drowsy and tired, but as soon as he saw us, he said, "Oh! Confound you fellows. Happy New Year to you. Never mix your liquors. I'm nearly dead."

"Thanks for your kindness, but you're over time," said Strickland. "To-day is the morning of the second. You've slept the clock round with a vengeance."

The door opened, and little Dumoise put his head in. He had come on foot, and fancied that we were laying out Fleete.

"I've brought a nurse," said Dumoise. "I suppose that she can come in for . . . what is necessary."

"By all means," said Fleete cheerily, sitting up in bed. "Bring on your nurses."

Dumoise was dumb. Strickland led him out and explained

that there must have been a mistake in the diagnosis. Dumoise remained dumb and left the house hastily. He considered that his professional reputation had been injured, and was inclined to make a personal matter of the recovery. Strickland went out too. When he came back, he said that he had been to call on the Temple of Hanuman to offer redress for the pollution of the god, and had been solemnly assured that no white man had ever touched the idol and that he was an incarnation of all the virtues labouring under a delusion. "What do you think?" said Strickland.

I said, " 'There are more things . . .' "

But Strickland hates that quotation. He says that I have worn it threadbare.

One other curious thing happened which frightened me as much as anything in all the night's work. When Fleete was dressed he came into the dining-room and sniffed. He had a quaint trick of moving his nose when he sniffed. "Horrid doggy smell, here," said he. "You should really keep those terriers of yours in better order. Try sulphur, Strick."

But Strickland did not answer. He caught hold of the back of a chair, and, without warning, went into an amazing fit of hysterics. It is terrible to see a strong man overtaken with hysteria. Then it struck me that we had fought for Fleete's soul with the Silver Man in that room, and had disgraced ourselves as Englishmen for ever, and I laughed and gasped and gurgled just as shamefully as Strickland, while Fleete thought that we had both gone mad. We never told him what we had done.

Some years later, when Strickland had married and was a church-going member of society for his wife's sake, we reviewed the incident dispassionately, and Strickland suggested that I should put it before the public.

I cannot myself see that this step is likely to clear up the mystery; because, in the first place, no one will believe a rather unpleasant story, and, in the second, it is well known to every right-minded man that the gods of the heathen are stone and brass, and any attempt to deal with them otherwise is justly condemned.

A MATTER OF FACT
1892

And if ye doubt the tale I tell,
Steer through the South Pacific swell;
Go where the branching coral hives
Unending strife of endless lives,
Where, leagued about the 'wildered boat,
The rainbow jellies fill and float;
And, lilting where the laver lingers,
The starfish trips on all her fingers;
Where, 'neath his myriad spines ashock,
The sea-egg ripples down the rock;
An orange wonder dimly guessed,
From darkness where the cuttles rest,
Moored o'er the darker deeps that hide
The blind white Sea-snake and his bride;
Who, drowsing, nose the long-lost ships
Let down through darkness to their lips.

—THE PALMS

ONCE a priest always a priest; once a Mason always a Mason; but once a journalist always and for ever a journalist.

There were three of us, all newspaper men, the only passengers on a little tramp-steamer that ran where her owners told her to go. She had once been in the Bilbao iron ore business, had been lent to the Spanish Government for service at Manilla; and was ending her days in the Cape Town coolie-trade, with occasional trips to Madagascar and even as far as England. We found her going to Southampton in ballast, and shipped in her because the fares were nominal. There was Keller, of an American paper, on his way back to the States from palace executions in Madagascar; there was a burly half Dutchman, called Zuyland, who owned and edited a paper up country near Johannesberg; and there was myself, who had solemnly put away all journalism, vowing to forget that I had ever known the difference between an imprint and a stereo advertisement.

Three minutes after Keller spoke to me, as the *Rathmines* cleared Cape Town, I had forgotten the aloofness I desired to feign, and was in heated discussion on the immorality of expanding telegrams beyond a certain fixed point. Then Zuyland came out of his state-room, and we were all at home instantly, because we were men of the same profession needing no introduction. We annexed the boat formally, broke open the passengers' bath-room door—on the Manilla lines the Dons do not wash—cleaned out the orange-peel and cigar-ends at the bottom of the bath, hired a Lascar to shave us throughout the voyage, and then asked each other's names.

Three ordinary men would have quarrelled through sheer boredom before they reached Southampton. We, by virtue of our craft, were anything but ordinary men. A large percentage of the tales of the world, the thirty-nine that cannot be told to ladies and the one that can, are common property coming of a common stock. We told them all, as a matter of form, with all their local and specific variants which are surprising. Then came, in the intervals of steady card-play, more personal histories of adventure and things seen and reported; panics among white folk, when the blind terror ran from man to man on the Brooklyn Bridge, and the people crushed each other to death they knew not why; fires, and faces that opened and shut their mouths horribly at red-hot window-frames; wrecks in frost and snow, reported from the sleet-sheathed rescue tug at the risk of frost-bite; long rides after diamond thieves; skirmishes on the veldt and in municipal committees with the Boers; glimpses of lazy, tangled Cape politics and the mule-rule in the Transvaal; card-tales, horse-tales, woman-tales by the score and the half hundred; till the first mate, who had seen more than us all put together, but lacked words to clothe his tales with, sat open-mouthed far into the dawn.

When the tales were done we picked up cards till a curious hand or a chance remark made one or other of us say, "That reminds me of a man who—or a business which—" and the anecdotes would continue while the *Rathmines* kicked her way northward through the warm water.

In the morning of one specially warm night we three were sitting immediately in front of the wheel-house where an old Swedish boatswain whom we called "Frithiof the Dane" was at the wheel pretending that he could not hear our stories. Once or twice Frithiof spun the spokes curiously, and Keller lifted his head from a long chair to ask, "What is it? Can't you get any pull on her?"

"There is a feel in the water," said Frithiof, "that I cannot understand. I think that we run downhills or somethings. She steers bad this morning."

Nobody seems to know the laws that govern the pulse of the big waters. Sometimes even a landsman can tell that the solid ocean is a-tilt, and that the ship is working herself up a long unseen slope; and sometimes the captain says, when neither full steam nor fair wind justify the length of a day's run, that the ship is sagging downhill; but how these ups and downs come about has not yet been settled authoritatively.

"No, it is a following sea," said Frithiof; "and with a following sea you shall not get good steerage way."

The sea was as smooth as a duck-pond, except for a regular oily swell. As I looked over the side to see where it might be following us from, the sun rose in a perfectly clear sky and struck the water with its light so sharply that it seemed as though the sea should clang like a burnished gong. The wake of the screw and the little white streak cut by the log-line hanging over the stern were the only marks on the water as far as eye could reach.

Keller rolled out of his chair and went aft to get a pineapple from the ripening stock that were hung inside the after awning.

"Frithiof, the log-line has got tired of swimming. It's coming home," he drawled.

"What?" said Frithiof, his voice jumping several octaves.

"Coming home," Keller repeated, leaning over the stern. I ran to his side and saw the log-line, which till then had been drawn tense over the stern railing, slacken, loop, and come up off the port quarter. Frithiof called up the speaking-tube to the bridge, and the bridge answered, "Yes, nine knots." Then Frithiof spoke again, and the answer was, "What do you want of the skipper?" and Frithiof bellowed, "Call him up."

By this time Zuyland, Keller, and myself had caught something of Frithiof's excitement, for any emotion on shipboard is most contagious. The captain ran out of his cabin, spoke to Frithiof, looked at the log-line, jumped on the bridge, and in a minute we felt the steamer swing round as Frithiof turned her.

"Going back to Cape Town?" said Keller.

Frithiof did not answer, but tore away at the wheel. Then he beckoned us three to help, and we held the wheel down till the *Rathmines* answered it, and we found ourselves looking into the white of our own wake, with the still oily sea tearing past our bows, though we were not going more than half steam ahead.

The captain stretched out his arm from the bridge and shouted. A minute later I would have given a great deal to have shouted too, for one-half of the sea seemed to shoulder itself above the other half, and came on in the shape of a hill. There was neither crest, comb, nor curl-over to it; nothing but black water with little waves chasing each other about the flanks. I saw it stream past and on a level with the *Rathmine's* bow-plates before the steamer made up her mind to rise, and I argued that this would be the last of all earthly voyages for me. Then we rose for ever and ever and ever, till I heard Keller saying in my ear, "The bowels of the deep, good Lord!" and the *Rathmines* stood poised, her screw racing and drumming on the slope of a hollow that stretched downwards for a good half-mile.

We went down that hollow, nose under for the most part, and the air smelt wet and muddy, like that of an emptied aquarium. There was a second hill to climb; I saw that much: but the water came aboard and carried me aft till it jammed me against the smoking-room door, and before I could catch breath or clear my eyes again we were rolling to and fro in torn water, with the scuppers pouring like eaves in a thunder-storm.

"There were three waves," said Keller; "and the stoke-hold's flooded."

The firemen were on deck waiting, apparently, to be drowned. The engineer came and dragged them below, and the crew, gasping, began to work the clumsy Board of Trade pump. That showed nothing serious, and when I understood that the *Rathmines* was really on the water, and not beneath it, I asked what had happened.

"The captain says it was a blow-up under the sea—a volcano," said Keller.

"It hasn't warmed anything," I said. I was feeling bitterly cold, and cold was almost unknown in those waters. I went below to change my clothes, and when I came up everything was wiped out by clinging white fog.

"Are there going to be any more surprises?" said Keller to the captain.

"I don't know. Be thankful you're alive, gentlemen. That's a tidal wave thrown up by a volcano. Probably the bottom of the sea has been lifted a few feet somewhere or other. I can't quite understand this cold spell. Our sea-thermometer says the surface water is 44°, and it should be 68° at least."

"It's abominable," said Keller, shivering. "But hadn't you better attend to the fog-horn? It seems to me that I heard something."

"Heard! Good heavens!" said the captain from the bridge, "I should think you did." He pulled the string of our fog-horn, which was a weak one. It sputtered and choked, because the stoke-hold was full of water and the fires were half-drowned, and at last gave out a moan. It was answered from the fog by one of the most appalling steam-sirens I have ever heard. Keller turned as white as I did, for the fog, the cold fog, was upon us, and any man may be forgiven for fearing the death he cannot see.

"Give her steam there!" said the captain to the engine-room. "Steam for the whistle, if we have to do dead slow."

We bellowed again, and the damp dripped off the awnings to the deck as we listened for the reply. It seemed to be astern this time, but much nearer than before.

"The *Pembroke Castle,* by gum!" said Keller, and then, viciously, "Well, thank God, we shall sink her too."

"It's a side-wheel steamer," I whispered. "Can't you hear the paddles?"

This time we whistled and roared till the steam gave out, and the answer nearly deafened us. There was a sound of frantic threshing in the water, apparently about fifty yards away, and something shot past in the whiteness that looked as though it were gray and red.

"The *Pembroke Castle* bottom up," said Keller, who, being a journalist, always sought for explanations. "That's the colours of a Castle liner. We're in for a big thing."

"The sea is bewitched," said Frithiof from the wheel-house. "There are two steamers."

Another siren sounded on our bow, and the little steamer rolled in the wash of something that had passed unseen.

"We're evidently in the middle of a fleet," said Keller quietly. "If one doesn't run us down, the other will. Phew! What in creation is that?"

I sniffed for there was a poisonous rank smell in the cold air—a smell that I had smelt before.

"If I was on land I should say that it was an alligator. It smells like musk," I answered.

"Not ten thousand alligators could make that smell," said Zuyland; "I have smelt them."

"Bewitched! Bewitched!" said Frithiof. "The sea she is turned upside down, and we are walking along the bottom."

Again the *Rathmines* rolled in the wash of some unseen ship, and a silver-gray wave broke over the bow, leaving on the deck a sheet of sediment—the gray broth that has its place in the fathomless deeps of the sea. A sprinkling of the wave fell on my face, and it was so cold that it stung as boiling water stings. The dead and most untouched deep water of the sea had been heaved to the top by the submarine volcano—the chill, still water that kills all life and smells of desolation and emptiness. We did not need either the blinding fog or that indescribable smell of musk to make us unhappy—we were shivering with cold and wretchedness where we stood.

"The hot air on the cold water makes this fog," said the captain. "It ought to clear in a little time."

"Whistle, oh! whistle, and let's get out of it," said Keller.

The captain whistled again, and far and far astern the invisible twin steam-sirens answered us. Their blasting shriek grew louder, till at last it seemed to tear out of the fog just above our quarter, and I cowered while the *Rathmines* plunged bows-under on a double swell that crossed.

"No more," said Frithiof, "it is not good any more. Let us get away, in the name of God."

"Now if a torpedo-boat with a *City of Paris* siren went mad and broke her moorings and hired a friend to help her, it's just conceivable that we might be carried as we are now. Otherwise this thing is——"

The last words died on Keller's lips, his eyes began to start from his head, and his jaw fell. Some six or seven feet above the port bulwarks, framed in fog, and as utterly unsupported as the full moon, hung a Face. It was not human, and it certainly was not animal, for it did not belong to this earth as known to man. The mouth was open, revealing a ridiculously tiny tongue—as absurd as the tongue of an elephant; there were tense wrinkles of white skin at the angles of the drawn lips; white feelers like those of a barbel sprang from the lower jaw, and there was no sign of teeth within the mouth. But the horror of the face lay in the eyes, for those were sightless—white, in sockets as white as scraped bone, and blind. Yet for all this the face, wrinkled as the mask of a lion is drawn in Assyrian sculpture, was alive with rage and terror. One long white feeler touched our bulwarks. Then the face disappeared with the swiftness of a blind worm popping into its burrow, and the next thing that I remember is my own voice in my own ears, saying gravely to the mainmast, "But the air-bladder ought to have been forced out of its mouth, you know."

Keller came up to me, ashy white. He put his hand into his pocket, took a cigar, bit it, dropped it, thrust his shaking thumb into his mouth and mumbled, "The giant gooseberry and the raining frogs! Gimme a light—gimme a light! I say, gimme a light." A little bead of blood dropped from his thumbnail.

I respected the motive, though the manifestation was absurd. "Stop, you'll bite your thumb off," I said, and Keller laughed brokenly as he picked up his cigar. Only Zuyland, leaning over the port bulwarks, seemed self-possessed. He declared later that he was very sick.

"We've seen it," he said, turning round. "That is it."

"What?" said Keller, chewing the unlighted cigar.

As he spoke the fog was blown into shreds, and we saw the sea, gray with mud, rolling on every side of us and empty of all life. Then in one spot it bubbled and became like the pot of ointment that the Bible speaks of. From that wide-ringed trouble a Thing came up—a gray and red Thing with a neck—a Thing that bellowed and writhed in pain. Frithiof drew in his breath and held it till the red letters of the ship's name, woven across his jersey, straggled and opened out as though they had been type badly set. Then he said with a little cluck in his throat, "Ah, me! It is blind. *Hur illa!* That thing is blind," and a murmur of pity went through us all, for we could see that the thing on the water was blind and in pain. Something had gashed and cut the great sides cruelly and the blood was spurting out. The gray ooze of the undermost sea lay in the monstrous wrinkles of the back and poured away in sluices. The blind white head flung back and battered the wounds, and the body in its torment rose clear of the red and gray waves till we saw a pair of quivering shoulders streaked with weed and rough with shells, but as white in the clear spaces as the hairless, nameless, blind, toothless head. Afterwards came a dot on the horizon and the sound of a shrill scream, and it was as though a shuttle shot all across the sea in one breath, and a second head and neck tore through the levels, driving a whispering wall of water to right and left. The two Things met—the one untouched and the other in its death throe—male and female, we said, the female coming to the male. She circled round him bellowing, and laid her neck across the curve of his great turtle-back, and he disappeared under water for an instant, but flung up again, grunting in agony while the blood ran. Once the entire head and neck shot clear of the water and stiffened, and I heard Keller saying, as though he was watching a street accident, "Give him air. For God's sake give him air!" Then the death struggle began, with crampings and twistings and jerkings of the white bulk to and fro, till our little steamer rolled again, and each gray wave coated her plates with the gray slime. The sun was clear, there was no wind, and we watched, the whole crew, stokers and all, in wonder and pity, but chiefly pity. The Thing was so helpless, and, save for his mate, so alone. No human eye should have beheld him; it was monstrous and indecent to exhibit him there in trade waters between atlas degrees of latitude. He had been spewed up, mangled and dying from his rest on the sea-floor, where he might have lived till the Judgment Day, and we saw the tides of his life go from him as an angry tide goes out across rocks in the teeth of a landward gale. The mate lay rocking on the water a little distance off, bellowing continually, and the smell of musk came down upon the ship making us cough.

At last the battle for life ended, in a batter of coloured seas. We saw the writhing neck fall like a flail, the carcase turn sideways, showing the glint of a white belly and the inset of a gigantic hind-leg or flapper. Then all sank, and sea boiled over it, while the mate swam round and round, darting her blind head in every direction. Though we might have feared that she would attack the steamer, no power on earth could have drawn any one of us from our places that hour. We watched, holding our breaths. The mate paused in her search; we could hear the wash beating along her sides; reared her neck as high as she could reach, blind and lonely in all that loneliness of the sea, and sent one desperate bellow booming across the swells as an oyster shell skips across a pond. Then she made off to the westward, the sun shining on the white head and the wake behind it, till nothing was left to see but a little pin point of silver on the horizon. We stood on our course again, and the *Rathmines,* coated with the sea-sediment, from bow to stern, looked like a ship made gray with terror.

. . . .

"We must pool our notes," was the first coherent remark from Keller. "We're three trained journalists—we hold absolutely the biggest scoop on record. Start fair."

I objected to this. Nothing is gained by collaboration in journalism when all deal with the same facts, so we went to work each according to his own lights. Keller triple-headed his account, talked about our "gallant captain," and wound up with an allusion to American enterprise in that it was a citizen of Dayton, Ohio, that had seen the sea-serpent. This sort of thing would have discredited the Creation, much more a mere sea tale, but as a specimen of the picture-writing of a half-civilized people it was very interesting. Zuyland took a heavy column and a half, giving approximate lengths and breadths and the whole list of the crew whom he had sworn on oath to testify to his facts. There was nothing fantastic or flamboyant in Zuyland. I wrote three-quarters of a leaded bourgeois column, roughly speaking, and refained from putting any journalese into it for reasons that had begun to appear to me.

Keller was insolent with joy. He was going to cable from Southampton to the New York *World,* mail his account to America on the same day, paralyze London with his three columns of loosely knitted headlines, and generally efface the earth. "You'll see how I work a big scoop when I get it," he said.

"Is this your first visit to England?" I asked.

"Yes," said he. "You don't seem to appreciate the beauty of our scoop. It's pyramidal—the death of the sea-serpent! Good heavens alive man, it's the biggest thing ever vouchsafed to a paper!"

"Curious to think that it will never appear in any paper, isn't it?" I said.

Zuyland was near me, and he nodded quickly.

"What do you mean?" said Keller. "If you're enough of a Britisher to throw this thing away, I sha'n't. I thought you were a newspaper man."

"I am. That's why I know. Don't be an ass, Keller. Remember, I'm seven hundred years your senior, and what your grandchildren may learn five hundred years hence, I learned from my grandfathers above five hundred years ago. You won't do it, because you can't."

This conversation was held in open sea, where everything seems possible, some hundred miles from Southampton. We passed the Needles Light at dawn, and the lifting day showed the stucco villas on the green and the awful orderliness of England—line upon line, wall upon wall, solid stone dock and monolithic pier. We waited an hour in the Customs shed, and there was ample time for the effect to soak in.

"Now, Keller, you face the music. The *Havel* goes out to-day. Mail by her, and I'll take you to the telegraph office," I said.

I heard Keller gasp as the influence of the land closed about him, cowing him as they say Newmarket Heath cows a young horse unused to open country.

"I want to retouch my stuff. Suppose we wait till we get to London?" he said.

Zuyland, by the way, had torn up his account and thrown it overboard that morning early. His reasons were my reasons.

In the train Keller began to revise his copy, and every time that he looked at the trim little fields, the red villas, and the embankments of the line, the blue pencil plunged remorselessly through the slips. He appeared to have dredged the dictionary for adjectives. I could think of none that he had not used. Yet he was a perfectly sound poker player and never showed more cards than were sufficient to take the pool.

"Aren't you going to leave him a single bellow?" I asked sympathetically. "Remember, everything goes in the States, from a trouser-button to a double eagle."

"That's just the curse of it," said Keller below his breath.

"We've played 'em for suckers so often that when it comes to the golden truth—I'd like to try this on a London paper. You have first call there, though."

"Not in the least. I'm not touching the thing in the papers. I shall be happy to leave 'em all to you; but surely you'll cable it home?"

"No. Not if I can make the scoop here and see the Britishers sit up."

"You won't do it with three column of slushy headline, believe me. They don't sit up as quickly as some people."

"I'm beginning to think that too. Does *nothing* make any difference in this country?" he said, looking out of the window. "How old is that farmhouse?"

"New. It can't be more than two hundred years at the most."

"Um. Fields, too?"

"That hedge there must have been clipped for about eighty years."

"Labour cheap—eh?"

"Pretty much. Well, I suppose you'd like to try the *Times*, wouldn't you?"

"No," said Keller, looking at Winchester Cathedral. "Might as well try to electrify a hay-rick. And to think that the *World* would take three columns and ask for more—with illustrations too! It's sickening."

"But the *Times* might," I began.

Keller flung his paper across the carriage, and it opened in its austere majesty of solid type—opened with the crackle of an encyclopædia.

"Might! You *might* work your way through the bow-plates of a cruiser. Look at that first page!"

"It strikes you that way, does it?" I said. "Then I'd recommend you to try a light and frivolous journal."

"With a thing like this of mine—of ours? It's sacred history!"

I showed him a paper which I conceived would be after his own heart, in that it was modelled on American lines.

"That's homey," he said, "but it's not the real thing. Now,

I should like one of these fat old *Times'* columns. Probably there'd be a bishop in the office, though."

When we reached London Keller disappeared in the direction of the Strand. What his experiences may have been I cannot tell, but it seems that he invaded the office of an evening paper at 11.45 a. m. (I told him English editors were most idle at that hour), and mentioned my name as that of a witness to the truth of his story.

"I was nearly fired out," he said furiously at lunch. "As soon as I mentioned you, the old man said that I was to tell you that they didn't want any more of your practical jokes, and that you knew the hours to call if you had anything to sell, and that they'd see you condemned before they helped to puff one of your infernal yarns in advance. Say, what record do you hold for truth in this city, anyway?"

"A beauty. You ran up against it, that's all. Why don't you leave the English papers alone and cable to New York? Everything goes over there."

"Can't you see that's just why?" he repeated.

"I saw it a long time ago. You don't intend to cable, then?"

"Yes, I do," he answered, in the over-emphatic voice of one who does not know his own mind.

That afternoon I walked him abroad and about, over the streets that run between the pavements like channels of grooved and tongued lava, over the bridges that are made of enduring stone, through subways floored and sided with yard-thick concrete, between houses that are never rebuilt, and by river steps hewn to the eye from the living rock. A black fog chased us into Westminster Abbey, and, standing there in the darkness, I could hear the wings of the dead centuries circling round the head of Litchfield A. Keller, journalist, of Dayton, Ohio, U. S. A., whose mission it was to make the Britishers sit up.

He stumbled gasping into the thick gloom, and the roar of the traffic came to his bewildered ears.

"Let's go to the telegraph office and cable," I said. "Can't you hear the New York *World* crying for news of the great sea-serpent, blind, white, and smelling of musk, stricken to death by a submarine volcano, assisted by his loving wife to die in mid-ocean, as visualized by an independent American citizen, a breezy, newsy, brainy newspaper man of Dayton, Ohio? 'Rah for the Buckeye State. Step lively! Both gates! Szz! Boom—ah!" Keller was a Princeton man, and he seemed to need encouragement.

"You've got me on your own ground," said he, tugging at his overcoat pocket. He pulled out his copy, with the cable forms—for he had written out his telegram—and put them all into my hand, groaning, "I pass. If I hadn't come to your cursed country—if I'd sent it off at Southampton—if I ever get you west of the Alleghanies, if——"

"Never mind, Keller. It isn't your fault. It's the fault of your country. If you had been seven hundred years older you'd have done what I'm going to do."

"What are you going to do?"

"Tell it as a lie."

"Fiction?" This with the full-blooded disgust of a journalist for the illegitimate branch of the profession.

"You can call it that if you like. I shall call it a lie."

And a lie it has become, for Truth is a naked lady, and if by accident she is drawn up from the bottom of the sea, it behoves a gentleman either to give her a print petticoat or to turn his face to the wall, and vow that he did not see.

"BRUGGLESMITH"

1891

This day the ship went down, and all hands was drowned but me.
—CLARK RUSSELL

THE first officer of the *Breslau* asked me to dinner on board, before the ship went round to Southampton to pick up her passengers. The *Breslau* was lying below London Bridge, her fore-hatches opened for cargo, and her deck littered with nuts and bolts, and screws and chains. The Black M'Phee had been putting some finishing touches to his adored engines, and M'Phee is the most tidy of chief engineers. If the leg of a cockroach gets into one of his slide-valves the whole ship knows it, and half the ship has to clean up the mess.

After dinner, which the first officer, M'Phee, and I ate in one little corner of the empty saloon, M'Phee returned to the engine-room to attend to some brass-fitters. The first officer and I smoked on the bridge and watched the lights of the crowded shipping till it was time for me to go home. It seemed, in the pauses of our conversation, that I could catch an echo of fearful bellowings from the engine-room, and the voice of M'Phee singing of home and the domestic affections.

"M'Phee has a friend aboard to-night—a man who was a boiler-maker at Greenock when M'Phee was a 'prentice," said the first officer. "I didn't ask him to dine with us because——"

"I see—I mean I hear," I answered. We talked on for a few minutes longer, and M'Phee came up from the engine-room with his friend on his arm.

"Let me present ye to this gentleman," said M'Phee. "He's a great admirer o' your wor-rks. He has just hear-rd o' them."

M'Phee could never pay a compliment prettily. The friend sat down suddenly on a bollard, saying that M'Phee had under-stated the truth. Personally, he on the bollard considered that Shakespeare was trembling in the balance solely on my account, and if the first officer wished to dispute this he was prepared to fight the first officer then or later, "as per invoice." "Man, if ye only knew," said he, wagging his head, "the times I've lain in my lonely bunk reading *Vanity Fair* an' sobbin'—ay, weepin' bitterly, at the pure fascination of it."

He shed a few tears for guarantee of good faith, and the first officer laughed. M'Phee resettled the man's hat, that had tilted over one eyebrow, and said:

"That'll wear off in a little. It's just the smell o' the engine-room," said M'Phee.

"I think I'll wear off myself," I whispered to the first officer. "Is the dinghy ready?"

The dinghy was at the gangway, which was down, and the first officer went forward to find a man to row me to the bank. He returned with a very sleepy Lascar, who knew the river.

"Are you going?" said the man on the bollard. "Well, I'll just see ye home. M'Phee, help me down the gangway. It has as many ends as a cat-o'-nine tails, and—losh!—how innumerable are the dinghys!"

"You'd better let him come with you," said the first officer. "Muhammad Jan, put the drunk sahib ashore first. Take the sober sahib to the next stairs."

I had my foot in the bow of the dinghy, the tide was making up-stream, when the man cannoned against me, pushed the Lascar back on the gangway, cast loose the painter, and the dinghy began to saw, stern-first, along the side of the *Breslau*.

"We'll have no exter-r-raneous races here," said the man. "I've known the Thames for thirty years——"

There was no time for argument. We were drifting under the *Breslau's* stern, and I knew that her propeller was half out of water, in the midst of an inky tangle of buoys, low-lying hawsers, and moored ships, with the tide roaring about them.

"What shall I do?" I shouted to the first officer.

"Find the Police Boat as soon as you can, and for God's sake get way on the dinghy. Steer with the oar. The rudder's unshipped and——"

I could hear no more. The dinghy slid away, bumped on a mooring-buoy, swung round and jigged off irresponsibly as I hunted for the oar. The man sat in the bow, his chin on his hands, smiling.

"Row, you ruffian," I said. "Get her out into the middle of the river——"

"It's a preevilege to gaze on the face o' genius. Let me go on thinking. There was 'Little Bar-rna-by Dorrit' and 'The Mystery o' the Bleak Druid.' I sailed in a ship called the *Druid* once—badly found she was. It all comes back to me so sweet. It all comes back to me. Man, ye steer like a genius!"

We just bumped another mooring-buoy and drifted on to the bows of a Norwegian timber-ship—I could see the great square holes on either side of the cutwater. Then we dived into a string of barges and scraped through them by the paint on our planks. It was a consolation to think that the dinghy was being reduced in value at every bump, but the question before me was when she would begin to leak. The man looked ahead into the pitchy darkness and whistled.

"Yon's a Castle liner; her ties are black. She's swinging across stream. Keep her port light on our starboard bow, and go large," he said.

"How can I keep anything anywhere? You're sitting on the oars. Row, man, if you don't want to drown."

He took the sculls, saying sweetly: "No harm comes to a drunken man. That's why I wished to come with *you*. Man, ye're not fit to be alone in a boat."

He flirted the dinghy round the big ship, and for the next ten minutes I enjoyed—positively enjoyed—an exhibition of first-class steering. We threaded in and out of the mercantile marine of Great Britain as a ferret threads a rabbit-hole, and we, he that is to say, sang joyously to each ship till men looked over bulwarks and cursed us. When we came to some moderately clear water he gave the sculls to me, and said:

"If ye could row as ye write, I'd respect you for all your vices. Yon's London Bridge. Take her through."

We shot under the dark ringing arch, and came out the other side, going up swiftly with the tide chanting songs of victory. Except that I wished to get home before morning, I was growing reconciled to the jaunt. There were one or two stars visible, and by keeping into the centre of the stream, I could not come to any very serious danger.

The man began to sing loudly:—

"The smartest clipper that you could find,
Yo ho! Oho!
Was the Marg'ret Evans *of the Black X Line*
A hundred years ago!

Incorporate that in your next book. Which is marvellous." Here he stood up in the bows and declaimed:—

"Ye Towers o' Julia, London's lasting wrong,
By mony a foul an' midnight murder fed—
Sweet Thames run softly till I end my song—
And yon's the grave as little as my bed.

I'm a poet mysel an' I can feel for others."

"Sit down," said I. "You'll have the boat over."

"Ay, I'm settin'—settin' like a hen." He plumped down heavily, and added, shaking his forefinger at me:—

"Lear-rn, prudent, cautious self-control
Is wisdom's root.

How did a man o' your parts come to be so drunk? Oh, it's a sinfu' thing, an' ye may thank God on all fours that I'm wi' you. What's yon boat?"

We had drifted far up the river, and a boat manned by four men, who rowed with a soothingly regular stroke, was overhauling us.

"It's the River Police," I said, at the top of my voice.

"Oh ay! If your sin do not find you out on dry land, it will find you out in the deep waters. Is it like they'll give us drink?"

"Exceedingly likely. I'll hail them." I hailed.

"What are you doing?" was the answer from the boat.

"It's the *Breslau's* dinghy broken loose," I began.

"It's a vara drunken man broke loose," roared my companion, "and I'm taking him home by water, for he canno stand on dry land." Here he shouted my name twenty times running, and I could feel the blushes racing over my body three deep.

"You'll be locked up in ten minutes, my friend," I said "and I don't think you'll be bailed either."

"H'sh, man, h'sh. They think I'm your uncle." He caugh

up a scull and began splashing the boat as it ranged alongside.

"You're a nice pair," said the sergeant at last.

"I am anything you please so long as you take this fiend away. Tow us in to the nearest station, and I'll make it worth your while," I said.

"Corruption—corruption," roared the man, throwing himself flat in the bottom of the boat. "Like unto the worms that perish, so is man. And all for the sake of a filthy half-crown to be arrested by the River Police at my time o' life!"

"For pity's sake, row," I shouted. "The man's drunk."

They rowed us to a flat—a fire or a police-station; it was too dark to see which. I could feel that they regarded me in no better light than my companion, and I could not explain, for I was holding the far end of the painter, ten long feet from all respectability.

We got out of the boat, my companion falling flat on his wicked face, and the sergeant asked us rude questions about the dinghy. My companion washed his hands of all responsibility. He was an old man; he had been lured into a stolen boat by a young man—probably a thief—he had saved the boat from wreck (this was absolutely true), and now he expected salvage in the shape of hot whisky and water. The sergeant turned to me. Fortunately I was in evening dress, and had a card to show. More fortunately still, the sergeant happened to know the *Breslau* and M'Phee. He promised to send the dinghy down next tide, and was not beyond accepting my thanks, in silver.

As this was satisfactorily arranged, I heard my companion say angrily to a constable, "If you will not give it to a dry man, ye maun to a drookit." Then he walked deliberately off the edge of the flat into the water. Somebody stuck a boathook into his clothes and hauled him out.

"Now," said he triumphantly, "under the rules o' the R-royal Humane Society, ye must give me hot whisky and water. Do not put temptation before the laddie. He's my nephew an' a good boy i' the main. Tho' why he should masquerade as Mister Thackeray on the high seas is beyond my comprehension. Oh the vanity o' youth! M'Phee told me ye were as vain as a peacock. I mind that now."

"You had better give him something to drink and wrap him up for the night. I don't know who he is," I said desperately, and when the man had settled down to a drink supplied on my representations, I escaped and found that I was near a bridge.

I went towards Fleet Street, intending to take a hansom and go home. After the first feeling of indignation died out, the absurdity of the experience struck me fully and I began to laugh aloud in the empty streets, to the scandal of a policeman. The more I reflected the more heartily I laughed, till my mirth was quenched by a hand on my shoulder, and turning I saw him who should have been in bed at the river police-station. He was damp all over; his wet silk hat rode far at the back of his head, and round his shoulders hung a striped yellow blanket, evidently the property of the State.

"The crackling o' thorns under a pot," said he, solemnly. "Laddie, have ye not thought o' the sin of idle laughter? My heart misgave me that ever ye'd get home, an' I've just come to convoy you a piece. They're sore uneducate down there by the river. They would na listen to me when I talked o' your wor-rks, so I e'en left them. Cast the blanket about you, laddie. It's fine and cold."

I groaned inwardly. Providence evidently intended that I should frolic through eternity with M'Phee's infamous acquaintance.

"Go away," I said; "go home, or I'll give you in charge."

He leaned against a lamp-post and laid his finger to his nose—his dishonourable, carnelian neb.

"I mind now that M'Phee told me ye were vainer than a peacock, an' your castin' me adrift in a boat shows ye were drunker than an owl. A good name is as a savoury bakemeat. I ha' nane." He smacked his lips joyously.

"Well, I know that," I said.

"Ay, but *ye* have. I mind now that M'Phee spoke o' your reputation that you're so proud of. Laddie, if ye gie me in charge—I'm old enough to be your father—I'll bla-ast your reputation as far as my voice can carry; for I'll call you by name till the cows come hame. It's no jestin' matter to be a friend to me. If you discard my friendship, ye must come to Vine Street wi' me for stealin' the *Breslau's* dinghy."

Then he sang at the top of his voice:—

"In the mor-rnin'
I' the mor-rnin' by the black van—
We'll toodle up to Vine Street i' the mornin'!

Yon's my own composeetion, but *I'm* not vain. We'll go home together, laddie, we'll go home together." And he sang "Auld Lang Syne" to show that he meant it.

A policeman suggested that we had better move on, and we moved on to the Law Courts near St. Clement Danes. My companion was quieter now, and his speech which up till that time had been distinct—it was a marvel to see how in his condition he could talk dialect—began to slur and slide and slummock. He bade me observe the architecture of the Law Courts and linked himself lovingly to my arm. Then he saw a policeman, and before I could shake him off, whirled me up to the man singing:—

"Every member of the Force,
Has a watch and chain of course—"

and threw his dripping blanket over the helmet of the Law. In any other country in the world we should have run an exceedingly good chance of being shot, or dirked, or clubbed —and clubbing is worse than being shot. But I reflected in that wet-cloth tangle that this was England, where the police are made to be banged and battered and bruised, that they may the better endure a police-court reprimand next morning. We three fell in a tangle, he calling on me by name—that was the tingling horror of it—to sit on the policeman's head and cut the traces. I wriggled clear first and shouted to the policeman to kill the blanket-man.

Naturally the policeman answered: "You're as bad as 'im,"

and chased me, as the smaller man, round St. Clement Danes into Holywell Street, where I ran into the arms of another policeman. That flight could not have lasted more than a minute and a half, but it seemed to me as long and as wearisome as the foot-bound flight of a nightmare. I had leisure to think of a thousand things as I ran, but most I thought of the great and god-like man who held a sitting in the north gallery of St. Clement Danes a hundred years ago. I know that he at least would have felt for me. So occupied was I with these considerations, that when the other policeman hugged me to his bosom and said: "What are you tryin' to do?" I answered with exquisite politeness: "Sir, let us take a walk down Fleet Street." "Bow Street'll do *your* business, I think," was the answer, and for a moment I thought so too, till it seemed I might wriggle out of it. Then there was a hideous scene, and it was complicated by my companion hurrying up with the blanket and telling me—always by name—that he would rescue me or perish in the attempt.

"Knock him down," I pleaded. "Club his head open first and I'll explain afterwards."

The first policeman, the one who had been outraged, drew his truncheon and cut my companion's head. The high silk hat crackled and the owner dropped like a log.

"Now you've done it," I said. "You've probably killed him."

Holywell Street never goes to bed. A small crowd gathered on the spot, and some one of German extraction cried: "You haf killed the man."

Another cried: "Take his bloomin' number. I saw him strook cruel 'ard. Yah!"

Now the street was empty when the trouble began, and, saving the two policemen and myself, no one had seen the blow. I said, therefore, in a loud and cheerful voice:—

"The man's a friend of mine. He's fallen down in a fit. Bobby, will you bring the ambulance?" Under my breath I added: "It's five shillings apiece, and the man didn't hit you."

"No, but 'im and you tried to scrob me," said the policeman.

This was not a thing to argue about.

"Is Dempsey on duty at Charing Cross?" I said.

"Wot d'you know of Dempsey, you bloomin' garrotter?" said the policeman.

"If Dempsey's there, he knows me. Get the ambulance quick, and I'll take him to Charing Cross."

"You're coming to Bow Street, *you* are," said the policeman crisply.

"The man's dying"—he lay groaning on the pavement—"get the ambulance," said I.

There is an ambulance at the back of St. Clement Danes, whereof I know more than most people. The policeman seemed to possess the keys of the box in which it lived. We trundled it out—it was a three-wheeled affair with a hood—and we bundled the body of the man upon it.

A body in an ambulance looks very extremely dead. The policeman softened at the sight of the stiff boot-heels.

"Now, then," said they, and I fancied that they still meant Bow Street.

"Let me see Dempsey for three minutes if he's on duty," I answered.

"Very good. He is."

Then I knew that all would be well, but before we started I put my head under the ambulance-hood to see if the man were alive. A guarded whisper caught my ear.

"Laddie, you maun pay me for a new hat. They've broken it. Dinna desert me now, laddie. I'm o'er old to go to Bow Street in my gray hairs for a fault of yours. Laddie, dinna desert me."

"You'll be lucky if you get off under seven years," I said to the policeman.

Moved by a very lively fear of having exceeded their duty, the two policemen left their beats, and the mournful procession wound down the empty Strand. Once west of the Adelphi, I knew I should be in my own country; and the policemen had reason to know that too, for as I was pacing proudly a little ahead of the catafalque, another policeman said "Good night, sir," to me as he passed.

"Now, you see," I said, with condescension. "I wouldn't be in your shoes for something. On my word, I've a great mind to march you two down to Scotland Yard."

"If the gentleman's a friend o' yours, per'aps—" said the policeman who had given the blow, and was reflecting on the consequences.

"Perhaps you'd like me to go away and say nothing about it," I said. Then there hove into view the figure of Constable Dempsey, glittering in his oilskins, and an angel of light to me. I had known him for months; he was an esteemed friend of mine, and we used to talk together in the early mornings. The fool seeks to ingratiate himself with Princes and Ministers; and courts and cabinets leave him to perish miserably. The wise man makes allies among the police and the hansoms, so that his friends spring up from the round-house and the cab-rank, and even his offences become triumphal processions.

"Dempsey," said I, "have the Police been on strike again? They've put some things on duty at St. Clement Danes that want to take me to Bow Street for garrotting."

"Lor', sir!" said Dempsey indignantly.

"Tell them I'm not a garrotter, nor a thief. It's simply disgraceful that a gentleman can't walk down the Strand without being man-handled by these roughs. One of them has done his best to kill my friend here; and I'm taking the body home. Speak for me, Dempsey."

There was no time for the much misrepresented policemen to say a word. Dempsey spoke to them in language calculated to alarm. They tried to explain, but Dempsey launched into a glowing catalogue of my virtues, as noted by him in the early hours. "And," he concluded vehemently, "'e writes for the papers, too. How'd *you* like to be written for in the papers —in verse, too, which is 'is 'abit. You leave 'im alone. 'Im an' me have been friends for months."

"What about the dead man?" said the policeman who had not given the blow.

"I'll tell you," I said relenting, and to the three policemen under the lights of Charing Cross assembled, I recounted faithfully and at length the adventures of the night, beginning with the *Breslau* and ending at St. Clement Danes. I described the sinful old ruffian in the ambulance in terms that made him wriggle where he lay, and never since the Metropolitan Police was founded did three policemen laugh as those three laughed. The Strand echoed to it, and the unclean birds of the night stood and wondered.

"Oh lor'!" said Dempsey wiping his eyes, "I'd ha' given anything to see that old man runnin' about with a wet blanket an' all! Excuse me, sir, but you ought to get took up every night for to make us 'appy." He dissolved into fresh guffaws.

There was a clinking of silver and the two policemen of St. Clement Danes hurried back to their beats, laughing as they ran.

"Take 'im to Charing Cross," said Dempsey between shouts. "They'll send the ambulance back in the morning."

"Laddie, ye've misca'ed me shameful names, but I'm o'er old to go to a hospital. Dinna desert me, laddie, tak me home to my wife," said the voice in the ambulance.

"He's none so bad. 'Is wife'll comb 'is hair for 'im proper," said Dempsey, who was a married man.

"Where d'you live?" I demanded.

"Brugglesmith," was the answer.

"What's that?" I said to Dempsey, more skilled than I in the portmanteau words of early dawn.

"Brook Green, 'Ammersmith," Dempsey translated promptly.

"Of course," I said. "That's just the sort of place he would choose to live in. I only wonder it was not Kew."

"Are you going to wheel him 'ome, sir?" said Dempsey.

"I'd wheel him home if he lived in——Paradise. He's not going to get out of this ambulance while I'm here. He'd drag me into a murder for tuppence."

"Then strap 'im up an' make sure," said Dempsey, and he deftly buckled two straps, that hung by the side of the ambulance, over the man's body. Brugglesmith—I know not his other name—was sleeping deeply. He even smiled in his sleep.

"That's all right," said Dempsey, and I moved off, wheeling my devil's perambulator before me. Trafalgar Square was empty except for the few that slept in the open. One of these wretches ranged alongside and begged for money, asserting that he had once been a gentleman.

"So have I," I said. "That was long ago. I'll give you a shilling if you'll help me to push this thing."

"Is it a murder?" said the vagabond, shrinking back. "I've not got to *that* yet."

"No. It's going to be one," I answered. "I have."

The man slunk back into the darkness and I pressed on, through Cockspur Street, and up to Piccadilly Circus, wondering what I should do with my treasure. All London was asleep, and I had only this drunken carcase to bear me company. It was silent—silent as chaste Piccadilly. A young man of my acquaintance came out of a pink-brick club as I passed. A faded carnation drooped from his button-hole; he had been playing cards, and was walking home before the dawn, when he overtook me.

"What are you doing?" he said.

I was far beyond any feeling of shame. "It's for a bet," said I. "Come and help."

"Laddie, who's yon?" said the voice beneath the hood.

"Good Lord!" said the young man, leaping across the pavement. Perhaps card-losses had told on his nerves. Mine were steel that night.

"The Lord, the Lord?" the passionless, incurious voice went on. "Dinna be profane, laddie. He'll come in His ain good time."

The young man looked at me with horror.

"It's all part of the bet," I answered. "Do come and push."

"W—where are you going to?" said he.

"Brugglesmith," said the voice within. "Laddie, d'ye ken my wife?"

"No," said I.

"Well, she's just a tremenjus wumman. Laddie, I want a drink. Knock at one o' these braw houses, laddie, an'—an'—ye may kiss the girl for your pains."

"Lie still, or I'll gag you," I said, savagely.

The young man with the carnation crossed to the other side of Piccadilly, and hailed the only hansom visible for miles. What he thought I cannot tell. Later I was told.

I pressed on—wheeling, eternally wheeling—to Brook Green, Hammersmith. There I would abandon Brugglesmith to the gods of that desolate land. We had been through so much together that I could not leave him bound in the street. Besides, he would call after me, and oh! it is a shameful thing to hear one's name ringing down the emptiness of London in the dawn.

So I went on, past Apsley House, even to the coffee-stall, but there was no coffee for Brugglesmith. And into Knightsbridge—respectable Knightsbridge—I wheeled my burden, the body of Brugglesmith.

"Laddie, what are ye going to do to me?" he said when opposite the barracks.

"Kill you," I said briefly, "or hand you over to your wife. Be quiet."

He would not obey. He talked incessantly—sliding in one sentence from clear cut dialect to wild and drunken jumble. At the Albert Hall he said that I was the "Hattle Gardle buggle," which I apprehend is the Hatton Garden burglar. At Kensington High Street he loved me as a son, but when my weary legs came to the Addison Road Bridge he implored me with tears to unloose the straps and to fight against the sin of vanity. No man molested us. It was as though a bar had been set between myself and all humanity till I had cleared my account with Brugglesmith. The glimmering of light grew in the sky; the cloudy brown of the wood pavement turned to heather-purple; I made no doubt that I should be allowed vengeance on Brugglesmith ere the evening.

At Hammersmith the heavens were steel-gray, and the day came weeping. All the tides of the sadness of an unprofitable dawning poured into the soul of Brugglesmith. He wept bitterly, because the puddles looked cold and houseless. I entered a half-waked public-house—in evening dress and an ulster, I marched to the bar—and got him whisky on condition that he should cease kicking at the canvas of the ambulance. Then he wept more bitterly, for that he had ever been associated with me, and so seduced into stealing the *Breslau's* dinghy.

The day was white and wan when I reached my long journey's end, and, putting back the hood, bade Brugglesmith declare where he lived. His eyes wandered disconsolately round the red and gray houses till they fell on a villa in whose garden stood a staggering board with the legend "To Let." It needed only this to break him down utterly, and with that breakage fled his fine fluency in his guttural northern tongue; for liquor levels all.

"Olely lil while," he sobbed. "Olely lil while. Home—falmy—besht of falmies—wife, too—*you* dole know my wife! Left them all a lil while ago. Now everything's sold—all sold. Wife—falmy—all sold. Lemmegellup!"

I unbuckled the straps cautiously. Brugglesmith rolled off his resting-place and staggered to the house.

"Wattle I do?" he said.

Then I understood the baser depths in the mind of Mephistopheles.

"Ring," I said; "perhaps they are in the attic or the cellar."

"You do' know my wife. She shleeps on soful in the dorlin' room waitin' meculhome. *You* do' know my wife."

He took off his boots, covered them with his tall hat, and craftily as a Red Indian picked his way up the garden path and smote the bell marked "Visitors" a severe blow with his clenched fist.

"Bell sole too. Sole electick bell! Wassor bell this? I can't riggle bell," he moaned despairingly.

"You pull it—pull it hard," I repeated, keeping a wary eye down the road. Vengeance was coming and I desired no witnesses.

"Yes, I'll pull it hard." He slapped his forehead with inspiration. "I'll pull it out."

Leaning back he grasped the knob with both hands and pulled. A wild ringing in the kitchen was his answer. Spitting on his hands he pulled with renewed strength, and shouted for his wife. Then he bent his ear to the knob, shook his head, drew out an enormous yellow and red handkerchief, tied it round the knob, turned his back to the door, and pulled over his shoulder.

Either the handkerchief or the wire, it seemed to me, was bound to give way. But I had forgotten the bell. Something cracked in the kitchen, and Brugglesmith moved slowly down the doorsteps, pulling valiantly. Three feet of wire followed him.

"Pull, oh pull!" I cried. "It's coming now!"

"Qui' ri'," he said. *"I'll* riggle bell."

He bowed forward, the wire creaking and straining behind him, the bell-knob clasped to his bosom, and from the noises within I fancied the bell was taking away with it half the wood-work of the kitchen and all the basement banisters as it came up.

"Get a purchase on her," I shouted, and he spun round, lapping that good copper wire about him. I opened the garden gate politely, and he passed out, spinning his own cocoon. Still the bell came up, hand over hand, and still the wire held fast. He was in the middle of the road now, whirling like an impaled cockchafer, and shouting madly for his wife and family. There he met with the ambulance, the bell within the house gave one last peal, and bounded from the far end of the hall to the inner side of the hall door, when it stayed fast. So did not my friend Brugglesmith. He fell upon his face embracing the ambulance as he did so, and the two turned over together in the toils of the never-sufficiently-to-be-advertised copper wire.

"Laddie," he gasped, his speech returning, "have I a legal remedy?"

"I will go and look for one," I said, and, departing, found two policemen, whom I told that daylight had surprised a burglar in Brook Green while he was stealing lead from an empty house. Perhaps they had better take care of that bootless thief. He seemed to be in difficulties.

I led the way to the spot, and behold! in the splendour of the dawning, the ambulance, wheels uppermost, was walkin down the muddy road on two stockinged feet—was shuffling to and fro in a quarter of a circle whose radius was copper wire, and whose centre was the bell-plate of the empty house.

Next to the amazing ingenuity with which Brugglesmith had contrived to lash himself under the ambulance, the thing that appeared to impress the constables most was the fact of the St. Clement Danes ambulance being at Brook Green, Hammersmith.

They even asked me, of all people in the world, whether I knew anything about it.

. . . .

They extricated him; not without pain and dirt. He explained that he was repelling boarding-attacks by a "Hattle Gardle buggle" who had sold his house, wife, and family. As to the bell-wire, he offered no explanation, and was borne off shoulder-high between the two policemen. Though his feet were not within six inches of the ground, they paddled swiftly, and I saw that in his magnificent mind he was running—furiously running.

Sometimes I have wondered whether he wished to find me.

MOWGLI'S BROTHERS
1894

Now Rann, the Kite, brings home the night
That Mang, the Bat, sets free—
The herds are shut in byre and hut,
For loosed till dawn are we.
This is the hour of pride and power,
Talon and tush and claw.
Oh, hear the call!—Good hunting all
That keep the Jungle Law!

—NIGHT-SONG IN THE JUNGLE

IT WAS seven o'clock of a very warm evening in the Seeonee hills when Father Wolf woke up from his day's rest, scratched himself, yawned, and spread out his paws one after the other to get rid of the sleepy feeling in the tips. Mother Wolf lay with her big gray nose dropped across her four tumbling, squealing cubs, and the moon shone into the mouth of the cave where they all lived. "Augrh!" said Father Wolf, "it is time to hunt again"; and he was going to spring downhill when a little shadow with a bushy tail crossed the threshold and whined: "Good luck go with you, O Chief of the Wolves; and good luck and strong white teeth go with the noble children, that they may never forget the hungry in this world."

It was the jackal—Tabaqui, the Dish-licker—and the wolves of India despise Tabaqui because he runs about making mischief, and telling tales, and eating rags and pieces of leather from the village rubbish-heaps. They are afraid of him too, because Tabaqui, more than any one else in the jungle, is apt to go mad, and then he forgets that he was ever afraid of any one, and runs through the forest biting everything in his way. Even the tiger hides when little Tabaqui goes mad, for madness is the most disgraceful thing that can overtake a wild creature. We call it hydrophobia, but they call it *dewanee*—the madness—and run.

"Enter, then, and look," said Father Wolf, stiffly; "but there is no food here."

"For a wolf, no," said Tabaqui; "but for so mean a person as myself a dry bone is a good feast. Who are we, the Gidur-log [the Jackal People], to pick and choose?" He scuttled to the back of the cave, where he found the bone of a buck with some meat on it, and sat cracking the end merrily.

"All thanks for this good meal," he said, licking his lips. "How beautiful are the noble children! How large are their eyes! And so young too! Indeed, indeed, I might have remembered that the children of kings are men from the beginning."

Now, Tabaqui knew as well as any one else that there is nothing so unlucky as to compliment children to their faces; and it pleased him to see Mother and Father Wolf look uncomfortable.

Tabaqui sat still, rejoicing in the mischief that he had made, and then he said spitefully:

"Shere Khan, the Big One, has shifted his hunting-grounds. He will hunt among these hills during the next moon, so he has told me."

Shere Khan was the tiger who lived near the Waingunga River, twenty miles away.

"He has no right!" Father Wolf began angrily. "By the Law of the Jungle he has no right to change his quarters without fair warning. He will frighten every head of game within ten miles; and I—I have to kill for two, these days."

"His mother did not call him Lungri [the Lame One] for nothing," said Mother Wolf, quietly. "He has been lame in one foot from his birth. That is why he has only killed cattle. Now the villagers of the Waingunga are angry with him, and he has come here to make *our* villagers angry. They will scour the jungle for him when he is far away, and we and our children must run when the grass is set alight. Indeed, we are very grateful to Shere Khan!"

"Shall I tell him of your gratitude?" said Tabaqui.

"Out!" snapped Father Wolf. "Out, and hunt with thy master. Thou hast done harm enough for one night."

"I go," said Tabaqui, quietly. "Ye can hear Shere Khan below in the thickets. I might have saved myself the message."

Father Wolf listened, and in the dark valley that ran down to a little river, he heard the dry, angry, snarly, singsong whine of a tiger who has caught nothing and does not care if all the jungle knows it.

"The fool!" said Father Wolf. "To begin a night's work with that noise! Does he think that our buck are like his fat Waingunga bullocks?"

"H'sh! It is neither bullock nor buck that he hunts tonight," said Mother Wolf; "it is Man." The whine had changed to a sort of humming purr that seemed to roll from every quarter of the compass. It was the noise that bewilders wood-cutters, and gipsies sleeping in the open, and makes them run sometimes into the very mouth of the tiger.

"Man!" said Father Wolf, showing all his white teeth. "Faugh! Are there not enough beetles and frogs in the tanks that he must eat Man—and on our ground too!"

The Law of the Jungle, which never orders anything without a reason, forbids every beast to eat Man except when he is killing to show his children how to kill, and then he must hunt outside the hunting-grounds of his pack or tribe. The real reason for this is that man-killing means, sooner or later, the arrival of white men on elephants, with guns, and hundreds of brown men with gongs and rockets and torches. Then everybody in the jungle suffers. The reason the beasts give among themselves is that Man is the weakest and most defenseless of all living things, and it is unsportsmanlike to touch him. They say too—and it is true—that man-eaters become mangy, and lose their teeth.

The purr grew louder, and ended in the full-throated "Aaarh!" of the tiger's charge.

Then there was a howl—an untigerish howl—from Shere Khan. "He has missed," said Mother Wolf. "What is it?"

Father Wolf ran out a few paces and heard Shere Khan

muttering and mumbling savagely, as he tumbled about in the scrub.

"The fool has had no more sense than to jump at a woodcutter's camp-fire, so he has burned his feet," said Father Wolf, with a grunt. "Tabaqui is with him."

"Something is coming uphill," said Mother Wolf, twitching one ear. "Get ready."

The bushes rustled a little in the thicket, and Father Wolf dropped with his haunches under him, ready for his leap. Then, if you had been watching, you would have seen the most wonderful thing in the world—the wolf checked in mid-spring. He made his bound before he saw what it was he was jumping at, and then he tried to stop himself. The result was that he shot up straight into the air for four or five feet, landing almost where he left ground.

"Man!" he snapped. "A man's cub. Look!"

Directly in front of him, holding on by a low branch, stood a naked brown baby who could just walk—as soft and as dimpled a little thing as ever came to a wolf's cave at night. He looked up into Father Wolf's face and laughed.

"Is that a man's cub?" said Mother Wolf. "I have never seen one. Bring it here."

A wolf accustomed to moving his own cubs can, if necessary, mouth an egg without breaking it, and though Father Wolf's jaws closed right on the child's back not a tooth even scratched the skin, as he laid it down among the cubs.

"How little! How naked, and—how bold!" said Mother Wolf, softly. The baby was pushing his way between the cubs to get close to the warm hide. "Ahai! He is taking his meal with the others. And so this is a man's cub. Now was there ever a wolf that could boast of a man's cub among her children?"

"I have heard now and again of such a thing, but never in our pack or in my time," said Father Wolf. "He is altogether without hair, and I could kill him with a touch of my foot. But see, he looks up and is not afraid."

The moonlight was blocked out of the mouth of the cave, for Shere Khan's great square head and shoulders were thrust into the entrance, Tabaqui, behind him, was squeaking: "My Lord, my Lord, it went in here!"

"Shere Khan does us great honour," said Father Wolf, but his eyes were very angry. "What does Shere Khan need?"

"My quarry. A man's cub went this way," said Shere Khan. "Its parents have run off. Give it to me."

Shere Khan had jumped at a wood-cutter's camp-fire, as Father Wolf had said, and was furious from the pain of his burned feet. But Father Wolf knew that the mouth of the cave was too narrow for a tiger to come in by. Even where he was, Shere Khan's shoulders and fore paws were cramped for want of room, as a man's would be if he tried to fight in a barrel.

"The Wolves are a free people," said Father Wolf. "They take orders from the Head of the Pack, and not from any striped cattle-killer. The man's cub is ours—to kill if we choose."

"Ye choose and ye do not choose! What talk is this of choosing? By the Bull that I killed, am I to stand nosing into your dog's den for my fair dues? It is I, Shere Khan, who speak!"

The tiger's roar filled the cave with thunder. Mother Wolf shook herself clear of the cubs and sprang forward, her eyes, like two green moons in the darkness, facing the blazing eyes of Shere Khan.

"And it is I, Raksha [the Demon], who answer. The man's cub is mine, Lungri—mine to me! He shall not be killed. He shall live to run with the Pack and to hunt with the Pack; and in the end, look you, hunter of little naked cubs—frog-eater—fish-killer, shall hunt *thee!* Now get hence, or by the Sambhur that I killed (I eat no starved cattle), back thou goest to thy mother, burned beast of the jungle, lamer than ever thou camest into the world! Go!"

Father Wolf looked on amazed. He had almost forgotten the days when he won Mother Wolf in fair fight from five other wolves, when she ran in the Pack and was not called the Demon for compliment's sake. Shere Khan might have faced Father Wolf, but he could not stand up against Mother Wolf, for he knew that where he was she had all the advantage of the ground, and would fight to the death. So he backed out of the cave-mouth growling, and when he was clear he shouted:

"Each dog barks in his own yard! We will see what the Pack will say to this fostering of man-cubs. The cub is mine, and to my teeth he will come in the end, O bush-tailed thieves!"

Mother Wolf threw herself down panting among the cubs, and Father Wolf said to her gravely:

"Shere Khan speaks this much truth. The cub must be shown to the Pack. Wilt thou still keep him, Mother?"

"Keep him!" she gasped. "He came naked, by night, alone and very hungry; yet he was not afraid! Look, he has pushed one of my babes to one side already. And that lame butcher would have killed him, and would have run off to the Waingunga while the villagers here hunted through all our lairs in revenge! Keep him? Assuredly I will keep him. Lie still, little frog. O thou Mowgli,—for Mowgli, the Frog, I will call thee,—the time will come when thou wilt hunt Shere Khan as he has hunted thee!"

"But what will our Pack say?" said Father Wolf.

The Law of the Jungle lays down very clearly that any wolf may, when he marries, withdraw from the Pack he belongs to; but as soon as his cubs are old enough to stand on their feet he must bring them to the Pack Council, which is generally held once a month at full moon, in order that the other wolves may identify them. After that inspection the cubs are free to run where they please, and until they have killed their first buck no excuse is accepted if a grown wolf of the Pack kills one of them. The punishment is death where the murderer can be found; and if you think for a minute you will see that this must be so.

Father Wolf waited till his cubs could run a little, and then on the night of the Pack Meeting took them and Mowgli and Mother Wolf to the Council Rock—a hilltop covered with stones and boulders where a hundred wolves could hide. Akela, the great gray Lone Wolf, who led all the Pack by strength and cunning, lay out at full length on his rock, and below him sat forty or more wolves of every size and colour, from badger-coloured veterans who could handle a buck alone, to young black three-year-olds who thought they could. The Lone Wolf had led them for a year now. He had fallen twice into a wolf-trap in his youth, and once he had been beaten and left for dead; so he knew the manners and customs of men.

There was very little talking at the Rock. The cubs tumbled over one another in the center of the circle where their mothers and fathers sat, and now and again a senior wolf would go quietly up to a cub, look at him carefully, and return to his place on noiseless feet. Sometimes a mother would push her cub far out into the moonlight, to be sure that he had not been overlooked. Akela from his rock would cry: "Ye know the Law—ye know the Law! Look well, O Wolves!" And the anxious mothers would take up the call: "Look—look well, O Wolves!"

At last—and Mother Wolf's neck-bristles lifted as the time came—Father Wolf pushed "Mowgli, the Frog," as they called him, into the centre, where he sat laughing and playing with some pebbles that glistened in the moonlight.

Akela never raised his head from his paws, but went on with the monotonous cry, "Look well!" A muffled roar came up from behind the rocks—the voice of Shere Khan crying, "The cub is mine; give him to me. What have the Free People to do with a man's cub?"

Akela never even twitched his ears. All he said was, "Look well, O Wolves! What have the Free People to do with the orders of any save the Free People? Look well!"

There was a chorus of deep growls, and a young wolf in his fourth year flung back Shere Khan's question to Akela: "What have the Free People to do with a man's cub?"

Now the Law of the Jungle lays down that if there is any dispute as to the right of a cub to be accepted by the Pack, he must be spoken for by at least two members of the Pack who are not his father and mother.

"Who speaks for this cub?" said Akela. "Among the Free People, who speaks?" There was no answer, and Mother Wolf got ready for what she knew would be her last fight, if things came to fighting.

Then the only other creature who is allowed at the Pack Council—Baloo, the sleepy brown bear who teaches the wolf cubs the Law of the Jungle, old Baloo—who can come and go where he pleases because he eats only nuts and roots and honey—rose up on his hind quarters and grunted.

"The man's cub—the man's cub?" he said. "*I* speak for the man's cub. There is no harm in a man's cub. I have no gift of words, but I speak the truth. Let him run with the Pack, and be entered with the others. I myself will teach him."

"We need yet another," said Akela. "Baloo has spoken, and he is our teacher for the young cubs. Who speaks besides Baloo?"

A black shadow dropped down into the circle. It was Bagheera, the Black Panther, inky black all over, but with the panther markings showing up in certain lights like the pattern of watered silk. Everybody knew Bagheera, and nobody cared to cross his path; for he was as cunning as Tabaqui, as bold as the wild buffalo, and as reckless as the wounded elephant. But he had a voice as soft as wild honey dripping from a tree, and a skin softer than down.

"O Akela, and ye, the Free People," he purred, "I have no right in your assembly; but the Law of the Jungle says that if there is a doubt which is not a killing matter in regard to a new cub, the life of that cub may be bought at a price. And the Law does not say who may or may not pay that price. Am I right?"

"Good! good!" said the young wolves, who are always hungry. "Listen to Bagheera. The cub can be bought for a price. It is the Law."

"Knowing that I have no right to speak here, I ask your leave."

"Speak then," cried twenty voices.

"To kill a naked cub is shame. Besides, he may make better sport for you when he is grown. Baloo has spoken in his behalf. Now to Baloo's word I will add one bull, and a fat one, newly killed, not half a mile from here, if ye will accept the man's cub according to the Law. Is it difficult?"

There was a clamour of scores of voices, saying:

"What matter? He will die in the winter rains. He will scorch in the sun. What harm can a naked frog do us? Let him run with the Pack. Where is the bull, Bagheera? Let him be accepted." And then came Akela's deep bay, crying: "Look well—look well, O Wolves!"

Mowgli was still playing with the pebbles, and he did not notice when the wolves came and looked at him one by one. At last they all went down the hill for the dead bull, and only Akela, Bagheera, Baloo, and Mowgli's own wolves were left. Shere Khan roared still in the night, for he was very angry that Mowgli had not been handed over to him.

"Ay, roar well," said Bagheera, under his whiskers; "for the time comes when this naked thing will make thee roar to another tune, or I know nothing of Man."

"It was well done," said Akela. "Men and their cubs are very wise. He may be a help in time."

"Truly, a help in time of need; for none can hope to lead the Pack forever," said Bagheera.

Akela said nothing. He was thinking of the time that comes to every leader of every pack when his strength goes from him and he gets feebler and feebler, till at last he is killed by the wolves and a new leader comes up—to be killed in his turn.

"Take him away," he said to Father Wolf, "and train him as befits one of the Free People."

And that is how Mowgli was entered into the Seeonee wolf-pack for the price of a bull and on Baloo's good word.

Now you must be content to skip ten or eleven whole years, and only guess at all the wonderful life that Mowgli led among the wolves, because if it were written out it would fill ever so many books. He grew up with the cubs, though they of course were grown wolves almost before he was a child, and Father Wolf taught him his business, and the meaning of things in the jungle, till every rustle in the grass, every breath of the warm night air, every note of the owls above his head, every scratch of a bat's claws as it roosted for a while in a tree, and every splash of every little fish jumping in a pool, meant just as much to him as the work of his office means to a business man. When he was not learning he sat out in the sun and slept, and ate, and went to sleep again; when he felt dirty or hot he swam in the forest pools; and when he wanted honey (Baloo told him that honey and nuts were just as pleasant to eat as raw meat) he climbed up for it, and that Bagheera showed him how to do.

Bagheera would lie out on a branch and call, "Come along, Little Brother," and at first Mowgli would cling like the sloth, but afterward he would fling himself through the branches almost as boldly as the gray ape. He took his place at the Council Rock, too, when the Pack met, and there he discovered that if he stared hard at any wolf, the wolf would be forced to drop his eyes, and so he used to stare for fun.

At other times he would pick the long thorns out of the pads of his friends, for wolves suffer terribly from thorns and burs in their coats. He would go down the hillside into the cultivated lands by night, and look very curiously at the villagers in their huts, but he had a mistrust of men because Bagheera showed him a square box with a drop-gate so cunningly hidden in the jungle that he nearly walked into it, and told him it was a trap.

He loved better than anything else to go with Bagheera into the dark warm heart of the forest, to sleep all through the drowsy day, and at night see how Bagheera did his killing. Bagheera killed right and left as he felt hungry, and so did Mowgli—with one exception. As soon as he was old enough to understand things, Bagheera told him that he must never touch cattle because he had been bought into the Pack at the price of a bull's life. "All the jungle is thine," said Bagheera, "and thou canst kill everything that thou art strong enough to kill; but for the sake of the bull that bought thee thou must never kill or eat any cattle young or old. That is the Law of the Jungle." Mowgli obeyed faithfully.

And he grew and grew strong as a boy must grow, who does not know that he is learning any lessons, and who has nothing in the world to think of except things to eat.

Mother Wolf told him once or twice that Shere Khan was not a creature to be trusted, and that some day he must kill Shere Khan; but though a young wolf would have remembered that advice every hour, Mowgli forgot it because he was only a boy—though he would have called himself a wolf if he had been able to speak in any human tongue.

Shere Khan was always crossing his path in the jungle, for as Akela grew older and feebler the lame tiger had come to be great friends with the younger wolves of the Pack, who followed him for scraps, a thing Akela would never have allowed if he had dared to push his authority to the proper bounds. Then Shere Khan would flatter them and wonder that such fine young hunters were content to be led by a dying wolf and a man's cub. "They tell me," Shere Khan would say, "that at Council ye dare not look him between the eyes"; and the young wolves would growl and bristle.

Bagheera, who had eyes and ears everywhere, knew something of this, and once or twice he told Mowgli in so many words that Shere Khan would kill him some day; and Mowgli would laugh and answer: "I have the Pack and I have thee; and Baloo, though he is so lazy, might strike a blow or two for my sake. Why should I be afraid?"

It was one very warm day that a new notion came to Bagheera—born of something that he had heard. Perhaps Ikki, the Porcupine, had told him; but he said to Mowgli when they were deep in the jungle, as the boy lay with his head on Bagheera's beautiful black skin: "Little Brother, how often have I told thee that Shere Khan is thy enemy?"

"As many times as there are nuts on that palm," said Mowgli, who, naturally, could not count. "What of it? I am sleepy, Bagheera, and Shere Khan is all long tail and loud talk, like Mao, the Peacock."

"But this is no time for sleeping. Baloo knows it, I know it, the Pack know it, and even the foolish, foolish deer know. Tabaqui has told thee too."

"Ho! ho!" said Mowgli. "Tabaqui came to me not long ago with some rude talk that I was a naked man's cub, and not fit to dig pig-nuts; but I caught Tabaqui by the tail and swung him twice against a palm-tree to teach him better manners."

"That was foolishness; for though Tabaqui is a mischief-maker, he would have told thee of something that concerned thee closely. Open those eyes, Little Brother! Shere Khan dares not kill thee in the jungle for fear of those that love thee; but remember, Akela is very old, and soon the day comes when he cannot kill his buck, and then he will be leader no more. Many of the wolves that looked thee over when thou wast brought to the Council first are old too, and the young wolves believe, as Shere Khan has taught them, that a man-cub has no place with the Pack. In a little time thou wilt be a man."

"And what is a man that he should not run with his brothers?" said Mowgli. "I was born in the jungle; I have obeyed the Law of the Jungle; and there is no wolf of ours from whose paws I have not pulled a thorn. Surely they are my brothers!"

Bagheera stretched himself at full length and half shut his eyes. "Little Brother," said he, "feel under my jaw."

Mowgli put up his strong brown hand, and just under Bagheera's silky chin, where the giant rolling muscles were all hid by the glossy hair, he came upon a little bald spot.

"There is no one in the jungle that knows that I, Bagheera, carry that mark—the mark of the collar; and yet, Little Brother, I was born among men, and it was among men that my mother died—in the cages of the King's Palace at Oodeypore. It was because of this that I paid the price for thee at the Council when thou wast a little naked cub. Yes, I too was born among men. I had never seen the jungle. They fed me behind bars from an iron pan till one night I felt that I was Bagheera, the Panther, and no man's plaything, and I broke the silly lock with one blow of my paw, and came away; and because I had learned the ways of men, I became more terrible in the jungle than Shere Khan. Is it not so?"

"Yes," said Mowgli; "all the jungle fear Bagheera—all except Mowgli."

"Oh, *thou* art a man's cub," said the Black Panther, very tenderly; "and even as I returned to my jungle, so thou must go back to men at last,—to the men who are thy brothers,—if thou art not killed in the Council."

"But why—but why should any wish to kill me?" said Mowgli.

"Look at me," said Bagheera; and Mowgli looked at him steadily between the eyes. The big panther turned his head away in half a minute.

"*That* is why," he said, shifting his paw on the leaves. "Not even I can look thee between the eyes, and I was born among men, and I love thee, Little Brother. The others they hate thee because their eyes cannot meet thine, because thou art wise; because thou hast pulled out thorns from their feet—because thou art a man."

"I did not know these things," said Mowgli, sullenly; and he frowned under his heavy black eyebrows.

"What is the Law of the Jungle? Strike first and then give tongue. By thy very carelessness they know that thou art a man. But be wise. It is in my heart that when Akela misses his next kill,—and at each hunt it costs him more to pin the buck,—the Pack will turn against him and against thee. They will hold a jungle Council at the Rock, and then—and then. . . . I have it!" said Bagheera, leaping up. "Go thou down quickly to the men's huts in the valley, and take some of the Red Flower which they grow there, so that when the time comes thou mayest have even a stronger friend than I or Baloo or those of the Pack that love thee. Get the Red Flower."

By Red Flower Bagheera meant fire, only no creature in the jungle will call fire by its proper name. Every beast lives in deadly fear of it, and invents a hundred ways of describing it.

"The Red Flower?" said Mowgli. "That grows outside their huts in the twilight. I will get some."

"There speaks the man's cub," said Bagheera, proudly. "Remember that it grows in little pots. Get one swiftly, and keep it by thee for time of need."

"Good!" said Mowgli. "I go. But art thou sure, O my Bagheera"—he slipped his arm round the splendid neck, and looked deep into the big eyes—"art thou sure that all this is Shere Khan's doing?"

"By the Broken Lock that freed me, I am sure, Little Brother."

"Then, by the Bull that bought me, I will pay Shere Khan full tale for this, and it may be a little over," said Mowgli; and he bounded away.

"That is a man. That is all a man," said Bagheera to himself, lying down again. "Oh, Shere Khan, never was a blacker hunting than that frog-hunt of thine ten years ago!"

Mowgli was far and far through the forest, running hard, and his heart was hot in him. He came to the cave as the evening mist rose, and drew breath, and looked down the valley. The cubs were out, but Mother Wolf, at the back of the cave, knew by his breathing that something was troubling her frog.

"What is it, Son?" she said.

"Some bat's chatter of Shere Khan," he called back. "I hunt among the ploughed fields to-night"; and he plunged downward through the bushes, to the stream at the bottom of the valley. There he checked, for he heard the yell of the Pack hunting, heard the bellow of a hunted Sambhur, and the snort as the buck turned at bay. Then there were wicked, bitter howls from the young wolves: "Akela! Akela! Let the Lone Wolf show his strength. Room for the leader of our Pack! Spring, Akela!"

The Lone Wolf must have sprung and missed his hold, for Mowgli heard the snap of his teeth and then a yelp as the Sambhur knocked him over with his fore foot.

He did not wait for anything more, but dashed on; and the yells grew fainter behind him as he ran into the croplands where the villagers lived.

"Bagheera spoke truth," he panted, as he nestled down in some cattle-fodder by the window of a hut. "To-morrow is one day for Akela and for me."

Then he pressed his face close to the window and watched the fire on the hearth. He saw the husbandman's wife get up and feed it in the night with black lumps; and when the morning came and the mists were all white and cold, he saw the man's child pick up a wicker pot plastered inside with earth, fill it with lumps of red-hot charcoal, put it under his blanket, and go out to tend the cows in the byre.

"Is that all?" said Mowgli. "If a cub can do it there is nothing to fear"; so he strode around the corner and met the boy, took the pot from his hand and disappeared into the mist while the boy howled with fear.

"They are very like me," said Mowgli, blowing into the pot, as he had seen the woman do. "This thing will die if I do not give it things to eat"; and he dropped twigs and dried bark on the red stuff. Half-way up the hill he met Bagheera with the morning dew shining like moonstones on his coat.

"Akela has missed," said the panther. "They would have killed him last night, but they needed thee also. They were looking for thee on the hill."

"I was among the ploughed lands. I am ready. Look!" Mowgli held up the fire-pot.

"Good! Now, I have seen men thrust a dry branch into that stuff, and presently the Red Flower blossomed at the end of it. Art thou not afraid?"

"No. Why should I fear? I remember—now if it is not a dream—how, before I was a wolf, I lay beside the Red Flower, and it was warm and pleasant."

All that day Mowgli sat in the cave tending his fire-pot and dipping dry branches into it to see how they looked. He found a branch that satisfied him, and in the evening when Tabaqui came to the cave and told him, rudely enough, that he was wanted at the Council Rock, he laughed till Tabaqui ran away. Then Mowgli went to the Council, still laughing.

Akela the Lone Wolf lay by the side of his rock as a sign that the leadership of the Pack was open, and Shere Khan with his following of scrap-fed wolves walked to and fro openly, being flattered. Bagheera lay close to Mowgli, and the fire-pot was between Mowgli's knees. When they were all gathered together, Shere Khan began to speak—a thing he would never have dared to do when Akela was in his prime.

"He has no right," whispered Bagheera. "Say so. He is a dog's son. He will be frightened."

Mowgli sprang to his feet. "Free People," he cried, "does

Shere Khan lead the Pack? What has a tiger to do with our leadership?"

"Seeing that the leadership is yet open, and being asked to speak"—Shere Khan began.

"By whom?" said Mowgli. "Are we *all* jackals, to fawn on this cattle-butcher? The leadership of the Pack is with the Pack alone."

There were yells of "Silence, thou man's cub!" "Let him speak; he has kept our law!" And at last the seniors of the Pack thundered: "Let the Dead Wolf speak!"

When a leader of the Pack has missed his kill, he is called the Dead Wolf as long as he lives, which is not long, as a rule.

Akela raised his old head wearily:

"Free people, and ye too, jackals of Shere Khan, for twelve seasons I have led ye to and from the kill, and in all that time not one has been trapped or maimed. Now I have missed my kill. Ye know how that plot was made. Ye know how ye brought me up to an untried buck to make my weakness known. It was cleverly done. Your right is to kill me here on the Council Rock now. Therefore I ask, 'Who comes to make an end of the Lone Wolf?' For it is my right, by the Law of the Jungle, that ye come one by one."

There was a long hush, for no single wolf cared to fight Akela to the death. Then Shere Khan roared: "Bah! What have we to do with this toothless fool? He is doomed to die! It is the man-cub who has lived too long. Free People, he was my meat from the first. Give him to me. I am weary of this man-wolf folly. He has troubled the jungle for ten seasons. Give me the man-cub, or I will hunt here always, and not give you one bone! He is a man—a man's child, and from the marrow of my bones I hate him!"

Then more than half the Pack yelled: "A man—a man! What has a man to do with us? Let him go to his own place."

"And turn all the people of the villages against us?" snarled Shere Khan. "No; give him to me. He is a man, and none of us can look him between the eyes."

Akela lifted his head again, and said: "He has eaten our

food; he has slept with us; he has driven game for us; he has broken no word of the Law of the Jungle."

"Also, I paid for him with a bull when he was accepted. The worth of a bull is little, but Bagheera's honour is something that he will perhaps fight for," said Bagheera in his gentlest voice.

"A bull paid ten years ago!" the Pack snarled. "What do we care for bones ten years old?"

"Or for a pledge?" said Bagheera, his white teeth bared under his lip. "Well are ye called the Free People!"

"No man's cub can run with the people of the jungle!" roared Shere Khan. "Give him to me."

"He is our brother in all but blood," Akela went on; "and ye would kill him here. In truth, I have lived too long. Some of ye are eaters of cattle, and of others I have heard that, under Shere Khan's teaching, ye go by dark night and snatch children from the villager's doorstep. Therefore I know ye to be cowards, and it is to cowards I speak. It is certain that I must die, and my life is of no worth or I would offer that in the man-cub's place. But for the sake of the Honour of the Pack,—a little matter that, by being without a leader, ye have forgotten,—I promise that if ye let the man-cub go to his own place, I will not, when my time comes to die, bare one tooth against ye. I will die without fighting. That will at least save the Pack three lives. More I cannot do; but, if ye will, I can save ye the shame that comes of killing a brother against whom there is no fault—a brother spoken for and bought into the Pack according to the Law of the Jungle."

"He is a man—a man—a man!" snarled the Pack; and most of the wolves began to gather round Shere Khan, whose tail was beginning to switch.

"Now the business is in thy hands," said Bagheera to Mowgli. "*We* can do no more except fight."

Mowgli stood upright—the fire-pot in his hands. Then he stretched out his arms, and yawned in the face of the Council; but he was furious with rage and sorrow, for, wolf-like, the wolves had never told him how they hated him.

"Listen, you!" he cried. "There is no need for this dog's

jabber. Ye have told me so often to-night that I am a man (though indeed I would have been a wolf with you to my life's end) that I feel your words are true. So I do not call ye my brothers any more, but *sag* [dogs], as a man should. What ye will do, and what ye will not do, is not yours to say. That matter is with *me;* and that we may see the matter more plainly, I, the man, have brought here a little of the Red Flower which ye, dogs, fear."

He flung the fire-pot on the ground, and some of the red coals lit a tuft of dried moss that flared up as all the Council drew back in terror before the leaping flames.

Mowgli thrust his dead branch into the fire till the twigs lit and crackled, and whirled it above his head among the cowering wolves.

"Thou art the master," said Bagheera, in an undertone. "Save Akela from the death. He was ever thy friend."

Akela, the grim old wolf who had never asked for mercy in his life, gave one piteous look at Mowgli as the boy stood all naked, his long black hair tossing over his shoulders in the light of the blazing branch that made the shadows jump and quiver.

"Good!" said Mowgli, staring around slowly, and thrusting out his lower lip. "I see that ye are dogs. I go from you to my own people—if they be my own people. The jungle is shut to me, and I must forget your talk and your companionship; but I will be more merciful than ye are. Because I was all but your brother in blood, I promise that when I am a man among men I will not betray ye to men as ye have betrayed me." He kicked the fire with his foot, and the sparks flew up. "There shall be no war between any of us and the Pack. But here is a debt to pay before I go." He strode forward to where Shere Khan sat blinking stupidly at the flames, and caught him by the tuft on his chin. Bagheera followed close, in case of accidents. "Up, dog!" Mowgli cried. "Up, when a man speaks, or I will set that coat ablaze!"

Shere Khan's ears lay flat back on his head, and he shut his eyes, for the blazing branch was very near.

"This cattle-killer said he would kill me in the Council because he had not killed me when I was a cub. Thus and thus, then, do we beat dogs when we are men! Stir a whisker, Lungri, and I ram the Red Flower down thy gullet!" He beat Shere Khan over the head with the branch, and the tiger whimpered and whined in an agony of fear.

"Pah! Singed jungle-cat—go now! But remember when next I come to the Council Rock, as a man should come, it will be with Shere Khan's hide on my head. For the rest, Akela goes free to live as he pleases. Ye will *not* kill him, because that is not my will. Nor do I think that ye will sit here any longer, lolling out your tongues as though ye were somebodies, instead of dogs whom I drive out—thus! Go!"

The fire was burning furiously at the end of the branch, and Mowgli struck right and left round the circle, and the wolves ran howling with the sparks burning their fur. At last there were only Akela, Bagheera, and perhaps ten wolves that had taken Mowgli's part. Then something began to hurt Mowgli inside him, as he had never been hurt in his life before, and he caught his breath and sobbed, and the tears ran down his face.

"What is it? What is it?" he said. "I do not wish to leave the jungle, and I do not know what this is. Am I dying, Bagheera?"

"No, Little Brother. Those are only tears such as men use," said Bagheera. "Now I know thou art a man, and a man's cub no longer. The jungle is shut indeed to thee henceforward. Let them fall, Mowgli; they are only tears." So Mowgli sat and cried as though his heart would break; and he had never cried in all his life before.

"Now," he said, "I will go to men. But first I must say farewell to my mother"; and he went to the cave where she lived with Father Wolf, and he cried on her coat, while the four cubs howled miserably.

"Ye will not forget me?" said Mowgli.

"Never while we can follow a trail," said the cubs. "Come to the foot of the hill when thou art a man, and we will talk to thee; and we will come into the crop-lands to play with thee by night."

"Come soon!" said Father Wolf. "Oh, wise little Frog, come again soon; for we be old, thy mother and I."

"Come soon," said Mother Wolf, "little naked son of mine; for, listen, child of man, I loved thee more than ever I loved my cubs."

"I will surely come," said Mowgli; "and when I come it will be to lay out Shere Khan's hide upon the Council Rock. Do not forget me! Tell them in the jungle never to forget me!"

The dawn was beginning to break when Mowgli went down the hillside alone to the crops to meet those mysterious things that are called men.

KAA'S HUNTING
1894

His spots are the joy of the Leopard: his horns are the Buffalo's pride—
Be clean, for the strength of the hunter is known by the gloss of his hide.

If ye find that the Bullock can toss you, or the heavy-browed Sambhur can gore;
Ye need not stop work to inform us; we knew it ten seasons before.

Oppress not the cubs of the stranger, but hail them as Sister and Brother,
For though they are little and fubsy, it may be the Bear is their mother.

"There is none like to me!" says the Cub in the pride of his earliest kill;
But the Jungle is large and the Cub he is small. Let him think and be still.

—MAXIMS OF BALOO

ALL that is told here happened some time before Mowgli was turned out of the Seeonee wolf-pack. It was in the days when Baloo was teaching him the Law of the Jungle. The big, serious, old brown bear was delighted to have so quick a pupil, for the young wolves will only learn as much of the Law of the Jungle as applies to their own pack and tribe, and run away as soon as they can repeat the Hunting Verse: "Feet that make no noise; eyes that can see in the dark; ears that can hear the winds in their lairs, and sharp white teeth —all these things are the marks of our brothers except Tabaqui and the Hyena, whom we hate." But Mowgli, as a man-cub, had to learn a great deal more than this. Sometimes Bagheera, the Black Panther, would come lounging through the jungle to see how his pet was getting on, and would purr with his head against a tree while Mowgli recited the day's lesson to Baloo. The boy could climb almost as well as he could swim, and swim almost as well as he could run; so Baloo, the Teacher of the Law, taught him the Wood and Water laws: how to tell a rotten branch from a sound one; how to speak politely to the wild bees when he came upon a hive of them fifty feet above-ground; what to say to Mang, the Bat, when he disturbed him in the branches at midday; and how to warn the water-snakes in the pools before he splashed down among them. None of the Jungle People like being disturbed, and all are very ready to fly at an intruder. Then, too, Mowgli was taught the Strangers' Hunting Call, which must be repeated aloud till it is answered, whenever one of the Jungle People hunts outside his own grounds. It means, translated: "Give me leave to hunt here because I am hungry"; and the answer is: "Hunt, then, for food, but not for pleasure."

All this will show you how much Mowgli had to learn by heart, and he grew very tired of repeating the same thing a hundred times; but, as Baloo said to Bagheera one day when Mowgli had been cuffed and had run off in a temper: "A man's cub is a man's cub, and he must learn *all* the Law of the Jungle."

"But think how small he is," said the Black Panther, who would have spoiled Mowgli if he had had his own way. "How can his little head carry all thy long talk?"

"Is there anything in the jungle too little to be killed? No.

That is why I teach him these things, and that is why I hit him, very softly, when he forgets."

"Softly! What dost thou know of softness, old Iron-feet?" Bagheera grunted. "His face is all bruised to-day by thy—softness. Ugh!"

"Better he should be bruised from head to foot by me who love him than that he should come to harm through ignorance," Baloo answered, very earnestly. "I am now teaching him the Master Words of the Jungle that shall protect him with the Birds and the Snake People, and all that hunt on four feet, except his own pack. He can now claim protection, if he will only remember the Words, from all in the jungle. Is not that worth a little beating?"

"Well, look to it then that thou dost not kill the man-cub. He is no tree-trunk to sharpen thy blunt claws upon. But what are those Master Words? I am more likely to give help than to ask it"—Bagheera stretched out one paw and admired the steel-blue ripping-chisel talons at the end of it—"Still I should like to know."

"I will call Mowgli and he shall say them—if he will. Come, Little Brother!"

"My head is ringing like a bee-tree," said a sullen voice over their heads, and Mowgli slid down a tree-trunk, very angry and indignant, adding, as he reached the ground: "I come for Bagheera and not for *thee*, fat old Baloo!"

"That is all one to me," said Baloo, though he was hurt and grieved. "Tell Bagheera, then, the Master Words of the Jungle that I have taught thee this day."

"Master Words for which people?" said Mowgli, delighted to show off. "The jungle has many tongues. I know them all."

"A little thou knowest, but not much. See, O Bagheera, they never thank their teacher! Not one small wolfling has come back to thank old Baloo for his teachings. Say the Word for the Hunting People, then,—great scholar!"

"We be of one blood, ye and I," said Mowgli, giving the words the Bear accent which all the Hunting People of the Jungle use.

"Good! Now for the Birds."

Mowgli repeated, with the Kite's whistle at the end of the sentencc.

"Now for the Snake People," said Bagheera.

The answer was a perfectly indescribable hiss, and Mowgli kicked up his feet behind, clapped his hands together to applaud himself, and jumped on Bagheera's back, where he sat sideways, drumming with his heels on the glossy skin and making the worst faces that he could think of at Baloo.

"There—there! That was worth a little bruise," said the Brown Bear, tenderly. "Some day thou wilt remember me." Then he turned aside to tell Bagheera how he had begged the Master Words from Hathi, the Wild Elephant, who knows all about these things, and how Hathi had taken Mowgli down to a pool to get the Snake Word from a water-snake, because Baloo could not pronounce it, and how Mowgli was now reasonably safe against all accidents in the jungle, because neither snake, bird, nor beast would hurt him.

"No one then is to be feared," Baloo wound up, patting his big furry stomach with pride.

"Except his own tribe," said Bagheera, under his breath; and then aloud to Mowgli: "Have a care for my ribs, Little Brother! What is all this dancing up and down?"

Mowgli had been trying to make himself heard by pulling at Bagheera's shoulder-fur and kicking hard. When the two listened to him he was shouting at the top of his voice: "And *so* I shall have a tribe of my own, and lead them through the branches all day long."

"What is this new folly, little dreamer of dreams?" said Bagheera.

"Yes, and throw branches and dirt at old Baloo," Mowgli went on. "They have promised me this, ah!"

"Whoof!" Baloo's big paw scooped Mowgli off Bagheera's back, and as the boy lay between the big fore paws he could see the bear was angry.

"Mowgli," said Baloo, "thou hast been talking with the Bandar-log—the Monkey People."

Mowgli looked at Bagheera to see if the panther was

angry too, and Bagheera's eyes were as hard as jade-stones.

"Thou hast been with the Monkey People—the gray apes —the people without a Law—the eaters of everything. That is great shame."

"When Baloo hurt my head," said Mowgli (he was still down on his back), "I went away, and the gray apes came down from the trees and had pity on me. No one else cared." He snuffled a little.

"The pity of the Monkey People!" Baloo snorted. "The stillness of the mountain stream! The coo of the summer sun! And then, man-cub?"

"And then—and then they gave me nuts and pleasant things to eat, and they—they carried me in their arms up to the top of the trees and said I was their blood-brother, except that I had no tail, and should be their leader some day."

"They have *no* leader," said Bagheera. "They lie. They have always lied."

"They were very kind, and bade me come again. Why have I never been taken among the Monkey People? They stand on their feet as I do. They do not hit me with hard paws. They play all day. Let me get up! Bad Baloo, let me up! I will go play with them again."

"Listen, man-cub," said the bear, and his voice rumbled like thunder on a hot night. "I have taught thee all the Law of the Jungle for all the Peoples of the Jungle—except the Monkey Folk who live in the trees. They have no Law. They are outcastes. They have no speech of their own but use the stolen words which they overhear when they listen and peep and wait up above in the branches. Their way is not our way. They are without leaders. They have no remembrance. They boast and chatter and pretend that they are a great people about to do great affairs in the jungle, but the falling of a nut turns their minds to laughter, and all is forgotten. We of the jungle have no dealings with them. We do not drink where the monkeys drink; we do not go where the monkeys go; we do not hunt where they hunt; we do not die where they die. Hast thou ever heard me speak of the Bandar-log till to-day?"

"No," said Mowgli in a whisper, for the forest was very still now that Baloo had finished.

"The Jungle People put them out of their mouths and out of their minds. They are very many, evil, dirty, shameless, and they desire, if they have any fixed desire, to be noticed by the Jungle People. But we do *not* notice them even when they throw nuts and filth on our heads."

He had hardly spoken when a shower of nuts and twigs spattered down through the branches; and they could hear coughings and howlings and angry jumpings high up in the air among the thin branches.

"The Monkey People are forbidden," said Baloo, "forbidden to the Jungle People. Remember."

"Forbidden," said Bagheera; "but I still think Baloo should have warned thee against them."

"I—I? How was I to guess he would play with such dirt. The Monkey People! Faugh!"

A fresh shower came down on their heads, and the two trotted away, taking Mowgli with them. What Baloo had said about the monkeys was perfectly true. They belonged to the tree-tops, and as beasts very seldom look up, there was no occasion for the monkeys and the Jungle People to cross one another's path. But whenever they found a sick wolf, or a wounded tiger or bear, the monkeys would torment him, and would throw sticks and nuts at any beast for fun and in the hope of being noticed. Then they would howl and shriek senseless songs, and invite the Jungle People to climb up their trees and fight them, or would start furious battles over nothing among themselves, and leave the dead monkeys where the Jungle People could see them.

They were always just going to have a leader and laws and customs of their own, but they never did, because their memories would not hold over from day to day, and so they settled things by making up a saying: "What the Bandar-log think now the Jungle will think later"; and that comforted them a great deal. None of the beasts could reach them, but on the other hand none of the beasts would notice them, and that was why they were so pleased when Mowgli came to play with them, and when they heard how angry Baloo was.

They never meant to do any more,—the Bandar-log never mean anything at all,—but one of them invented what seemed to him a brilliant idea, and he told all the others that Mowgli would be a useful person to keep in the tribe, because he could weave sticks together for protection from the wind; so, if they caught him, they could make him teach them. Of course Mowgli, as a wood-cutter's child, inherited all sorts of instincts, and used to make little play huts of fallen branches without thinking how he came to do it. The Monkey People, watching in the trees, considered these huts most wonderful. This time, they said, they were really going to have a leader and become the wisest people in the jungle—so wise that every one else would notice and envy them. Therefore they followed Baloo and Bagheera and Mowgli through the jungle very quietly till it was time for the midday nap, and Mowgli, who was very much ashamed of himself, slept between the panther and the bear, resolving to have no more to do with the Monkey People.

The next thing he remembered was feeling hands on his legs and arms,—hard, strong little hands,—and then a swash of branches in his face; and then he was staring down through the swaying boughs as Baloo woke the jungle with his deep cries and Bagheera bounded up the trunk with every tooth bared. The Bandar-log howled with triumph, and scuffled away to the upper branches where Bagheera dared not follow, shouting: "He has noticed us! Bagheera has noticed us! All the Jungle People admire us for our skill and our cunning!" Then they began their flight; and the flight of the Monkey People through tree-land is one of the things nobody can describe. They have their regular roads and cross-roads, uphills and downhills, all laid out from fifty to seventy or a hundred feet aboveground, and by these they can travel even at night if necessary.

Two of the strongest monkeys caught Mowgli under the arms and swung off with him through the tree-tops, twenty feet at a bound. Had they been alone they could have gone twice as fast, but the boy's weight held them back. Sick and giddy as Mowgli was he could not help enjoying the wild rush, though the glimpses of earth far down below frightened him, and the terrible check and jerk at the end of the swing over nothing but empty air brought his heart between his teeth.

His escort would rush him up a tree till he felt the weak topmost branches crackle and bend under them, and, then, with a cough and a whoop, would fling themselves into the air outward and downward, and bring up hanging by their hands or their feet to the lower limbs of the next tree. Sometimes he could see for miles and miles over the still green jungle, as a man on the top of a mast can see for miles across the sea, and then the branches and leaves would lash him across the face, and he and his two guards would be almost down to earth again.

So bounding and crashing and whooping and yelling, the whole tribe of Bandar-log swept along the tree-roads with Mowgli their prisoner.

For a time he was afraid of being dropped; then he grew angry, but he knew better than to struggle; and then he began to think. The first thing was to send back word to Baloo and Bagheera, for, at the pace the monkeys were going, he knew his friends would be left far behind. It was useless to look down, for he could see only the top sides of the branches, so he stared upward and saw, far away in the blue, Rann, the Kite, balancing and wheeling as he kept watch over the jungle waiting for things to die. Rann noticed that the monkeys were carrying something, and dropped a few hundred yards to find out whether their load was good to eat. He whistled with surprise when he saw Mowgli being dragged up to a tree-top, and heard him give the Kite call for "We be of one blood, thou and I." The waves of the branches closed over the boy, but Rann balanced away to the next tree in time to see the little brown face come up again. "Mark my trail!" Mowgli shouted. "Tell Baloo of the Seeonee Pack, and Bagheera of the Council Rock."

"In whose name, Brother?" Rann had never seen Mowgli before, though of course he had heard of him.

"Mowgli, the Frog. Man-cub they call me! Mark my tra—il!"

The last words were shrieked as he was being swung through the air, but Rann nodded, and rose up till he looked no bigger than a speck of dust, and there he hung, watching with his telescope eyes the swaying of the tree-tops as Mowgli's escort whirled along.

"They never go far," he said with a chuckle. "They never do what they set out to do. Always pecking at new things are the Bandar-log. This time, if I have any eyesight, they have pecked down trouble for themselves, for Baloo is no fledgling and Bagheera can, as I know, kill more than goats."

Then he rocked on his wings, his feet gathered up under him, and waited.

Meanwhile, Baloo and Bagheera were furious with rage and grief. Bagheera climbed as he had never climbed before, but the branches broke beneath his weight, and he slipped down, his claws full of bark.

"Why didst thou not warn the man-cub!" he roared to poor Baloo, who had set off at a clumsy trot in the hope of overtaking the monkeys. "What was the use of half slaying him with blows if thou didst not warn him?"

"Haste! O haste! We—we may catch them yet!" Baloo panted.

"At that speed! It would not tire a wounded cow. Teacher of the Law, cub-beater—a mile of that rolling to and fro would burst thee open. Sit still and think! Make a plan. This is no time for chasing. They may drop him if we follow too close."

"*Arrula! Whoo!* They may have dropped him already, being tired of carrying him. Who can trust the Bandar-log? Put dead bats on my head! Give me black bones to eat! Roll me into the hives of the wild bees that I may be stung to death, and bury me with the hyena; for I am the most miserable of bears! *Arulala! Wahooa!* O Mowgli, Mowgli! Why did I not warn thee against the Monkey Folk instead of breaking thy head? Now perhaps I may have knocked the day's lesson out of his mind, and he will be alone in the jungle without the Master Words!"

Baloo clasped his paws over his ears and rolled to and fro, moaning.

"At least he gave me all the Words correctly a little time ago," said Bagheera, impatiently. "Baloo, thou hast neither memory nor respect. What would the jungle think if I, the Black Panther, curled myself up like Ikki, the Porcupine, and howled?"

"What do I care what the jungle thinks? He may be dead by now."

"Unless and until they drop him from the branches in sport, or kill him out of idleness, I have no fear for the man-cub. He is wise and well-taught, and, above all, he has the eyes that make the Jungle People afraid. But (and it is a great evil) he is in the power of the Bandar-log, and they, because they live in trees, have no fear of any of our people." Bagheera licked his one fore paw thoughtfully.

"Fool that I am! Oh, fat, brown, root-digging fool that I am!" said Baloo, uncoiling himself with a jerk. "It is true what Hathi, the Wild Elephant, says: *'To each his own fear'*; and they, the Bandar-log, fear Kaa, the Rock Snake. He can climb as well as they can. He steals the young monkeys in the night. The mere whisper of his name makes their wicked tails cold. Let us go to Kaa."

"What will he do for us? He is not of our tribe, being footless and with most evil eyes," said Bagheera.

"He is very old and very cunning. Above all, he is always hungry," said Baloo, hopefully. "Promise him many goats."

"He sleeps for a full month after he has once eaten. He may be asleep now, and even were he awake, what if he would rather kill his own goats?" Bagheera, who did not know much about Kaa, was naturally suspicious.

"Then in that case, thou and I together, old hunter, may make him see reason." Here Baloo rubbed his faded brown shoulder against the panther, and they went off to look for Kaa, the Rock Python.

They found him stretched out on a warm ledge in the afternoon sun, admiring his beautiful new coat for he had been in retirement for the last ten days changing his skin, and now he was very splendid—darting his big blunt-nosed head along the ground, and twisting the thirty feet of his body into fantastic knots and curves, and licking his lips as he thought of his dinner to come.

"He has not eaten," said Baloo, with a grunt of relief, as soon as he saw the beautifully mottled brown and yellow jacket. "Be careful, Bagheera! He is always a little blind after he has changed his skin, and very quick to strike."

Kaa was not a poison snake—in fact he rather despised the Poison Snakes for cowards; but his strength lay in his hug, and when he had once lapped his huge coils round anybody there was no more to be said. "Good hunting!" cried Baloo, sitting up on his haunches. Like all snakes of his breed Kaa was rather deaf, and did not hear the call at first. Then he curled up ready for any accident, his head lowered.

"Good hunting for us all," he answered. "Oho, Baloo, what dost thou do here? Good hunting, Bagheera. One of us at least needs food. Is there any news of game afoot? A doe now, or even a young buck? I am as empty as a dried well."

"We are hunting," said Baloo, carelessly. He knew that you must not hurry Kaa. He is too big.

"Give me permission to come with you," said Kaa. "A blow more or less is nothing to thee, Bagheera or Baloo, but I—I have to wait and wait for days in a wood path and climb half a night on the mere chance of a young ape. *Pss naw!* The branches are not what they were when I was young. Rotten twigs and dry boughs are they all."

"Maybe thy great weight has something to do with the matter," said Baloo.

"I am a fair length—a fair length," said Kaa, with a little pride. "But for all that, it is the fault of this new-grown timber. I came very near to falling on my last hunt,—very near indeed,—and the noise of my slipping, for my tail was not tight wrapped round the tree, waked the Bandar-log, and they called me most evil names."

"'Footless, yellow earthworm,'" said Bagheera under his whiskers, as though he were trying to remember something.

"Sssss! Have they ever called me *that?"* said Kaa.

"Something of that kind it was that they shouted to us last moon, but we never noticed them. They will say anything—even that thou hast lost all thy teeth, and dare not face anything bigger than a kid, because (they are indeed shameless, these Bandar-log)—because thou art afraid of the he-goats' horns," Bagheera went on sweetly.

Now a snake, especially a wary old python like Kaa, very seldom shows that he is angry, but Baloo and Bagheera could see the big swallowing muscles on either side of Kaa's throat ripple and bulge.

"The Bandar-log have shifted their grounds," he said, quietly. "When I came up into the sun today I heard them whooping among the tree-tops."

"It—it is the Bandar-log that we follow now," said Baloo; but the words stuck in his throat, for this was the first time in his memory that one of the Jungle People had owned to being interested in the doings of the monkeys.

"Beyond doubt, then, it is no small thing that takes two such hunters—leaders in their own jungle, I am certain—on the trail of the Bandar-log," Kaa replied, courteously, as he swelled with curiosity.

"Indeed," Baloo began, "I am no more than the old, and sometimes very foolish, Teacher of the Law to the Seeonee wolf-cubs, and Bagheera here—"

"Is Bagheera," said the Black Panther, and his jaws shut with a snap, for he did not believe in being humble. "The trouble is this, Kaa. Those nut-stealers and pickers of palm-leaves have stolen away our man-cub, of whom thou hast perhaps heard."

"I heard some news from Ikki (his quills make him presumptuous) of a man-thing that was entered into a wolf-pack, but I did not believe. Ikki is full of stories half heard and very badly told."

"But it is true. He is such a man-cub as never was," said Baloo. "The best and wisest and boldest of man-cubs. My own pupil, who shall make the name of Baloo famous through all the jungles, and besides, I—we—love him, Kaa."

"Ts! Ts!" said Kaa, shaking his head to and fro. "I have also known what love is. There are tales I could tell that—"

"That need a clear night when we are all well fed to praise properly," said Bagheera, quickly. "Our man-cub is in the hands of the Bandar-log now, and we know that of all the Jungle People they fear Kaa alone."

"They fear me alone. They have good reason," said Kaa. "Chattering, foolish, vain—vain, foolish, and chattering—are the monkeys. But a man-thing in their hands is in no good luck. They grow tired of the nuts they pick, and throw them down. They carry a branch half a day, meaning to do great things with it, and then snap it in two. That manling is not to be envied. They called me also—'yellow fish,' was it not?"

"Worm—worm—earthworm," said Bagheera; "as well as other things which I cannot now say for shame."

"We must remind them to speak well of their master. *Aaa-sssh!* We must help their wandering memories. Now, whither went they with thy cub?"

"The jungle alone knows. Toward the sunset, I believe," said Baloo. "We had thought that thou wouldst know, Kaa."

"I? How? I take them when they come in my way, but I do not hunt the Bandar-log—or frogs—or green scum on a water-hole, for that matter."

"Up, up! Up, up! *Hillo! Illo! Illo!* Look up, Baloo of the Seeonee Wolf Pack!"

Baloo looked up to see where the voice came from, and there was Rann, the Kite, sweeping down with the sun shining on the upturned flanges of his wings. It was near Rann's bedtime, but he had ranged all over the jungle looking for the bear, and missed him in the thick foliage.

"What is it?" said Baloo.

"I have seen Mowgli among the Bandar-log. He bade me tell you. I watched. The Bandar-log have taken him beyond the river to the Monkey City—to the Cold Lairs. They may stay there for a night, or ten nights, or an hour. I have told the bats to watch through the dark time. That is my message. Good hunting, all you below!"

"Full gorge and a deep sleep to you, Rann!" cried Bagheera. "I will remember thee in my next kill, and put aside the head for thee alone, O best of kites!"

"It is nothing. It is nothing. The boy held the Master Word. I could have done no less," and Rann circled up again to his roost.

"He has not forgotten to use his tongue," said Baloo, with a chuckle of pride. "To think of one so young remembering the Master Word for the birds while he was being pulled across trees!"

"It was most firmly driven into him," said Bagheera. "But I am proud of him, and now we must go to the Cold Lairs."

They all knew where that place was, but few of the Jungle People ever went there, because what they called the Cold Lairs was an old deserted city, lost and buried in the jungle, and beasts seldom use a place that men have once used. The wild boar will, but the hunting-tribes do not. Besides, the monkeys lived there as much as they could be said to live anywhere, and no self-respecting animal would come within eyeshot of it except in times of drouth, when the half-ruined tanks and reservoirs held a little water.

"It is half a night's journey—at full speed," said Bagheera. Baloo looked very serious. "I will go as fast as I can," he said, anxiously.

"We dare not wait for thee. Follow, Baloo. We must go on the quick-foot—Kaa and I."

"Feet or no feet, I can keep abreast of all thy four," said Kaa, shortly.

Baloo made one effort to hurry, but had to sit down panting, and so they left him to come on later, while Bagheera hurried forward, at the rocking panther-canter. Kaa said nothing, but, strive as Bagheera might, the huge Rock Python held level with him. When they came to a hill-stream, Bagheera gained, because he bounded across while Kaa swam, his head and two feet of his neck clearing the water, but on level ground Kaa made up the distance.

"By the Broken Lock that freed me," said Bagheera, when twilight had fallen, "thou art no slow-goer."

"I am hungry," said Kaa. "Besides, they called me speckled frog."

"Worm—earthworm, and yellow to boot."

"All one. Let us go on," and Kaa seemed to pour himself along the ground, finding the shortest road with his steady eyes, and keeping to it.

In the Cold Lairs the Monkey People were not thinking of Mowgli's friends at all. They had brought the boy to the Lost City, and were very pleased with themselves for the time. Mowgli had never seen an Indian city before, and though this was almost a heap of ruins it seemed very wonderful and splendid. Some king had built it long ago on a little hill. You could still trace the stone causeways that led up to the ruined gates where the last splinters of wood hung to the worn, rusted hinges. Trees had grown into and out of the walls; the battlements were tumbled down and decayed, and wild creepers hung out of the windows of the towers on the walls in bushy hanging clumps.

A great roofless palace crowned the hill, and the marble of the courtyards and the fountains was split and stained with red and green, and the very cobblestones in the courtyard where the king's elephants used to live had been thrust up and apart by grasses and young trees. From the palace you could see the rows and rows of roofless houses that made up the city, looking like empty honeycombs filled with blackness; the shapeless block of stone that had been an idol in the square where four roads met; the pits and dimples at street corners where the public wells once stood, and the shattered domes of temples with wild figs sprouting on their sides.

The monkeys called the place their city, and pretended to despise the Jungle People because they lived in the forest. And yet they never knew what the buildings were made for nor how to use them. They would sit in circles on the hall of the king's council-chamber, and scratch for fleas and pretend to be men; or they would run in and out of the roofless houses and collect pieces of plaster and old bricks in a corner, and forget where they had hidden them, and fight and cry in scuffling crowds, and then break off to play up and down the terraces of the king's garden, where they would shake the rose-trees and the oranges in sport to see the fruit and flowers fall. They explored all the passages and dark tunnels in the palace and the hundreds of little dark rooms; but they never remembered what they had seen and what they had not, and so drifted about in ones and twos or crowds, telling one another that they were doing as men did. They drank at the tanks and made the water all muddy, and then they fought over it, and then they would all rush together in mobs and shout: "There are none in the jungle so wise and good and clever and strong and gentle as the Bandar-log." Then all would begin again till they grew tired of the city and went back to the tree-tops, hoping the Jungle People would notice them.

Mowgli, who had been trained under the Law of the Jungle, did not like or understand this kind of life. The monkeys dragged him into the Cold Lairs late in the afternoon, and instead of going to sleep, as Mowgli would have done after a long journey, they joined hands and danced about and sang their foolish songs.

One of the monkeys made a speech, and told his companions that Mowgli's capture marked a new thing in the history of the Bandar-log, for Mowgli was going to show them how to weave sticks and canes together as a protection against rain and cold. Mowgli picked up some creepers and began to work them in and out, and the monkeys tried to imitate; but in a very few minutes they lost interest and began to pull their friends' tails or jump up and down on all fours, coughing.

"I want to eat," said Mowgli. "I am a stranger in this part of the jungle. Bring me food, or give me leave to hunt here."

Twenty or thirty monkeys bounded away to bring him nuts and wild pawpaws; but they fell to fighting on the road, and it was too much trouble to go back with what was left of the fruit. Mowgli was sore and angry as well as hungry and he roamed through the empty city giving the Strangers' Hunting Call from time to time, but no one answered him, and Mowgli felt that he had reached a very bad place indeed.

"All that Baloo has said about the Bandar-log is true," he thought to himself. "They have no Law, no Hunting Call, and no leaders—nothing but foolish words and little picking, thievish hands. So if I am starved or killed here, it will be all my own fault. But I must try to return to my own jungle. Baloo will surely beat me, but that is better than chasing silly rose-leaves with the Bandar-log."

But no sooner had he walked to the city wall than the monkeys pulled him back, telling him that he did not know how happy he was, and pinching him to make him grateful. He set his teeth and said nothing, but went with the shouting monkeys to a terrace above the red sand-stone reservoirs that were half full of rain-water. There was a ruined summer-house of white marble in the centre of the terrace, built for queens dead a hundred years ago. The domed roof had half fallen in and blocked up the underground passage from the palace by which the queens used to enter; but the walls were made of screens of marble tracery—beautiful, milk-white fret-work, set with agates and cornelians and jasper and lapis lazuli, and as the moon came up behind the hill it shone through the openwork, casting shadows on the ground like black-velvet embroidery.

Sore, sleepy, and hungry as he was, Mowgli could not help laughing when the Bandar-log began twenty at a time, to tell him how great and wise and strong and gentle they were, and how foolish he was to wish to leave them. "We are great. We are free. We are wonderful. We are the most wonderful people in all the jungle! We all say so, and so it must be true," they shouted. "Now as you are a new listener and can carry our words back to the Jungle People so that they may notice us in future, we will tell you all about our most excellent selves."

Mowgli made no objection, and the monkeys gathered by hundreds and hundreds on the terrace to listen to their own speakers singing the praises of the Bandar-log, and whenever a speaker stopped for want of breath they would all shout together: "This is true; we all say so."

Mowgli nodded and blinked, and said "Yes" when they asked him a question, and his head spun with the noise. "Tabaqui, the Jackal, must have bitten all these people," he said to himself, "and now they have the madness. Certainly this is *dewanee*—the madness. Do they never go to sleep? Now there is a cloud coming to cover that moon. If it were only a big enough cloud I might try to run away in the darkness. But I am tired."

That same cloud was being watched by two good friends in the ruined ditch below the city wall, for Bagheera and Kaa, knowing well how dangerous the Monkey People were in large numbers, did not wish to run any risks. The monkeys never fight unless they are a hundred to one, and few in the jungle care for those odds.

"I will go to the west wall," Kaa whispered, "and come down swiftly with the slope of the ground in my favour. They will not throw themselves upon *my* back in their hundreds, but—"

"I know it," said Bagheera. "Would that Baloo were here; ut we must do what we can. When that cloud covers the noon I shall go to the terrace. They hold some sort of counil there over the boy."

"Good hunting," said Kaa, grimly, and glided away to the vest wall. That happened to be the least ruined of any, and he big snake was delayed a while before he could find a way p the stones.

The cloud hid the moon, and as Mowgli wondered what vould come next he heard Bagheera's light feet on the terrace. he Black Panther had raced up the slope almost without a ound, and was striking—he knew better than to waste time n biting—right and left among the monkeys, who were seated ound Mowgli in circles fifty and sixty deep. There was a owl of fright and rage, and then as Bagheera tripped on the olling, kicking bodies beneath him, a monkey shouted: "There only one here! Kill him! Kill!" a scuffling mass of monkeys, iting, scratching, tearing, and pulling, closed over Bagheera, while five or six laid hold of Mowgli, dragged him up the wall of the summer-house, and pushed him through the hole of the broken dome. A man-trained boy would have been badly bruised, for the fall was a good ten feet, but Mowgli fell as Baloo had taught him to fall, and landed light.

"Stay there," shouted the monkeys, "till we have killed thy friend. Later we will play with thee, if the Poison People leave thee alive."

"We be of one blood, ye and I," said Mowgli, quickly giving the Snake's Call. He could hear rustling and hissing in the rubbish all round him, and gave the Call a second time to make sure.

"Down hoods all," said half a dozen low voices. Every old ruin in India becomes sooner or later a dwelling-place of snakes, and the old summer-house was alive with cobras. "Stand still, Little Brother, lest thy feet do us harm."

Mowgli stood as quietly as he could, peering through the openwork and listening to the furious din of the fight round the Black Panther—the yells and chatterings and scufflings, and Bagheera's deep, hoarse cough as he backed and bucked and twisted and plunged under the heaps of his enemies. For the first time since he was born, Bagheera was fighting for his life.

"Baloo must be at hand; Bagheera would not have come alone," Mowgli thought; and then he called aloud: "To the tank, Bagheera! Roll to the water-tanks! Roll and plunge Get to the water!"

Bagheera heard, and the cry that told him Mowgli wa safe gave him new courage. He worked his way desperately inch by inch, straight for the reservoirs, hitting in silence.

Then from the ruined wall nearest the jungle rose up th rumbling war-shout of Baloo. The old bear had done hi best, but he could not come before. "Bagheera," he shoutec "I am here! I climb! I haste! *Ahuwora!* The stones slip unde my feet! Wait my coming, O most infamous Bandar-log!"

He panted up the terrace only to disappear to the head i a wave of monkeys, but he threw himself squarely on hi haunches, and spreading out his fore paws, hugged as man as he could hold, and then began to hit with a regular *bat-bat-bat,* like the flipping strokes of a paddle-wheel.

A crash and a splash told Mowgli that Bagheera had fought his way to the tank, where the monkeys could not follow. The panther lay gasping for breath, his head just out of water, while the monkeys stood three deep on the red stone steps, dancing up and down with rage, ready to spring upon him from all sides if he came out to help Baloo. It was then that Bagheera lifted up his dripping chin, and in despair gave the Snake's Call for protection,—"We be of one blood, ye and I,"—for he believed that Kaa had turned tail at the last minute. Even Baloo, half smothered under the monkeys on the edge of the terrace, could not help chuckling as he heard the big Black Panther asking for help.

Kaa had only just worked his way over the west wall, landing with a wrench that dislodged a coping-stone into the ditch. He had no intention of losing any advantage of the ground, and coiled and uncoiled himself once or twice, to be sure that every foot of his long body was in working order. All that while the fight with Baloo went on, and the monkeys yelled in the tank round Bagheera, and Mang, the Bat, flying to and fro, carried the news of the great battle over the jungle, till even Hathi, the Wild Elephant, trumpeted, and, far away, scattered bands of the Monkey Folk woke and came leaping along the tree-roads to help their comrades in the Cold Lairs, and the noise of the fight roused all the day-birds for miles round.

Then Kaa came straight, quickly, and anxious to kill. The fighting strength of a python is in the driving blow of his head, backed by all the strength and weight of his body. If you can imagine a lance, or a battering-ram, or a hammer, weighing nearly half a ton driven by a cool, quiet mind living in the handle of it, you can imagine roughly what Kaa was like when he fought. A python four or five feet long can knock a man down if he hits him fairly in the chest, and Kaa was thirty feet long, as you know. His first stroke was delivered into the heart of the crowd round Baloo—was sent home with shut mouth in silence, and there was no need of a second. The monkeys scattered with cries of "Kaa! It is Kaa! Run! Run!"

Generations of monkeys have been scared into good behaviour by the stories their elders told them of Kaa, the night-thief, who could slip along the branches as quietly as moss grows, and steal away the strongest monkey that ever lived; of old Kaa, who could make himself look so like a dead branch or a rotten stump that the wisest were deceived till the branch caught them, and then—

Kaa was everything that the monkeys feared in the jungle, for none of them knew the limits of his power, none of them could look him in the face, and none had ever come alive out of his hug. And so they ran, stammering with terror, to the walls and the roofs of the houses, and Baloo drew a deep breath of relief. His fur was much thicker than Bagheera's, but he had suffered sorely in the fight. Then Kaa opened his mouth for the first time and spoke one long hissing word, and the far-away monkeys, hurrying to the defense of the Cold Lairs, stayed where they were, cowering, till the loaded branches bent and crackled under them. The monkeys on the walls and the empty houses stopped their cries, and in the stillness that fell upon the city Mowgli heard Bagheera shaking his wet sides as he came up from the tank.

Then the clamour broke out again. The monkeys leaped higher up the walls; they clung round the necks of the big stone idols and shrieked as they skipped along the battlements; while Mowgli, dancing in the summer-house, put his eye to the screenwork and hooted owl-fashion between his front teeth, to show his derision and contempt.

"Get the man-cub out of that trap; I can do no more," Bagheera gasped. "Let us take the man-cub and go. They may attack again."

"They will not move till I order them. Stay you sssso!" Kaa hissed, and the city was silent once more. "I could not come before, Brother, but, I *think* I heard thee call"—this was to Bagheera.

"I—I may have cried out in the battle," Bagheera answered. "Baloo, art thou hurt?"

"I am not sure that they have not pulled me into a hundred little bearlings," said Baloo, gravely shaking one leg after the other. "Wow! I am sore. Kaa, we owe thee, I think, our lives —Bagheera and I."

"No matter. Where is the manling?"

"Here, in a trap. I cannot climb out," cried Mowgli. The curve of the broken dome was above his head.

"Take him away. He dances like Mao, the Peacock. He will crush our young," said the cobras inside.

"Hah!" said Kaa, with a chuckle, "he has friends everywhere, this manling. Stand back, Manling; and hide you, O Poison People. I break down the wall."

Kaa looked carefully till he found a discoloured crack in the marble tracery showing a weak spot, made two or three light taps with his head to get the distance, and then lifting up six feet of his body clear of the ground, sent home half a dozen full-power, smashing blows, nose-first. The screen-work broke and fell away in a cloud of dust and rubbish, and Mowgli leaped through the opening and flung himself between Baloo and Bagheera—an arm round each big neck.

"Art thou hurt?" said Baloo, hugging him softly.

"I am sore, hungry, and not a little bruised; but, oh, they have handled ye grievously, my Brothers! Ye bleed."

"Others also," said Bagheera, licking his lips and looking at the monkey-dead on the terrace and round the tank.

"It is nothing, it is nothing if thou art safe, O my pride of all little frogs!" whimpered Baloo.

"Of that we shall judge later," said Bagheera, in a dry voice that Mowgli did not at all like. "But here is Kaa, to whom we owe the battle and thou owest thy life. Thank him according to our customs, Mowgli."

Mowgli turned and saw the great python's head swaying a foot above his own.

"So this is the manling," said Kaa. "Very soft is his skin, and he is not so unlike the Bandar-log. Have a care, Manling, that I do not mistake thee for a monkey some twilight when I have newly changed my coat."

"We be of one blood, thou and I," Mowgli answered. "I

take my life from thee, to-night. My kill shall be thy kill if ever thou art hungry, O Kaa."

"All thanks, Little Brother," said Kaa, though his eyes twinkled. "And what may so bold a hunter kill? I ask that I may follow when next he goes abroad."

"I kill nothing,—I am too little,—but I drive goats toward such as can use them. When thou art empty come to me and see if I speak the truth. I have some skill in these [he held out his hands], and if ever thou art in a trap, I may pay the debt which I owe to thee, to Bagheera, and to Baloo, here. Good hunting to ye all, my masters."

"Well said," growled Baloo, for Mowgli had returned thanks very prettily. The python dropped his head lightly for a minute on Mowgli's shoulder. "A brave heart and a courteous tongue," said he. "They shall carry thee far through the jungle, Manling. But now go hence quickly with thy friends. Go and sleep, for the moon sets, and what follows it is not well that thou shouldst see."

The moon was sinking behind the hills and the lines of trembling monkeys huddled together on the walls and battlements looked like ragged, shaky fringes of things. Baloo went down to the tank for a drink, and Bagheera began to put his fur in order, as Kaa glided out into the centre of the terrace and brought his jaws together with a ringing snap that drew all the monkeys' eyes upon him.

"The moon sets," he said. "Is there yet light to see?"

From the walls came a moan like the wind in the tree-tops: "We see, O Kaa!"

"Good! Begins now the Dance—the Dance of the Hunger of Kaa. Sit still and watch."

He turned twice or thrice in a big circle, weaving his head from right to left. Then he began making loops and figures of eight with his body, and soft, oozy triangles that melted into squares and five-side figures, and coiled mounds, never resting, never hurrying, and never stopping his low, humming song. It grew darker and darker, till at last the dragging, shifting coils disappeared, but they could hear the rustle of the scales.

Baloo and Bagheera stood still as stone, growling in their throats, their neck-hair bristling, and Mowgli watched and wondered.

"Bandar-log," said the voice of Kaa at last, "can ye stir foot or hand without my order? Speak!"

"Without thy order we cannot stir foot or hand, O Kaa!"

"Good! Come all one pace nearer to me."

The lines of the monkeys swayed forward helplessly, and Baloo and Bagheera took one stiff step forward with them.

"Nearer!" hissed Kaa, and they all moved again.

Mowgli laid his hands on Baloo and Bagheera to get them away, and the two great beasts started as though they had been waked from a dream.

"Keep thy hand on my shoulder," Bagheera whispered. "Keep it there, or I must go back—must go back to Kaa. *Aah!*"

"It is only old Kaa making circles on the dust," said Mowgli; "let us go"; and the three slipped off through a gap in the walls to the jungle.

"Whoof!" said Baloo, when he stood under the still trees again. "Never more will I make an ally of Kaa," and he shook himself all over.

"He knows more than we," said Bagheera, trembling. "In a little time, had I stayed, I should have walked down his throat."

"Many will walk that road before the moon rises again," said Baloo. "He will have good hunting—after his own fashion."

"But what was the meaning of it all?" said Mowgli, who did not know anything of a python's powers of fascination. "I saw no more than a big snake making foolish circles till the dark came. And his nose was all sore. Ho! Ho!"

"Mowgli," said Bagheera, angrily, "his nose was sore on *thy* account; as my ears and sides and paws, and Baloo's neck and shoulders are bitten on *thy* account. Neither Baloo nor Bagheera will be able to hunt with pleasure for many days."

"It is nothing," said Baloo; "we have the man-cub again."

"True; but he has cost us most heavily in time which might have been spent in good hunting, in wounds, in hair,—I am half plucked along my back,—and last of all, in honour. For, remember, Mowgli, I, who am the Black Panther, was forced to call upon Kaa for protection, and Baloo and I were both made stupid as little birds by the Hunger-Dance. All this, Man-cub, came of thy playing with the Bandar-log."

"True; it is true," said Mowgli, sorrowfully. "I am an evil man-cub, and my stomach is sad in me."

"*Mf!* What says the Law of the Jungle, Baloo?"

Baloo did not wish to bring Mowgli into any more trouble, but he could not tamper with the Law, so he mumbled, "Sorrow never stays punishment. But remember, Bagheera, he is very little."

"I will remember; but he has done mischief; and blows must be dealt now. Mowgli, hast thou anything to say?"

"Nothing. I did wrong. Baloo and thou art wounded. It is just."

Bagheera gave him half a dozen love-taps; from a panther's point of view they would hardly have waked one of his own cubs, but for a seven-year-old boy they amounted to as severe a beating as you could wish to avoid. When it was all over Mowgli sneezed, and picked himself up without a word.

"Now," said Bagheera, "jump on my back, Little Brother, and we will go home."

One of the beauties of Jungle Law is that punishment settles all scores. There is no nagging afterward.

Mowgli laid his head down on Bagheera's back and slept so deeply that he never waked when he was put down by Mother Wolf's side in the home-cave.

ROAD-SONG OF THE BANDAR-LOG

1894

Here we go in a flung festoon,
Half-way up to the jealous moon!
Don't you envy our pranceful bands?
Don't you wish you had extra hands?

Wouldn't you like if your tails were—*so*—
Curved in the shape of a Cupid's bow?
  Now you're angry, but—never mind,
  Brother, thy tail hangs down behind!

Here we sit in a branchy row,
Thinking of beautiful things we know;
Dreaming of deeds that we mean to do,
All complete, in a minute or two—
Something noble and grand and good,
Won by merely wishing we could.
  Now we're going to—never mind,
  Brother, thy tail hangs down behind!

All the talk we ever have heard
Uttered by bat or beast or bird—
Hide or fin or scale or feather—
Jabber it quickly and all together!
Excellent! Wonderful! Once again!
Now we are talking just like men.
  Let's pretend we are . . . never mind,
  Brother, thy tail hangs down behind!
  This is the way of the Monkey-kind.

Then join our leaping lines that scumfish through the pines,
That rocket by where, light and high, the wild-grape swings,
By the rubbish in our wake, and the noble noise we make,
Be sure, be sure, we're going to do some splendid things!

"RIKKI-TIKKI-TAVI"
1893

At the hole where he went in
Red-Eye called to Wrinkle-Skin.
Hear what little Red-Eye saith:
"Nag, come up and dance with death!"

Eye to eye and head to head,
(Keep the measure, Nag.)
This shall end when one is dead;
(At thy pleasure, Nag.)

Turn for turn and twist for twist—
(Run and hide thee, Nag.)
Hah! The hooded Death has missed!
(Woe betide thee, Nag!)

THIS is the story of the great war that Rikki-tikki-tavi fought single-handed, through the bath-rooms of the big bungalow in Segowlee cantonment. Darzee, the tailor-bird, helped him, and Chuchundra, the muskrat, who never comes out into the middle of the floor, but always creeps round by the wall, gave him advice; but Rikki-tikki did the real fighting.

He was a mongoose, rather like a little cat in his fur and his tail, but quite like a weasel in his head and his habits. His eyes and the end of his restless nose were pink; he could scratch himself anywhere he pleased, with any leg, front or back, that he chose to use; he could fluff up his tail till it looked like a bottle-brush, and his war-cry as he scuttled through the long grass, was: *"Rikk-tikk-tikki-tikki-tchk!"*

One day, a high summer flood washed him out of the burrow where he lived with his father and mother, and carried him, kicking and clucking, down a roadside ditch. He found a little wisp of grass floating there, and clung to it till he lost his senses. When he revived, he was lying in the hot sun on the middle of a garden path, very draggled indeed, and a small boy was saying: "Here's a dead mongoose. Let's have a funeral."

"No," said his mother; "let's take him in and dry him. Perhaps he isn't really dead."

They took him into the house, and a big man picked him up between his finger and thumb and said he was not dead but half choked; so they wrapped him in cotton-wool, and warmed him, and he opened his eyes and sneezed.

"Now," said the big man (he was an Englishman who had just moved into the bungalow); "don't frighten him, and we'll see what he'll do."

It is the hardest thing in the world to frighten a mongoose, because he is eaten up from nose to tail with curiosity. The motto of all the mongoose family is, "Run and find out"; and Rikki-tikki was a true mongoose. He looked at the cotton-wool, decided that it was not good to eat, ran all round the table, sat up and put his fur in order, scratched himself, and jumped on the small boy's shoulder.

"Don't be frightened, Teddy," said his father. "That's his way of making friends."

"Ouch! He's tickling under my chin," said Teddy.

Rikki-tikki looked down between the boy's collar and neck, snuffed at his ear, and climbed down to the floor, where he sat rubbing his nose.

"Good gracious," said Teddy's mother, "and that's a wild creature! I suppose he's so tame because we've been kind to him."

"All mongooses are like that," said her husband. "If Teddy doesn't pick him up by the tail, or try to put him in a cage, he'll run in and out of the house all day long. Let's give him something to eat."

They gave him a little piece of raw meat. Rikki-tikki liked it immensely, and when it was finished he went out into the veranda and sat in the sunshine and fluffed up his fur to make it dry to the roots. Then he felt better.

"There are more things to find out about in this house," he said to himself, "than all my family could find out in all their lives. I shall certainly stay and find out."

He spent all that day roaming over the house. He nearly drowned himself in the bath-tubs, put his nose into the ink on a writing-table, and burned it on the end of the big man's cigar, for he climbed up in the big man's lap to see how writing was done. At nightfall he ran into Teddy's nursery to watch how kerosene lamps were lighted, and when Teddy went to bed Rikki-tikki climbed up too; but he was a restless companion, because he had to get up and attend to every noise all through the night, and find out what made it. Teddy's mother and father came in, the last thing, to look at their boy, and Rikki-tikki was awake on the pillow. "I don't like that," said Teddy's mother; "he may bite the child." "He'll do no such thing," said the father. "Teddy's safer with that little beast than if he had a bloodhound to watch him. If a snake came into the nursery now—"

But Teddy's mother wouldn't think of anything so awful.

Early in the morning Rikki-tikki came to early breakfast in the veranda riding on Teddy's shoulder, and they gave him banana and some boiled egg; and he sat on all their laps one after the other, because every well-brought-up mongoose always hopes to be a house-mongoose some day and have rooms to run about in, and Rikki-tikki's mother (she used to live in the General's house at Segowlee) had carefully told Rikki what to do if ever he came across white men.

Then Rikki-tikki went out into the garden to see what was to be seen. It was a large garden, only half cultivated, with bushes as big as summer-houses of Marshal Niel roses, lime and orange trees, clumps of bamboos, and thickets of high grass. Rikki-tikki licked his lips. "This is a splendid hunting-ground," he said, and his tail grew bottle-brushy at the thought of it, and he scuttled up and down the garden, snuffing here and there till he heard very sorrowful voices in a thorn-bush.

It was Darzee, the tailor-bird, and his wife. They had made a beautiful nest by pulling two big leaves together and stitching them up the edges with fibers, and had filled the hollow with cotton and downy fluff. The nest swayed to and fro, as they sat on the rim and cried.

"What is the matter?" asked Rikki-tikki.

"We are very miserable," said Darzee. "One of our babies fell out of the nest yesterday and Nag ate him."

"H'm!" said Rikki-tikki, "that is very sad—but I am a stranger here. Who is Nag?"

Darzee and his wife only cowered down in the nest without answering, for from the thick grass at the foot of the bush there came a low hiss—a horrid cold sound that made Rikki-tikki jump back two clear feet. Then inch by inch out of the grass rose up the head and spread hood of Nag, the big black cobra, and he was five feet long from tongue to tail. When he had lifted one-third of himself clear of the ground, he stayed balancing to and fro exactly as a dandelion-tuft balances in the wind, and he looked at Rikki-tikki with the wicked snake's eyes that never change their expression, whatever the snake may be thinking of.

"Who is Nag?" he said. "*I* am Nag. The great god Brahm put his mark upon all our people when the first cobra spread his hood to keep the sun off Brahm as he slept. Look, and be afraid!"

He spread out his hood more than ever, and Rikki-tikki saw the spectacle-mark on the back of it that looks exactly like the eye part of a hook-and-eye fastening. He was afraid for the minute; but it is impossible for a mongoose to stay frightened for any length of time, and though Rikki-tikki had never met a live cobra before, his mother had fed him on dead ones, and he knew that all a grown mongoose's business in life was to fight and eat snakes. Nag knew that too, and at the bottom of his cold heart he was afraid.

"Well," said Rikki-tikki, and his tail began to fluff up again, "marks or no marks, do you think it is right for you to eat fledglings out of a nest?"

Nag was thinking to himself, and watching the least little movement in the grass behind Rikki-tikki. He knew that mongooses in the garden meant death sooner or later for him and his family; but he wanted to get Rikki-tikki off his guard. So he dropped his head a little, and put it on one side.

"Let us talk," he said. "You eat eggs. Why should not I eat birds?"

"Behind you! Look behind you!" sang Darzee.

Rikki-tikki knew better than to waste time in staring. He jumped up in the air as high as he could go, and just under him whizzed by the head of Nagaina, Nag's wicked wife. She had crept up behind him as he was talking, to make an end of him; and he heard her savage hiss as the stroke missed. He came down almost across her back, and if he had been an old mongoose he would have known that then was the time to break her back with one bite; but he was afraid of the terrible lashing return-stroke of the cobra. He bit, indeed, but did not bite long enough, and he jumped clear of the whisking tail, leaving Nagaina torn and angry.

"Wicked, wicked Darzee!" said Nag, lashing up as high as he could reach toward the nest in the thorn-bush; but Darzee had built it out of reach of snakes, and it only swayed to and fro.

Rikki-tikki felt his eyes growing red and hot (when a mongoose's eyes grow red, he is angry), and he sat back on his tail and hind legs like a little kangaroo, and looked all around him, and chattered with rage. But Nag and Nagaina had disappeared into the grass. When a snake misses its stroke, it never says anything or gives any sign of what it means to do next. Rikki-tikki did not care to follow them, for he did not feel sure that he could manage two snakes at once. So he trotted off to the gravel path near the house, and sat down to think. It was a serious matter for him.

If you read the old books of natural history, you will find they say that when the mongoose fights the snake and happens to get bitten, he runs off and eats some herb that cures him. That is not true. The victory is only a matter of quickness of eye and quickness of foot,—snake's blow against mongoose's jump,—and as no eye can follow the motion of a snake's head when it strikes, that makes things much more wonderful than any magic herb. Rikki-tikki knew he was a young mongoose, and it made him all the more pleased to think that he had managed to escape a blow from behind. It gave him confidence in himself, and when Teddy came running down the path, Rikki-tikki was ready to be petted.

But just as Teddy was stooping, something flinched a little in the dust, and a tiny voice said: "Be careful. I am death!" It was Karait, the dusty brown snakeling that lies for choice on the dusty earth; and his bite is as dangerous as the cobra's. But he is so small that nobody thinks of him, and so he does the more harm to people.

Rikki-tikki's eyes grew red again, and he danced up to Karait with the peculiar rocking, swaying motion that he had inherited from his family. It looks very funny, but it is so perfectly balanced a gait that you can fly off from it at any angle you please; and in dealing with snakes this is an advantage. If Rikki-tikki had only known, he was doing a much more dangerous thing than fighting Nag for Karait is so small, and can turn so quickly, that unless Rikki bit him close to the back of the head, he would get the return-stroke in his eye or lip. But Rikki did not know: his eyes were all red, and he rocked back and forth, looking for a good place to hold. Karait struck out. Rikki jumped sideways and tried to run in, but the wicked little dusty gray head lashed within a fraction of his shoulder, and he had to jump over the body, and the head followed his heels close.

Teddy shouted to the house: "Oh, look here! Our mongoose is killing a snake"; and Rikki-tikki heard a scream from Teddy's mother. His father ran out with a stick, but by the time he came up, Karait had lunged out once too far, and Rikki-tikki had sprung, jumped on the snake's back, dropped his head far between his fore legs, bitten as high up the back as he could get hold, and rolled away. That bite paralyzed Karait, and Rikki-tikki was just going to eat him up from the tail, after the custom of his family at dinner, when he remembered that a full meal makes a slow mongoose, and if he wanted all his strength and quickness ready, he must keep himself thin.

He went away for a dust-bath under the castor-oil bushes.

while Teddy's father beat the dead Karait. "What is the use of that?" thought Rikki-tikki. "I have settled it all"; and then Teddy's mother picked him up from the dust and hugged him, crying that he had saved Teddy from death, and Teddy's father said that he was a providence, and Teddy looked on with big scared eyes. Rikki-tikki was rather amused at all the fuss, which, of course, he did not understand. Teddy's mother might just as well have petted Teddy for playing in the dust. Rikki was thoroughly enjoying himself.

That night, at dinner, walking to and fro among the wine-glasses on the table, he could have stuffed himself three times over with nice things; but he remembered Nag and Nagaina, and though it was very pleasant to be patted and petted by Teddy's mother, and to sit on Teddy's shoulder, his eyes would get red from time to time, and he would go off into his long war-cry of *"Rikk-tikk-tikki-tikki-tchk!"*

Teddy carried him off to bed, and insisted on Rikki-tikki sleeping under his chin. Rikki-tikki was too well bred to bite or scratch, but as soon as Teddy was asleep he went off for his nightly walk round the house, and in the dark he ran up against Chuchundra, the muskrat, creeping round by the wall. Chuchundra is a broken-hearted little beast. He whimpers and cheeps all the night, trying to make up his mind to run into the middle of the room, but he never gets there.

"Don't kill me," said Chuchundra, almost weeping. "Rikki-tikki, don't kill me."

"Do you think a snake-killer kills muskrats?" said Rikki-tikki scornfully.

"Those who kill snakes get killed by snakes," said Chuchundra, more sorrowfully than ever. "And how am I to be sure that Nag won't mistake me for you some dark night?"

"There's not the least danger," said Rikki-tikki; "but Nag is in the garden, and I know you don't go there."

"My cousin Chua, the rat, told me—" said Chuchundra, and then he stopped.

"Told you what?"

"H'sh! Nag is everywhere, Rikki-tikki. You should have talked to Chua in the garden."

"I didn't—so you must tell me. Quick, Chuchundra, or I'll bite you!"

Chuchundra sat down and cried till the tears rolled off his whiskers. "I am a very poor man," he sobbed. "I never had spirit enough to run out into the middle of the room. H'sh! I mustn't tell you anything. Can't you *hear*, Rikki-tikki?"

Rikki-tikki listened. The house was as still as still, but he thought he could just catch the faintest *scratch-scratch* in the world,—a noise as faint as that of a wasp walking on a window-pane,—the dry scratch of a snake's scales on brick-work.

"That's Nag or Nagaina," he said to himself; "and he is crawling into the bath-room sluice. You're right, Chuchundra; I should have talked to Chua."

He stole off to Teddy's bath-room, but there was nothing there, and then to Teddy's mother's bath-room. At the bottom of the smooth plaster wall there was a brick pulled out to make a sluice for the bath-water, and as Rikki-tikki stole in by the masonry curb where the bath is put, he heard Nag and Nagaina whispering together outside in the moonlight.

"When the house is emptied of people," said Nagaina to her husband, "*he* will have to go away, and then the garden will be our own again. Go in quietly, and remember that the big man who killed Karait is the first one to bite. Then come out and tell me, and we will hunt for Rikki-tikki together."

"But are you sure that there is anything to be gained by killing the people?" said Nag.

"Everything. When there were no people in the bungalow, did we have any mongoose in the garden? So long as the bungalow is empty, we are king and queen of the garden; and remember that as soon as our eggs in the melon-bed hatch (as they may to-morrow), our children will need room and quiet."

"I had not thought of that," said Nag. "I will go, but there is no need that we should hunt for Rikki-tikki afterward. I will kill the big man and his wife, and the child if I can, and come away quietly. Then the bungalow will be empty, and Rikki-tikki will go."

Rikki-tikki tingled all over with rage and hatred at this, and then Nag's head came through the sluice, and his five feet of cold body followed it. Angry as he was, Rikki-tikki was very frightened as he saw the size of the big cobra. Nag coiled himself up, raised his head, and looked into the bathroom in the dark, and Rikki could see his eyes glitter.

"Now, if I kill him here, Nagaina will know; and if I fight him on the open floor, the odds are in his favour. What am I to do?" said Rikki-tikki-tavi.

Nag waved to and fro, and then Rikki-tikki heard him drinking from the biggest water-jar that was used to fill the bath. "That is good," said the snake. "Now, when Karait was killed, the big man had a stick. He may have that stick still, but when he comes in to bathe in the morning he will not have a stick. I shall wait here till he comes. Nagaina—do you hear me?—I shall wait here in the cool till daytime."

There was no answer from outside, so Rikki-tikki knew Nagaina had gone away. Nag coiled himself down, coil by coil, round the bulge at the bottom of the water-jar, and Rikki-tikki stayed still as death. After an hour he began to move, muscle by muscle, toward the jar. Nag was asleep, and Rikki-tikki looked at his big back, wondering which would be the best place for a good hold. "If I don't break his back at the first jump," said Rikki, "he can still fight; and if he fights—O Rikki!" He looked at the thickness of the neck below the hood, but that was too much for him; and a bite near the tail would only make Nag savage.

"It must be the head," he said at last; "the head above the hood; and, when I am once there, I must not let go."

Then he jumped. The head was lying a little clear of the water-jar, under the curve of it; and, as his teeth met, Rikki braced his back against the bulge of the red earthenware to hold down the head. This gave him just one second's purchase, and he made the most of it. Then he was battered to and fro as a rat is shaken by a dog—to and fro on the floor, up and down, and round in great circles; but his eyes were red, and he held on as the body cartwhipped over the floor, upsetting the tin dipper and the soap-dish and the flesh-brush, and banged against the tin side of the bath. As he held he closed his jaws tighter and tighter, for he made sure he would be banged to death, and, for the honour of his family, he preferred to be found with his teeth locked. He was dizzy, aching, and felt shaken to pieces when something went off like a thunder-clap just behind him; a hot wind knocked him senseless and red fire singed his fur. The big man had been wakened by the noise, and had fired both barrels of a shot-gun into Nag just behind the hood.

Rikki-tikki held on with his eyes shut, for now he was quite sure he was dead; but the head did not move, and the big man picked him up and said: "It's the mongoose again, Alice; the little chap has saved *our* lives now." Then Teddy's mother came in with a very white face, and saw what was left of Nag, and Rikki-tikki dragged himself to Teddy's bed-room and spent half the rest of the night shaking himself tenderly to find out whether he really was broken into forty pieces, as he fancied.

When morning came he was very stiff, but well pleased with his doings. "Now I have Nagaina to settle with, and she will be worse than five Nags, and there's no knowing when the eggs she spoke of will hatch. Goodness! I must go and see Darzee," he said.

Without waiting for breakfast, Rikki-tikki ran to the thorn-bush where Darzee was singing a song of triumph at the top of his voice. The news of Nag's death was all over the garden, for the sweeper had thrown the body on the rubbish-heap.

"Oh, you stupid tuft of feathers!" said Rikki-tikki, angrily. "Is this the time to sing?"

"Nag is dead—is dead—is dead!" sang Darzee. "The valiant Rikki-tikki caught him by the head and held fast. The big man brought the bang-stick and Nag fell in two pieces! He will never eat my babies again."

"All that's true enough; but where's Nagaina?" said Rikki-tikki, looking carefully round him.

"Nagaina came to the bath-room sluice and called for Nag," Darzee went on; "and Nag came out on the end of a stick—the sweeper picked him up on the end of a stick and threw him upon the rubbish-heap. Let us sing about the great, the red-eyed Rikki-tikki!" and Darzee filled his throat and sang.

"If I could get up to your nest, I'd roll all your babies out!" said Rikki-tikki. "You don't know when to do the right thing at the right time. You're safe enough in your nest there, but it's war for me down here. Stop singing a minute, Darzee."

"For the great, the beautiful Rikki-tikki's sake I will stop," said Darzee. "What is it, O Killer of the terrible Nag?"

"Where is Nagaina, for the third time?"

"On the rubbish-heap by the stables, mourning for Nag. Great is Rikki-tikki with the white teeth."

"Bother my white teeth! Have you ever heard where she keeps her eggs?"

"In the melon-bed, on the end nearest the wall, where the sun strikes nearly all day. She had them there weeks ago."

"And you never thought it worth while to tell me? The end nearest the wall, you said?"

"Rikki-tikki, you are not going to eat her eggs?"

"Not eat exactly; no. Darzee, if you have a grain of sense you will fly off to the stables and pretend that your wing is broken, and let Nagaina chase you away to this bush! I must get to the melon-bed, and if I went there now she'd see me."

Darzee was a feather-brained little fellow who could never hold more than one idea at a time in his head; and just because he knew that Nagaina's children were born in eggs like his own, he didn't think at first that it was fair to kill them. But his wife was a sensible bird, and she knew that cobras' eggs meant young cobras later on; so she flew off from the nest, and left Darzee to keep the babies warm, and continue his song about the death of Nag. Darzee was very like a man in some ways.

She fluttered in front of Nagaina by the rubbish-heap, and cried out, "Oh, my wing is broken! The boy in the house threw a stone at me and broke it." Then she fluttered more desperately than ever.

Nagaina lifted up her head and hissed, "You warned Rikki-tikki when I would have killed him. Indeed and truly, you've chosen a bad place to be lame in." And she moved toward Darzee's wife, slipping along over the dust.

"The boy broke it with a stone!" shrieked Darzee's wife.

"Well! It may be some consolation to you when you're dead to know that I shall settle accounts with the boy. My husband lies on the rubbish-heap this morning, but before night the boy in the house will lie very still. What is the use of running away? I am sure to catch you. Little fool, look at me!"

Darzee's wife knew better than to do *that,* for a bird who looks at a snake's eyes gets so frightened that she cannot move. Darzee's wife fluttered on, piping sorrowfully, and never leaving the ground, and Nagaina quickened her pace.

Rikki-tikki heard them going up the path from the stables, and he raced for the end of the melon-patch near the wall. There, in the warm litter about the melons, very cunningly hidden, he found twenty-five eggs, about the size of a bantam's eggs, but with whitish skin instead of shell.

"I was not a day too soon," he said; for he could see the baby cobras curled up inside the skin, and he knew that the minute they were hatched they could each kill a man or a mongoose. He bit off the tops of the eggs as fast as he could, taking care to crush the young cobras, and turned over the litter from time to time to see whether he had missed any. At last there were only three eggs left, and Rikki-tikki began to chuckle to himself, when he heard Darzee's wife screaming:

"Rikki-tikki, I led Nagaina toward the house, and she has gone into the veranda, and—oh, come quickly—she means killing!"

Rikki-tikki smashed two eggs, and tumbled backward down the melon-bed with the third egg in his mouth, and scuttled to the veranda as hard as he could put foot to the ground. Teddy and his mother and father were there at early breakfast; but Rikki-tikki saw that they were not eating anything. They sat stone-still, and their faces were white. Nagaina was coiled up on the matting by Teddy's chair, within easy striking distance of Teddy's bare leg, and she was swaying to and fro singing a song of triumph.

"Son of the big man that killed Nag," she hissed, "stay still. I am not ready yet. Wait a little. Keep very still, all you three. If you move I strike, and if you do not move I strike. Oh, foolish people, who killed my Nag!"

Teddy's eyes were fixed on his father, and all his father could do was to whisper, "Sit still, Teddy. You mustn't move. Teddy, keep still."

Then Rikki-tikki came up and cried: "Turn round, Nagaina; turn and fight!"

"All in good time," said she, without moving her eyes. "I will settle my account with *you* presently. Look at your friends, Rikki-tikki. They are still and white; they are afraid. They dare not move, and if you come a step nearer I strike."

"Look at your eggs," said Rikki-tikki, "in the melon-bed near the wall. Go and look, Nagaina."

The big snake turned half round, and saw the egg on the veranda. "Ah-h! Give it to me," she said.

Rikki-tikki put his paws one on each side of the egg, and his eyes were blood-red. "What price for a snake's egg? For a young cobra? For a young king-cobra? For the last—the very last of the brood? The ants are eating all the others down by the melon-bed."

Nagaina spun clear round, forgetting everything for the sake of the one egg; and Rikki-tikki saw Teddy's father shoot out a big hand, catch Teddy by the shoulder and drag him across the little table with the tea-cups, safe and out of reach of Nagaina.

"Tricked! Tricked! Tricked! *Rikk-tck-tck!*" chuckled Rikki-tikki. "The boy is safe, and it was I—I—I that caught Nag by the hood last night in the bath-room." Then he began to jump up and down, all four feet together, his head close to the floor. "He threw me to and fro, but he could not shake me off. He was dead before the big man blew him in two. I did it. *Rikki-tikki-tck-tck!* Come then, Nagaina. Come and fight with me. You shall not be a widow long."

Nagaina saw that she had lost her chance of killing Teddy, and the egg lay between Rikki-tikki's paws. "Give me the egg, Rikki-tikki. Give me the last of my eggs, and I will go away and never come back," she said, lowering her hood.

"Yes, you will go away, and you will never come back; for you will go to the rubblish-heap with Nag. Fight, widow! The big man has gone for his gun! Fight!"

Rikki-tikki was bounding all around Nagaina, keeping just out of the reach of her stroke, his little eyes like hot coals. Nagaina gathered herself together, and flung out at him. Rikki-tikki jumped up and backward. Again and again and again she struck, and each time her head came with a whack on the matting of the veranda and she gathered herself together like a watch-spring. Then Rikki-tikki danced in a circle to get behind her, and Nagaina spun round to keep her head to his head, so that the rustle of her tail on the matting sounded like dry leaves blown along by the wind.

He had forgotten the egg. It still lay on the veranda, and Nagaina came nearer and nearer to it, till at last, while Rikki-tikki was drawing breath, she caught it in her mouth, turned to the veranda steps, and flew like an arrow down the path, with Rikki-tikki behind her. When the cobra runs for her life, she goes like a whiplash flicked across a horse's neck.

Rikki-tikki knew that he must catch her, or all the trouble would begin again. She headed straight for the long grass by the thorn-bush, and as he was running Rikki-tikki heard Darzee still singing his foolish little song of triumph. But Darzee's wife was wiser. She flew off her nest as Nagaina came along, and flapped her wings about Nagaina's head. If Darzee had helped they might have turned her; but Nagaina only lowered her hood and went on. Still, the instant's delay brought Rikki-tikki up to her, and as she plunged into the rat-hole where she and Nag used to live, his little white teeth were clenched on her tail, and he went down with her—and very few mongooses, however wise and old they may be, care to follow a cobra into its hole. It was dark in the hole; and Rikki-tikki never knew when it might open out and give Nagaina room to turn and strike at him. He held on savagely, and struck out his feet to act as brakes on the dark slope of the hot, moist earth.

Then the grass by the mouth of the hole stopped waving, and Darzee said: "It is all over with Rikki-tikki! We must sing his death-song. Valiant Rikki-tikki is dead! For Nagaina will surely kill him underground."

So he sang a very mournful song that he made up all on the spur of the minute, and just as he got to the most touching part the grass quivered again, and Rikki-tikki, covered with dirt, dragged himself out of the hole leg by leg, licking his whiskers. Darzee stopped with a little shout. Rikki-tikki shook some of the dust out of his fur and sneezed. "It is all over," he said. "The widow will never come out again." And the red ants that live between the grass stems heard him, and began to troop down one after another to see if he had spoken the truth.

Rikki-tikki curled himself up in the grass and slept where he was—slept and slept till it was late in the afternoon, for he had done a hard day's work.

"Now," he said, when he awoke, "I will go back to the house. Tell the Coppersmith, Darzee, and he will tell the garden that Nagaina is dead."

The Coppersmith is a bird who makes a noise exactly like the beating of a little hammer on a copper pot; and the reason he is always making it is because he is the town-crier to every Indian garden, and tells all the news to everybody who cares to listen. As Rikki-tikki went up the path, he heard his "attention" notes like a tiny dinner-gong; and then the steady *"Ding-dong-tock!* Nag is dead—*dong!* Nagaina is dead! *Ding-dong-tock!"* That set all the birds in the garden singing, and the frogs croaking; for Nag and Nagaina used to eat frogs as well as little birds.

When Rikki got to the house, Teddy and Teddy's mother (she looked very white still, for she had been fainting) and Teddy's father came out and almost cried over him; and that night he ate all that was given him till he could eat no more, and went to bed on Teddy's shoulder, where Teddy's mother saw him when she came to look late at night.

"He saved our lives and Teddy's life," she said to her husband. "Just think, he saved all our lives."

Rikki-tikki woke up with a jump, for all the mongooses are light sleepers.

"Oh, it's you," said he. "What are you bothering for? All the cobras are dead; and if they weren't I'm here."

Rikki-tikki had a right to be proud of himself; but he did not grow too proud, and he kept that garden as a mongoose should keep it, with tooth and jump and spring and bite, till never a cobra dared show its head inside the walls.

DARZEE'S CHAUNT

(SUNG IN HONOUR OF RIKKI-TIKKI-TAVI)

Singer and tailor am I—
Doubled the joys that I know—
Proud of my lilt through the sky,
Proud of the house that I sew—
Over and under, so weave I my music—so weave I the house that I sew.

Sing to your fledglings again,
Mother, oh lift up your head!
Evil that plagued us is slain,
Death in the garden lies dead.
Terror that hid in the roses is impotent—flung on the dung-hill and dead!

Who hath delivered us, who?
Tell me his nest and his name.
Rikki, the valiant, the true,
Tikki, with eyeballs of flame.
Rik-tikki-tikki, the ivory-fanged, the hunter with eyeballs of flame.

Give him the Thanks of the Birds,
Bowing with tail-feathers spread!
Praise him with nightingale words—
Nay, I will praise him instead.
Hear! I will sing you the praise of the bottle-tailed Rikki, with eyeballs of red!

(Here Rikki-tikki interrupted, and the rest of the song is lost.)

.007

1897

A LOCOMOTIVE is, next to a marine engine, the most sensitive thing man ever made; and No. .007, besides being sensitive, was new. The red paint was hardly dry on his spotless bumper-bar, his headlight shone like a fireman's helmet, and his cab might have been a hard-wood-finish parlour. They had run him into the round-house after his trial—he had said good-bye to his best friend in the shops, the overhead travelling-crane—the big world was just outside; and the other locos were taking stock of him. He looked at the semicircle of bold, unwinking headlights, heard the low purr and mutter of the steam mounting in the gauges—scornful hisses of contempt as a slack valve lifted a little—and would have given a month's oil for leave to crawl through his own driving-wheels into the brick ash-pit beneath him. .007 was an eight-wheeled "American" loco, slightly different from others of his type, and as he stood he was worth ten thousand dollars on the Company's books. But if you had bought him at his own valuation, after half an hour's waiting in the darkish, echoing round-house, you would have saved exactly nine thousand nine hundred and ninety-nine dollars and ninety-eight cents.

A heavy Mogul freight, with a short cow-catcher and a fire-box that came down within three inches of the rail, began the impolite game, speaking to a Pittsburgh Consolidation, who was visiting.

"Where did this thing blow in from?" he asked, with a dreamy puff of light steam.

"It's all I can do to keep track of our makes," was the answer, "without lookin' after *your* back-numbers. Guess it's something Peter Cooper left over when he died."

.007 quivered; his steam was getting up, but he held his tongue. Even a hand-car knows what sort of locomotive it was that Peter Cooper experimented upon in the far-away Thirties. It carried its coal and water in two apple-barrels, and was not much bigger than a bicycle.

Then up and spoke a small, newish switching-engine, with a little step in front of his bumper-timber, and his wheels so close together that he looked like a broncho getting ready to buck.

"Something's wrong with the road when a Pennsylvania gravel-pusher tells us anything about our stock, *I* think. That kid's all right. Eustis designed him, and Eustis designed me. Ain't that good enough?"

.007 could have carried the switching-loco round the yard in his tender, but he felt grateful for even this little word of consolation.

"We don't use hand-cars on the Pennsylvania," said the Consolidation. "That—er—peanut-stand 's old enough and ugly enough to speak for himself."

"He hasn't bin spoken to yet. He's bin spoke *at*. Hain't ye any manners on the Pennsylvania?" said the switching-loco.

"You ought to be in the yard, Poney," said the Mogul, severely. "We're all long-haulers here."

"That's what you think," the little fellow replied. "You'll know more 'fore the night's out. I've bin down to Track 17, and the freight there—oh, Christmas!"

"I've trouble enough in my own division," said a lean, light suburban loco with very shiny brake-shoes. "My commuters wouldn't rest till they got a parlour-car. They've hitched it back of all, and it hauls worse'n a snow-plough. I'll snap her off some day sure, and then they'll blame every one except their fool-selves. They'll be askin' me to haul a vestibuled next!"

"They made you in New Jersey, didn't they?" said Poney.

"Thought so. Commuters and truck-wagons ain't any sweet haulin', but I tell *you* they're a heap better'n cuttin' out refrigerator-cars or oil-tanks. Why, I've hauled——"

"Haul! You?" said the Mogul, contemptuously. "It's all you can do to bunt a cold-storage car up the yard. Now, I—" he paused a little to let the words sink in—"I handle the Flying Freight—e-leven cars worth just anything you please to mention. On the stroke of eleven I pull out; and I'm timed for thirty-five an hour. Costly—perishable—fragile—immediate—that's me! Suburban traffic's only but one degree better than switching. Express freight's what pays."

"Well, I ain't given to blowing, as a rule," began the Pittsburgh Consolidation.

"No? You was sent in here because you grunted on the grade," Poney interrupted.

"Where I grunt, you'd lie down, Poney; but, as I was saying, I don't blow much. Notwithstandin', *if* you want to see freight that is freight moved lively, you should see me warbling through the Alleghanies with thirty-seven ore-cars behind me, and my brakemen fightin' tramps so's they can't attend to my tooter. I have to do all the holdin' back then, and, though I say it, I've never had a load get away from me yet. *No,* sir. Haulin' 's one thing, but judgment and discretion's another. You want judgment in my business."

"Ah! But—but are you not paralyzed by a sense of your overwhelming responsibilities?" said a curious, husky voice from a corner.

"Who's that?" .007 whispered to the Jersey commuter.

"Compound—experiment—N. G. She's bin switchin' in the B. & A. yards for six months, when she wasn't in the shops. She's economical (*I* call it mean) in her coal, but she takes it out in repairs. Ahem! I presume you found Boston somewhat isolated, madam, after your New York season?"

"I am never so well occupied as when I am alone." The Compound seemed to be talking from half-way up her smoke-stack.

"Sure," said the irreverent Poney, under his breath. "They don't hanker after her any in the yard."

"But, with my constitution and temperament—my work lies in Boston—I find your *outrecuidance*——"

"Outer which?" said the Mogul freight. "Simple cylinders are good enough for me."

"Perhaps I should have said *faroucherie,*" hissed the Compound.

"I don't hold with any make of papier-mâché wheel," the Mogul insisted.

The Compound sighed pityingly, and said no more.

"Git 'em all shapes in this world, don't ye?" said Poney. "That's Mass'chusetts all over. They half start, an' then they stick on a dead-centre, an' blame it all on other folk's ways o' treatin' them. Talkin' o' Boston, Comanche told me, last night, he had a hot-box just beyond the Newtons, Friday. That was why, *he* says, the Accommodation was held up. Made out no end of a tale, Comanche did."

"If I'd heard that in the shops, with my boiler out for repairs, I'd know 't was one o' Comanche's lies," the New Jersey commuter snapped. "Hot-box! Him! What happened was they'd put an extra car on, and he just lay down on the grade and squealed. They had to send 127 to help him through. Made it out a hot-box, did he? Time before that he said he was ditched! Looked me square in the headlight and told me that as cool as—as a water-tank in a cold wave. Hot-box! You ask 127 about Comanche's hot-box. Why, Comanche he was side-tracked, and 127 (*he* was just about as mad as they make 'em on account o' being called out at ten o'clock at night) took hold and snapped her into Boston in seventeen minutes. Hot-box! Hot fraud! That's what Comanche is."

Then .007 put both drivers and his pilot into it, as the saying is, for he asked what sort of thing a hot-box might be?

"Paint my bell sky-blue!" said Poney, the switcher. "Make me a surface-railroad loco with a hard-wood skirtin'-board round my wheels. Break me up and cast me into five-cent sidewalk-fakirs' mechanical toys! Here's an eight-wheel coupled 'American' don't know what a hot-box is! Never heard of an emergency-stop either, did ye? Don't know what ye carry jack-screws for? You're too innocent to be left alone with your own tender. Oh, you—you flat-car!"

There was a roar of escaping steam before any one could answer, and .007 nearly blistered his paint off with pure mortification.

"A hot-box," began the Compound, picking and choosing her words as though they were coal, "a hot-box is the penalty exacted from inexperience by haste. Ahem!"

"Hot-box!" said the Jersey Suburban. "It's the price you pay for going on the tear. It's years since I've had one. It's a disease that don't attack short-haulers, as a rule."

"We never have hot-boxes on the Pennsylvania," said the Consolidation. "They get 'em in New York—same as nervous prostration."

"Ah, go home on a ferry-boat," said the Mogul. "You think because you use worse grades than our road 'u'd allow, you're a kind of Alleghany angel. Now, I'll tell you what you . . . Here's my folk. Well, I can't stop. See you later, perhaps."

He rolled forward majestically to the turn-table, and swung like a man-of-war in a tideway, till he picked up his track. "But as for you, you pea-green swivelin' coffee-pot (this to .007), you go out and learn something before you associate with those who've made more mileage in a week than you'll roll up in a year. Costly—perishable—fragile—immediate—that's me! S'long."

"Split my tubes if that's actin' polite to a new member o' the Brotherhood," said Poney. "There wasn't any call to trample on ye like that. But manners was left out when Moguls was made. Keep up your fire, kid, an' burn your own smoke. 'Guess we'll all be wanted in a minute."

Men were talking rather excitedly in the round-house. One man, in a dingy jersey, said that he hadn't any locomotives to waste on the yard. Another man, with a piece of crumpled paper in his hand, said that the yard-master said that he was to say that if the other man said anything, he (the other man) was to shut his head. Then the other man waved his arms, and wanted to know if he was expected to keep locomotives in his hip-pocket. Then a man in a black Prince Albert, without a collar, came up dripping, for it was a hot August night, and said that what *he* said went; and between the three of them the locomotives began to go, too—first the Compound; then the Consolidation; the .007.

Now, deep down in his fire-box, .007 had cherished a hope that as soon as his trial was done, he would be led forth with songs and shoutings, and attached to a green-and-chocolate vestibuled flyer, under charge of a bold and noble engineer, who would pat him on his back, and weep over him, and call him his Arab steed. (The boys in the shops where he was built used to read wonderful stories of railroad life, and .007 expected things to happen as he had heard.) But there did not seem to be many vestibuled fliers in the roaring, rumbling, electric-lighted yards, and his engineer only said:

"Now, what sort of a fool-sort of an injector has Eustis loaded on to this rig this time?" And he put the lever over with an angry snap, crying: "Am I supposed to switch with this thing, hey?"

The collarless man mopped his head, and replied that, in the present state of the yard and freight and a few other things, the engineer would switch and keep on switching till the cows came home. .007 pushed out gingerly, his heart in his headlight, so nervous that the clang of his own bell almost made him jump the track. Lanterns waved, or danced up and down, before and behind him; and on every side, six tracks deep, sliding backward and forward, with clashings of couplers and squeals of hand-brakes, were cars—more cars than .007 had dreamed of. There were oil-cars, and hay-cars, and stock-cars full of lowing beasts, and ore-cars, and potato-cars with stovepipe-ends sticking out in the middle; cold-storage and refrigerator cars dripping ice-water on the tracks; ventilated fruit- and milk-cars; flat-cars with truck-wagons full of market-stuff; flat-cars loaded with reapers and binders, all red and green and gilt under the sizzling electric lights; flat-cars piled high with strong-scented hides, pleasant hemlock-plank, or bundles of shingles; flat-cars creaking to the weight of thirty-ton castings, angle-irons, and rivet-boxes for some new bridge; and hundreds and hundreds and hundreds of box-cars loaded, locked, and chalked. Men—hot and angry—crawled among and between and under the thousand wheels; men took flying jumps through his cab, when he halted for a moment; men sat on his pilot as he went forward, and on his tender as he returned; and regiments of men ran along the tops of the box-cars beside him, screwing down brakes, waving their arms, and crying curious things.

He was pushed forward a foot at a time; whirled backward, his rear drivers clinking and clanking, a quarter of a mile; jerked into a switch (yard-switches are very stubby and unaccommodating), bunted into a Red D, or Merchant's Transport car, and, with no hint or knowledge of the weight behind him, started up anew. When his load was fairly on the move, three or four cars would be cut off, and .007 would bound forward, only to be held hiccupping on the brake. Then he would wait a few minutes, watching the whirled lanterns, deafened with the clang of the bells, giddy with the vision of the sliding cars, his brake-pump panting forty to the minute, his front coupler lying sideways on his cow-catcher, like a tired dog's tongue in his mouth, and the whole of him covered with half-burnt coal-dust.

" 'T isn't so easy switching with a straight-backed tender," said his little friend of the round-house, bustling by at a trot. "But you're comin' on pretty fair. 'Ever seen a flyin' switch? No? Then watch me."

Poney was in charge of a dozen heavy flat-cars. Suddenly he shot away from them with a sharp *"Whutt!"* A switch opened in the shadows ahead; he turned up it like a rabbit as it snapped behind him, and the long line of twelve-foot-high lumber jolted on into the arms of a full-sized road-loco, who acknowledged receipt with a dry howl.

"My man's reckoned the smartest in the yard at that trick," he said, returning. "Gives me cold shivers when another fool tries it, though. That's where my short wheel-base comes in. Like as not you'd have your tender scraped off if *you* tried it."

.007 had no ambitions that way, and said so.

"No? Of course this ain't your regular business, but say, don't you think it's interestin'? Have you seen the yard-master? Well, he's the greatest man on earth, an' don't you forget it. When are we through? Why, kid, it's always like this, day *an'* night—Sundays an' week-days. See that thirty-car freight slidin' in four, no, five tracks off? She's all mixed freight, sent here to be sorted out into straight trains. That's why we're cuttin' out the cars one by one." He gave a vigorous push to a west-bound car as he spoke, and started back with a little snort of surprise, for the car was an old friend—an M. T. K. box-car.

"Jack my drivers, but it's Homeless Kate! Why, Kate, ain't there *no* gettin' you back to your friends? There's forty chasers out for you from your road, if there's one. Who's holdin' you now?"

"Wish I knew," whimpered Homeless Kate. "I belong in Topeka, but I've bin to Cedar Rapids; I've bin to Winnipeg; I've bin to Newport News; I've bin all down the old Atlanta and West Point; an' I've bin to Buffalo. Maybe I'll fetch up at Haverstraw. I've only bin out ten months, but I'm home-sick—I'm just achin' homesick."

"Try Chicago, Katie," said the switching-loco; and the battered old car lumbered down the track, jolting: "I want to be in Kansas when the sunflowers bloom."

"'Yard's full o' Homeless Kates an' Wanderin' Willies," he explained to .007. "I knew an old Fitchburg flat-car out seventeen months; an' one of ours was gone fifteen 'fore ever we got track of her. Dunno quite how our men fix it. 'Swap around, I guess. Anyway, I've done *my* duty. She's on her way to Kansas, via Chicago; but I'll lay my next boilerful she'll be held there to wait consignee's convenience, and sent back to us with wheat in the fall."

Just then the Pittsburgh Consolidation passed, at the head of a dozen cars.

"I'm goin' home," he said proudly.

"Can't get all them twelve on to the flat. Break 'em in half, Dutchy!" cried Poney. But it was .007 who was backed down to the last six cars, and he nearly blew up with surprise when he found himself pushing them on to a huge ferry-boat. He had never seen deep water before, and shivered as the flat drew away and left his bogies within six inches of the black, shiny tide.

After this he was hurried to the freight-house, where he saw the yard-master, a smallish, white-faced man in shirt, trousers, and slippers, looking down upon a sea of trucks, a mob of bawling truckmen, and squadrons of backing, turning, sweating, spark-striking horses.

"That's shippers' carts loadin' on to the receivin' trucks," said the small engine, reverently. "But *he* don't care. He lets 'em cuss. He's the Czar—King—Boss! He says 'Please,' and then they kneel down an' pray. There's three or four strings o' to-day's freight to be pulled before he can attend to *them*. When he waves his hand that way, things happen."

A string of loaded cars slid out down the track, and a string of empties took their place. Bales, crates, boxes, jars, carboys, frails, cases, and packages flew into them from the freight-house as though the cars had been magnets and they iron filings.

"Ki-yah!" shrieked little Poney. "Ain't it great?"

A purple-faced truckman shouldered his way to the yard-master, and shook his fist under his nose. The yard-master never looked up from his bundle of freight-receipts. He crooked his forefinger slightly, and a tall young man in a red shirt, lounging carelessly beside him, hit the truckman under the left ear, so that he dropped, quivering and clucking, on a hay-bale.

"Eleven, seven, ninety-seven, L. Y. S.; fourteen ought ought three; nineteen thirteen; one one four; seventeen ought twenty-one M. B.; *and* the ten west-bound. All straight except the two last. Cut 'em off at the junction. An' *that* 's all right. Pull that string." The yard-master, with mild blue eyes, looked out over the howling truckmen at the waters in the moonlight beyond, and hummed:

"All things bright and beautiful,
All creatures great and small,
All *things wise and wonderful,*
The Lawd Gawd He made all!"

.007 moved out the cars and delivered them to the regular road-engine. He had never felt quite so limp in his life before.

"Curious, ain't it?" said Poney, puffing, on the next track. "You an' me, if we got that man under our bumpers, we'd work him into red waste an' not know what we'd done; but—up there—with the steam hummin' in his boiler that awful quiet way . . ."

"I know," said .007. "Makes me feel as if I'd dropped my fire an' was getting cold. He is the greatest man on earth."

They were at the far north end of the yard now, under a switch-tower, looking down on the four-track way of the main traffic. The Boston Compound was to haul .007's string to some far-away northern junction over an indifferent road-bed, and she mourned aloud for the ninety-six pound rails of the B. & A.

"You're young; you're young," she coughed. "You don't realize your responsibilities."

"Yes, he does," said Poney, sharply; "but he don't lie down under 'em." Then, with a side-spurt of steam, exactly like a tough spitting: "There ain't more than fifteen thousand dollars' worth o' freight behind her anyway, and she goes on as if 't were a hundred thousand—same as the Mogul's. Excuse me, madam, but you've the track. . . . She's stuck on a dead-centre again—bein' specially designed not to."

The Compound crawled across the tracks on a long slant, groaning horribly at each switch, and moving like a cow in a snow-drift. There was a little pause along the yard after her tail-lights had disappeared, switches locked crisply, and every one seemed to be waiting.

"Now I'll show you something worth," said Poney. "When the Purple Emperor ain't on time, it's about time to amend the Constitution. The first stroke of twelve is——"

"Boom!" went the clock in the big yard-tower, and far away .007 heard a full, vibrating *"Yah! Yah! Yah!"* A head-light twinkled on the horizon like a star, grew an overpowering blaze, and whooped up the humming track to the roaring music of a happy giant's song:

"With a michnai—ghignai—shtingal! Yah! Yah! Yah!
Ein—zwei—drei—Mutter! Yah! Yah! Yah!
She climb upon der shteeple,
Und she frighten all der people.
Singin' michnai—ghignai—shtingal! Yah! Yah!"

The last defiant "yah! yah!" was delivered a mile and a half beyond the passenger-depot; but .007 had caught one glimpse of the superb six-wheel-coupled racing-locomotive, who hauled the pride and glory of the road—the gilt-edged Purple Emperor, the millionaires' south-bound express, laying the miles over his shoulder as a man peels a shaving from a soft board. The rest was a blur of maroon enamel, a bar of white light from the electrics in the cars, and a flicker of nickel-plated hand-rail on the rear platform.

"Ooh!" said .007.

"Seventy-five miles an hour these five miles. Baths, I've heard; barber's shop; ticker; and a library and the rest to match. Yes, sir; seventy-five an hour! But he'll talk to you in the round-house just as democratic as I would. And I—cuss my wheel-base!—I'd kick clean off the track at half his gait. He's the Master of our Lodge. Cleans up at our house. I'll introduce you some day. He's worth knowin'! There ain't many can sing that song, either."

.007 was too full of emotions to answer. He did not hear a raging of telephone-bells in the switch-tower, nor the man, as he leaned out and called to .007's engineer: "Got any steam?"

"'Nough to run her a hundred mile out o' this, if I could," said the engineer, who belonged to the open road and hated switching.

"Then get. The Flying Freight's ditched forty mile out, with fifty rod o' track ploughed up. No; no one's hurt, but both tracks are blocked. Lucky the wreckin'-car an' derrick are this end of the yard. Crew'll be along in a minute. Hurry! You've the track."

"Well, I could jest kick my little sawed-off self," said Poney, as .007 was backed, with a bang, on to a grim and grimy car like a caboose, but full of tools—a flat-car and a derrick behind it. "Some folks are one thing, and some are another, but *you*'re in luck, kid. They push a wrecking-car. Now, don't get rattled. Your wheel-base will keep you on the track, and there ain't any curves worth mentionin'. Oh, say! Comanche told me there's one section o' saw-edged track that's liable to jounce ye a little. Fifteen an' a half out, *after* the grade at Jackson's crossin'. You'll know it by a farmhouse an' a windmill an' five maples in the dooryard. Windmill's west o' the maples. An' there's an eighty-foot iron bridge in the middle o' that section with no guard-rails. See you later. Luck!"

Before he knew well what had happened, .007 was flying up the track into the dumb, dark world. Then fears of the night beset him. He remembered all he had ever heard of landslides, rain-piled boulders, blown trees, and strayed cattle, all that the Boston Compound had ever said of responsibility, and a great deal more that came out of his own head. With a very quavering voice he whistled for his first grade-crossing (an event in the life of a locomotive), and his nerves were in no way restored by the sight of a frantic horse and a white-faced man in a buggy less than a yard from his right shoulder. Then he was sure he would jump the track; felt his flanges mounting the rail at every curve; knew that his first grade would make him lie down even as Comanche had done at the Newtons. He whirled down the grade to Jackson's crossing, saw the windmill west of the maples, felt the badly laid rails spring under him, and sweated big drops all over his boiler. At each jarring bump he believed an axle had smashed, and he took the eighty-foot bridge without the guard-rail like a hunted cat on the top of a fence. Then a wet leaf stuck against the glass of his headlight and threw a flying shadow on the track, so that he thought it was some little dancing animal that would feel soft if he ran over it; and anything soft underfoot frightens a locomotive as it does an elephant. But the men behind seemed quite calm. The wrecking-crew were climbing carelessly from the caboose to the tender—even jesting with the engineer, for he heard a shuffling of feet among the coal, and the snatch of a song, something like this:

"Oh, the Empire State must learn to wait,
And the Cannon-ball go hang!
When the West-bound's ditched, and the tool-car's hitched,
And it's 'way for the Breakdown Gang (Tara-ra!)
'Way for the Breakdown Gang!"

"Say! Eustis knew what he was doin' when he designed this rig. She's a hummer. New, too."

"Snff! Phew! She *is* new. That ain't paint. That's——"

A burning pain shot through .007's right rear driver—a crippling, stinging pain.

"This," said .007, as he flew, "is a hot-box. Now I know what it means. I shall go to pieces, I guess. My first road-run, too!"

"Het a bit, ain't she?" the fireman ventured to suggest to the engineer.

"She'll hold for all we want of her. We're 'most there. Guess you chaps back had better climb into your car," said the engineer, his hand on the brake-lever. "I've seen men snapped off——"

But the crew fled back with laughter. They had no wish to be jerked on to the track. The engineer half turned his wrist, and .007 found his drivers pinned firm.

"Now it's come!" said .007, as he yelled aloud, and slid like a sleigh. For the moment he fancied that he would jerk bodily from off his underpinning.

"That must be the emergency-stop that Poney guyed me about," he gasped, as soon as he could think. "Hot-box—emergency-stop. They both hurt; but now I can talk back in the round-house."

He was halted, all hissing hot, a few feet in the rear of what doctors would call a compound-comminuted car. His engineer was kneeling down among his drivers, but he did not call .007 his "Arab steed," nor cry over him, as the engineers did in the newspapers. He just bad-worded .007, and pulled yards of charred cotton-waste from about the axles, and hoped he might some day catch the idiot who had packed it. Nobody else attended to him, for Evans, the Mogul's engineer, a little cut about the head, but very angry, was exhibiting, by lantern-light, the mangled corpse of a slim blue pig.

"'T were n't even a decent-sized hog," he said. "'T were a shote."

"Dangerousest beasts they are," said one of the crew. "Get under the pilot an' sort o' twiddle ye off the track, don't they?"

"Don't they?" roared Evans, who was a red-headed Welshman. "You talk as if I was ditched by a hog every fool-day o' the week. *I* ain't friends with all the cussed half-fed shotes in the State o' New York. No, indeed! Yes, this is him—an' look what he's done!"

It was not a bad night's work for one stray piglet. The Flying Freight seemed to have flown in every direction, for the Mogul had mounted the rails and run diagonally a few hundred feet from right to left, taking with him such cars as cared to follow. Some did not. They broke their couplers and lay down, while rear cars frolicked over them. In that game, they had ploughed up and removed and twisted a good deal of the left-hand track. The Mogul himself had waddled into a corn-field, and there he knelt—fantastic wreaths of green twisted round his crank-pins; his pilot covered with solid clods of field, on which corn nodded drunkenly; his fire put out with dirt (Evans had done that as soon as he recovered his senses); and his broken headlight half full of half-burnt moths. His tender had thrown coal all over him, and he looked like a disreputable buffalo who had tried to wallow in a general store. For there lay scattered over the landscape, from the burst cars, type-writers, sewing-machines, bicycles in crates, a consignment of silver-plated imported harness, French dresses and gloves, a dozen finely moulded hard-wood mantels, a fifteen-foot naphtha-launch, with a solid brass bedstead crumpled around her bows, a case of telescopes and microscopes, two coffins, a case of very best candies, some gilt-edged dairy produce, butter and eggs in an omelette, a broken box of expensive toys, and a few hundred other luxuries. A camp of tramps hurried up from nowhere, and generously volunteered to help the crew. So the brakemen, armed with coupler-pins, walked up and down on one side, and the freight-conductor and the fireman patrolled the other with their hands in their hip-pockets. A long-bearded man came out of a house beyond the corn-field, and told Evans that if the accident had happened a little later in the year, all his corn would have been burned, and accused Evans of carelessness. Then he ran away, for Evans was at his heels shrieking: "'T was his hog done it—his hog done it! Let me kill him! Let me kill him!" Then the wrecking-crew laughed; and the farmer put his head out of a window and said that Evans was no gentleman.

But .007 was very sober. He had never seen a wreck before, and it frightened him. The crew still laughed, but they worked at the same time; and .007 forgot horror in amazement at the way they handled the Mogul freight. They dug round him with spades; they put ties in front of his wheels, and jack-screws under him; they embraced him with the derrick-chain and tickled him with crowbars; while .007 was hitched on to wrecked cars and backed away till the knot broke or the cars rolled clear of the track. By dawn thirty or forty men were at work, replacing and ramming down the ties, gauging the rails and spiking them. By daylight all cars who could move had gone on in charge of another loco; the track was freed for traffic; and .007 had hauled the old Mogul over a small pavement of ties, inch by inch, till his flanges bit the rail once more, and he settled down with a clank. But his spirit was broken, and his nerve was gone.

"'T were n't even a hog," he repeated dolefully; "'t were a shote; and you—*you* of all of 'em—had to help me on."

"But how in the whole long road did it happen?" asked 007, sizzling with curiosity.

"Happen! It didn't happen! It just come! I sailed right on top of him around that last curve—thought he was a skunk. Yes; he was all as little as that. He hadn't more 'n squealed once 'fore I felt my bogies lift (he'd rolled right under the pilot), and I couldn't catch the track again to save me. Swivelled clean off, I was. Then I felt him sling himself along, all greasy, under my left leadin' driver, and, oh, Boilers! that mounted the rail. I heard my flanges zippin' along the ties, an' the next I knew I was playin' 'Sally, Sally Waters' in the corn, my tender shuckin' coal through my cab, an' old man Evans lyin' still an' bleedin' in front o' me. Shook? There ain't a stay or a bolt or a rivet in me that ain't sprung to glory somewhere."

"Umm!" said .007. "What d'you reckon you weigh?"

"Without these lumps o' dirt I'm all of a hundred thousand pound."

"And the shote?"

"Eighty. Call him a hundred pound at the outside. He's worth about four 'n' a half dollars. Ain't it awful? Ain't it enough to give you nervous prostration? Ain't it paralyzin'? Why, I come just around that curve—" and the Mogul told the tale again, for he was very badly shaken.

"Well, it's all in the day's run, I guess," said .007, soothingly; "an'—an' a corn-field's pretty soft fallin'."

"If it had bin a sixty-foot bridge, an' I could ha' slid off into deep water an' blown up an' killed both men, same as others have done, I wouldn't ha' cared; but to be ditched by a shote—an' you to help me out—in a corn-field—an' an old hayseed in his nightgown cussin' me like as if I was a sick truck-horse! . . . Oh, it's awful! Don't call me Mogul! I'm a sewin'-machine. They'll guy my sand-box off in the yard."

And .007, his hot-box cooled and his experience vastly enlarged, hauled the Mogul freight slowly to the round-house.

"Hello, old man! Bin out all night, hain't ye?" said the irrepressible Poney, who had just come off duty. "Well, I must say you look it. Costly—perishable—fragile—immediate—that's you! Go to the shops, take them vine-leaves out o' your hair, an' git 'em to play the hose on you."

"Leave him alone, Poney," said .007, severely, as he was swung on the turn-table, "or I'll——"

"'Didn't know the old granger was any special friend o' yours, kid. He wasn't over-civil to you last time I saw him."

"I know it; but I've seen a wreck since then, and it has about scared the paint off me. I'm not going to guy any one as long as I steam—not when they're new to the business an anxious to learn. And I'm not goin' to guy the old Mogul either, though I did find him wreathed around with roastin'-ears. 'T was a little bit of a shote—not a hog—just a shote, Poney—no bigger'n a lump of anthracite—I saw it—that made all the mess. Anybody can be ditched, I guess."

"Found that out already, have you? Well, that's a good beginnin'." It was the Purple Emperor, with his high, tight, plate-glass cab and green velvet cushion, waiting to be cleaned for his next day's fly.

"Let me make you two gen'lemen acquainted," said Poney. "This is our Purple Emperor, kid, whom you were admirin' and, I may say, envyin' last night. This is a new brother, worshipful sir, with most of his mileage ahead of him, but, so far as a serving-brother can, I'll answer for him."

" 'Happy to meet you," said the Purple Emperor, with a glance round the crowded round-house. "I guess there are enough of us here to form a full meetin'. Ahem! By virtue of the authority vested in me as Head of the Road, I hereby declare and pronounce No. .007 a full and accepted Brother of the Amalgamated Brotherhood of Locomotives, and as such entitled to all shop, switch, track, tank, and round-house privileges throughout my jurisdiction, in the Degree of Superior Flier, it bein' well known and credibly reported to me that our Brother has covered forty-one miles in thirty-nine minutes and a half on an errand of mercy to the afflicted. At a convenient time, I myself will communicate to you the Song and Signal of this Degree whereby you may be recognized in the darkest night. Take your stall, newly entered Brother among Locomotives!"

. . . . . .

Now, in the darkest night, even as the Purple Emperor said, if you will stand on the bridge across the freight-yard, looking down upon the four-track way, at 2:30 A. M., neither before nor after, when the White Moth, that takes the overflow from the Purple Emperor, tears south with her seven vestibuled cream-white cars, you will hear, as the yard-clock makes the half-hour, a far-away sound like the bass of a violoncello, and then, a hundred feet to each word:

"With a michnai—ghignai—shtingal! Yah! Yah! Yah!
Ein—zwei—drei—Mutter! Yah! Yah! Yah!
She climb upon der shteeple,
Und she frighten all der people,
Singin' michnai—ghignai—shtingal! Yah! Yah!"

That is .007 covering his one hundred and fifty-six miles in two hundred and twenty-one minutes.

"BREAD UPON THE WATERS"
1896

IF YOU remember my improper friend Brugglesmith, you will also bear in mind his friend McPhee, Chief Engineer of the *Breslau,* whose dingey Brugglesmith tried to steal. His apologies for the performances of Brugglesmith may one day be told in their proper place; the tale before us concerns McPhee. He was never a racing engineer, and took special pride in saying as much before the Liverpool men; but he had a thirty-two years' knowledge of machinery and the humours of ships. One side of his face had been wrecked through the bursting of a pressure-gauge in the days when men knew less than they do now, and his nose rose grandly out of the wreck, like a club in a public riot. There were cuts and lumps on his head, and he would guide your forefinger through his short iron-grey hair and tell you how he had come by his trade-marks. He owned all sorts of certificates of extra-competency, and at the bottom of his cabin chest of drawers, where he kept the photograph of his wife, were two or three Royal Humane Society medals for saving lives at sea. Professionally—it was different when crazy steerage-passengers jumped overboard—professionally, McPhee does not approve of saving life at sea, and he has often told me that a new Hell awaits stokers and trimmers who sign for a strong man's pay and fall sick the second day out. He believes in throwing boots at fourth and fifth engineers when they wake him up at night with word that a bearing is red-hot, all because a lamp's glare is reflected red from the twirling metal. He believes that there are only two poets in the world; one being Robert Burns, of course, and the other Gerald Massey. When he has time for novels he reads Wilkie Collins and Charles Reade—chiefly the latter—and knows whole pages of "Very Hard Cash" by heart. In the saloon his table is next to the captain's, and he drinks only water while his engines work.

He was good to me when we first met, because I did not ask questions, and believed in Charles Reade as a most shamefully neglected author. Later he approved of my writings to the extent of one pamphlet of twenty-four pages that I wrote for Holdock, Steiner & Chase, owners of the line, when they bought some ventilating patent and fitted it to the cabins of the *Breslau, Spandau,* and *Koltzau.* The purser of the *Breslau* recommended me to Holdock's secretary for the job; and Holdock, who is a Wesleyan Methodist, invited me to his house, and gave me dinner with the governess when the others had finished, and placed the plans and specifications in my hand, and I wrote the pamphlet that same afternoon. It was called "Comfort in the Cabin," and brought me seven pound ten, cash down—an important sum of money in those days; and the governess, who was teaching Master John Holdock his scales, told me that Mrs. Holdock had told her to keep an eye on me, in case I went away with coats from the hat-rack. McPhee liked that pamphlet enormously, for it was composed in the Bouverie-Byzantine style, with baroque and rococo embellishments; and afterwards he introduced me to Mrs. McPhee, who succeeded Dinah in my heart; for Dinah was half a world away, and it is wholesome and antiseptic to love such a woman as Janet McPhee. They lived in a little twelve-pound house, close to the shipping. When McPhee was away Mrs. McPhee read the Lloyds column in the papers, and called on the wives of senior engineers of equal social standing. Once or twice, too, Mrs. Holdock visited Mrs. McPhee in a brougham with celluloid fittings, and I have reason to believe that, after she had played owner's wife long enough, they talked scandal. The Holdocks lived in an old-fashioned house with a big brick garden not a mile from the McPhees, for they stayed by their money as their money stayed by them; and in summer you met their brougham solemnly junketing by Theydon Bois or Loughton. But I was Mrs. McPhee's friend, for she allowed me to convoy her westward, sometimes, to theatres where she sobbed or laughed or shivered with a simple heart; and she introduced me to a new world of doctors' wives, captains' wives, and engineers' wives, whose whole talk and thought centred in and about ships and lines of ships you have never heard of. There were sailing-ships, with stewards and mahogany and maple saloons, trading to Australia, taking cargoes of consumptives and hopeless drunkards for whom a sea-voyage was recommended; there were frowzy little West African boats, full of rats and cockroaches, where men died anywhere but in their bunks; there were Brazilian boats whose cabins could be hired for merchandise, that went out loaded nearly awash; there were Zanzibar and Mauritius steamers and wonderful reconstructed boats that plied to the other side of Borneo. These were loved and known, for they earned our bread and a little butter, and we despised the big Atlantic boats, and made fun of the P. & O. and Orient liners, and swore by our respective owners —Wesleyan, Baptist, or Presbyterian, as the case might be.

I had only just come back to England when Mrs. McPhee invited me to dinner at three o'clock in the afternoon, and the notepaper was almost bridal in its scented creaminess. When I reached the house I saw that there were new curtains in the window that must have cost forty-five shillings a pair; and as Mrs. McPhee drew me into the little marble-papered hall, she looked at me keenly, and cried:

"Have ye not heard? What d' ye think o' the hat-rack?"

Now, that hat-rack was oak—thirty shillings, at least.

McPhee came down-stairs with a sober foot—he steps as lightly as a cat, for all his weight, when he is at sea—and shook hands in a new and awful manner—a parody of old Holdock's style when he says good-bye to his skippers. I perceived at once that a legacy had come to him, but I held my peace, though Mrs. McPhee begged me every thirty seconds to eat a great deal and say nothing. It was rather a mad sort of meal, because McPhee and his wife took hold of hands like little children (they always do after voyages), and nodded and winked and choked and gurgled, and hardly ate a mouthful.

A female servant came in and waited; though Mrs. McPhee had told me time and again that she would thank no one to do her housework while she had her health. But this was a servant with a cap, and I saw Mrs. McPhee swell and swell under her *garance*-coloured gown. There is no small free-board to Janet McPhee, nor is *garance* any subdued tint; and with all this unexplained pride and glory in the air I felt like watching fireworks without knowing the festival. When the maid had removed the cloth she brought a pineapple that would have cost half a guinea at that season (only McPhee has his own way of getting such things), and a Canton china bowl of dried lichis, and a glass plate of preserved ginger, and a small jar of sacred and Imperial chow-chow that perfumed the room. McPhee gets it from a Dutchman in Java, and I think he doctors it with liqueurs. But the crown of the feast was some Madeira of the kind you can only come by if you know the wine and the man. A little maize-wrapped fig of clotted Madeira cigars went with the wine, and the rest was a pale blue smoky silence; Janet, in her splendour, smiling on us two, and patting McPhee's hand.

"We 'll drink," said McPhee, slowly, rubbing his chin, "to the eternal damnation o' Holdock, Steiner & Chase."

Of course I answered "Amen," though I had made seven pound ten shillings out of the firm. McPhee's enemies were mine, and I was drinking his Madeira.

"Ye 've heard nothing?" said Janet. "Not a word, not a whisper?"

"Not a word, nor a whisper. On my word, I have not."

"Tell him, Mac," said she; and that is another proof of Janet's goodness and wifely love. A smaller woman would have babbled first, but Janet is five feet nine in her stockings.

"We 're rich," said McPhee. I shook hands all round.

"We 're damned rich," he added. I shook hands all round a second time.

"I 'll go to sea no more—unless—there 's no sayin'—a private yacht, maybe—wi' a small an' handy auxiliary."

"It 's not enough for *that,*" said Janet. "We 're fair rich —well-to-do, but no more. A new gown for church, and one for the theatre. We 'll have it made west."

"How much is it?" I asked.

"Twenty-five thousand pounds." I drew a long breath. "An' I 've been earnin' twenty-five an' twenty pound a month!" The last words came away with a roar, as though the wide world was conspiring to beat him down.

"All this time I 'm waiting," I said. "I know nothing since last September. Was it left you?"

They laughed aloud together. "It was left," said McPhee, choking. "Ou, ay, it was left. That 's vara good. Of course it was left. Janet, d' ye note that? It was left. Now if you 'd put *that* in your pamphlet it would have been vara jocose. It *was* left." He slapped his thigh and roared till the wine quivered in the decanter.

The Scotch are a great people, but they are apt to hang over a joke too long, particularly when no one can see the point but themselves.

"When I rewrite my pamphlet I 'll put it in, McPhee. Only I must know something more first."

McPhee thought for the length of half a cigar, while Janet caught my eye and led it round the room to one new thing after another—the new vine-pattern carpet, the new chiming rustic clock between the models of the Colombo outrigger-boats, the new inlaid sideboard with a purple cut-glass flower-stand, the fender of gilt and brass, and last, the new black-and-gold piano.

"In October o' last year the Board sacked me," began

McPhee. "In October o' last year the *Breslau* came in for winter overhaul. She 'd been runnin' eight months—two hunder an' forty days—an' I was three days makin' up my indents, when she went to dry-dock. All told, mark you, it was this side o' three hunder pound—to be preceese, two hunder an' eighty-six pound four shillings. There 's not another man could ha' nursed the *Breslau* for eight months to that tune. Never again—never again! They may send their boats to the bottom, for aught I care."

"There 's no need," said Janet, softly. "We 're done wi' Holdock, Steiner & Chase."

"It 's irritatin', Janet, it 's just irritatin'. I ha' been justified from first to last, as the world knows, but—but I canna forgie 'em. Ay, wisdom is justified o' her children; an' any other man than me wad ha' made the indent eight hunder. Hay was our skipper—ye 'll have met him. They shifted him to the *Torgau,* an' bade me wait for the *Breslau* under young Bannister. Ye 'll obsairve there 'd been a new election on the Board. I heard the shares were sellin' hither an' yon, an' the major part of the Board was new to me. The old Board would ne'er ha' done it. They trusted me. But the new Board were all for reorganization. Young Steiner—Steiner's son—the Jew, was at the bottom of it, an' they did not think it worth their while to send me word. The first *I* knew—an' I was Chief Engineer—was the notice of the line's winter sailin's, and the *Breslau* timed for sixteen days between port an' port! Sixteen days, man! She 's a good boat, but eighteen is her summer time, mark you. Sixteen was sheer flytin', kitin' nonsense, an' so I told young Bannister.

" 'We 've got to make it,' he said. 'Ye should not ha' sent in a three hunder pound indent.'

" 'Do they look for their boats to be run on air?' I said. 'The Board 's daft.'

" 'E'en tell 'em so,' he says. 'I'm a married man, an' my fourth 's on the ways now, she says.' "

"A boy—wi' red hair," Janet put in. Her own hair is the splendid red-gold that goes with a creamy complexion.

"My word, I was an angry man that day! Forbye I was

fond o' the old *Breslau,* I looked for a little consideration from the Board after twenty years' service. There was Board-meetin' on Wednesday, an' I slept overnight in the engine-room, takin' figures to support my case. Well, I put it fair and square before them all. 'Gentlemen,' I said, 'I 've run the *Breslau* eight seasons, an' I believe there 's no fault to find wi' my wark. But if ye haud to this'—I waggled the advertisement at 'em—'this that *I* 've never heard of it till I read it at breakfast, I do assure you on my professional reputation, she can never do it. That is to say, she can for a while, but at a risk no thinkin' man would run.'

" 'What the deil d' ye suppose we pass your indents for?' says old Holdock. 'Man, we' re spendin' money like water.'

" 'I 'll leave it in the Board's hands,' I said, 'if two hunder an' eighty-seven pound is anything beyond right and reason for eight months.' I might ha' saved my breath, for the Board was new since the last election, an' there they sat, the damned deevidend-huntin' ship-chandlers, deaf as the adders o' Scripture.

" 'We must keep faith wi' the public,' said young Steiner.

" 'Keep faith wi' the *Breslau,* then,' I said. 'She's served you well, an' your father before you. She 'll need her bottom restiffenin' an' new bed-plates, an' turnin' out the forward boilers, an' re-turnin' all three cylinders, an' refacin' all guides, to begin with it 's a three months' job.'

" 'Because one employé is afraid?' says young Steiner. 'Maybe a piano in the Chief Engineer's cabin would be more to the point.'

"I crushed my cap in my hands, an' thanked God we 'd no bairns an' a bit put by.

" 'Understand, gentlemen,' I said. 'If the *Breslau* is made a sixteen-day boat, ye 'll find another engineer.'

" 'Bannister makes no objection,' said Holdock.

" 'I 'm speakin' for myself,' I said. 'Bannister has bairns.' An' then I lost my temper. 'Ye can run her into Hell an' out again if ye pay pilotage,' I said, 'but ye run without me.'

" 'That 's insolence,' said young Steiner.

" 'At your pleasure,' I said, turnin' to go.

"'Ye can consider yourself dismissed. We must preserve discipline among our employés,' said old Holdock, an' he looked round to see that the Board was with him. They knew nothin'—God forgie 'em—an' they nodded me out o' the line after twenty years—after twenty years.

"I went out an' sat down by the hall porter to get my wits again. I 'm thinkin' I swore at the Board. Then auld McRimmon—o' McNaughten & McRimmon—came oot o' his office, that 's on the same floor, an' looked at me, proppin' up one eyelid wi' his forefinger. Ye know they call him the Blind Deevil, forbye he 's onythin' but blind, an' no deevil in his dealin's wi' me—McRimmon o' the Black Bird Line.

"'What 's here, Mister McPhee?' said he.

"I was past prayin' for by then. 'A Chief Engineer sacked after twenty years' service because he 'll not risk the *Breslau* on the new timin', an' be damned to ye, McRimmon,' I said.

"The auld man sucked in his lips an' whistled. 'Ah,' said he, 'the new timin'. I see!' He doddered into the Board-room I 'd just left, an' the Dandie-dog that is just his blind man's leader stayed wi' me. *That* was providential. In a minute he was back again. 'Ye've cast your bread on the watter, McPhee, an' be damned to you,' he says. 'Whaur 's my dog? My word, is he on your knee? There 's more discernment in a dog than a Jew. What garred ye curse your Board, McPhee? It 's expensive.'

"'They 'll pay more for the *Breslau*,' I said. 'Get off my knee, ye smotherin' beast.'

"'Bearin 's hot, eh?' said McRimmon. 'It 's thirty year since a man daur curse me to my face. Time was I 'd ha' cast ye doon the stairway for that.'

"'Forgie 's all!' I said. He was wearin' to eighty, as I knew. 'I was wrong, McRimmon; but when a man 's shown the door for doin' his plain duty he 's not always ceevil.'

"'So I hear,' says McRimmon. 'Ha' ye ony objection to a tramp freighter? It 's only fifteen a month, but they say the Blind Deevil feeds a man better than others. She 's my *Kite*. Come ben. Ye can thank Dandie, here. I 'm no used to thanks. An' noo,' says he, 'what possessed ye to throw up your berth wi' Holdock?'

" 'The new timin',' said I. 'The *Breslau* will not stand it.'

" 'Hoot, oot,' said he. 'Ye might ha' crammed her a little —enough to show ye were drivin' her—an' brought her in twa days behind. What 's easier than to say ye slowed for bearin's, eh? All my men do it, and—I believe 'em.'

" 'McRimmon,' says I, 'what 's her virginity to a lassie?'

"He puckered his dry face an' twisted in his chair. 'The warld an' a',' says he. 'My God, the vara warld an' a'! But what ha' you or me to do wi' virginity, this late along?'

" 'This,' I said. 'There 's just one thing that each one of us in his trade or profession will *not* do for ony consideration whatever. If I run to time I run to time, barrin' always the risks o' the high seas. Less than that, under God, I have not done. More than that, by God, I will not do! There 's no trick o' the trade I 'm not acquaint wi'—'

" 'So I 've heard,' says McRimmon, dry as a biscuit.

" 'But yon matter o' fair runnin' 's just my Shekinah, ye 'll understand. I daurna tamper wi' *that*. Nursing weak engines is fair craftsmanship; but what the Board ask is cheatin', wi' the risk o' manslaughter addeetional.' Ye 'll note I know my business.

"There was some more talk, an' next week I went aboard the *Kite,* twenty-five hunder ton, simple compound, a Black Bird tramp. The deeper she rode, the better she 'd steam. I 've snapped as much as eleven out of her, but eight point three was her fair normal. Good food forward an' better aft, all indents passed wi'out marginal remarks, the best coal, new donkeys, and good crews. There was nothin' the old man would not do, except paint. That was his deeficulty Ye could no more draw paint than his last teeth from him. He 'd come down to dock, an' his boats a scandal all along the watter, an' he 'd whine an' cry an' say they looked all he could desire. Every owner has his *non plus ultra,* I 've obsairved. Paint was McRimmon's. But you could get round his engines without riskin' your life, an', for all his blindness, I 've seen him reject five flawed intermediates, one after the other, on a nod from me; an' his cattle-fittin's were guaranteed for North Atlantic winter weather. Ye ken what *that* means? McRimmon an' the Black Bird Line, God bless him!

"Oh, I forgot to say she would lie down an' fill her forward deck green, an' snore away into a twenty-knot gale forty-five to the minute, three an' a half knots an hour, the engines runnin' sweet an' true as a bairn breathin' in its sleep. Bell was skipper; an' forbye there 's no love lost between crews an' owners, we were fond o' the auld Blind Deevil an' his dog, an' I 'm thinkin' he liked us. He was worth the windy side o' twa million sterlin', an' no friend to his own blood-kin. Money 's an awfu' thing—overmuch—for a lonely man.

"I'd taken her out twice, there an' back again, when word came o' the *Breslau's* breakdown, just as I prophesied. Calder was her engineer—he 's not fit to run a tug down the Solent—and he fairly lifted the engines off the bed-plates, an' they fell down in heaps, by what I heard. So she filled from the after stuffin'-box to the after bulkhead, an' lay star-gazing, with seventy-nine squealin' passengers in the saloon, till the *Camaralzaman* o' Ramsey & Gold's Cartagena line gave her a tow to the tune o' five thousand seven hunder an' forty pound, wi' costs in the Admiralty Court. She was helpless, ye 'll understand, an' in no case to meet ony weather. Five thousand seven hunder an' forty pounds, *with* costs, an' exclusive o' new engines! They 'd ha' done better to ha' kept me—on the old timin'.

"But, even so, the new Board were all for retrenchment. Young Steiner, the Jew, was at the bottom of it. They sacked men right an' left, that would not eat the dirt the Board gave 'em. They cut down repairs; they fed crews wi' leavin's an' scrapin's; and, reversin' McRimmon's practice, they hid their defeeciencies wi' paint an' cheap gildin'. *Quem Deus vult perrdere prrius dementat,* ye remember.

"In January we went to dry-dock, an' in the next dock lay the *Grotkau,* their big freighter that was the *Dolabella* o' Piegan, Piegan & Walsh's line in '84—a Clyde-built iron boat, a flat-bottomed, pigeon-breasted, under-engined, bull-nosed bitch of a five thousand ton freighter, that would neither steer, nor steam, nor stop when ye asked her. Whiles she 'd attend to her helm, whiles she 'd take charge, whiles she 'd wait to scratch herself, an' whiles she 'd buttock into a dock-head. But Holdock and Steiner had bought her cheap, and painted her all over like the Hoor o' Babylon, an' we called her the *Hoor* for short." (By the way, McPhee kept to that name throughout the rest of his tale; so you must read accordingly.) "I went to see young Bannister—he had to take what the Board gave him, an' he an' Calder were shifted together from the *Breslau* to this abortion—an' talkin' to him I went into the dock under her. Her plates were pitted till the men that were paint, paint, paintin' her laughed at it. But the warst was at the last. She 'd a great clumsy iron twelve-foot Thresher propeller—Aitcheson designed the *Kite's*—and just on the tail o' the shaft, behind the boss, was a red weepin' crack ye could ha' put a penknife to. Man, it was an awfu' crack!

" 'When d' ye ship a new tail-shaft?' I said to Bannister.

"He knew what I meant. 'Oh, yon 's a superfeecial flaw,' says he, not lookin' at me.

" 'Superfeecial Gehenna!' I said. 'Ye 'll not take her oot wi' a solution o' continuity that like.'

" 'They 'll putty it up this evening,' he said. 'I 'm a married man, an'—ye used to know the Board.'

"I e'en said what was gied me in that hour. Ye know how a dry-dock echoes. I saw young Steiner standin' listenin' above me, an', man, he used language provocative of a breach o' the peace. I was a spy and a disgraced employé, an' a corrupter o' young Bannister's morals, an' he 'd prosecute me for libel. He went away when I ran up the steps— I'd ha' thrown him into the dock if I 'd caught him—an' there I met McRimmon, wi' Dandie pullin' on the chain, guidin' the auld man among the railway lines.

" 'McPhee,' said he, 'ye're no paid to fight Holdock, Steiner, Chase & Company, Limited, when ye meet. What 's wrong between you?"

" 'No more than a tail-shaft rotten as a kail-stump. For ony sakes go an' look, McRimmon. It 's a comedietta.'

" 'I 'm feared o' yon conversational Hebrew,' said he. 'Whaur 's the flaw, an' what like?'

" 'A seven-inch crack just behind the boss. There 's no power on earth will fend it just jarrin' off.'

" 'When?'

" 'That 's beyon' my knowledge,' I said.

" 'So it is; so it is,' said McRimmon. 'We 've all oor leemitations. Ye 're certain it was a crack?'

" 'Man, it 's a crevasse,' I said, for there were no words to describe the magnitude of it. 'An' young Bannister 's sayin' it 's no more than a superfeecial flaw!'

" 'Weell, I tak' it oor business is to mind oor business. If ye 've ony friends aboard her, McPhee, why not bid them to a bit dinner at Radley's?'

" 'I was thinkin' o' tea in the cuddy,' I said. 'Engineers o' tramp freighters cannot afford hotel prices.'

" 'Na! na!' says the auld man, whimperin'. 'Not the cuddy. They 'll laugh at my *Kite*, for she 's no plastered with paint like the *Hoor*. Bid them to Radley's, McPhee, an' send me the bill. Thank Dandie, here, man. I 'm no used to thanks.' Then he turned him round. (I was just thinkin' the vara same thing.) 'Mister McPhee,' said he, 'this is *not* senile dementia.'

" 'Preserve 's!' I said, clean jumped oot o' mysel'. 'I was but thinkin' you 're fey, McRimmon.'

"Dod, the auld deevil laughed till he nigh sat down on Dandie. 'Send me the bill,' says he. 'I 'm long past champagne, but tell me how it tastes the morn.'

"Bell and I bid young Bannister and Calder to dinner at Radley's. They 'll have no laughin' an' singin' there, but we took a private room—like yacht-owners fra' Cowes."

McPhee grinned all over, and lay back to think.

"And then?" said I.

"We were no drunk in ony preceese sense o' the word, but Radley 's showed me the dead men. There were six magnums o' dry champagne an' maybe a bottle o' whisky."

"Do you mean to tell me that you four got away with a magnum and a half a piece, besides whisky?" I demanded.

McPhee looked down upon me from between his shoulders with toleration.

"Man, we were not settin' down to drink," he said. "They

no more than made us wutty. To be sure, young Bannister laid his head on the table an' greeted like a bairn, an' Calder was all for callin' on Steiner at two in the morn an' painting him galley-green; but they 'd been drinkin' the afternoon. Lord, how they twa cursed the Board, an' the *Grotkau*, an' the tail-shaft, an' the engines, an' a'! They didna talk o' superfeecial flaws that night. I mind young Bannister an' Calder shakin' hands on a bond to be revenged on the Board at ony reasonable cost this side o' losing their certificates. Now mark ye how false economy ruins business. The Board fed them like swine (I have good reason to know it), an' I 've obsairved wi' my ain people that if ye touch his stomach ye wauken the deil in a Scot. Men will tak' a dredger across the Atlantic if they 're well fed, an' fetch her somewhere on the broadside o' the Americas; but bad food 's bad service the warld over.

"The bill went to McRimmon, an' he said no more to me till the week-end, when I was at him for more paint, for we 'd heard the *Kite* was chartered Liverpool-side.

" 'Bide whaur ye 're put,' said the Blind Deevil. 'Man, do ye wash in champagne? The *Kite* 's no leavin' here till I gie the order, an'—how am I to waste paint on her, wi' the *Lammergeyer* docked for who knows how long an' a' ?'

"She was our big freighter—McIntyre was engineer—an' I knew she 'd come from overhaul not three months. That morn I met McRimmon's head-clerk—ye 'll not know him—fair bitin' his nails off wi' mortification.

" 'The auld man 's gone gyte,' says he. 'He's withdrawn the *Lammergeyer*.'

" 'Maybe he has reasons,' says I.

" 'Reasons! He 's daft!'

" 'He 'll no be daft till he begins to paint,' I said.

" 'That 's just what he 's done—and South American freights higher than we 'll live to see them again. He 's laid her up to paint her—to paint her—to paint her!' says the little clerk, dancin' like a hen on a hot plate.

"Five thousand ton o' potential freight rottin' in dry-dock, man; an' he dolin' the paint out in quarter-pound-tins, for it cuts him to the heart, mad though he is. An' the *Grotkau*—

the *Grotkau* of all conceivable bottoms—soaking up every pound that should be ours at Liverpool!'

"I was staggered wi' this folly—considerin' the dinner at Radley's in connection wi' the same.

" 'Ye may well stare, McPhee,' says the head-clerk. 'There's engines, an' rollin' stock, an' iron bridges—d' ye know what freights are noo?—an' pianos, an' millinery, an' fancy Brazil cargo o' every species pourin' into the *Grotkau*—the *Grotkau* o' the Jerusalem firm—and the *Lammergeyer* 's bein' painted!'

"Losh, I thought he 'd drop dead wi' the fits.

"I could say no more than 'Obey orders, if ye break owners,' but on the *Kite* we believed McRimmon was mad; an' McIntyre of the *Lammergeyer* was for lockin' him up by some patent legal process he 'd found in a book o' maritime law. An' a' that week South American freights rose an' rose. It was sinfu'!

"Syne Bell got orders to tak' the *Kite* round to Liverpool in water-ballast, and McRimmon came to bid 's good-bye, yammerin' an' whinin' o'er the acres o' paint he 'd lavished on the *Lammergeyer*.

" 'I look to you to retrieve it,' says he. 'I look to you to reimburse me! 'Fore God, why are ye not cast off? Are ye dawdlin' in dock for a purpose?'

" 'What odds, McRimmon?' says Bell. 'We 'll be a day behind the fair at Liverpool. The *Grotkau* 's got all the freight that might ha' been ours an' the *Lammergeyer's*.' McRimmon laughed an' chuckled—the pairfect eemage o' senile dementia. Ye ken his eyebrows wark up an' down like a gorilla's.

" 'Ye're under sealed orders,' said he, tee-heein' an' scratchin' himself. 'Yon 's they'—to be opened *seriatim*.

"Says Bell, shufflin' the envelopes when the auld man had gone ashore: 'We 're to creep round a' the south coast, standin' in for orders—this weather, too. There 's no question o' his lunacy now.'

"Well, we buttocked the auld *Kite* along—vara bad weather we made—standin' in all alongside for telegraphic orders, which are the curse o' skippers. Syne we made over to Holyhead, an' Bell opened the last envelope for the last instructions. I was wi' him in the cuddy, an' he threw it over to me, cryin': 'Did ye ever know the like, Mac?"

"I'll no say what McRimmon had written. but he was far from mad. There was a sou'wester brewin' when we made the mouth o' the Mersey, a bitter cold morn wi' a grey-green sea and a grey-green sky—Liverpool weather, as they say; an' there we lay choppin', an' the crew swore. Ye canna keep secrets aboard ship. They thought McRimmon was mad, too.

"Syne we saw the *Grotkau* rollin' oot on the top o' flood, deep an' double deep, wi' her new painted funnel an' her new-painted boats an' a'. She looked her name, an', moreover, she coughed like it. Calder tauld me at Radley's what ailed his engines, but my own ear would ha' told me twa mile awa', by the beat o' them. Round we came, plungin' an' squatterin' in her wake, an' the wind cut wi' good promise o' more to come. By six it blew hard but clear, an' before the middle watch it was a sou'wester in airnest.

"'She 'll edge into Ireland, this gait,' says Bell. I was with him on the bridge, watchin' the *Grotkau's* port light. Ye canna see green so far as red, or we 'd ha' kept to leeward. We 'd no passengers to consider, an' (all eyes being on the *Grotkau*) we fair walked into a liner rampin' home to Liverpool. Or, to be preceese, Bell no more than twisted the *Kite* oot from under her bows, and there was a little damnin' betwix' the twa bridges. Noo a passenger"—McPhee regarded me benignantly—"wad ha' told the papers that as soon as he got to the Customs. We stuck to the *Grotkau's* tail that night an' the next twa days—she slowed down to five knot by my reckonin'—and we lapped along the weary way to the Fastnet."

"But you don't go by the Fastnet to get to any South American port, do you?" I said.

"*We* do not. We prefer to go as direct as may be. But we were followin' the *Grotkau,* an' she 'd no walk into that gale for ony consideration. Knowin' what I did to her discredit, I couldna blame young Bannister. It was warkin' up to a North Atlantic winter gale, snow an' sleet an' a perishin' wind. Eh, it was like the Deil walkin' abroad o' the surface o' the deep, whuppin' off the top o' the waves before he made up his mind. They 'd bore up against it so far, but the minute she was clear o' the Skelligs she fair tucked up her skirts an' ran for it by Dunmore Head. Wow, she rolled!

" 'She 'll be makin' Smerwick,' says Bell.

" 'She 'd ha' tried for Ventry by noo if she meant that,' I said.

" 'They 'll roll the funnel oot o' her, this gait,' says Bell. 'Why canna Bannister keep her head to sea?'

" 'It 's the tail-shaft. Ony rollin' 's better than pitchin' wi' superfeecial cracks in the tail-shaft. Calder knows that much,' I said.

" 'It 's ill wark retreevin' steamers this weather,' said Bell. His beard and whiskers were frozen to his oilskin, an' the spray was white on the weather side of him. Pairfect North Atlantic winter weather!

"One by one the sea raxed away our three boats, an' the davits were crumpled like ram's horns.

" 'Yon 's bad,' said Bell, at the last. 'Ye canna pass a hawser wi'oot a boat.' Bell was a vara judeecious man—for an Aberdonian.

"I'm not one that fashes himself for eventualities outside the engine-room, so I e'en slipped down betwixt waves to see how the *Kite* fared. Man, she 's the best geared boat of her class that ever left Clyde! Kinloch, my second, knew her as well as I did. I found him dryin' his socks on the main-steam, an' combin' his whiskers wi' the comb Janet gied me last year, for the warld an' a' as though we were in port. I tried the feed, speered into the stoke-hole, thumbed all bearin's, spat on the thrust for luck, gied 'em my blessin', an' took Kinloch's socks before I went up to the bridge again.

"Then Bell handed me the wheel, an' went below to warm himself. When he came up my gloves were frozen to the spokes an' the ice clicked over my eyelids. Pairfect North Atlantic winter weather, as I was sayin'.

"The gale blew out by night, but we lay in smotherin' cross-seas that made the auld *Kite* chatter from stem to stern. I slowed to thirty-four, I mind—no, thirty-seven. There was a long swell the morn, an' the *Grotkau* was headin' into it west awa'.

"'She 'll win to Rio yet, tail-shaft or no tail-shaft,' says Bell.

"'Last night shook her,' I said. 'She 'll jar it off yet, mark my word.'

"We were then, maybe, a hunder and fifty mile west-sou'-west o' Slyne Head, by dead reckonin'. Next day we made a hunder an' thirty—ye 'll note we were not racin'-boats—an' the day after a hunder an' sixty-one, an' that made us, we 'll say, Eighteen an' a bittock west, an' maybe Fifty-one an' a bittock north, crossin' all the North Atlantic liner lanes on the long slant, always in sight o' the *Grotkau,* creepin' up by night and fallin' awa' by day. After the gale it was cold weather wi' dark nights.

"I was in the engine-room on Friday night, just before the middle watch, when Bell whustled down the tube: 'She 's done it'; an' up I came.

"The *Grotkau* was just a fair distance south, an' one by one she ran up the three red lights in a vertical line—the sign of a steamer not under control.

"'Yon 's a tow for us,' said Bell, lickin' his chops. 'She 'll be worth more than the *Breslau.* We 'll go down to her, McPhee!'

"'Bide a while,' I said. 'The seas fair throng wi' ships here.'

"'Reason why,' said Bell. 'It 's a fortune gaun beggin'. What d' ye think, man?'

"'Gie her till daylight. She knows we 're here. If Bannister needs help he 'll loose a rocket.'

"'Wha told ye Bannister's need? We 'll ha' some rag-an'-bone tramp snappin' her up under oor nose,' said he; an' he put the wheel over. We were goin' slow.

"'Bannister wad like better to go home on a liner an' eat in the saloon. Mind ye what they said o' Holdock & Steiner's food that night at Radley's? Keep her awa', man—keep her awa'. A tow 's a tow, but a derelict 's big salvage.'

"'E-eh!' said Bell. 'Yon's an inshot o' yours, Mac. I love

ye like a brother. We 'll bide whaur we are till daylight'; an' he kept her awa'.

"Syne up went a rocket forward, an' twa on the bridge, an' a blue light aft. Syne a tar-barrel forward again.

" 'She's sinkin',' said Bell. 'It 's all gaun, an' I 'll get no more than a pair o' night-glasses for pickin' up young Bannister—the fool!'

" 'Fair an' soft again,' I said. 'She 's signallin' to the south of us. Bannister knows as well as I that one rocket would bring the *Breslau*. He 'll no be wastin' fireworks for nothin'. Hear her ca'!'

"The *Grotkau* whustled an' whustled for five minutes, an' then there were more fireworks—a regular exhibeetion.

" 'That 's no for men in the regular trade,' says Bell. 'Ye 're right, Mac. That 's for a cuddy full o' passengers.' He blinked through the night-glasses when it lay a bit thick to southward.

" 'What d' ye make of it?' I said.

" 'Liner,' he says. 'Yon 's her rocket. Ou, ay; they 've waukened the gold-strapped skipper, an'—noo they've waukened the passengers. They 're turnin' on the electrics, cabin by cabin. Yon 's anither rocket! They 're comin' up to help the perishin' in deep watters.'

" 'Gie me the glass,' I said. But Bell danced on the bridge, clean dementit. 'Mails—mails—mails!' said he. 'Under contract wi' the Government for the due conveyance o' the mails; an' as such, Mac, ye 'll note, she may rescue life at sea, but she canna tow!—she canna tow! Yon 's her night-signal. She 'll be up in half an hour!'

" 'Gowk!' I said, 'an' we blazin' here wi' all oor lights. Oh, Bell, ye 're a fool!'

"He tumbled off the bridge forward, an' I tumbled aft, an' before ye could wink our lights were oot, the engine-room hatch was covered, an' we lay pitch-dark, watchin' the lights o' the liner come up that the *Grotkau* 'd been signallin' to. Twenty knot an hour she came, every cabin lighted, an' her boats swung awa'. It was grandly done, an' in the inside of an hour. She stopped like Mrs. Holdock's machine; down went the gangway, down went the boats, an' in ten minutes we heard the passengers cheerin', an' awa' she fled.

" 'They 'll tell o' this all the days they live,' said Bell. 'A rescue at sea by night, as pretty as a play. Young Bannister an' Calder will be drinkin' in the saloon, an' six months hence the Board o' Trade 'll gie the skipper a pair o' binoculars. It 's vara philanthropic all round.'

"We 'll lay by till day—ye may think we waited for it wi' sore eyes—an' there sat the *Grotkau,* her nose a bit cocked, just leerin' at us. She looked paifectly ridiculous.

" 'She 'll be fillin' aft,' says Bell; 'for why is she down by the stern? The tail-shaft 's punched a hole in her, an'—we 've no boats. There 's three hunder thousand pound sterlin', at a conservative estimate, droonin' before our eyes. What 's to do?' An' his bearin's got hot again in a minute: he was an incontinent man.

" 'Run her as near as ye daur,' I said. 'Gie me a jacket an' a life-line, an' I 'll swum for it.' There was a bit lump of a sea, an' it was cold in the wind—vara cold; but they 'd gone overside like passengers, young Bannister an' Calder an' a', leaving the gangway down on the lee-side. It would ha' been a flyin' in the face o' manifest Providence to overlook the invitation. We were within fifty yards o' her while Kinloch was garmin' me all over wi' oil behind the galley; an' as we ran past I went outboard for the salvage o' three hunder thousand pound. Man, it was perishin' cold, but I 'd done my job judgmatically, an' came scrapin' all along her side slap on to the lower gratin' o' the gangway. No one more astonished than me, I assure ye. Before I 'd caught my breath I 'd skinned both my knees on the gratin', an' was climbin' up before she rolled again. I made my line fast to the rail, an' squattered aft to young Bannister's cabin, whaur I dried me wi' everything in his bunk, an' put on every conceivable sort o' rig I found till the blood was circulatin'. Three pair drawers, I mind I found—to begin upon—an' I needed them all. It was the coldest cold I remember in all my experience.

"Syne I went aft to the engine-room. The *Grotkau* sat on her own tail, as they say. She was vara short-shafted, an' her gear was all aft. There was four or five foot o' water in the engine-room slummockin' to and fro, black an' greasy; maybe there was six foot. The stoke-hold doors were screwed home, an' the stoke-hold was tight enough, but for a minute the mess in the engine-room deceived me. Only for a minute, though, an' that was because I was not, in a manner o' speakin', as calm as ordinar'. I looked again to mak' sure. 'T was just black wi' bilge: dead watter that must ha' come in fortuitously, ye ken."

"McPhee, I 'm only a passenger," I said, "but you don't persuade me that six foot o' water can come into an engine-room fortuitously."

"Who 's tryin' to persuade one way or the other?" McPhee retorted. "I 'm statin' the facts o' the case—the simple, natural facts. Six or seven foot o' dead watter in the engine-room is a vara depressin' sight if ye think there 's like to be more comin'; but I did not consider that such was likely, and so, ye 'll note, I was not depressed."

"That 's all very well, but I want to know about the water," I said.

"I 've told ye. There was six feet or more there, wi' Calder's cap floatin' on top."

"Where did it come from?"

"Weel, in the confusion o' things after the propeller had dropped off an' the engines were racin' an' a', it 's vara possible that Calder might ha' lost it off his head an' no troubled himself to pick it up again. I remember seein' that cap on him at Southampton."

"I don't want to know about the cap. I 'm asking where the water came from and what it was doing there, and why you were so certain that it was n't a leak, McPhee?"

"For good reason—for good an' sufficient reason."

"Give it to me, then."

"Weel, it 's a reason that does not properly concern myself only. To be preceese, I 'm of opinion that it was due, the watter, in part to an error o' judgment in another man. We can a' mak' mistakes."

"Oh, I beg your pardon!"

"I got me to the rail again, an', 'What 's wrang?' said Bell, hailin'.

" 'She 'll do,' I said. 'Send 's o'er a hawser, an' a man to steer. I 'll pull him in by the life-line.'

"I could see heads bobbin' back an' forth, an' a whuff or two o' strong words. Then Bell said: 'They 'll not trust themselves—one of 'em—in this watter—except Kinloch, an' I 'll no spare him.'

" 'The more salvage to me, then,' I said. 'I 'll make shift *solo*.'

"Says one dock-rat, at this: 'D' ye think she 's safe?'

" 'I 'll guarantee ye nothing,' I said, 'except maybe a hammerin' for keepin' me this long.'

"Then he sings out: 'There 's no more than one lifebelt, an' they canna find it, or I 'd come.'

" 'Throw him over, the Jezebel,' I said, for I was oot o' patience; an' they took haud o' that volunteer before he knew what was in store, and hove him over, in the bight of my life-line. So I e'en hauled him up on the sag of it, hand over fist—a vara welcome recruit when I 'd tilted the salt watter oot of him: for, by the way, he could na swim.

"Syne they bent a twa-inch rope to the life-line, an' a hawser to that, an' I led the rope o'er the drum of a hand-winch forward, an' we sweated the hawser inboard an' made it fast to the *Grotkau's* bitts.

"Bell brought the *Kite* so close I feared she 'd roll in an' do the *Grotkau's* plates a mischief. He hove anither life-line to me, an' went astern, an' we had all the weary winch work to do again wi' a second hawser. For all that, Bell was right: we 'd a long tow before us, an' though Providence had helped us that far, there was no sense in leavin' too much to its keepin'. When the second hawser was fast, I was wet wi' sweat, an' I cried Bell to tak' up his slack an' go home. The other man was by way o' helpin' the work wi' askin' for drinks but I e'en told him he must hand reef an' steer, beginnin' with steerin', for I was goin' to turn in. He steered—oh, ay, he steered, in a manner o' speakin'. At the least, he grippit the spokes an' twiddled 'em an' looked wise, but I doubt if the *Hoor* ever felt it. I turned in there an' then, to young Bannister's bunk, an' slept past expression. I waukened ragin' wi' hunger, a fair lump o' sea runnin', the *Kite* snorin' awa' four knots an hour; an' the *Grotkau* slappin' her nose under, an' yawin' an' standin' over at discretion. She was a most disgracefu' tow. But the shameful thing of all was the food. I raxed me a meal fra galley-shelves an' pantries an' lazareetes an' cubby-holes that I would not ha' gied to the mate of a Cardiff collier; an' ye ken we say a Cardiff mate will eat clinkers to save waste. I 'm sayin' it was simply vile! The crew had written what *they* thought of it on the new paint o' the fo'c'sle, but I had not a decent soul wi' me to complain on. There was nothin' for me to do save watch the hawsers an' the *Kite's* tail squatterin' down in white watter when she lifted to a sea; so I got steam on the after donkey-pump, an' pumped oot the engine-room. There 's no sense in leavin' watter loose in a ship. When she was dry, I went doun the shaft-tunnel, an' found she was leakin' a little through the stuffin'-box, but nothin' to make wark. The propeller had e'en jarred off, as I knew it must, an' Calder had been waitin' for it to go wi' his hand on the gear. He told me as much when I met him ashore. There was nothin' started or strained. It had just slipped awa' to the bed o' the Atlantic as easy as a man dyin' wi' due warnin'—a most providential business for all concerned. Syne I took stock o' the *Grotkau's* upper works. Her boats had been smashed on the davits, an' here an' there was the rail missin', an' a ventilator or two had fetched awa', an' the bridge-rails were bent by the seas; but her hatches were tight, and she 'd taken no sort of harm. Dod, I came to hate her like a human bein', for I was eight weary days aboard, starvin'—ay, starvin'—within a cable's length o' plenty. All day I laid in the bunk reading the 'Woman-Hater,' the grandest book Charlie Reade ever wrote, an' pickin' a toothful here an' there. It was weary, weary work. Eight days, man, I was aboard the *Grotkau,* an' not one full meal did I make. Sma' blame her crew would not stay by her. The other man? Oh I warked him wi' a vengeance to keep him warm.

"It came on to blow when we fetched soundin's, an' that

kept me standin' by the hawsers, lashed to the capstan, breathin' twixt green seas. I near died o' cauld an' hunger, for the *Grotkau* towed like a barge, an' Bell howkit her along through or over. It was vara thick up-Channel, too. We were standin' in to make some sort o' light, an' we near walked over twa three fishin'-boats, an' they cried us we were overclose to Falmouth. Then we were near cut down by a drunken foreign fruiter that was blunderin' between us an' the shore, and it got thicker an' thicker that night, an' I could feel by the tow Bell did not know whaur he was. Losh, we knew in the morn, for the wind blew the fog oot like a candle, an' the sun came clear; and as surely as McRimmon gied me my cheque, the shadow o' the Eddystone lay across our tow-rope! We were that near—ay, we were that near! Bell fetched the *Kite* round with the jerk that came close to tearin' the bitts out o' the *Grotkau,* an' I mind I thanked my Maker in young Bannister's cabin when we were inside Plymouth break-water.

"The first to come aboard was McRimmon, wi' Dandie. Did I tell you our orders were to take anything we found into Plymouth? The auld deil had just come down overnight, puttin' two an' two together from what Calder had told him when the liner landed the *Grotkau's* men. He had preceesely hit oor time. I 'd hailed Bell for something to eat, an' he sent it o'er in the same boat wi' McRimmon, when the auld man came to me. He grinned an' slapped his legs and worked his eyebrows the while I ate.

" 'How do Holdock, Steiner & Chase feed their men?' said he.

" 'Ye can see,' I said, knockin' the top off another beer-bottle. 'I did not sign to be starved, McRimmon.'

" 'Nor to swum, either,' said he, for Bell had tauld him how I carried the line aboard. 'Well, I 'm thinkin' you 'll be no loser. What freight could we ha' put into the *Lammergeyer* would equal salvage on four hunder thousand pounds—hull an' cargo? Eh, McPhee? This cuts the liver out o' Holdock, Steiner, Chase & Company, Limited. Eh, McPhee? An' I 'm sufferin' from senile dementia now? Eh, McPhee? An' I 'm not daft, am I, till I begin to paint the *Lammergeyer?* Eh,

McPhee? Ye may weel lift your leg, Dandie! I ha' the laugh o' them all. Ye found watter in the engine-room?'

"'To speak wi'oot prejudice,' I said, 'there was some watter.'

"'They thought she was sinkin' after the propeller went. She filled wi' extraordinary rapeedity. Calder said it grieved him an' Bannister to abandon her.'

"I thought o' the dinner at Radley's, an' what like o' food I 'd eaten for eight days.

"'It would grieve them sore,' I said.

"'But the crew would not hear o' stayin' and workin' her back under canvas. They 're gaun up an' down sayin' they 'd ha' starved first.'

"'They 'd ha' starved if they 'd stayed,' said I.

"'I tak' it, fra Calder's account, there was a mutiny a'most.'

"'Ye know more than I, McRimmon,' I said. 'Speakin' wi'oot prejudice, for we 're all in the same boat, *who* opened the bilge-cock?'

"'Oh, that 's it—is it?' said the auld man, an' I could see he was surprised. 'A bilge-cock, ye say?'

"'I believe it was a bilge-cock. They were all shut when I came aboard, but some one had flooded the engine-room eight feet over all, and shut it off with the worm-an'-wheel gear from the second gratin' afterwards.'

"'Losh!' said McRimmon. 'The ineequity o' man 's beyond belief. But it 's awfu' discreditable to Holdock, Steiner & Chase, if that came oot in court.'

"'It 's just my own curiosity,' I said.

"'Aweel, Dandie 's afflicted wi' the same disease. Dandie, strive against curiosity, for it brings a little dog into traps an' suchlike. Whaur was the *Kite* when yon painted liner took off the *Grotkau's* people?'

"'Just there or thereabouts,' I said.

"'An' which o' you twa thought to cover your lights?' said he, winkin'.

"'Dandie, I said to the dog, 'we must both strive against curiosity. It 's an unremunerative business. What 's our chance o' salvage, Dandie?'

"He laughed till he choked. 'Tak' what I gie you, McPhee, an' be content,' he said. 'Lord, how a man wastes time when he gets old. Get aboard the *Kite,* mon, as soon as ye can. I 've clean forgot there 's a Baltic charter yammerin' for you at London. That 'll be your last voyage, I 'm thinkin', excep' by way o' pleasure.'

"Steiner's men were comin' aboard to take charge an' tow her round, an' I passed young Steiner in a boat as I went to the *Kite*. He looked down his nose; but McRimmon pipes up: 'Here 's the man ye owe the *Grotkau* to—at a price, Steiner—at a price! Let me introduce Mr. McPhee to you. Maybe ye 've met before; but ye 've vara little luck in keepin' your men—ashore or afloat!'

"Young Steiner looked angry enough to eat him as he chuckled an' whustled in his dry old throat.

" 'Ye 've not got your award yet,' Steiner says.

" 'Na, na,' says the auld man, in a screech ye could hear to the Hoe, 'but I 've twa million sterlin', an' no bairns, ye Judeeas Apella, if ye mean to fight; an' I 'll match ye p'und for p'und till the last p'und 's oot. Ye ken *me,* Steiner! I 'm McRimmon o' McNaughten & McRimmon!'

" 'Dod,' he said betwix' his teeth, sittin' back in the boat, 'I 've waited fourteen year to break that Jew-firm, an' God be thankit I 'll do it now.'

"The *Kite* was in the Baltic while the auld man was warkin' his warks, but I know the assessors valued the *Grotkau,* all told, at over three hunder and sixty thousand—her manifest was a treat o' richness—an' McRimmon got a third for salvin' an abandoned ship. Ye see, there 's vast deeference between towin' a ship wi' men on her an' pickin' up a derelict—a vast deeference—in pounds sterlin'. Moreover, twa three o' the *Grotkau's* crew were burnin' to testify about food, an' there was a note o' Calder to the Board, in regard to the tail-shaft, that would ha' been vara damagin' if it had come into court. They knew better than to fight.

"Syne the *Kite* came back, an' McRimmon paid off me an' Bell personally, an' the rest of the crew *pro rata,* I believe it 's ca'ed. My share—oor share, I should say—was just twenty-five thousand pound sterlin'."

At this point Janet jumped up and kissed him.

"Five-and-twenty thousand pound sterlin'. Noo, I 'm fra the North, and I 'm not the like to fling money awa' rashly, but I 'd gie six months' pay—one hunder an' twenty pounds—to know *who* flooded the engine-room of the *Grotkau.* I 'm fairly well acquaint wi' McRimmon's eediosyncrasies, and *he* 'd no hand in it. It was not Calder, for I 've asked him, an' he wanted to fight me. It would be in the highest degree unprofessional o' Calder—not fightin', but openin' bilge-cocks—but for a while I thought it was him. Ay, I judged it might be him —under temptation."

"What 's your theory?" I demanded.

"Weel, I 'm inclined to think it was one o' those singular providences that remind us we 're in the hands o' Higher Powers."

"It could n't open and shut itself?"

"I did not mean that; but some half-starvin' oiler or, maybe, trimmer must ha' opened it awhile to mak' sure o' leavin' the *Grotkau.* It 's a demoralizin' thing to see an engine-room flood up after any accident to the gear—demoralizin' and deceptive both. Aweel, the man got what he wanted, for they went aboard the liner cryin' that the *Grotkau* was sinkin'. But it's curious to think o' the consequences. In a' human probability, he 's bein' damned in heaps at the present moment aboard another tramp freighter; an' here am I, wi' five-an'-twenty thousand pound invested, resolute to go to sea no more —providential 's the preceese word—except as a passenger, ye 'll understand, Janet."

. . . .

McPhee kept his word. He and Janet went for a voyage as passengers in the first-class saloon. They paid seventy pounds for their berths; and Janet found a very sick woman in the second-class saloon, so that for sixteen days she lived below, and chatted with the stewardesses at the foot of the second-saloon stairs while her patient slept. McPhee was a passenger for exactly twenty-four hours. Then the engineers' mess—where the oilcloth tables are—joyfully took him to its bosom, and for the rest of the voyage that company was richer by the unpaid services of a highly certificated engineer.

THE BRUSHWOOD BOY
1895

Girls and boys, come out to play.
The moon is shining as bright as day!
Leave your supper and leave your sleep,
And come with your playfellows out in the street!
Up the ladder and down the wall—

A CHILD of three sat up in his crib and screamed at the top of his voice, his fists clinched and his eyes full of terror. At first no one heard, for his nursery was in the west wing, and the nurse was talking to a gardener among the laurels. Then the housekeeper passed that way, and hurried to soothe him. He was her special pet, and she disapproved of the nurse.

"What was it, then? What was it, then? There's nothing to frighten him, Georgie dear."

"It was—it was a policeman! He was on the Down—I saw him! He came in. Jane *said* he would."

"Policemen don't come into houses, dearie. Turn over, and take my hand."

"I saw him—on the Down. He came here. Where is your hand, Harper?"

The housekeeper waited till the sobs changed to the regular breathing of sleep before she stole out.

"Jane, what nonsense have you been telling Master Georgie about policemen?"

"I have n't told him anything."

"You have. He's been dreaming about them."

"We met Tisdall on Dowhead when we were in the donkey-cart this morning. P'r'aps that's what put it into his head."

"Oh! Now you are n't going to frighten the child into fits with your silly tales, and the master know nothing about it. If ever I catch you again," etc.

. . . .

A child of six was telling himself stories as he lay in bed. It was a new power, and he kept it a secret. A month before it had occurred to him to carry on a nursery tale left unfinished by his mother, and he was delighted to find the tale as it came out of his own head just as surprising as though he were listening to it "all new from the beginning." There was a prince in that tale, and he killed dragons, but only for one night. Ever afterwards Georgie dubbed himself prince, pasha, giant-killer, and all the rest (you see, he could not tell any one, for fear of being laughed at), and his tales faded gradually into dreamland, where adventures were so many that he could not recall the half of them. They all began in the same way, or, as Georgie explained to the shadows of the night-light, there was "the same starting-off place"—a pile of brushwood stacked somewhere near a beach; and round this pile Georgie found himself running races with little boys and girls. These ended, ships ran high up the dry land and opened into cardboard boxes; or gilt-and-green iron railings that surrounded beautiful gardens turned all soft and could be walked through and overthrown so long as he remembered it was only a dream. He could never hold that knowledge more than a few seconds ere things became real, and instead of pushing down houses full of grown-up people (a just revenge), he sat miserably upon gigantic door-steps trying to sing the multiplication-table up to four times six.

The princess of his tales was a person of wonderful beauty (she came from the old illustrated edition of Grimm, now out of print), and as she always applauded Georgie's valour among the dragons and buffaloes, he gave her the two finest names he had ever heard in his life—Annie and Louise, pronounced "Annie*an*louise." When the dreams swamped the stories, she would change into one of the little girls round the brushwood-pile, still keeping her title and crown. She saw Georgie drown once in a dream-sea by the beach (it was the day after he had been taken to bathe in a real sea by his nurse); and he said as he sank: "Poor Annie*an*louise! She'll be sorry for me now!" But "Annie*an*louise" walked slowly on the beach, called, "'Ha! ha!' said the duck, laughing," which to a waking mind might not seem to bear on the situation. It consoled Georgie at once, and must have been some kind of spell, for it raised the bottom of the deep, and he waded out with a twelve-inch flower-pot on each foot. As he was strictly forbidden to meddle with flower-pots in real life, he felt triumphantly wicked.

. . . .

The movements of the grown-ups, whom Georgie tolerated, but did not pretend to understand, removed his world, when he was seven years old, to a place called "Oxford-on-a-visit." Here were huge buildings surrounded by vast prairies, with streets of infinite length, and, above all, something called the "buttery," which Georgie was dying to see, because he knew it must be greasy, and therefore delightful. He perceived how correct were his judgments when his nurse led him through a stone arch into the presence of an enormously fat man, who asked him if he would like some bread and cheese. Georgie was used to eat all round the clock, so he took what "buttery" gave him, and would have taken some brown liquid called "auditale" but that his nurse led him away to an afternoon performance of a thing called "Pepper's Ghost." This was intensely thrilling. People's heads came off and flew all over the stage, and skeletons danced bone by bone, while Mr. Pepper himself, beyond question a man of the worst, waved his arms and flapped a long gown, and in a deep bass voice (Georgie had never heard a man sing before) told of his sorrows unspeakable. Some grown-up or other tried to explain that the illusion was made with mirrors, and that there was no need to be frightened. Georgie did not know what illusions were, but he did know that a mirror was the looking-glass with the ivory handle on his mother's dressing-table. Therefore the "grown-up" was "just saying things" after the distressing custom of "grown-ups," and Georgie cast about for amusement between scenes. Next to him sat a little girl dressed all in black, her hair combed off her forehead exactly like the girl in the book called "Alice in Wonderland," which had been given him on his last birthday. The little girl looked at Georgie, and Georgie looked at her. There seemed to be no need of any further introduction.

"I've got a cut on my thumb," said he. It was the first work of his first real knife, a savage triangular hack, and he esteemed it a most valuable possession.

"I'm tho thorry!" she lisped. "Let me look—pleathe."

"There's a di-ack-lum plaster on, but it's all raw under," Georgie answered, complying.

"Dothent it hurt?"—her grey eyes were full of pity and interest.

"Awf'ly. Perhaps it will give me lockjaw."

"It lookth very horrid. I'm *tho* thorry!" She put a forefinger to his hand, and held her head sidewise for a better view.

Here the nurse turned, and shook him severely. "You mustn't talk to strange little girls, Master Georgie."

"She isn't strange. She's very nice. I like her, an' I've showed her my new cut."

"The idea! You change places with me."

She moved him over, and shut out the little girl from his view, while the grown-up behind renewed the futile explanations.

"I am *not* afraid, truly," said the boy, wriggling in despair; "but why don't you go to sleep in the afternoons, same as Provost of Oriel?"

Georgie had been introduced to a grown-up of that name, who slept in his presence without apology. Georgie understood that he was the most important grown-up in Oxford; hence he strove to gild his rebuke with flatteries. This grown-up did not seem to like it, but he collapsed, and Georgie lay back in his seat, silent and enraptured. Mr. Pepper was singing again, and the deep, ringing voice, the red fire, and the misty, waving gown all seemed to be mixed up with the little girl who had been so kind about his cut. When the performance was ended she nodded to Georgie, and Georgie nodded in return. He spoke no more than was necessary till bedtime, but meditated on new colours and sounds and lights and music and things as far as he understood them; the deep-mouthed agony of Mr. Pepper mingling with the little girl's lisp. That night he made a new tale, from which he shamelessly removed the Rapunzel-Rapunzel-let-down-your-hair princess, gold crown, Grimm edition, and all, and put a new Annie*an*louise in her place. So it was perfectly right and natural that when he came to the brushwood-pile he should find her waiting for him, her hair combed off her forehead more like Alice in Wonderland than ever, and the races and adventures began.

. . . .

Ten years at an English public school do not encourage dreaming. Georgie won his growth and chest measurement, and a few other things which did not appear in the bills, under a system of cricket, foot-ball, and paper-chases, from four to five days a week, which provided for three lawful cuts of a ground-ash if any boy absented himself from these entertainments. He became a rumple-collared, dusty-hatted fag of the Lower Third, and a light half-back at Little Side foot-ball; was pushed and prodded through the slack back-waters of the Lower Fourth, where the raffle of a school generally accumulates; won his "second-fifteen" cap at foot-ball, enjoyed the dignity of a study with two companions in it, and began to look forward to office as a sub-prefect. At last he blossomed into full glory as head of the school, ex-officio captains of the games; head of his house, where he and his lieutenants preserved discipline and decency among seventy boys from twelve to seventeen; general arbiter in the quarrels that spring up among the touchy Sixth—and intimate friend and ally of the Head himself. When he stepped forth in the black jersey, white knickers, and black stockings of the First Fifteen, the new match-ball under his arm, and his old and frayed cap at the back of his head, the small fry of the lower forms stood apart and worshipped, and the "new caps" of the team talked to him ostentatiously, that the world might see. And so, in summer, when he came back to the pavilion after a slow but eminently safe game, it mattered not whether he had made nothing or, as once happened, a hundred and three, the school shouted just the same, and women-folk who had come to look at the match looked at Cottar—Cottar, *major;* "that's Cottar!" Above all, he was responsible for that thing called the tone of the school, and few realize with what passionate devotion a certain type of boy throws himself into this work. Home was a far-away country, full of ponies and fishing and shooting, and men-visitors who interfered with one's plans; but school was the real world, where things of vital importance happened, and crises arose that must be dealt with promptly and quietly. Not for nothing was it written, "Let the Consuls look to it that the Republic takes no harm," and Georgie was glad to be back in authority when the holidays ended. Behind him, but not too near, was the wise and temperate Head, now suggesting the wisdom of the serpent, now counselling the mildness of the dove; leading him on to see, more by half-hints than by any direct word, how boys and men are all of a piece, and how he who can handle the one will assuredly in time control the other.

For the rest, the school was not encouraged to dwell on its emotions, but rather to keep in hard condition, to avoid false quantities, and to enter the army direct, without the help of the expensive London crammer, under whose roof young blood learns too much. Cottar, *major,* went the way of hundreds before him. The Head gave him six months' final polish, taught him what kind of answers best please a certain kind of examiners, and handed him over to the properly constituted authorities, who passed him into Sandhurst. Here he had sense enough to see that he was in the Lower Third once more, and behaved with respect toward his seniors, till they in turn respected him, and he was promoted to the rank of corporal, and sat in authority over mixed peoples with all the vices of men and boys combined. His reward was another string of athletic cups, a good-conduct sword, and, at last, Her Majesty's commission as a subaltern in a first-class line regiment. He did not know that he bore with him from school and college a character worth much fine gold, but was pleased to find his mess so kindly. He had plenty of money of his own; his training had set the public-school mask upon his face, and had taught him how many were the "things no fellow can do." By virtue of the same training he kept his pores open and his mouth shut.

The regular working of the Empire shifted his world to India, where he tasted utter loneliness in subaltern's quarters, —one room and one bullock-trunk,—and, with his mess, learned the new life from the beginning. But there were horses in the land—ponies at reasonable price; there was polo for such as could afford it; there were the disreputable remnants of a pack of hounds; and Cottar worried his way along without too much despair. It dawned on him that a regiment in India was nearer the chance of active service than he had conceived, and that a man might as well study his profession. A major of the new school backed this idea with enthusiasm, and he and Cottar accumulated a library of military works, and read and argued and disputed far into the nights. But the adjutant said the old thing: "Get to know your men, young un, and they'll follow you anywhere. That's all you want—know your men." Cottar thought he knew them fairly well at cricket and the regimental sports, but he never realized the true inwardness of them till he was sent off with a detachment of twenty to sit down in a mud fort near a rushing river which was spanned by a bridge of boats. When the floods came they went forth and hunted strayed pontoons along the banks. Otherwise there was nothing to do, and the men got drunk, gambled, and quarrelled. They were a sickly crew, for a junior subaltern is by custom saddled with the worst men. Cottar endured their rioting as long as he could and then sent down-country for a dozen pairs of boxing-gloves.

"I wouldn't blame you for fightin'," said he, "if you only knew how to use your hands; but you don't. Take these things, and I'll show you." The men appreciated his efforts. Now, instead of blaspheming and swearing at a comrade, and threatening to shoot him, they could take him apart, and soothe themselves to exhaustion. As one explained whom Cottar found with a shut eye and a diamond-shaped mouth spitting blood through an embrasure: "We tried it with the gloves, sir, for twenty minutes, and *that* done us no good, sir. Then we took off the gloves and tried it that way for another twenty minutes, same as you showed us, sir, an' that done us a world o' good. 'T wasn't fightin', sir; there was a bet on."

Cottar dared not laugh, but he invited his men to other sports, such as racing across country in shirt and trousers after a trail of torn paper, and to single-stick in the evenings, till the native population, who had a lust for sport in every form, wished to know whether the white men understood wrestling. They sent in an ambassador, who took the soldiers by the neck and threw them about the dust; and the entire command were all for this new game. They spent money on learning new falls and holds, which was better than buying other doubtful commodities; and the peasantry grinned five deep round the tournaments.

That detachment, who had gone up in bullock-carts, returned to headquarters at an average rate of thirty miles a day, fair heel-and-toe; no sick, no prisoners, and no court martials pending. They scattered themselves among their friends, singing the praises of their lieutenant and looking for causes of offense.

"How did you do it, young un?" the adjutant asked.

"Oh, I sweated the beef off 'em, and then I sweated some muscle on to 'em. It was rather a lark."

"If that's your way of lookin' at it, we can give you all the larks you want. Young Davies isn't feelin' quite fit, and he's next for detachment duty. Care to go for him?"

" 'Sure he wouldn't mind? I don't want to shove myself forward, you know."

"You needn't bother on Davies's account. We'll give you the sweepin's of the corps, and you can see what you can make of 'em."

"All right," said Cottar. "It's better fun than loafin' about cantonments."

"Rummy thing," said the adjutant, after Cottar had returned to his wilderness with twenty other devils worse than the first. "If Cottar only knew it, half the women in the station would give their eyes—confound 'em!—to have the young un in tow."

"That accounts for Mrs. Elery sayin' I was workin' my nice new boy too hard," said a wing commander.

"Oh, yes; and 'Why doesn't he come to the band-stand in the evenings?' and 'Can't I get him to make up a four at tennis with the Hammon girls?'" the adjutant snorted. "Look at young Davies makin' an ass of himself over mutton-dressed-as-lamb old enough to be his mother!"

"No one can accuse young Cottar of runnin' after women, white *or* black," the major replied thoughtfully. "But, then, that's the kind that generally goes the worst mucker in the end."

"Not Cottar. I've only run across one of his muster before —a fellow called Ingles, in South Africa. He was just the same hard-trained, athletic-sports build of animal. Always kept himself in the pink of condition. Didn't do him much good, though. 'Shot at Wesselstroom the week before Majuba. Wonder how the young un will lick his detachment into shape."

Cottar turned up six weeks later, on foot, with his pupils. He never told his experiences, but the men spoke enthusiastically, and fragments of it leaked back to the colonel through sergeants, bâtmen, and the like.

There was great jealousy between the first and second detachments, but the men united in adoring Cottar, and their way of showing it was by sparing him all the trouble that men know how to make for an unloved officer. He sought popularity as little as he had sought it at school, and therefore it came to him. He favoured no one—not even when the company sloven pulled the company cricket-match out of the fire with an unexpected forty-three at the last moment. There was very little getting round him, for he seemed to know by instinct exactly when and where to head off a malingerer; but he did not forget that the difference between a dazed and sulky junior of the upper school and a bewildered, browbeaten lump of a private fresh from the depot was very small indeed. The sergeants, seeing these things, told him secrets generally hid from young officers. His words were quoted as barrack authority on bets in canteen and at tea; and the veriest shrew of the corps, bursting with charges against other women who had used the cooking-ranges out of turn, forbore to speak when Cottar, as the regulations ordained, asked of a morning if there were "any complaints."

"I'm full o' complaints," said Mrs. Corporal Morrison, "an' I'd kill O'Halloran's fat sow of a wife any day, but ye know how it is. 'E puts 'is head just inside the door, an' looks down 'is blessed nose so bashful, an' 'e whispers, 'Any complaints?' Ye can't complain after that. *I* want to kiss him. Some day I think I will. Heigh-ho! she'll be a lucky woman that gets Young Innocence. See 'im now, girls. Do ye blame me?"

Cottar was cantering across to polo, and he looked a very satisfactory figure of a man as he gave easily to the first excited bucks of his pony, and slipped over a low mud wall to the practice-ground. There were more than Mrs. Corporal Morrison who felt as she did. But Cottar was busy for eleven hours of the day. He did not care to have his tennis spoiled by petticoats in the court; and after one long afternoon at a garden-party, he explained to his major that this sort of thing was "futile piffle," and the major laughed. Theirs was not a married mess, except for the colonel's wife, and Cottar stood in awe of the good lady. She said "my regiment," and the world knows what that means. None the less, when they wanted her to give away the prizes after a shooting-match, and she refused because one of the prize-winners was married to a girl who had made a jest of her behind her broad back, the mess ordered Cottar to "tackle her," in his best calling-kit. This he did, simply and laboriously, and she gave way altogether.

"She only wanted to know the facts of the case," he explained. "I just told her, and she saw at once."

"Ye-es," said the adjutant. "I expect that's what she did. Comin' to the Fusiliers' dance to-night, Galahad?"

"No, thanks. I've got a fight on with the major." The virtuous apprentice sat up till midnight in the major's quarters, with a stop-watch and a pair of compasses, shifting little painted lead-blocks about a four-inch map.

Then he turned in and slept the sleep of innocence, which is full of healthy dreams. One peculiarity of his dreams he noticed at the beginning of his second hot weather. Two or three times a month they duplicated or ran in series. He would find himself sliding into dreamland by the same road—a road that ran along a beach near a pile of brushwood. To the right lay the sea, sometimes at full tide, sometimes withdrawn to the very horizon; but he knew it for the same sea. By that road he would travel over a swell of rising ground covered with short, withered grass, into valleys of wonder and unreason. Beyond the ridge, which was crowned with some sort of street-lamp, anything was possible; but up to the lamp it seemed to him that he knew the road as well as he knew the parade-ground. He learned to look forward to the place; for, once there, he was sure of a good night's rest, and Indian hot weather can be rather trying. First, shadowy under closing eyelids, would come the outline of the brushwood-pile, next the white sand of the beach-road, almost overhanging the black, changeful sea; then the turn inland and uphill to the single light. When he was unrestful for any reason, he would tell himself how he was sure to get there—sure to get there—if he shut his eyes and surrendered to the drift of things. But one night after a foolishly hard hour's polo (the thermometer was 94° in his quarters at ten o'clock), sleep stood away from him altogether, though he did his best to find the well-known road, the point where true sleep began. At last he saw the brushwood-pile, and hurried along to the ridge, for behind him he felt was the wide-awake, sultry world. He reached the lamp in safety, tingling with drowsiness, when a policeman—a common country policeman—sprang up before him and touched him on the shoulder ere he could dive into the dim valley below. He was filled with terror,—the hopeless terror of dreams,—for the policeman said, in the awful, distinct voice of dream-people, "I am Policeman Day coming back from the City of Sleep. You come with me." Georgie knew it was true—that just beyond him in the valley lay the lights of the City of Sleep, where he would have been sheltered, and that this Policeman-Thing had full power and authority to head him back to miserable wakefulness. He found himself looking at the moonlight on the wall, dripping with fright; and he never overcame that horror, though he met the Policeman several times that hot weather, and his coming was the forerunner of a bad night.

But other dreams—perfectly absurd ones—filled him with an incommunicable delight. All those that he remembered began by the brushwood-pile. For instance, he found a small clockwork steamer (he had noticed it many nights before) lying by the sea-road and stepped into it, whereupon it moved with surpassing swiftness over an absolutely level sea. This was glorious, for he felt he was exploring great matters; and it stopped by a lily carved in stone, which, most naturally, floated on the water. Seeing the lily was labelled "Hong-Kong," Georgie said: "Of course. This is precisely what I expected Hong-Kong would be like. How magnificent!" Thousands of miles farther on it halted at yet another stone lily, labelled "Java"; and this, again, delighted him hugely, because he knew that now he was at the world's end. But the little boat ran on and on till it lay in a deep fresh-water lock, the sides of which were carven marble, green with moss. Lily-pads lay on the water, and reeds arched above. Someone moved among the reeds—someone whom Georgie knew he had travelled to this world's end to reach. Therefore everything was entirely well with him. He was unspeakably happy, and vaulted over the ship's side to find this person. When his feet touched that still water, it changed, with the rustle of unrolling maps, to nothing less than a sixth quarter of the globe, beyond the most remote imagining of man—a place where islands were coloured yellow and blue, their lettering strung across their faces. They gave on unknown seas, and Georgie's urgent desire was to return swiftly across this floating atlas to known bearings. He told himself repeatedly that it was no good to hurry; but still he hurried desperately, and the islands slipped and slid under his feet, the straits yawned and widened, till he found himself utterly lost in the world's fourth dimension, with no hope of return. Yet only a little distance away he could see the old world with the rivers and mountain-chains marked according to the Sandhurst rules of map-making. Then that person for whom he had come to the Lily Lock (that was its name) ran up across unexplored territories, and showed him a way. They fled hand in hand till they reached a road that spanned ravines, and ran along the edge of precipices, and was tunnelled through mountains. "This goes to our brushwood-pile," said his companion; and all his trouble was at an end. He took a pony, because he understood that this was the Thirty-Mile Ride and he must ride swiftly, and raced through the clattering tunnels and round the curves, always downhill, till he heard the sea to his left, and saw it raging under a full moon, against sandy cliffs. It was heavy going, but he recognized the nature of the country, the dark-purple downs inland, and the bents that whistled in the wind. The road was eaten away in places, and the sea lashed at him—black, foamless tongues of smooth and glossy rollers; but he was sure that there was less danger from the sea than from "Them," whoever "They" were, inland to his right. He knew, too, that he would be safe if he could reach the down with the lamp on it. This came as he expected: he saw the one light a mile ahead along the beach, dismounted, turned to the right, walked quietly over to the brushwood-pile, found the little steamer had returned to the beach whence he had unmoored it, and—must have fallen asleep, for he could remember no more. "I'm gettin' the hang of the geography of that place," he said to himself, as he shaved next morning. "I must have made some sort of circle. Let's see. The Thirty-Mile Ride (now how the deuce did I know it was called the Thirty-Mile Ride?) joins the sea-road beyond the first down where the lamp is. And that atlas-country lies at the back of the Thirty-Mile Ride, somewhere out to the right beyond the hills and tunnels. Rummy things, dreams. 'Wonder what makes mine fit into each other so?"

He continued on his solid way through the recurring duties of the seasons. The regiment was shifted to another station, and he enjoyed road-marching for two months, with a good deal of mixed shooting thrown in, and when they reached their new cantonments he became a member of the local Tent Club, and chased the mighty boar on horseback with a short stabbing-spear. There he met the *mahseer* of the Poonch, beside whom the tarpon is as a herring, and he who lands him can say that he is a fisherman. This was as new and as fascinating as the big-game shooting that fell to his portion, when he had himself photographed for the mother's benefit, sitting on the flank of his first tiger.

Then the adjutant was promoted, and Cottar rejoiced with him, for he admired the adjutant greatly, and marvelled who might be big enough to fill his place; so that he nearly collapsed when the mantle fell on his own shoulders, and the colonel said a few sweet things that made him blush. An adjutant's position does not differ materially from that of head of the school, and Cottar stood in the same relation to the colonel as he had to his old Head in England. Only, tempers wear out in hot weather, and things were said and done that tried him sorely, and he made glorious blunders, from which the regimental sergeant-major pulled him with a loyal soul and a shut mouth. Slovens and incompetents raged against him; the weak-minded strove to lure him from the ways of justice; the small-minded—yea, men whom Cottar believed would never do "things no fellow can do"—imputed motives mean and circuitous to actions that he had not spent a thought upon; and he tasted injustice, and it made him very sick. But his consolation came on parade, when he looked down the full companies, and reflected how few were in hospital or cells, and wondered when the time would come to try the machine of his love and labour.

But they needed and expected the whole of a man's working-day, and maybe three or four hours of the night. Curiously enough, he never dreamed about the regiment as he was popularly supposed to. The mind, set free from the day's doings, generally ceased working altogether, or, if it moved at all, carried him along the old beach-road to the downs, the lamp-post, and, once in a while, to terrible Policeman Day. The second time that he returned to the world's lost continent (this was a dream that repeated itself again and again, with variations, on the same ground) he knew that if he only sat still the person from the Lily Lock would help him, and he was not disappointed. Sometimes he was trapped in mines of vast depth hollowed out of the heart of the world, where men in torment chanted echoing songs; and he heard this person coming along through the galleries, and everything was made safe and delightful. They met again in low-roofed Indian railway-carriages that halted in a garden surrounded by gilt-and-green railings, where a mob of stony white people, all unfriendly, sat at breakfast-tables covered with roses, and separated Georgie from his companion, while underground voices sang deep-voiced songs. Georgie was filled with enormous despair till they two met again. They foregathered in the middle of an endless, hot tropic night, and crept into a huge house that stood, he knew, somewhere north of the railway-station where the people ate among the roses. It was surrounded with gardens, all moist and dripping; and in one room, reached through leagues of whitewashed passages, a Sick Thing lay in bed. Now the least noise, Georgie knew, would unchain some waiting horror, and his companion knew it, too; but when their eyes met across the bed, Georgie was disgusted to see that she was a child—a little girl in strapped shoes, with her black hair combed back from her forehead.

"What disgraceful folly!" he thought. "Now she could do nothing whatever if Its head came off."

Then the Thing coughed, and the ceiling shattered down in plaster on the mosquito-netting, and "They" rushed in from all quarters. He dragged the child through the stifling garden, voices chanting behind them, and they rode the Thirty-Mile Ride under whip and spur along the sandy beach by the booming sea, till they came to the downs, the lamp-post, and the brushwood-pile, which was safety. Very often dreams would break up about them in this fashion, and they would be separated, to endure awful adventures alone. But the most amusing times were when he and she had a clear understanding that it was all make-believe, and walked through mile-wide roaring rivers without even taking off their shoes, or set light to populous cities to see how they would burn, and were rude as any children to the vague shadows met in their rambles. Later in the night they were sure to suffer for this, either at the hands of the Railway People eating among the roses, or in the tropic uplands at the far end of the Thirty-Mile Ride. Together, this did not much affright them; but often Georgie would hear her shrill cry of "Boy! Boy!" half a world away, and hurry to her rescue before "They" maltreated her.

He and she explored the dark-purple downs as far inland from the brushwood-pile as they dared, but that was always a dangerous matter. The interior was filled with "Them," and "They" went about singing in the hollows, and Georgie and she felt safer on or near the seaboard. So thoroughly had he come to know the place of his dreams that even waking he accepted it as a real country, and made a rough sketch of it. He kept his own counsel, of course; but the permanence of the land puzzled him. His ordinary dreams were as formless and as fleeting as any healthy dreams could be, but once at the brushwood-pile he moved within known limits and could see where he was going. There were months at a time when nothing notable crossed his sleep. Then the dreams would come in a batch of five or six, and next morning the map that he kept in his writing-case would be written up to date, for Georgie was a most methodical person. There was, indeed, a danger—his seniors said so—of his developing into a regular "Auntie Fuss" of an adjutant, and when an officer once takes to old-maidism there is more hope for the virgin of seventy than for him.

But fate sent the change that was needed, in the shape of a little winter campaign on the Border, which, after the manner of little campaigns, flashed out into a very ugly war; and Cottar's regiment was chosen among the first.

"Now," said a major, "this'll shake the cobwebs out of us all—especially you, Galahad; and we can see what your hen-with-one-chick attitude has done for the regiment."

Cottar nearly wept with joy as the campaign went forward. They were fit—physically fit beyond the other troops; they were good children in camp, wet or dry, fed or unfed; and they followed their officers with the quick suppleness and trained obedience of a first-class foot-ball fifteen. They were cut off from their apology for a base, and cheerfully cut their way back to it again; they crowned and cleaned out hills full of the

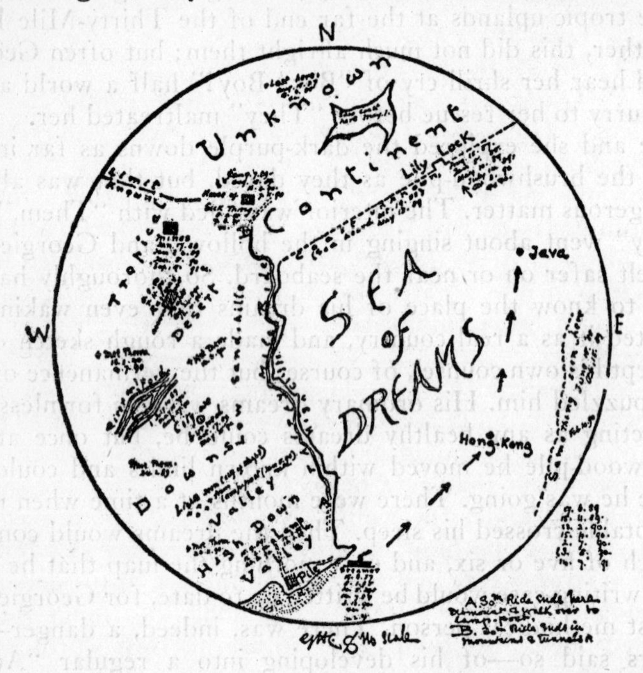

enemy with the precision of well-broken dogs of chase; and in the hour of retreat, when, hampered with the sick and wounded of the column, they were persecuted down eleven miles of waterless valley, they, serving as rear-guard, covered themselves with a great glory in the eyes of fellow-professionals. Any regiment can advance, but few know how to retreat with a sting in the tail. Then they turned to made roads, most often under fire, and dismantled some inconvenient mud redoubts. They were the last corps to be withdrawn when the rubbish of the campaign was all swept up; and after a month in standing camp, which tries morals severely, they departed to their own place in column of fours, singing:

"'E's goin' to do without 'em—
Don't want 'em any more;
'E's goin' to do without 'em,
As 'e's often done before.
'E's goin' to be a martyr
On a 'ighly novel plan.
An' all the boys and girls will say,
'Ow! what a nice young man—man—man!
Ow! what a nice young man!'"

There came out a "Gazette" in which Cottar found that he had been behaving with "courage and coolness and discretion" in all his capacities; that he had assisted the wounded under fire, and blown in a gate, also under fire. Net result, his captaincy and a brevet majority, coupled with the Distinguished Service Order.

As to his wounded, he explained that they were both heavy men, whom he could lift more easily than any one else. "Otherwise, of course, I should have sent out one of my men; and, of course, about that gate business, we were safe the minute we were well under the walls." But this did not prevent his men from cheering him furiously whenever they saw him, or the mess from giving him a dinner on the eve of his departure to England. (A year's leave was among the things he had "snaffled out of the campaign," to use his own words.) The doctor, who had taken quite as much as was good for him, quoted poetry about "a good blade carving the casques of men," and so on, and everybody told Cottar that he was an excellent person; but when he rose to make his maiden speech they shouted so that he was understood to say, "It isn't any use tryin' to speak with you chaps rottin' me like this. Let's have some pool."

. . . .

It is not unpleasant to spend eight-and-twenty days in an easy-going steamer on warm waters, in the company of a woman who lets you see that you are head and shoulders superior to the rest of the world, even though that woman may be, and most often is, ten counted years your senior. P. O. boats are not lighted with the disgustful particularity of Atlantic liners. There is more phosphorescence at the bows, and greater silence and darkness by the hand-steering gear aft.

Awful things might have happened to Georgie but for the little fact that he had never studied the first principles of the game he was expected to play. So when Mrs. Zuleika, at Aden, told him how motherly an interest she felt in his welfare, medals, brevet, and all, Georgie took her at the foot of the letter, and promptly talked of his own mother, three hundred miles nearer each day, of his home, and so forth, all the way up the Red Sea. It was much easier than he had supposed to converse with a woman for an hour at a time. Then Mrs. Zuleika, turning from parental affection, spoke of love in the abstract as a thing not unworthy of study, and in discreet twilights after dinner demanded confidences. Georgie would have been delighted to supply them, but he had none, and did not know it was his duty to manufacture them. Mrs. Zuleika expressed surprise and unbelief, and asked those questions which deep asks of deep. She learned all that was necessary to conviction, and, being very much a woman, resumed (Georgie never knew that she had abandoned) the motherly attitude.

"Do you know," she said, somewhere in the Mediterranean, "I think you're the very dearest boy I have ever met in my life, and I'd like you to remember me a little. You will when you are older, but I want you to remember me now. You'll make some girl very happy."

"Oh! Hope so," said Georgie, gravely; "but there's heaps of time for marryin' an' all that sort of thing, ain't there?"

"That depends. Here are your bean-bags for the Ladies' Competition. I think I'm growing too old to care for these *tamashas*."

They were getting up sports, and Georgie was on the committee. He never noticed how perfectly the bags were sewn, but another woman did, and smiled—once. He liked Mrs. Zuleika greatly. She was a bit old, of course, but uncommonly nice. There was no nonsense about her.

A few nights after they passed Gibraltar his dream returned to him. She who waited by the brushwood-pile was no longer a little girl, but a woman with black hair that grew into a "widow's peak," combed back from her forehead. He knew her for the child in black, the companion of the last six years, and, as it had been in the time of the meetings on the Lost Continent, he was filled with delight unspeakable. "They," for some dreamland reason, were friendly or had gone away that night, and the two flitted together over all their country, from the brushwood-pile up the Thirty-Mile Ride, till they saw the House of the Sick Thing, a pin-point in the distance to the left; stamped through the Railway Waiting-room where the roses lay on the spread breakfast-tables; and returned, by the ford and the city they had once burned for sport, to the great swells of the downs under the lamp-post. Wherever they moved a strong singing followed them underground, but this night there was no panic. All the land was empty except for themselves, and at the last (they were sitting by the lamp-post hand in hand) she turned and kissed him. He woke with a start, staring at the waving curtain of the cabin door; he could almost have sworn that the kiss was real.

Next morning the ship was rolling in a Biscay sea, and people were not happy; but as Georgie came to breakfast, shaven, tubbed, and smelling of soap, several turned to look at him because of the light in his eyes and the splendour of his countenance.

"Well, you look beastly fit," snapped a neighbour. "Any one left you a legacy in the middle of the Bay?"

Georgie reached for the curry, with a seraphic grin. "I suppose it's the gettin' so near home, and all that. I do feel rather festive this mornin'. 'Rolls a bit, doesn't she?"

Mrs. Zuleika stayed in her cabin till the end of the voyage, when she left without bidding him farewell, and wept passionately on the dock-head for pure joy of meeting her children, who, she had often said, were so like their father.

Georgie headed for his own country, wild with delight of his first long furlough after the lean seasons. Nothing was changed in that orderly life, from the coachman who met him at the station to the white peacock that stormed at the carriage from the stone wall above the shaven lawns. The house took toll of him with due regard to precedence—first the mother; then the father; then the housekeeper, who wept and praised God; then the butler, and so on down to the under-keeper, who had been dog-boy in Georgie's youth, and called him "Master Georgie," and was reproved by the groom who had taught Georgie to ride.

"Not a thing changed," he sighed contentedly, when the three of them sat down to dinner in the late sunlight, while the rabbits crept out upon the lawn below the cedars, and the big trout in the ponds by the home paddock rose for their evening meal.

"*Our* changes are all over, dear," cooed the mother; "and now I am getting used to your size and your tan (you're very brown, Georgie), I see you haven't changed in the least. You're exactly like the pater."

The father beamed on this man after his own heart,—"youngest major in the army, and should have had the V. C., sir,"—and the butler listened with his professional mask off when Master Georgie spoke of war as it is waged to-day, and his father cross-questioned.

They went out on the terrace to smoke among the roses, and the shadow of the old house lay long across the wonderful English foliage, which is the only living green in the world.

"Perfect! By Jove, it's perfect!" Georgie was looking at the round-bosomed woods beyond the home paddock, where the white pheasant boxes were ranged; and the golden air was full of a hundred sacred scents and sounds. Georgie felt his father's arm tighten in his.

"It's not half bad—but *hodie mihi, cras tibi,* isn't it? I suppose you'll be turning up some fine day with a girl under your arm, if you haven't one now, eh?"

"You can make your mind easy, sir. I haven't one."

"Not in all these years?" said the mother.

"I hadn't time, mummy. They keep a man pretty busy, these days, in the service, and most of our mess are unmarried, too."

"But you must have met hundreds in society—at balls, and so on?"

"I'm like the Tenth, mummy: I don't dance."

"Don't dance! What have you been doing with yourself then—backing other men's bills?" said the father.

"Oh, yes; I've done a little of that too; but you see, as things are now, a man has all his work cut out for him to keep abreast of his profession, and my days were always too full to let me lark about half the night."

"Hmm!"—suspiciously.

"It's never too late to learn. We ought to give some kind of housewarming for the people about, now you've come back. Unless you want to go straight up to town, dear?"

"No. I don't want anything better than this. Let's sit still and enjoy ourselves. I suppose there will be something for me to ride if I look for it?"

"Seeing I've been kept down to the old brown pair for the last six weeks because all the others were being got ready for Master Georgie, I should say there might be," the father chuckled. "They're reminding me in a hundred ways that I must take the second place now."

"Brutes!"

"The pater doesn't mean it, dear; but every one had been trying to make your home-coming a success; and you *do* like it, don't you?"

"Perfect! Perfect! There's no place like England—when you've done your work."

"That's the proper way to look at it, my son."

And so up and down the flagged walk till their shadows grew long in the moonlight, and the mother went indoors and played such songs as a small boy once clamoured for, and the squat silver candlesticks were brought in, and Georgie climbed to the two rooms in the west wing that had been his nursery and his playroom in the beginning. Then who should come to tuck him up for the night but the mother? And she sat down on the bed, and they talked for a long hour, as mother and son should, if there is to be any future for the Empire. With a simple woman's deep guile she asked questions and suggested answers that should have waked some sign in the face on the pillow, and there was neither quiver of eyelid nor quickening of breath, neither evasion nor delay in reply. So she blessed him and kissed him on the mouth, which is not always a mother's property, and said something to her husband later, at which he laughed profane and incredulous laughs.

All the establishment waited on Georgie next morning, from the tallest six-year-old, "with a mouth like a kid glove, Master Georgie," to the under-keeper strolling carelessly along the horizon, Georgie's pet rod in his hand, and "There's a four-pounder risin' below the lasher. You don't 'ave 'em in Injia, Mast—Major Georgie." It was all beautiful beyond telling even though the mother insisted on taking him out in the landau (the leather had the hot Sunday smell of his youth) and showing him off to her friends at all the houses for six miles round; and the pater bore him up to town and a lunch at the club, where he introduced him, quite carelessly, to not less than thirty ancient warriors whose sons were not the youngest majors in the army and had not the D. S. O. After that it was Georgie's turn; and remembering his friends, he filled up the house with that kind of officer who live in cheap lodgings at Southsea or Montpelier Square, Brompton—good men all, but not well off. The mother perceived that they needed girls to play with; and as there was no scarcity of girls, the house hummed like a dovecote in spring. They tore up the place for amateur theatricals; they disappeared in the gardens when they ought to have been rehearsing; they swept off every available horse and vehicle, especially the governess cart and the fat pony; they fell into the trout-ponds; they picnicked and they tennised; and they sat on gates in the twilight, two by two, and Georgie found that he was not in the least necessary to their entertainment.

"My word!" said he, when he saw the last of their dear backs. "They told me they've enjoyed 'emselves, but they haven't done half the things they said they would."

"I know they've enjoyed themselves—immensely," said the mother. "You're a public benefactor, dear."

"Now we can be quiet again, can't we?"

"Oh, quite. I've a very dear friend of mine that I want you to know. She couldn't come with the house so full, because she's an invalid, and she was away when you first came. She's a Mrs. Lacy."

"Lacy! I don't remember the name about here."

"No; they came after you went to India—from Oxford. Her husband died there, and she lost some money, I believe. They bought The Firs on the Bassett Road. She's a very sweet woman, and we're very fond of them both."

"She's a widow, didn't you say?"

"She has a daughter. Surely I said so, dear?"

"Does she fall into trout-ponds, and gas and giggle, and 'Oh, Major Cottah!' and all that sort of thing?"

"No, indeed. She's a very quiet girl, and very musical. She always came over here with her music books—composing, you know; and she generally works all day, so you won't——"

" 'Talking about Miriam?" said the pater, coming up. The mother edged toward him within elbow-reach. There was no finesse about Georgie's father. "Oh, Miriam's a dear girl. Plays beautifully. Rides beautifully, too. She's a regular pet of the household. Used to call me——" The elbow went home, and ignorant but obedient always, the pater shut himself off.

"What used she to call you, sir?"

"All sorts of pet names. I'm very fond of Miriam."

"Sounds Jewish—Miriam."

"Jew! You'll be calling yourself a Jew next. She's one of the Herefordshire Lacys. When her aunt dies——" Again the elbow.

"Oh, you won't see anything of her, Georgie. She's busy with her music or her mother all day. Besides, you're going up to town to-morrow, aren't you? I thought you said something about an Institute meeting?" The mother spoke.

"Go up to town *now!* What nonsense!" Once more the pater was shut off.

"I had some idea of it, but I'm not quite sure," said the son of the house. Why did the mother try to get him away because a musical girl and her invalid parent were expected? He did not approve of unknown females calling his father pet names. He would observe these pushing persons who had been only seven years in the county.

All of which the delighted mother read in his countenance, herself keeping an air of sweet disinterestedness.

"They'll be here this evening for dinner. I'm sending the carriage over for them, and they won't stay more than a week."

"Perhaps I shall go up to town. I don't quite know yet." Georgie moved away irresolutely. There was a lecture at the United Services Institute on the supply of ammunition in the field, and the one man whose theories most irritated Major Cottar would deliver it. A heated discussion was sure to follow, and perhaps he might find himself moved to speak. He took his rod that afternoon and went down to thrash it out among the trout.

"Good sport, dear!" said the mother, from the terrace.

"'Fraid it won't be, mummy. All those men from town, and the girls particularly, have put every trout off his feed for weeks. There isn't one of 'em that cares for fishin'—really. Fancy stampin' and shoutin' on the bank, and tellin' every fish for half a mile exactly what you're goin' to do, and then chuckin' a brute of a fly at him! By Jove, it would scare *me* if I was a trout!"

But things were not as bad as he had expected. The black gnat was on the water, and the water was strictly preserved. A three-quarter-pounder at the second cast set him for the campaign, and he worked down-stream, crouching behind the reed and meadow-sweet; creeping between a hornbeam hedge and a foot-wide strip of bank, where he could see the trout, but where they could not distinguish him from the background; lying almost on his stomach to switch the blue-upright sidewise through the checkered shadows of a gravelly ripple under overarching trees. But he had known every inch of the water since he was four feet high. The aged and astute between sunk roots, with the large and fat that lay in the frothy scum below some strong rush of water, sucking as lazily as carp, came to trouble in their turn, at the hand that imitated so delicately the flicker and wimple of an egg-dropping fly. Consequently, Georgie found himself five miles from home when he ought to have been dressing for dinner. The housekeeper had taken good care that her boy should not go empty, and before he changed to the white moth he sat down to excellent claret with sandwiches of potted egg and things that adoring women make and men never notice. Then back, to surprise the otter grubbing for fresh-water mussels, the rabbits on the edge of the beechwoods foraging in the clover, and the policeman-like white owl stooping to the little field-mice, till the moon was strong, and he took his rod apart, and went home through well-remembered gaps in the hedges. He fetched a compass round the house, for, though he might have broken every law of the establishment every hour, the law of his boyhood was unbreakable; after fishing you went in by the south garden back-door, cleaned up in the outer scullery, and did not present yourself to your elders and your betters till you had washed and changed.

"Half-past ten, by Jove! Well, we'll make the sport an excuse. They wouldn't want to see me the first evening, at any rate. Gone to bed, probably." He skirted by the open French windows of the drawing-room. "No, they haven't. They look very comfy in there."

He could see his father in his own particular chair, the mother in hers, and the back of a girl at the piano by the big potpourri-jar. The gardens looked half divine in the moonlight, and he turned down through the roses to finish his pipe.

A prelude ended, and there floated out a voice of the kind that in his childhood he used to call "creamy"—a full, true contralto; and this is the song that he heard every syllable of it:

Over the edge of the purple down,
Where the single lamplight gleams,
Know ye the road to the Merciful Town
That is hard by the Sea of Dreams—
Where the poor may lay their wrongs away,
And the sick may forget to weep?
But we—pity us! Oh, pity us!
We wakeful; ah, pity us!—
We must go back with Policeman Day—
Back from the City of Sleep!

Weary they turn from the scroll and crown,
Fetter and prayer and plough—
They that go up to the Merciful Town,
For her gates are closing now.
It is their right in the Baths of Night
Body and soul to steep:
But we—pity us! ah, pity us!
We wakeful; oh, pity us!—
We must go back with Policeman Day—
Back from the City of Sleep!

Over the edge of the purple down,
Ere the tender dreams begin,
Look—we may look—at the Merciful Town,
But we may not enter in!
Outcasts all, from her guarded wall
Back to our watch we creep:
We—pity us! ah, pity us!
We wakeful; oh, pity us!—
We that go back with Policeman Day—
Back from the City of Sleep!

At the last echo he was aware that his mouth was dry and unknown pulses were beating in the roof of it. The housekeeper, who would have it that he must have fallen in and caught a chill, was waiting to catch him on the stairs, and, since he neither saw nor answered her, carried a wild tale abroad that brought his mother knocking at the door.

"Anything happened, dear? Harper said she thought you weren't——"

"No; it's nothing. I'm all right, mummy. *Please* don't bother."

He did not recognize his own voice, but that was a small matter beside what he was considering. Obviously, most obviously, the whole coincidence was crazy lunacy. He proved it to the satisfaction of Major George Cottar, who was going up to town to-morrow to hear a lecture on the supply of ammunition in the field; and having so proved it, the soul and brain and heart and body of Georgie cried joyously: "That's the Lily

Lock girl—the Lost Continent girl—the Thirty-Mile Ride girl—the Brushwood girl! *I* know her!"

He waked, stiff and cramped in his chair, to reconsider the situation by sunlight, when it did not appear normal. But a man must eat, and he went to breakfast, his heart between his teeth, holding himself severely in hand.

"Late, as usual," said the mother. "'My boy, Miss Lacy."

A tall girl in black raised her eyes to his, and Georgie's life training deserted him—just as soon as he realized that she did not know. He stared coolly and critically. There was the abundant black hair, growing in a widow's peak, turned back from the forehead, with that peculiar ripple over the right ear; there were the grey eyes set a little close together; the short upper lip, resolute chin, and the known poise of the head. There was also the small well-cut mouth that had kissed him.

"Georgie—*dear!*" said the mother, amazedly, for Miriam was flushing under the stare.

"I—I beg your pardon!" he gulped. "I don't know whether the mother has told you, but I'm rather an idiot at times, specially before I've had my breakfast. It's—it's a family failing."

He turned to explore among the hot-water dishes on the sideboard, rejoicing that she did not know—she did not know.

His conversation for the rest of the meal was mildly insane, though the mother thought she had never seen her boy look half so handsome. How could any girl, least of all one of Miriam's discernment, forbear to fall down and worship? But deeply Miriam was displeased. She had never been stared at in that fashion before, and promptly retired into her shell when Georgie announced that he had changed his mind about going to town, and would stay to play with Miss Lacy if she had nothing better to do.

"Oh, but don't let me throw you out. I'm at work. I've things to do all the morning."

"What possessed Georgie to behave so oddly?" the mother sighed to herself. "Miriam's a bundle of feelings—like her mother."

"You compose—don't you? Must be a fine thing to be able

to do that. ["Pig—oh, pig!" thought Miriam.] I think I heard you singin' when I came in last night after fishin'. All about a Sea of Dreams, wasn't it? [Miriam shuddered to the core of the soul that afflicted her.] Awfully pretty song. How d' you think of such things?"

"You only composed the music, dear, didn't you?"

"The words too. I'm sure of it," said Georgie, with a sparkling eye. No; she did not know.

"Yeth; I wrote the words too." Miriam spoke slowly, for she knew she lisped when she was nervous.

"Now how *could* you tell, Georgie?" said the mother, as delighted as though the youngest major in the army were ten years old, showing off before company.

"I was sure of it, somehow. Oh, there are heaps of things about me, mummy, that you don't understand. Looks as if it were goin' to be a hot day—for England. Would you care for a ride this afternoon, Miss Lacy? We can start out after tea, if you'd like it."

Miriam could not in decency refuse, but any woman might see she was not filled with delight.

"That will be very nice, if you take the Bassett Road. It will save me sending Martin down to the village," said the mother, filling in gaps.

Like all good managers, the mother had her one weakness—a mania for little strategies that should economize horses and vehicles. Her men-folk complained that she turned them into common carriers, and there was a legend in the family that she had once said to the pater on the morning of a meet: "If you *should* kill near Bassett, dear, and if it isn't too late, would you mind just popping over and matching me this?"

"I knew that was coming. You'd never miss a chance, mother. If it's a fish or a trunk I won't." Georgie laughed.

"It's only a duck. They can do it up very neatly at Mallett's," said the mother, simply. "You won't mind, will you? We'll have a scratch dinner at nine, because it's so hot."

The long summer day dragged itself out for centuries; but at last there was tea on the lawn, and Miriam appeared.

She was in the saddle before he could offer to help, with

the clean spring of the child who mounted the pony for the Thirty-Mile Ride. The day held mercilessly, though Georgie got down thrice to look for imaginary stones in Rufus's foot. One cannot say even simple things in broad light, and this that Georgie meditated was not simple. So he spoke seldom, and Miriam was divided between relief and scorn. It annoyed her that the great hulking thing should know she had written the words of the song overnight; for though a maiden may sing her most secret fancies aloud, she does not care to have them trampled over by the male Philistine. They rode into the little red-brick street of Bassett, and Georgie made untold fuss over the disposition of that duck. It must go in just such a package, and be fastened to the saddle in just such a manner, though eight o'clock had struck and they were miles from dinner.

"We must be quick!" said Miriam, bored and angry.

"There's no great hurry; but we can cut over Dowhead Down, and let 'em out on the grass. That will save us half an hour."

The horses capered on the short, sweet-smelling turf, and the delaying shadows gathered in the valley as they cantered over the great dun down that overhangs Bassett and the Western coaching-road. Insensibly the pace quickened without thought of mole-hills; Rufus, gentleman that he was, waiting on Miriam's Dandy till they should have cleared the rise. Then down the two-mile slope they raced together, the wind whistling in their ears, to the steady throb of eight hoofs and the light click-click of the shifting bits.

"Oh, that was glorious!" Miriam cried, reining in. "Dandy and I are old friends, but I don't think we've ever gone better together."

"No; but you've gone quicker, once or twice."

"Really? When?"

Georgie moistened his lips. "Don't you remember the Thirty-Mile Ride—with me—when 'They' were after us—on the beach-road, with the sea to the left—going toward the lamp-post on the downs?"

The girl gasped. "What—what do you mean?" she said hysterically.

"The Thirty-Mile Ride, and—and all the rest of it."

"You mean——? I didn't sing anything about the Thirty-Mile Ride. I know I didn't. I have never told a living soul."

"You told about Policeman Day, and the lamp at the top of the downs, and the City of Sleep. It all joins on, you know—it's the same country—and it was easy enough to see where you had been."

"Good God!—It joins on—of course it does; but—I have been—you have been—— Oh, let's walk, please, or I shall fall off!"

Georgie ranged alongside, and laid a hand that shook below her bridle-hand, pulling Dandy into a walk. Miriam was sobbing as he had seen a man sob under the touch of the bullet.

"It's all right—it's all right," he whispered feebly. "Only—only it's true, you know."

"True! Am I mad?"

"Not unless I'm mad as well. *Do* try to think a minute quietly. How could any one conceivably know anything about the Thirty-Mile Ride having anything to do with you, unless he had been there?"

"But where? But *where?* Tell me!"

"There—wherever it may be—in our country, I suppose. Do you remember the first time you rode it—the Thirty-Mile Ride, I mean? You must."

"It was all dreams—all dreams!"

"Yes, but tell, please; because I know."

"Let me think. I—we were on no account to make any noise—on no account to make any noise." She was staring between Dandy's ears, with eyes that did not see, and a suffocating heart.

"Because 'It' was dying in the big house?" Georgie went on, reining in again.

"There was a garden with green-and-gilt railings—all hot. Do *you* remember?"

"I ought to. I was sitting on the other side of the bed before 'It' coughed and 'They' came in."

"You!"—the deep voice was unnaturally full and strong, and the girl's wide-opened eyes burned in the dusk as she stared him through and through. "Then you're the Boy—my Brushwood Boy, and I've known you all my life!"

She fell forward on Dandy's neck. Georgie forced himself out of the weakness that was overmastering his limbs, and slid an arm round her waist. The head dropped on his shoulder, and he found himself with parched lips saying things that up till then he believed existed only in printed works of fiction. Mercifully the horses were quiet. She made no attempt to draw herself away when she recovered, but lay still, whispering, "Of course you're the Boy, and I didn't know—I didn't know."

"I knew last night; and when I saw you at breakfast—"

"Oh, *that* was why! I wondered at the time. You would, of course."

"I couldn't speak before this. Keep your head where it is, dear. It's all right now—all right now, isn't it?"

"But how was it *I* didn't know—after all these years and years? I remember—oh, what lots of things I remember!"

"Tell me some. I'll look after the horses."

"I remember waiting for you when the steamer came in. Do you?"

"At the Lily Lock, beyond Hong-Kong and Java?"

"Do *you* call it that, too?"

"You told me it was when I was lost in the continent. That was you that showed me the way through the mountains?"

"When the islands slid? It must have been, because you're the only one I remember. All the others were 'Them.'"

"Awful brutes they were, too."

"I remember showing you the Thirty-Mile Ride the first time. You ride just as you used to—then. You *are* you!"

"That's odd. I thought that of you this afternoon. Isn't it wonderful?"

"What does it all mean? Why should you and I of the millions of people in the world have this—this thing between us? What does it mean? I'm frightened."

"This!" said Georgie. The horses quickened their pace. They thought they had heard an order. "Perhaps when we die we may find out more, but it means this now."

There was no answer. What could she say? As the world went, they had known each other rather less than eight and a half hours, but the matter was one that did not concern the world. There was a very long silence, while the breath in their nostrils drew cold and sharp as it might have been a fume of ether.

"That's the second," Georgie whispered. "You remember, don't you?"

"It's not!"—furiously. "It's not!"

"On the downs the other night—months ago. You were just as you are now, and we went over the country for miles and miles."

"It was all empty, too. They had gone away. Nobody frightened us. I wonder why, Boy?"

"Oh, if you remember *that,* you must remember the rest. Confess!"

"I remember lots of things, but I *know* I didn't. I never have—till just now."

"You *did,* dear."

"I know I didn't, because—oh, it's no use keeping anything back!—because I truthfully meant to."

"And truthfully did."

"No; meant to; but some one else came by."

"There wasn't any one else. There never has been."

"There was—there always is. It was another woman—out there on the sea. I saw her. It was the 26th of May. I've got it written down somewhere."

"Oh, *you*'ve kept a record of your dreams, too? That's odd about the other woman, because I happened to be on the sea just then."

"I was right. How do I know what you've done when you were awake—and I thought it was only *you!*"

"You never were more wrong in your life. What a little temper you've got! Listen to me a minute, dear." And Georgie, though he knew it not, committed black perjury. "It—it isn't the kind of thing one says to any one, because they'd laugh; but on my word and honour, darling, I've never been kissed by a living soul outside my own people in all my life.

Don't laugh, dear. I wouldn't tell any one but you, but it's the solemn truth."

"I knew! You are you. Oh, I *knew* you'd come some day; but I didn't know you were you in the least till you spoke."

"Then give me another."

"And you never cared or looked anywhere? Why, all the round world must have loved you from the very minute they saw you, Boy."

"They kept it to themselves if they did. No; I never cared."

"And we shall be late for dinner—horribly late. Oh, how can I look at you in the light before your mother—and mine!"

"We'll play you're Miss Lacy till the proper time comes. What's the shortest limit for people to get engaged? S'pose we have got to go through all the fuss of an engagement, haven't we?"

"Oh, I don't want to talk about that. It's so commonplace. I've thought of something that you don't know. I'm sure of it. What's my name?"

"Miri—no, it isn't, by Jove! Wait half a second, and it'll come back to me. You aren't—you can't! Why, *those* old tales—before I went to school! I've never thought of 'em from that day to this. Are you the original, only Annie*an*louise?"

"It was what you always called me ever since the beginning. Oh! We've turned into the avenue, and we must be an hour late."

"What does it matter? The chain goes as far back as those days? It must, of course—of course it must. I've got to ride round with this pestilent old bird—confound him!"

" ' "Ha! ha!" said the duck, laughing'—do you remember *that?*"

"Yes, I do—flower-pots on my feet, and all. We've been together all this while; and I've got to say good-bye to you till dinner. *Sure* I'll see you at dinner-time? *Sure* you won't sneak up to your room, darling, and leave me all the evening? Good-bye, dear—good-bye."

"Good-bye, Boy, good-bye. Mind the arch! Don't let Rufus bolt into his stables. Good-bye. Yes, I'll come down to dinner: but—what shall I do when I see you in the light!"

THE LAST TERM
1899

IT WAS within a few days of the holidays, the term-end examinations, and, more important still, the issue of the College paper which Beetle edited. He had been cajoled into that office by the blandishments of Stalky and McTurk and the extreme rigour of study law. Once installed, he discovered, as others have done before him, that his duty was to do the work while his friends criticized. Stalky christened it the *Swillingford Patriot,* in pious memory of Sponge—and McTurk compared the output unfavourably with Ruskin and De Quincey. Only the Head took an interest in the publication, and his methods were peculiar. He gave Beetle the run of his brown-bound, tobacco-scented library; prohibiting nothing, recommending nothing. There Beetle found a fat arm-chair, a silver inkstand, and unlimited pens and paper. There were scores and scores of ancient dramatists; there were Hakluyt, his voyages; French translations of Muscovite authors called Pushkin and Lermontoff; little tales of a heady and bewildering nature, interspersed with unusual songs—Peacock was that writer's name; there was Borrow's *Lavengro;* an odd theme, purporting to be a translation of something, called a "Rubáiyát," which the Head said was a poem not yet come to its own; there were hundreds of volumes of verse—Crashaw; Dryden; Alexander Smith; L. E. L.; Lydia Sigourney; Fletcher and a purple island; Donne; Marlowe's *Faust;* and —this made McTurk (to whom Beetle conveyed it) sheer drunk for three days—Ossian; *The Earthly Paradise; Atalanta in Calydon;* and Rossetti—to name only a few. Then the Head, drifting in under pretense of playing censor to the paper, would read here a verse and here another of these poets, opening up avenues. And, slow breathing, with half-shut eyes above his cigar, would he speak of great men living, and journals, long dead, founded in their riotous youth; of years when all the planets were little new-lit stars trying to find their places in the uncaring void, and he, the Head, knew them as young men know one another. So the regular work went to the dogs, Beetle being full of other matters and meters, hoarded in secret and only told to McTurk of an afternoon, on the sands, walking high and disposedly round the wreck of the Armada galleon, shouting and declaiming against the long-ridged seas.

Thanks in large part to their house-master's experienced distrust, the three for three consecutive terms had been passed over for promotion to the rank of prefect—an office that went by merit, and carried with it the honour of the ground-ash, and liberty, under restrictions, to use it.

"But," said Stalky, "come to think of it, we've done more giddy jesting with the Sixth since we've been passed over than any one else in the last seven years."

He touched his neck proudly. It was encircled by the stiffest of stick-up collars, which custom decreed could be worn only by the Sixth. And the Sixth saw those collars and said no word. "Pussy," Abanazar, or Dick Four of a year ago would have seen them discarded in five minutes or . . . But the Sixth of that term was made up mostly of young but brilliantly clever boys, pets of the housemasters, too anxious for their dignity to care to come to open odds with the resourceful three. So they crammed their caps at the extreme back of their heads, instead of a trifle over one eye as the Fifth should, and rejoiced in patent-leather boots on week-days, and marvellous made-up ties on Sundays—no man rebuking. McTurk was going up for Cooper's Hill, and Stalky for Sandhurst, in the spring; and the Head had told them both that, unless they absolutely collapsed during the holidays, they were safe. As a trainer of colts, the Head seldom erred in an estimate of form.

He had taken Beetle aside that day and given him much

good advice, not one word of which did Beetle remember when he dashed up to the study, white with excitement, and poured out the wondrous tale. It demanded a great belief.

"*You* begin on a hundred a year?" said McTurk unsympathetically. "Rot!"

"*And* my passage out! It's all settled. The Head says he's been breaking me in for this for ever so long, and I never knew—I never knew. One don't begin with writing straight off, y'know. Begin by filling in telegrams and cutting things out o' papers with scissors."

"Oh, scissors! What an ungodly mess you'll make of it," said Stalky. "But, anyhow, this will be your last term, too. Seven years, my dearly beloved 'earers—though not prefects."

"Not half bad years, either," said McTurk. "I shall be sorry to leave the old Coll.; shan't you?"

They looked out over the sea creaming along the Pebble Ridge in the clear winter light. "Wonder where we shall all be this time next year?" said Stalky absently.

"This time five years," said McTurk.

"Oh," said Beetle, "my leavin's between ourselves. The Head hasn't told any one. I know he hasn't, because Prout grunted at me to-day that if I were more reasonable—yah!—I might be a prefect next term. I suppose he's hard up for his prefects."

"Let's finish up with a row with the Sixth," suggested McTurk.

"Dirty little schoolboys!" said Stalky, who already saw himself a Sandhurst cadet. "What's the use?"

"Moral effect," quoth McTurk. "Leave an imperishable tradition, and all the rest of it."

"Better go into Bideford an' pay up our debts," said Stalky. "I've got three quid out of my father—*ad hoc*. Don't owe more than thirty bob, either. Cut along, Beetle, and ask the Head for leave. Say you want to correct the *Swillingford Patriot*."

"Well, I do," said Beetle. "It'll be my last issue, and I'd like it to look decent. I'll catch him before he goes to his lunch."

Ten minutes later they wheeled out in line, by grace released from five o'clock call-over, and all the afternoon lay before them. So also unluckily did King, who never passed without witticisms. But brigades of Kings could not have ruffled Beetle that day.

"Aha! Enjoying the study of light literature, my friends," said he, rubbing his hands. "Common mathematics are not for such soaring minds as yours, are they?"

("One hundred a year," thought Beetle, smiling into vacancy.)

"Our open incompetence takes refuge in the flowery paths of inaccurate fiction. But a day of reckoning approaches, Beetle mine. I myself have prepared a few trifling foolish questions in Latin prose which can hardly be evaded even by your practised arts of deception. Ye-es, Latin prose. I think, if I may say so—but we shall see when the papers are set—'Ulpian serves *your* need.' Aha! *'Elucescebat,* quoth our friend.' We shall see! We shall see!"

Still no sign from Beetle. He was on a steamer, his passage paid into the wide and wonderful world—a thousand leagues beyond Lundy Island.

King dropped him with a snarl.

"He doesn't know. He'll go on correctin' exercises an' jawin' an' showin' off before the little boys next term—and next." Beetle hurried after his companions up the steep path of the furze-clad hill behind the College.

They were throwing pebbles on the top of the gasometer, and the grimy gas-man in charge bade them desist. They watched him oil a turncock sunk in the ground between two furze-bushes.

"Cokey, what's that for?" said Stalky.

"To turn the gas on to the kitchens," said Cokey. "If so be I didn't turn her on, yeou young gen'lemen 'ud be larnin' your book by candlelight."

"Um!" said Stalky, and was silent for at least a minute.

"Hullo! Where are you chaps going?"

A bend of the lane brought them face to face with Tulke, senior prefect of King's house—a smallish, white-haired boy, of the type that must be promoted on account of its intellect, and ever afterwards appeals to the Head to support its authority when zeal has outrun discretion.

The three took no sort of notice. They were on lawful pass. Tulke repeated his question hotly, for he had suffered many slights from Number Five study, and fancied that he had at last caught them tripping.

"What the devil is that to you?" Stalky replied with his sweetest smile.

"Look here, I'm not goin'—I'm not goin' to be sworn at by the Fifth!" sputtered Tulke.

"Then cut along and call a prefects' meeting," said McTurk, knowing Tulke's weakness.

The prefect became inarticulate with rage.

"Mustn't yell at the Fifth that way," said Stalky. "It's vile bad form."

"Cough it up, ducky!" McTurk said calmly.

"I—I want to know what you chaps are doing out of bounds?" This with an important flourish of his ground-ash.

"Ah," said Stalky. "Now we're gettin' at it. Why didn't you ask that before?"

"Well, I ask it now. What are you doing?"

"We're admiring you, Tulke," said Stalky. "We think you're no end of a fine chap, don't we?"

"We do! We do!" A dog-cart with some girls in it swept round the corner, and Stalky promptly kneeled before Tulke in the attitude of prayer; so Tulke turned a colour.

"I've reason to believe——" he began.

"Oyez! Oyez! Oyez!" shouted Beetle, after the manner of Bideford's town crier, "Tulke has reason to believe! Three cheers for Tulke!"

They were given. "It's all our giddy admiration," said Stalky. "You know how we love you, Tulke. We love you so much we think you ought to go home and die. You're too good to live, Tulke."

"Yes," said McTurk. "*Do* oblige us by dyin'. Think how lovely you'd look stuffed!"

Tulke swept up the road with an unpleasant glare in his eye.

"That means a prefects' meeting—sure pop," said Stalky. "Honour of the Sixth involved, and all the rest of it. Tulke'll write notes all this afternoon, and Carson will call us up after tea. They daren't overlook that."

"Bet you a bob he follows us!" said McTurk. "He's King's pet, and it's scalps to both of 'em if we're caught out. We must be virtuous."

"Then I move we go to Mother Yeo's for a last gorge. We owe her about ten bob, and Mary'll weep sore when she knows we're leaving," said Beetle.

"She gave me an awful wipe on the head last time—Mary," said Stalky.

"She does if you don't duck," said McTurk. "But she generally kisses one back. Let's try Mother Yeo."

They sought a little bottle-windowed half dairy, half restaurant, a dark-browed, two-hundred-year-old house, at the head of a narrow side street. They had patronized it from the days of their fagdom, and were very much friends at home.

"We've come to pay our debts, mother," said Stalky, sliding his arm round the fifty-six-inch waist of the mistress of the establishment. "To pay our debts and say good-bye—and—and we're awf'ly hungry."

"Aie!" said Mother Yeo, "makkin' love to me! I'm shaamed of 'ee."

" 'Rackon us wouldn't du no such thing if Mary was here," said McTurk, lapsing into the broad North Devon that the boys used on their campaigns.

"Who'm takin' my name in vain?" The inner door opened, and Mary, fair-haired, blue-eyed, and apple-cheeked, entered with a bowl of cream in her hands. McTurk kissed her. Beetle followed suit, with exemplary calm. Both boys were promptly cuffed.

"Niver kiss the maid when 'e can kiss the mistress," said Stalky, shamelessly winking at Mother Yeo, as he investigated a shelf of jams.

"Glad to see one of 'ee don't want his head slapped no more," said Mary invitingly, in that direction.

"Neu! Reckon I can get 'em give me," said Stalky, his back turned.

"Not by me—yeou little masterpiece!"

"Niver asked 'ee. There's maids to Northam. Yiss—an' Appledore." An unreproducible sniff, half contempt, half reminiscence, rounded the retort.

"Aie! Yeou won't niver come to no good end. Whutt be 'baout, smellin' the cream?"

"'Tees bad," said Stalky. "Zmell 'un."

Incautiously Mary did as she was bid.

"Bidevoor kiss."

"Niver amiss," said Stalky, taking it without injury.

"Yeou—yeou—yeou——" Mary began, bubbling with mirth.

"They'm better to Northam—more rich, laike—an' us gets them give back again," he said, while McTurk solemnly waltzed Mother Yeo out of breath, and Beetle told Mary the sad news, as they sat down to clotted cream, jam, and hot bread.

"Yiss. Yeou'll niver zee us no more, Mary. We'm goin' to be passons an' missioners."

"Steady the Buffs!" said McTurk, looking through the blind. "Tulke *has* followed us. He's comin' up the street now."

"They've niver put us out o' bounds," said Mother Yeo. "Bide yeou still, my little dearrs." She rolled into the inner room to make the score.

"Mary," said Stalky, suddenly, with tragic intensity. "Do 'ee lov' me, Mary?"

"Iss—fai! Talled 'ee zo since yeou was zo high!" the damsel replied.

"Zee 'un comin' up street, then?" Stalky pointed to the unconscious Tulke. "He've niver been kissed by no sort or manner o' maid in hees borned laife, Mary. Oh, 'tees shaamful!"

"Whutt's to do with me? 'Twill come to 'un in the way o' nature, I rackon." She nodded her head sagaciously. "You niver want me to kiss un—sure-*ly?*"

"Give 'ee half-a-crown if 'ee will," said Stalky, exhibiting the coin.

Half-a-crown was much to Mary Yeo, and a jest was more; but——

"Yeu'm afraid," said McTurk, at the psychological moment.

"Aie!" Beetle echoed, knowing her weak point. "There's not a maid to Northam 'ud think twice. An' yeou such a fine maid, tu!"

McTurk planted one foot firmly against the inner door lest Mother Yeo should return inopportunely, for Mary's face was set. It was then that Tulke found his way blocked by a tall daughter of Devon—that county of easy kisses, the pleasantest under the sun. He dodged aside politely. She reflected a moment, and laid a vast hand upon his shoulder.

"Where be 'ee gwaine tu, my dearr?" said she.

Over the handkerchief he had crammed into his mouth Stalky could see the boy turn scarlet.

"Gie I a kiss! Don't they larn 'ee manners to College?"

Tulke gasped and wheeled. Solemnly and conscientiously Mary kissed him twice, and the luckless prefect fled.

She stepped into the shop, her eyes full of simple wonder.

"Kissed 'un?" said Stalky, handing over the money.

"Iss, fai! But, oh, my little body, *he*'m no Colleger. 'Zeemed tu-minded to cry, laike."

"Well, we won't. You couldn't make us cry that way," said McTurk. "Try."

Whereupon Mary cuffed them all round.

As they went out with tingling ears, said Stalky, generally, "Don't think there'll be much of a prefects' meeting."

"Won't there, just!" said Beetle. "Look here: If he kissed her—which is our tack—he is a cynically immoral hog, and his conduct is blatant indecency. *Confer orationes Regis furiosissimi,* when he collared me readin' 'Don Juan.' "

" 'Course he kissed her," said McTurk. "In the middle of the street. With his house-cap on!"

"Time, 3:57 P. M. Make a note o' that. What d'you mean, Beetle?" said Stalky.

"Well! He's a truthful little beast. He may say he was kissed."

"And then?"

"Why, then!" Beetle capered at the mere thought of it. "Don't you see? The corollary to the giddy proposition is that the Sixth can't protect 'emselves from outrages an' ravishin's. Want nursemaids to look after 'em! We've only got to whisper that to the Coll. Jam for the Sixth! Jam for us! Either way it's jammy!"

"By Gum!" said Stalky. "Our last term's endin' well. Now you cut along an' finish up your old rag, and Turkey and me will help. We'll go in the back way. No need to bother Randall."

"Don't play the giddy garden-goat, then!" Beetle knew what help meant, though he was by no means averse to showing his importance before his allies. The little loft behind Randall's printing-office was his own territory, where he saw himself already controlling the *Times*. Here, under the guidance of the inky apprentice, he had learned to find his way more or less circuitously about the case, and considered himself an expert compositor.

The school paper in its locked formes lay on a stone-topped table, a proof by the side; but not for worlds would Beetle have corrected from the mere proof. With a mallet and a pair of tweezers, he knocked out mysterious wedges of wood that released the forme, picked a letter here and inserted a letter there, reading as he went along and stopping much to chuckle over his own contributions.

"You won't show off like that," said McTurk, "when you've got to do it for your living. Upside down and backwards, isn't it? Let's see if I can read it."

"Get out!" said Beetle. "Go and read those formes in the rack there, if you think you know so much."

"Formes in a rack! What's that? Don't be so beastly professional."

McTurk drew off with Stalky to prowl about the office. They left little unturned.

"Come here a shake, Beetle. What's this thing?" said Stalky, in a few minutes. "Looks familiar."

Said Beetle, after a glance: "It's King's Latin prose exam. paper. *In—In Verrem: actio prima*. What a lark!"

"Think o' the pure-souled, high-minded boys who'd give their eyes for a squint at it!" said McTurk.

"No, Willie dear," said Stalky; "that would be wrong and painful to our kind teachers. You wouldn't crib, Willie, would you?"

"Can't read the beastly stuff, anyhow," was the reply. "Besides, we're leavin' at the end o' the term, so it makes no difference to us."

" 'Member what the Considerate Bloomer did to Spraggon's account of the Puffin'ton Hounds? We must sugar Mr. King's milk for him," said Stalky, all lighted from within by a devilish joy. "Let's see what Beetle can do with those forceps he's so proud of."

"Don't see how you can make Latin prose much more cockeyed than it is, but we'll try," said Beetle, transposing an *aliud* and *Asiæ* from two sentences. "Let's see! We'll put that full-stop a little further on, and begin the sentence with the next capital Hurrah! Here's three lines that can move up all in a lump."

" 'One of those scientific rests for which this eminent huntsman is so justly celebrated.' " Stalky knew the Puffington run by heart.

"Hold on! Here's a *vol—voluntate quidnam* all by itself," said McTurk.

"I'll attend to her in a shake. *Quidnam* goes after *Dolabella*."

"Good old Dolabella," murmured Stalky. "Don't break him. Vile prose Cicero wrote, didn't he? He ought to be grateful for——"

"Hullo!" said McTurk, over another forme. "What price a giddy ode? *Qui—quis*—oh, it's *Quis multa gracilis*, o' course."

"Bring it along. We've sugared the milk here," said Stalky, after a few minutes' zealous toil. "Never thrash your hounds unnecessarily."

"*Quis munditiis?* I swear that's not bad," began Beetle,

plying the tweezers. "Don't that interrogation look pretty? *Heu quoties fidem!* That sounds as if the chap were anxious an' excited. *Cui flavam religas in rosa*—Whose flavour is relegated to a rose. *Mutatosque Deos flebit in antro.*"

"Mute gods weepin' in a cave," suggested Stalky. "'Pon my Sam, Horace needs as much lookin' after as—Tulke."

They edited him faithfully till it was too dark to see.

. . . .

"'Aha! *Elucescebat,* quoth our friend.' Ulpian serves my need, does it? If King can make anything out of *that,* I'm a blue-eyed squatteroo," said Beetle, as they slid out of the loft window into a back alley of old acquaintance and started on a three-mile trot to the College. But the revision of the classics had detained them too long. They halted, blown and breathless, in the furze at the back of the gasometer, the College lights twinkling below, ten minutes at least late for tea and lock-up.

"It's no good," puffed McTurk. "Bet a bob Foxy is waiting for defaulters under the lamp by the Fives Court. It's a nuisance, too, because the Head gave us long leave, and one doesn't like to break it."

"'Let me now from the bonded ware'ouse of my knowledge,'" began Stalky.

"Oh, rot! Don't Jorrock. Can we make a run for it?" snapped McTurk.

"'Bishops' boots Mr. Radcliffe also condemned, an' spoke 'ighly in favour of tops cleaned with champagne an' abricot jam.' Where's that thing Cokey was twiddlin' this afternoon?"

They heard him groping in the wet, and presently beheld a great miracle. The lights of the Coastguard cottages near the sea went out; the brilliantly illuminated windows of the Golf Club disappeared, and were followed by the frontages of the two hotels. Scattered villas dulled, twinkled, and vanished. Last of all, the College lights died also. They were left in the pitchy darkness of a windy winter's night.

" 'Blister my kidneys. It *is* a frost. The dahlias are dead!' " said Stalky. "Bunk!"

They squattered through the dripping gorse as the College hummed like an angry hive and the dining rooms chorused, "Gas! gas! gas!" till they came to the edge of the sunk path that divided them from their study. Dropping that ha-ha like bullets, and rebounding like boys, they dashed to their study, in less than two minutes had changed into dry trousers and coat, and, ostentatiously slippered, joined the mob in the dining-hall, which resembled the storm-centre of a South American revolution.

" 'Hellish dark and smells of cheese.' " Stalky elbowed his way into the press, howling lustily for gas. "Cokey must have gone for a walk. Foxy'll have to find him."

Prout, as the nearest house-master, was trying to restore order, for rude boys were flicking butter-pats across chaos, and McTurk had turned on the fags' tea-urn, so that many were parboiled and wept with an unfeigned dolour. The Fourth and Upper Third broke into the school song, the *"Vive la Compagnie,"* to the accompaniment of drumming knife-handles; and the junior forms shrilled bat-like shrieks and raided one another's victuals. Two hundred and fifty boys in high condition, seeking for more light, are truly earnest inquirers.

When a most vile smell of gas told them that supplies had been renewed, Stalky, waistcoat unbuttoned, sat gorgedly over what might have been his fourth cup of tea. "And that's all right," he said. "Hullo! 'Ere's Pomponius Ego!"

It was Carson, the head of the school, a simple, straight-minded soul, and a pillar of the First Fifteen, who crossed over from the prefects' table and in a husky, official voice invited the three to attend in his study in half an hour.

"Prefects' meetin'! Prefects' meetin'!" hissed the tables, and they imitated barbarically the actions and effects of the ground-ash.

"How are we goin' to jest with 'em?" said Stalky, turning half-face to Beetle. "It's your play this time!"

"Look here," was the answer, "all I want you to do is not

to laugh. I'm goin' to take charge o' young Tulke's immorality—*à la* King, and it's goin' to be serious. If you can't help laughin' don't look at me, or I'll go pop."

"I see. All right," said Stalky.

McTurk's lank frame stiffened in every muscle and his eyelids dropped half over his eyes. That last was a war-signal.

The eight or nine seniors, their faces very set and sober, were ranged in chairs round Carson's severely Philistine study. Tulke was not popular among them, and a few who had had experience of Stalky & Co. doubted that he might, perhaps, have made an ass of himself. But the dignity of the Sixth was to be upheld. So Carson began hurriedly:

"Look here, you chaps, I've—we've sent for you to tell you you're a good deal too cheeky to the Sixth—have been for some time—and—and we've stood about as much as we're goin' to, and it seems you've been cursin' and swearin' at Tulke on the Bideford road this afternoon, and we're goin' to show you you can't do it. That's all."

"Well, that's awfully good of you," said Stalky, "but we happen to have a few rights of our own, too. You can't, just because you happen to be made prefects, haul up seniors and jaw 'em on spec., like a house-master. *We* aren't fags, Carson. This kind of thing may do for Davies Tertius, but it won't do for us."

"It's only old Prout's lunacy that we weren't prefects long ago. You know that," said McTurk. "You haven't any tact."

"Hold on," said Beetle. "A prefects' meetin' has to be reported to the Head. I want to know if the Head backs Tulke in this business?"

"Well—well, it isn't exactly a prefects' meeting," said Carson. "We only called you in to warn you."

"But all the prefects are here," Beetle insisted. "Where's the difference?"

"My Gum!" said Stalky. "Do you mean to say you've just called us in for a jaw—after comin' to us before the whole school at tea an' givin' 'em the impression it was a prefects' meeting? 'Pon my Sam, Carson, you'll get into trouble, you will."

"Hole-an'-corner business—hole-an'-corner business," said McTurk, wagging his head. "Beastly suspicious."

The Sixth looked at each other uneasily. Tulke had called three prefects' meetings in two terms, till the Head had informed the Sixth that they were expected to maintain discipline without the recurrent menace of his authority. Now, it seemed that they had made a blunder at the outset, but any right-minded boy would have sunk the legality and been properly impressed by the Court. Beetle's protest was distinct "cheek."

"Well, you chaps deserve a lickin'," cried one Naughten incautiously. Then was Beetle filled with a noble inspiration.

"For interferin' with Tulke's amours, eh?" Tulke turned a rich sloe colour. "Oh, no, you don't!" Beetle went on. "You've had your innings. We've been sent up for cursing and swearing at you, and we're goin' to be let off with a warning? *Are* we? Now then, you're going to catch it."

"I—I—I——" Tulke began. "Don't let that young devil start jawing."

"If you've anything to say you must say it decently," said Carson.

"Decently? I will. Now look here. When we went into Bideford we met this ornament of the Sixth—is that decent enough?—hanging about on the road with a nasty look in his eye. We didn't know *then* why he was so anxious to stop us, *but* at five minutes to four, when we were in Yeo's shop, we saw Tulke *in* broad daylight, *with* his house-cap on, kissin' an' huggin' a woman *on* the pavement. Is that decent enough for you?"

"I didn't—I wasn't."

"We saw you!" said Beetle. "And now—I'll be decent, Carson—you sneak back with her kisses" (not for nothing had Beetle perused the later poets) "hot on your lips and call prefects' meetings, which aren't prefects' meetings, to uphold the honour of the Sixth." A new and heaven-cleft path opened before him that instant. "And how do we know," he shouted—"how do we know how many of the Sixth are mixed up in this abominable affair?"

"Yes, that's what we want to know," said McTurk, with simple dignity.

"We meant to come to you about it quietly, Carson, but you *would* have the meeting," said Stalky sympathetically.

The Sixth were too taken aback to reply. So, carefully modelling his rhetoric on King, Beetle followed up the attack, surpassing and surprising himself.

"It—it isn't so much the cynical immorality of the biznai, as the blatant indecency of it, that's so awful. As far as we can see, it's impossible for us to go into Bideford without runnin' up against some prefect's unwholesome amours. There's nothing to snigger over, Naughten. *I* don't pretend to know much about these things—but it seems to me a chap must be pretty far dead in sin" (that was a quotation from the school chaplain) "when he takes to embracing his paramours" (that was Hakluyt) "before all the city" (a reminiscence of Milton). "He might at least have the decency—you're authorities on decency, I believe—to wait till dark. But he didn't. You didn't! Oh, Tulke. You—you incontinent little animal!"

"Here, shut up a minute. What's all this about, Tulke?" said Carson.

"I—look here. I'm awfully sorry. I never thought Beetle would take this line."

"Because—you've—no decency—you—thought—I hadn't," cried Beetle all in one breath.

"Tried to cover it all up with a conspiracy, did you?" said Stalky.

"Direct insult to all three of us," said McTurk. "A most filthy mind you have, Tulke."

"I'll shove you fellows outside the door if you go on like this," said Carson angrily.

"That proves it's a conspiracy," said Stalky, with the air of a virgin martyr.

"I—I was goin' along the street—I swear I was," cried Tulke, "and—and I'm awfully sorry about it—a woman came up and kissed me. I swear I didn't kiss her."

There was a pause, filled by Stalky's long, liquid whistle of contempt, amazement, and derision.

"On my honour," gulped the persecuted one. "Oh, do stop him jawing."

"Very good," McTurk interjected. "We are compelled, of course, to accept your statement."

"Confound it!" roared Naughten. "You aren't head-prefect here, McTurk."

"Oh, well," returned the Irishman, "you know Tulke better than we do. I am only speaking for ourselves. *We* accept Tulke's words. But all I can say is that if I'd been collared in a similarly disgustin' situation, and had offered the same explanation Tulke has, I—I wonder what you'd have said. However, it seems on Tulke's word of honour——"

"And Tulkus—beg pardon—*kiss,* of course—Tulkiss is an honourable man," put in Stalky.

"—that the Sixth can't protect 'emselves from bein' kissed when they go for a walk!" cried Beetle, taking up the running with a rush. "Sweet business, isn't it? Cheerful thing to tell the fags, ain't it? We aren't prefects, of course, but we aren't kissed very much. Don't think that sort of thing ever enters our heads; does it, Stalky?"

"Oh, no!" said Stalky, turning aside to hide his emotions. McTurk's face merely expressed lofty contempt and a little weariness.

"Well, you seem to know a lot about it," interposed a prefect.

"Can't help it—when you chaps shove it under our noses." Beetle dropped into a drawling parody of King's most biting colloquial style—the gentle rain after the thunder-storm. "Well, it's all very sufficiently vile and disgraceful, isn't it? I don't know who comes out of it worst: Tulke, who happens to have been caught; or the other fellows who haven't. And we—" here he wheeled fiercely on the other two—"we've got to stand up and be jawed by them because we've disturbed their intrigues."

"Hang it! I only wanted to give you a word of warning," said Carson, thereby handing himself bound to the enemy.

"Warn? You?" This with the air of one who finds loathsome gifts in his locker. "Carson, *would* you be good enough to tell us what conceivable thing there is that you are entitled to warn us about after this exposure? Warn? Oh, it's a little too much! Let's go somewhere where it's clean."

The door banged behind their outraged innocence.

"Oh, Beetle! Beetle! Beetle! Golden Beetle!" sobbed Stalky, hurling himself on Beetle's panting bosom as soon as they reached the study. "However did you do it?"

"Dear-r man!" said McTurk, embracing Beetle's head with both arms, while he swayed it to and fro on the neck, in time to this ancient burden—

"Pretty lips—sweeter than—cherry or plum,
Always look—jolly and—never look glum;
Seem to say—Come away. Kissy!—come, come!
Yummy-yum! Yummy-yum! Yummy-yum-yum!"

"Look out. You'll smash my gig-lamps," puffed Beetle, emerging. "Wasn't it glorious? Didn't I *Eric* 'em splendidly? Did you spot my cribs from King? Oh, blow!" His countenance clouded. "There's one adjective I didn't use—obscene. Don't know how I forgot that. It's one of King's pet ones, too."

"Never mind. They'll be sendin' ambassadors round in half a shake to beg us not to tell the school. It's a deuced serious business for them," said McTurk. "Poor Sixth—poor old Sixth!"

"Immoral young rips," Stalky snorted. "What an example to pure-souled boys like you and me!"

And the Sixth in Carson's study sat aghast, glowering at Tulke, who was on the edge of tears.

"Well," said the head-prefect acidly. "You've made a pretty average ghastly mess of it, Tulke."

"Why—why didn't you lick that young devil Beetle before he began jawing?" Tulke wailed.

"I knew there'd be a row," said a prefect of Prout's house. "But you would insist on the meeting, Tulke."

"Yes, and a fat lot of good it's done us," said Naughten. "They come in here and jaw our heads off when we ought to be jawin' them. Beetle talks to us as if we were a lot of blackguards and—and all that. And when they've hung us up to dry, they go out and slam the door like a housemaster. All your fault, Tulke."

"But I didn't kiss her."

"You ass! If you'd said you *had* and stuck to it, it would have been ten times better than what you did," Naughten retorted. "Now they'll tell the whole school—and Beetle'll make up a lot of beastly rhymes and nick-names."

"But, hang it, she kissed me!" Outside of his work, Tulke's mind moved slowly.

"I'm not thinking of you. I'm thinking of *us*. I'll go up to their study and see if I can make 'em keep quiet!"

"Tulke's awf'ly cut up about this business——" Naughten began, ingratiatingly, when he found Beetle.

"Who's kissed him this time?"

"—and I've come to ask you chaps, and especially you, Beetle, not to let the thing be known all over the school. Of course, fellows as senior as you are can easily see why."

"Um!" said Beetle, with the cold reluctance of one who foresees an unpleasant public duty. "I suppose I must go and talk to the Sixth again."

"Not the least need, my dear chap, I assure you," said Naughten hastily. "I'll take any message you care to send."

But the chance of supplying the missing adjective was too tempting. So Naughten returned to that still undissolved meeting, Beetle, white, icy, and aloof, at his heels.

"There seems," he began, with laboriously crisp articulation, "there seems to be a certain amount of uneasiness among you as to the steps we may think fit to take in regard to this last revelation of the—ah—obscene. If it is any consolation to you to know that we have decided—for the honour of the school, you understand—to keep our mouths shut as to these—ah—obscenities, you—ah—have it."

He wheeled, his head among the stars, and strode statelily back to his study, where Stalky and McTurk lay side by side upon the table wiping their tearful eyes—too weak to move.

. . . . . .

The Latin prose paper was a success beyond their wildest dreams. Stalky and McTurk were, of course, out of all examinations (they did extra-tuition with the Head), but Beetle attended with zeal.

"This, I presume, is a par-ergon on your part," said King, as he dealt out the papers. "One final exhibition ere you are translated to loftier spheres? A last attack on the classics? It seems to confound you already."

Beetle studied the print with knit brows. "I can't make head or tail of it," he murmured. "What does it mean?"

"No, no!" said King, with scholastic coquetry. "We depend upon *you* to give us the meaning. This is an examination, Beetle mine, not a guessing-competition. You will find your associates have no difficulty in——"

Tulke left his place and laid the paper on the desk. King looked, read, and turned a ghastly green.

"Stalky's missing a heap," thought Beetle. "Wonder how King'll get out of it?"

"There seems," King began with a gulp, "a certain modicum of truth in our Beetle's remark. I am—er—inclined to believe that the worthy Randall must have dropped this in forme—if you know what that means. Beetle, you purport to be an editor. Perhaps you can enlighten the form as to formes."

"What, sir? Whose form? I don't see that there's any verb in this sentence at all, an'—an'—the Ode is all different, somehow."

"I was about to say, before you volunteered your criticism, that an accident must have befallen the paper in type, and that the printer reset it by the light of nature. No—" he held the thing at arm's length—"our Randall is not an authority on Cicero or Horace."

"Rather mean to shove it off on Randall," whispered Beetle to his neighbour. "King must ha' been as screwed as an owl when he wrote it out."

"But we can amend the error by dictating it."

"No, sir." The answer came pat from a dozen throats at once. "That cuts the time for the exam. Only two hours allowed, sir. 'Tisn't fair. It's a printed-paper exam. How're we goin' to be marked for it? It's all Randall's fault. It isn't *our* fault, anyhow. An exam.'s an exam.," etc., etc.

Naturally Mr. King considered this was an attempt to undermine his authority, and, instead of beginning dictation at once, delivered a lecture on the spirit in which examinations should be approached. As the storm subsided, Beetle fanned it afresh.

"Eh? What? What was that you were saying to MacLagan?"

"I only said I thought the papers ought to have been looked at before they were given out, sir."

"Hear, hear!" from a back bench.

Mr. King wished to know whether Beetle took it upon himself personally to conduct the traditions of the school. His zeal for knowledge ate up another fifteen minutes, during which the prefects showed unmistakable signs of boredom.

"Oh, it was a giddy time," said Beetle, afterwards, in dismantled Number Five. "He gibbered a bit, and I kept him on the gibber, and then he dictated about a half of Dolabella & Co."

"Good old Dolabella! Friend of mine. Yes?" said Stalky, pensively.

"Then we had to ask him how every other word was spelt, of course, and he gibbered a lot more. He cursed me and MacLagan (Mac played up like a trump) and Randall, and the 'materialized ignorance of the unscholarly middle classes,' 'lust for mere marks,' and all the rest. It was what you might call a final exhibition—a last attack—a giddy par-ergon."

"But o' course he was blind squiffy when he wrote the paper. I hope you explained *that?*" said Stalky.

"Oh, yes. I told Tulke so. I said an immoral prefect an' drunken house-master were legitimate inferences. Tulke nearly blubbed. He's awfully shy of us since Mary's time."

Tulke preserved that modesty till the last moment—till the journey-money had been paid, and the boys were filling the brakes that took them to the station. Then the three tenderly constrained him to wait a while.

"You see, Tulke, you may be a prefect," said Stalky; "but I've left the Coll. Do you see, Tulke, dear?"

"Yes, I see. Don't bear malice, Stalky."

"Stalky? Curse your impudence, you young cub," shouted Stalky, magnificent in top-hat, stiff collar, spats, and high-waisted, snuff-coloured ulster. "I want you to understand that *I'm* Mister Corkran, an' you're a dirty little schoolboy."

"Besides bein' frabjously immoral," said McTurk. "Wonder you aren't ashamed to foist your company on pure-minded boys like us."

"Come on, Tulke," cried Naughten, from the prefects' brake.

"Yes, we're comin'. Shove up and make room, you Collegers. You've all got to be back next term, with your 'Yes, sir,' and 'Oh, sir,' an' 'No, sir,' an' 'Please, sir'; but before we say good-bye we're going to tell you a little story. Go on, Dickie" (this to the driver); "we're quite ready. Kick that hat-box under the seat, an' don't crowd your Uncle Stalky."

"As nice a lot of high-minded youngsters as you'd wish to see," said McTurk, gazing round with bland patronage. "A trifle immoral, but then—boys will be boys. It's no good tryin' to look stuffy, Carson. *Mister* Corkran will now oblige with the story of Tulke an' Mary Yeo!"

From FROM SEA TO SEA *1899*

AN INTERVIEW WITH MARK TWAIN 1890

THEY said in Buffalo that he was in Hartford, Conn.; and again they said "perchance he is gone upon a journey to Portland"; and a big, fat drummer vowed that he knew the great man intimately, and that Mark was spending the summer in Europe—which information so upset me that I embarked upon the wrong train, and was incontinently turned out by the conductor three-quarters of a mile from the station, amid the wilderness of railway tracks. Have you ever, encumbered with great-coat and valise, tried to dodge diversely-minded locomotives when the sun was shining in your eyes? But I forgot that you have not seen Mark Twain, you people of no account!

Saved from the jaws of the cowcatcher, me wandering devious a stranger met.

"Elmira is the place. Elmira in the State of New York—this State, not two hundred miles away;" and he added, perfectly unnecessarily, "Slide, Kelley, slide."

I slid on the West Shore line, I slid till midnight, and they dumped me down at the door of a frowzy hotel in Elmira. Yes, they knew all about "that man Clemens," but reckoned he was not in town; had gone East somewhere. I had better possess my soul in patience till the morrow, and then dig up the "man Clemens'" brother-in-law, who was interested in coal.

The idea of chasing half a dozen relatives in addition to Mark Twain up and down a city of thirty thousand inhabitants kept me awake. Morning revealed Elmira, whose streets were desolated by railway tracks, and whose suburbs were given up to the manufacture of door-sashes and window-frames. It was surrounded by pleasant, fat, little hills, rimmed with timber and topped with cultivation. The Chemung River flowed generally up and down the town, and had just finished flooding a few of the main streets.

The hotel-man and the telephone-man assured me that the much-desired brother-in-law was out of town, and no one seemed to know where "the man Clemens" abode. Later on I discovered that he had not summered in that place for more than nineteen seasons, and so was comparatively a new arrival.

A friendly policeman volunteered the news that he had seen Twain or "some one very like him" driving a buggy the day before. This gave me a delightful sense of nearness. Fancy living in a town where you could see the author of *Tom Sawyer,* or "some one very like him," jolting over the pavements in a buggy!

"He lives out yonder at East Hill," said the policeman; "three miles from here."

Then the chase began—in a hired hack, up an awful hill, where sunflowers blossomed by the roadside, and crops waved, and *Harper's Magazine* cows stood in eligible and commanding attitudes knee-deep in clover, all ready to be transferred to photogravure. The great man must have been persecuted by outsiders aforetime, and fled up the hill for refuge.

Presently the driver stopped at a miserable, little, white wood shanty, and demanded "Mister Clemens."

"I know he's a big-bug and all that," he explained, "but you can never tell what sort of notions those sort of men take into their heads to live in, anyways."

There rose up a young lady who was sketching thistle-tops and goldenrod, amid a plentiful supply of both, and set the pilgrimage on the right path.

"It's a pretty Gothic house on the left-hand side a little way farther on."

"Gothic h——," said the driver. "Very few of the city hacks take this drive, specially if they know they are coming out here," and he glared at me savagely.

It was a very pretty house, anything but Gothic, clothed with ivy, standing in a very big compound, and fronted by a verandah full of chairs and hammocks. The roof of the verandah was a trellis-work of creepers, and the sun peeping through moved on the shining boards below.

Decidedly this remote place was an ideal one for work, if a man could work among these soft airs and the murmur of the long-eared crops.

Appeared suddenly a lady used to dealing with rampageous outsiders. "Mr. Clemens has just walked downtown. He is at his brother-in-law's house."

Then he was within shouting distance, after all, and the chase had not been in vain. With speed I fled, and the driver, skidding the wheel and swearing audibly, arrived at the bottom of that hill without accidents. It was in the pause that followed between ringing the brother-in-law's bell and getting an answer that it occurred to me for the first time Mark Twain might possibly have other engagements than the entertainment of escaped lunatics from India, be they never so full of admiration. And in another man's house—anyhow, what had I come to do or say? Suppose the drawing-room should be full of people,—suppose a baby were sick, how was I to explain that I only wanted to shake hands with him?

Then things happened somewhat in this order. A big, darkened drawing-room; a huge chair; a man with eyes, a mane of grizzled hair, a brown mustache covering a mouth as delicate as a woman's, a strong, square hand shaking mine, and the slowest, calmest, levellest voice in all the world saying:—

"Well, you think you owe me something, and you've come to tell me so. That's what I call squaring a debt handsomely."

"Piff!" from a cob-pipe (I always said that a Missouri meerschaum was the best smoking in the world), and, behold! Mark Twain had curled himself up in the big armchair, and I was smoking reverently, as befits one in the presence of his superior.

The thing that struck me first was that he was an elderly man; yet, after a minute's thought, I perceived that it was otherwise, and in five minutes, the eyes looking at me, I saw that the grey hair was an accident of the most trivial. He was quite young. I was shaking his hand. I was smoking his cigar, and I was hearing him talk—this man I had learned to love and admire fourteen thousand miles away.

Reading his books, I had striven to get an idea of his personality, and all my preconceived notions were wrong and beneath the reality. Blessed is the man who finds no disillusion when he is brought face to face with a revered writer. That was a moment to be remembered; the landing of a twelve-pound salmon was nothing to it. I had hooked Mark Twain, and he was treating me as though under certain circumstances I might be an equal.

About this time I became aware that he was discussing the copyright question. Here, so far as I remember, is what he said. Attend to the words of the oracle through this unworthy medium transmitted. You will never be able to imagine the long, slow surge of the drawl, and the deadly gravity of the countenance, the quaint pucker of the body, one foot thrown over the arm of the chair, the yellow pipe clinched in one corner of the mouth, and the right hand casually caressing the square chin:—

"Copyright? Some men have morals, and some men have—other things. I presume a publisher is a man. He is not born. He is created—by circumstances. Some publishers have morals. Mine have. They pay me for the English productions of my books. When you hear men talking of Bret Harte's works and other works and my books being pirated, ask them to be sure of their facts. I think they'll find the books are paid for. It was ever thus.

"I remember an unprincipled and formidable publisher. Perhaps he's dead now. He used to take my short stories—I can't call it steal or pirate them. It was beyond these things altogether. He took my stories one at a time and made a book of it. If I wrote an essay on dentistry or theology or any little thing of that kind—just an essay that long (he indicated half an inch on his finger), any sort of essay—that publisher would amend and improve my essay.

"He would get another man to write some more to it or cut it about exactly as his needs required. Then he would publish a book called *Dentistry by Mark Twain,* that little essay and some other things not mine added. Theology would make another book, and so on. I do not consider that fair. It's an insult. But he's dead now, I think. I didn't kill him.

"There is a great deal of nonsense talked about international copyright. The proper way to treat a copyright is to make it exactly like real-estate in every way.

"It will settle itself under these conditions. If Congress were to bring in a law that a man's life was not to extend over a hundred and sixty years, somebody would laugh. That law wouldn't concern anybody. The man would be out of the jurisdiction of the court. A term of years in copyright comes to exactly the same thing. No law can make a book live or cause it to die before the appointed time.

"Tottletown, Cal., was a new town, with a population of three thousand—banks, fire-brigade, brick buildings, and all the modern improvements. It lived, it flourished, and it disappeared. To-day no man can put his foot on any remnant of Tottletown, Cal. It's dead. London continues to exist. Bill Smith, author of a book read for the next year or so, is real-estate in Tottletown. William Shakespeare, whose works are extensively read, is real-estate in London. Let Bill Smith, equally with Mr. Shakespeare now deceased, have as complete a control over his copyright as he would over his real-estate. Let him gamble it away, drink it away, or—give it to the church. Let his heirs and assigns treat it in the same manner.

"Every now and again I go up to Washington, sitting on a board to drive that sort of view into Congress. Congress takes its arguments against international copyright delivered ready made, and—Congress isn't very strong. I put the real-estate view of the case before one of the Senators.

"He said: 'Suppose a man has written a book that will live for ever?'

"I said: 'Neither you nor I will ever live to see that man, but we'll assume it. What then?'

"He said: 'I want to protect the world against that man's heirs and assigns, working under your theory.'

"I said: 'You think that all the world has no commercial

sense. The book that will live for ever can't be artificially kept up at inflated prices. There will always be very expensive editions of it and cheap ones issuing side by side.'

"Take the case of Sir Walter Scott's novels," Mark Twain continued, turning to me. "When the copyright notes protected them, I bought editions as expensive as I could afford, because I liked them. At the same time the same firm were selling editions that a cat might buy. They had their real estate, and not being fools, recognized that one portion of the plot could be worked as a gold mine, another as a vegetable garden, and another as a marble quarry. Do you see?"

What I saw with the greatest clearness was Mark Twain being forced to fight for the simple proposition that a man has as much right to the work of his brains (think of the heresy of it!) as to the labour of his hands. When the old lion roars, the young whelps growl. I growled assentingly, and the talk ran on from books in general to his own in particular.

Growing bold, and feeling that I had a few hundred thousand folk at my back, I demanded whether Tom Sawyer married Judge Thatcher's daughter and whether we were ever going to hear of Tom Sawyer as a man.

"I haven't decided," quoth Mark Twain, getting up, filling his pipe, and walking up and down the room in his slippers. "I have a notion of writing the sequel to *Tom Sawyer* in two ways. In one I would make him rise to great honour and go to Congress, and in the other I should hang him. Then the friends and enemies of the book could take their choice."

Here I lost my reverence completely, and protested against any theory of the sort, because, to me at least, Tom Sawyer was real.

"Oh, he *is* real," said Mark Twain. "He's all the boy that I have known or recollect; but that would be a good way of ending the book"; then, turning round, "because, when you come to think of it, neither religion, training, nor education avails anything against the force of circumstances that drive a man. Suppose we took the next four and twenty years of Tom Sawyer's life, and gave a little joggle to the circumstances that controlled him. He would, logically and according to the joggle, turn out a rip or an angel."

"Do you believe that, then?"

"I think so. Isn't it what you call Kismet?"

"Yes; but don't give him two joggles and show the result, because he isn't your property any more. He belongs to us."

He laughed—a large, wholesome laugh—and this began a dissertation on the rights of a man to do what he liked with his own creations, which being a matter of purely professional interest, I will mercifully omit.

Returning to the big chair, he, speaking of truth and the like in literature, said that an autobiography was the one work in which a man, against his own will and in spite of his utmost striving to the contrary, revealed himself in his true light to the world.

"A good deal of your life on the Mississippi is autobiographical, isn't it?" I asked.

"As near as it can be—when a man is writing to a book and about himself. But in genuine autobiography, I believe it is impossible for a man to tell the truth about himself or to avoid impressing the reader with the truth about himself.

"I made an experiment once. I got a friend of mine—a man painfully given to speak the truth on all occasions—a man who wouldn't dream of telling a lie—and I made him write his autobiography for his own amusement and mine. He did it. The manuscript would have made an octavo volume, but—good, honest man that he was—in every single detail of his life that I knew about he turned out, on paper, a formidable liar. He could not help himself.

"It is not in human nature to write the truth about itself. None the less the reader gets a general impression from an autobiography whether the man is a fraud or a good man. The reader can't give his reasons any more than a man can explain why a woman struck him as being lovely when he doesn't remember her hair, eyes, teeth, or figure. And the impression that the reader gets is a correct one."

"Do you ever intend to write an autobiography?"

"If I do, it will be as other men have done—with the most

earnest desire to make myself out to be the better man in every little business that has been to my discredit; and I shall fail, like the others, to make my readers believe anything except the truth."

This naturally led to a discussion on conscience. Then said Mark Twain, and his words are mighty and to be remembered:—

"Your conscience is a nuisance. A conscience is like a child. If you pet it and play with it and let it have everything that it wants, it becomes spoiled and intrudes on all your amusements and most of your griefs. Treat your conscience as you would treat anything else. When it is rebellious, spank it—be severe with it, argue with it, prevent it from coming to play with you at all hours, and you will secure a good conscience; that is to say, a properly trained one. A spoiled one simply destroys all the pleasure in life. I think I have reduced mine to order. At least, I haven't heard from it for some time. Perhaps I have killed it from over-severity. It's wrong to kill a child, but, in spite of all I have said, a conscience differs from a child in many ways. Perhaps it's best when it's dead."

Here he told me a little—such things as a man may tell a stranger—of his early life and upbringing, and in what manner he had been influenced for good by the example of his parents. He spoke always through his eyes, a light under the heavy eyebrows; anon crossing the room with a step as light as a girl's, to show me some book or other; then resuming his walk up and down the room, puffing at the cob-pipe. I would have given much for nerve enough to demand the gift of that pipe—value, five cents when new. I understood why certain savage tribes ardently desired the liver of brave men slain in combat. That pipe would have given me, perhaps, a hint of his keen insight into the souls of men. But he never laid it aside within stealing reach.

Once, indeed, he put his hand on my shoulder. It was an investiture of the Star of India, blue silk, trumpets, and diamond-studded jewel, all complete. If hereafter, in the changes and chances of this mortal life, I fall to cureless ruin, I will tell the superintendent of the workhouse that Mark

Twain once put his hand on my shoulder; and he shall give me a room to myself and a double allowance of paupers' tobacco.

"I never read novels myself," said he, "except when the popular persecution forces me to—when people plague me to know what I think of the last book that every one is reading."

"And how did the latest persecution affect you?"

"Robert?" said he, interrogatively.

I nodded.

"I read it, of course, for the workmanship. That made me think I had neglected novels too long—that there might be a good many books as graceful in style somewhere on the shelves; so I began a course of novel reading. I have dropped it now; it did not amuse me. But as regards Robert, the effect on me was exactly as though a singer of street ballads were to hear excellent music from a church organ. I didn't stop to ask whether the music was legitimate or necessary. I listened, and I liked what I heard. I am speaking of the grace and beauty of the style."

"You see," he went on, "every man has his private opinion about a book. But that is my private opinion. If I had lived in the beginning of things, I should have looked around the township to see what popular opinion thought of the murder of Abel before I openly condemned Cain. I should have had my private opinion, of course, but I shouldn't have expressed it until I had felt the way. You have my private opinion about that book. I don't know what my public ones are exactly. They won't upset the earth."

He recurled himself into the chair and talked of other things.

"I spend nine months of the year at Hartford. I have long ago satisfied myself that there is no hope of doing much work during those nine months. People come in and call. They call at all hours, about everything in the world. One day I thought I would keep a list of interruptions. It began this way:—

"A man came and would see no one but Mr. Clemens. He was an agent for photogravure reproductions of Salon pictures. I very seldom use Salon pictures in my books.

"After that man another man, who refused to see any one but Mr. Clemens, came to make me write to Washington about something. I saw him. I saw a third man, then a fourth. By this time it was noon. I had grown tired of keeping the list. I wished to rest.

"But the fifth man was the only one of the crowd with a card of his own. He sent up his card. 'Ben Koontz, Hannibal, Mo.' I was raised in Hannibal. Ben was an old schoolmate of mine. Consequently I threw the house wide open and rushed with both hands out at a big, fat, heavy man, who was not the Ben I had ever known—nor anything like him.

" 'But *is* it you, Ben?' I said. 'You've altered in the last thousand years.'

"The fat man said: 'Well, I'm not Koontz exactly, but I met him down in Missouri, and he told me to be sure and call on you, and he gave me his card, and'—here he acted the little scene for my benefit—'if you can wait a minute till I can get out the circulars—I'm not Koontz exactly, but I'm travelling with the fullest line of rods you ever saw.' "

"And what happened?" I asked breathlessly.

"I shut the door. He was not Ben Koontz—exactly—not my old school-fellow, but I had shaken him by both hands in love, and . . . I had been bearded by a lightning-rod man in my own house.

"As I was saying, I do very little work in Hartford. I come here for three months every year, and I work four or five hours a day in a study down the garden of that little house on the hill. Of course, I do not object to two or three interruptions. When a man is in the full swing of his work these little things do not affect him. Eight or ten or twenty interruptions retard composition."

I was burning to ask him all manner of impertinent questions, as to which of his works he himself preferred, and so forth; but, standing in awe of his eyes, I dared not. He spoke on, and I listened, grovelling.

It was a question of mental equipment that was on the carpet, and I am still wondering whether he meant what he said.

"Personally I never care for fiction or story-books. What I like to read about are facts and statistics of any kind. If they are only facts about the raising of radishes, they interest me. Just now, for instance, before you came in"—he pointed to an encyclopædia on the shelves—"I was reading an article about 'Mathematics.' Perfectly pure mathematics.

"My own knowledge of mathematics stops at 'twelve times twelve,' but I enjoyed that article immensely. I didn't understand a word of it; but facts, or what a man believes to be facts, are always delightful. That mathematical fellow believed in his facts. So do I. Get your facts first, and"—the voice dies away to an almost inaudible drone—"then you can distort 'em as much as you please."

Bearing this precious advice in my bosom, I left; the great man assuring me with gentle kindness that I had not interrupted him in the least. Once outside the door, I yearned to go back and ask some questions—it was easy enough to think of them now—but his time was his own, though his books belonged to me.

I should have ample time to look back to that meeting across the graves of the days. But it was sad to think of the things he had not spoken about.

In San Francisco the men of *The Call* told me many legends of Mark's apprenticeship in their paper five and twenty years ago; how he was a reporter delightfully incapable of reporting according to the needs of the day. He preferred, so they said, to coil himself into a heap and meditate until the last minute. Then he would produce copy bearing no sort of relationship to his legitimate work—copy that made the editor swear horribly, and the readers of *The Call* ask for more.

I should like to have heard Mark's version of that, with some stories of his joyous and variegated past. He has been journeyman printer (in those days he wandered from the banks of the Missouri even to Philadelphia), pilot cub and full-blown pilot, soldier of the South (that was for three weeks only), private secretary to a Lieutenant-Governor of Nevada (that displeased him), miner, editor, special correspondent in the Sandwich Islands, and the Lord only knows what else. If so experienced a man could by any means be made drunk, it would be a glorious thing to fill him up with composite liquors, and, in the language of his own country, "let him retrospect." But these eyes will never see that orgy fit for the gods!

THE LIGHT THAT FAILED

1891

CHAPTER I

So we settled it all when the storm was done
As comf'y as comf'y could be;
And I was to wait in the barn, my dears,
Because I was only three,
And Teddy would run to the rainbow's foot,
Because he was five and a man;
And that's how it all began, my dears,
And that's how it all began.

—BIG BARN STORIES

WHAT do you think she'd do if she caught us? We oughtn't to have it, you know," said Maisie.

"Beat me, and lock you up in your bedroom," Dick answered, without hesitation. "Have you got the cartridges?"

"Yes; they're in my pocket, but they are joggling horribly. Do pin-fire cartridges go off of their own accord?"

"Don't know. Take the revolver, if you are afraid, and let me carry them."

"I'm *not* afraid." Maisie strode forward swiftly, a hand in her pocket and her chin in the air. Dick followed with a small pin-fire revolver.

The children had discovered that their lives would be unendurable without pistol-practice. After much forethought and self-denial, Dick had saved seven shillings and sixpence, the price of a badly constructed Belgian revolver. Maisie could only contribute half a crown to the syndicate for the purchase of a hundred cartridges. "You can save better than I can, Dick," she explained; "I like nice things to eat, and it doesn't matter to you. Besides, boys ought to do these things."

Dick grumbled a little at the arrangement, but went out

and made the purchases, which the children were then on their way to test. Revolvers did not lie in the scheme of their daily life as decreed for them by the guardian who was incorrectly supposed to stand in the place of a mother to these two orphans. Dick had been under her care for six years, during which time she had made her profit of the allowances supposed to be expended on his clothes, and, partly through thoughtlessness, partly through a natural desire to pain,—she was a widow of some years anxious to marry again,—had made his days burdensome on his young shoulders. Where he had looked for love, she gave him first aversion and then hate. Where he growing older had sought a little sympathy, she gave him ridicule. The many hours that she could spare from the ordering of her small house she devoted to what she called the home-training of Dick Heldar. Her religion, manufactured in the main by her own intelligence and a keen study of the Scriptures, was an aid to her in this matter. At such times as she herself was not personally displeased with Dick, she left him to understand that he had a heavy account to settle with his Creator; wherefore Dick learned to loathe his God as intensely as he loathed Mrs. Jennett; and this is not a wholesome frame of mind for the young. Since she chose to regard him as a hopeless liar, when dread of pain drove him to his first untruth he naturally developed into a liar, but an economical and self-contained one, never throwing away the least unnecessary fib, and never hesitating at the blackest, were it only plausible, that might make his life a little easier. The treatment taught him at least the power of living alone, —a power that was of service to him when he went to a public school and the boys laughed at his clothes, which were poor in quality and much mended. In the holidays he returned to the teachings of Mrs. Jennett, and, that the chain of discipline might not be weakened by association with the world, was generally beaten, on one count or another, before he had been twelve hours under her roof.

The autumn of one year brought him a companion in bondage, a long-haired, gray-eyed little atom, as self-contained as himself, who moved about the house silently and for the first few weeks spoke only to the goat that was her chiefest friend on earth and lived in the back-garden. Mrs. Jennett objected to the goat on the grounds that he was un-Christian,—which he certainly was. "Then," said the atom, choosing her words very deliberately, "I shall write to my lawyer-peoples and tell them that you are a very bad woman. Amomma is mine, mine, mine!" Mrs. Jennett made a movement to the hall, where certain umbrellas and canes stood in a rack. The atom understood as clearly as Dick what this meant. "I have been beaten before," she said, still in the same passionless voice; "I have been beaten worse than you can ever beat me. If you beat me I shall write to my lawyer-peoples and tell them that you do not give me enough to eat. I am not afraid of you." Mrs. Jennett did not go into the hall, and the atom, after a pause to assure herself that all danger of war was past, went out, to weep bitterly on Amomma's neck.

Dick learned to know her as Maisie, and at first mistrusted her profoundly, for he feared that she might interfere with the small liberty of action left to him. She did not, however; and she volunteered no friendliness until Dick had taken the first steps. Long before the holidays were over, the stress of punishment shared in common drove the children together, if it were only to play into each other's hands as they prepared lies for Mrs. Jennett's use. When Dick returned to school, Maisie whispered, "Now I shall be all alone to take care of myself; but," and she nodded her head bravely, "I can do it. You promised to send Amomma a grass collar. Send it soon." A week later she asked for that collar by return of post, and was not pleased when she learned that it took time to make. When at last Dick forwarded the gift, she forgot to thank him for it.

Many holidays had come and gone since that day, and Dick had grown into a lanky hobbledehoy more than ever conscious of his bad clothes. Not for a moment had Mrs. Jennett relaxed her tender care of him, but the average canings of a public school—Dick fell under punishment about three times a month—filled him with contempt for her powers. "She doesn't hurt," he explained to Maisie, who urged him to rebellion, "and she is kinder to you after she has whacked me." Dick shambled through the days unkempt in body and savage in soul, as the smaller boys of the school learned to know, for when the spirit moved him he would hit them, cunningly and with science. The same spirit made him more than once try to tease Maisie, but the girl refused to be made unhappy. "We are both miserable as it is," said she. "What is the use of trying to make things worse? Let's find things to do, and forget things."

The pistol was the outcome of that search. It could only be used on the muddiest foreshore of the beach, far away from bathing-machines and pier-heads, below the grassy slopes of Fort Keeling. The tide ran out nearly two miles on that coast, and the many-coloured mud-banks, touched by the sun, sent up a lamentable smell of dead weed. It was late in the afternoon when Dick and Maisie arrived on their ground, Amomma trotting patiently behind them.

"Mf!" said Maisie, sniffing the air. "I wonder what makes the sea so smelly? I don't like it."

"You never like anything that isn't made just for you," said Dick bluntly. "Give me the cartridges, and I'll try first shot. How far does one of these little revolvers carry?"

"Oh, half a mile," said Maisie, promptly. "At least it makes an awful noise. Be careful with the cartridges; I don't like those jagged stick-up things on the rim. Dick, do be careful."

"All right. I know how to load. I'll fire at the breakwater out there."

He fired, and Amomma ran away bleating. The bullet threw up a spurt of mud to the right of the weed-wreathed piles.

"Throws high and to the right. You try, Maisie. Mind, it's loaded all round."

Maisie took the pistol and stepped delicately to the verge of the mud, her hand firmly closed on the butt, her mouth and left eye screwed up. Dick sat down on a tuft of bank and laughed. Amomma returned very cautiously. He was accustomed to strange experiences in his afternoon walks, and, finding the cartridge-box unguarded, made investigations with his nose. Maisie fired, but could not see where the bullet went.

"I think it hit the post," she said, shading her eyes and looking out across the sailless sea.

"I know it has gone out to the Marazion Bell-buoy," said Dick, with a chuckle. "Fire low and to the left; then perhaps you'll get it. Oh, look at Amomma!—he's eating the cartridges!"

Maisie turned, the revolver in her hand, just in time to see Amomma scampering away from the pebbles Dick threw after him. Nothing is sacred to a billy goat. Being well fed and the adored of his mistress, Amomma had naturally swallowed two loaded pin-fire cartridges. Maisie hurried up to assure herself that Dick had not miscounted the tale.

"Yes, he's eaten two."

"Horrid little beast! Then they'll joggle about inside him and blow up, and serve him right. . . . Oh, Dick! have I killed you?"

Revolvers are tricky things for young hands to deal with. Maisie could not explain how it had happened, but a veil of reeking smoke separated her from Dick, and she was quite certain that the pistol had gone off in his face. Then she heard him sputter, and dropped on her knees beside him crying, "Dick, you aren't hurt, are you? I didn't mean it."

"Of course you didn't," said Dick, coming out of the smoke and wiping his cheek. "But you nearly blinded me. That powder stuff stings awfully." A neat little splash of gray lead on a stone showed where the bullet had gone. Maisie began to whimper.

"Don't," said Dick, jumping to his feet and shaking himself. "I'm not a bit hurt."

"No, but I might have killed you," protested Maisie, the corners of her mouth drooping. "What should I have been then?"

"Gone home and told Mrs. Jennett." Dick grinned at the thought; then, softening, "Please don't worry about it. Besides, we are wasting time. We've got to get back to tea. I'll take the revolver for a bit."

Maisie would have wept on the least encouragement, but Dick's indifference, albeit his hand was shaking as he picked up the pistol, restrained her. She lay panting on the beach while Dick methodically bombarded the breakwater. "Got it at last!" he exclaimed, as a lock of weed flew from the wood

"Let me try," said Maisie, imperiously. "I'm all right now."

They fired in turns till the rickety little revolver nearly shook itself to pieces, and Amomma the outcast—because he might blow up at any moment—browsed in the background and wondered why stones were thrown at him. Then they found a balk of timber floating in a pool which was commanded by the seaward slope of Fort Keeling, and they sat down together before this new target.

"Next holidays," said Dick, as the now thoroughly fouled revolver kicked wildly in his hand, "we'll get another pistol,—central fire,—that will carry farther."

"There won't be any next holidays for me," said Maisie. "I'm going away."

"Where to?"

"I don't know. My lawyers have written to Mrs. Jennett, and I've got to be educated somewhere,—in France, perhaps,—I don't know where; but I shall be glad to go away."

"I shan't like it a bit. I suppose I shall be left. Look here, Maisie, is it really true you're going? Then these holidays will be the last I shall see anything of you; and I go back to school next week. I wish——"

The young blood turned his cheeks scarlet. Maisie was picking grass-tufts and throwing them down the slope at a yellow sea-poppy nodding all by itself to the illimitable levels of the mud-flats and the milk-white sea beyond.

"I wish," she said, after a pause, "that I could see you again sometime. You wish that, too?"

"Yes, but it would have been better if—if—you had—shot straight over there—down by the breakwater."

Maisie looked with large eyes for a moment. And this was the boy who only ten days before had decorated Amomma's horns with cut-paper ham-frills and turned him out, a bearded derision, among the public ways! Then she dropped her eyes: this was not the boy.

"Don't be stupid," she said reprovingly, and with swift instinct attacked the side-issue. "How selfish you are! Just think what I should have felt if that horrid thing had killed you! I'm quite miserable enough already."

"Why? Because you're going away from Mrs. Jennett?"

"No."

"From me, then?"

No answer for a long time. Dick dared not look at her. He felt, though he did not know, all that the past four years had been to him, and this the more acutely since he had no knowledge to put his feelings in words.

"I don't know," she said. "I suppose it is."

"Maisie, you must know. *I'm* not supposing."

"Let's go home," said Maisie, weakly.

But Dick was not minded to retreat.

"I can't say things," he pleaded, "and I'm awfully sorry for teasing you about Amomma the other day. It's all different now, Maisie, can't you see? And you might have told me that you were going, instead of leaving me to find out."

"You didn't. I did tell. Oh, Dick, what's the use of worrying?"

"There isn't any; but we've been together years and years, and I didn't know how much I cared."

"I don't believe you ever did care."

"No, I didn't; but I do,—I care awfully now, Maisie," he gulped,—"Maisie, darling, say you care too, please."

"I do, indeed I do; but it won't be any use."

"Why?"

"Because I am going away."

"Yes, but if you promise before you go. Only say—will you?" A second "darling" came to his lips more easily than the first. There were few endearments in Dick's home or school life; he had to find them by instinct. Dick caught the little hand blackened with the escaped gas of the revolver.

"I promise," she said solemnly; "but if I care there is no need for promising."

"And you do care?" For the first time in the past few minutes their eyes met and spoke for them who had no skill in speech. . . .

"Oh, Dick, don't! Please don't! It was all right when we said good-morning; but now it's all different!" Amomma looked on from afar. He had seen his property quarrel frequently, but he had never seen kisses exchanged before. The yellow sea-poppy was wiser, and nodded its head approvingly. Considered as a kiss, that was a failure, but since it was the first, other than those demanded by duty, in all the world that either had ever given or taken, it opened to them new worlds, and every one of them glorious, so that they were lifted above the consideration of any worlds at all, especially those in which tea is necessary, and sat still, holding each other's hands and saying not a word.

"You can't forget now," said Dick, at last. There was that on his cheek that stung more than gun-powder.

"I shouldn't have forgotten anyhow," said Maisie, and they looked at each other and saw that each was changed from the companion of an hour ago to a wonder and a mystery they could not understand. The sun began to set, and a night-wind thrashed along the bents of the fore-shore.

"We shall be awfully late for tea," said Maisie. "Let's go home."

"Let's use the rest of the cartridges first," said Dick; and he helped Maisie down the slope of the fort to the sea,—a descent that she was quite capable of covering at full speed. Equally gravely Maisie took the grimy hand. Dick bent forward clumsily; Maisie drew the hand away, and Dick blushed.

"It's very pretty," he said.

"Pooh!" said Maisie, with a little laugh of gratified vanity. She stood close to Dick as he loaded the revolver for the last time and fired over the sea with a vague notion at the back of his head that he was protecting Maisie from all the evils in the world. A puddle far across the mud caught the last rays of the sun and turned into a wrathful red disc. The light held Dick's attention for a moment, and as he raised his revolver there fell upon him a renewed sense of the miraculous, in that he was standing by Maisie who had promised to care for him for an indefinite length of time till such date as—— A gust of the growing wind drove the girl's long black hair across his face as she stood with her hand on his shoulder calling Amomma "a little beast," and for a moment he was in the dark,—a darkness that stung. The bullet went singing out to the empty sea.

"Spoilt my aim," said he, shaking his head. "There aren't any more cartridges; we shall have to run home." But they did not run. They walked very slowly, arm in arm. And it was a matter of indifference to them whether the neglected Amomma with two pin-fire cartridges in his inside blew up or trotted beside them; for they had come into a golden heritage and were disposing of it with all the wisdom of all their years.

"And I shall be——" quoth Dick, valiantly. Then he checked himself: "I don't know what I shall be. I don't seem to be able to pass any exams., but I can make awful caricatures of the masters. Ho! ho!"

"Be an artist, then," said Maisie. "You're always laughing at my trying to draw; and it will do you good."

"I'll never laugh at anything you do," he answered. "I'll be an artist, and I'll do things."

"Artists always want money, don't they?"

"I've got a hundred and twenty pounds a year of my own. My guardians tell me I'm to have it when I come of age. That will be enough to begin with."

"Ah, I'm rich," said Maisie. "I've got three hundred a year all my own when I'm twenty-one. That's why Mrs. Jennett is kinder to me than she is to you. I wish, though, that I had somebody that belonged to me,—just a father or a mother."

"You belong to me," said Dick, "for ever and ever."

"Yes, we belong—for ever. It's very nice." She squeezed his arm. The kindly darkness hid them both, and, emboldened because he could only just see the profile of Maisie's cheek with the long lashes veiling the gray eyes, Dick at the front door delivered himself of the words he had been boggling over for the last two hours.

"And I—love you, Maisie," he said, in a whisper that seemed to him to ring across the world,—the world that he would to-morrow or the next day set out to conquer.

There was a scene, not, for the sake of discipline, to be reported, when Mrs. Jennett would have fallen upon him, first for disgraceful unpunctuality, and secondly for nearly killing himself with a forbidden weapon.

"I was playing with it, and it went off by itself," said Dick, when the powder-pocked cheek could no longer be hidden, "but if you think you're going to lick me you're wrong. You are never going to touch me again. Sit down and give me my tea. You can't cheat us out of that, anyhow."

Mrs. Jennett gasped and became livid. Maisie said nothing, but encouraged Dick with her eyes, and he behaved abominably all that evening. Mrs. Jennett prophesied an immediate judgment of Providence and a descent into Tophet later, but Dick walked in Paradise and would not hear. Only when he was going to bed Mrs. Jennett recovered and asserted herself. He had bidden Maisie good-night with down-drooped eyes and from a distance.

"If you aren't a gentleman you might try to behave like one," said Mrs. Jennett, spitefully. "You've been quarrelling with Maisie again."

This meant that the usual good-night kiss had been omitted. Maisie, white to the lips, thrust her cheek forward with a fine air of indifference, and was duly pecked by Dick, who tramped out of the room red as fire. That night he dreamed a wild dream. He had won all the world and brought it to Maisie in a cartridge-box, but she turned it over with her foot, and, instead of saying "Thank you," cried—

"Where is the grass collar you promised for Amomma? Oh, how selfish you are!"

CHAPTER II

Then we brought the lances down, then the bugles blew,
When we went to Kandahar, ridin' two an' two,
Ridin', ridin', ridin', two an' two,
Ta-ra-ra-ra-ra-ra-ra,
All the way to Kandahar, ridin' two an' two.

—BARRACK-ROOM BALLAD

"I'M NOT angry with the British public, but I wish we had a few thousand of them scattered among these rocks. They wouldn't be in such a hurry to get at their morning papers then. Can't you imagine the regulation householder—Lover of Justice, Constant Reader, Paterfamilias, and all that lot—frizzling on hot gravel?"

"With a blue veil over his head, and his clothes in strips. Has any man here a needle? I've got a piece of sugar-sack."

"I'll lend you a packing-needle for six square inches of it then. Both my knees are worn through."

"Why not six square acres, while you're about it? But lend me the needle, and I'll see what I can do with the selvage. I don't think there's enough to protect my royal body from the cold blast as it is. What are you doing with that everlasting sketch-book of yours, Dick?"

"Study of our Special Correspondent repairing his wardrobe," said Dick, gravely, as the other man kicked off a pair of sorely worn riding-breeches and began to fit a square of coarse canvas over the most obvious open space. He grunted disconsolately as the vastness of the void developed itself.

"Sugar-bags, indeed! Hi! you pilot man there! lend me all the sails of that whale-boat."

A fez-crowned head bobbed up in the stern-sheets, divided itself into exact halves with one flashing grin, and bobbed down again. The man of the tattered breeches, clad only in a Norfolk jacket and a gray flannel shirt, went on with his clumsy sewing, while Dick chuckled over the sketch.

Some twenty whale-boats were nuzzling a sand-bank which was dotted with English soldiery of half a dozen corps, bathing or washing their clothes. A heap of boat-rollers, commissariat-boxes, sugar-bags, and flour- and small-arm-ammunition-cases showed where one of the whale-boats had been compelled to unload hastily; and a regimental carpenter was swearing aloud as he tried, on a wholly insufficient allowance of white lead, to plaster up the sun-parched gaping seams of the boat herself.

"First the bloomin' rudder snaps," said he to the world in general; "then the mast goes; an' then, s' 'elp me, when she can't do nothin' else, she opens 'erself out like a cock-eyed Chinese lotus."

"Exactly the case with my breeches, whoever you are," said the tailor, without looking up. "Dick, I wonder when I shall see a decent shop again."

There was no answer, save the incessant angry murmur of the Nile as it raced round a basalt-walled bend and foamed across a rock-bridge half a mile upstream. It was as though the brown weight of the river would drive the white men back to their own country. The indescribable scent of Nile mud in the air told that the stream was falling and that the next few miles would be no light thing for the whale-boats to overpass. The desert ran down almost to the banks, where, among gray, red, and black hillocks, a camel-corps was encamped. No man dared even for a day lose touch of the slow-moving boats; there had been no fighting for weeks past, and throughout all that time the Nile had never spared them. Rapid had followed rapid, rock rock, and island-group island-group, till the rank and file had long since lost all count of direction and very nearly of time. They were moving somewhere, they did not know why, to do something, they did not know what. Before them lay the Nile, and at the other end of it was one Gordon, fighting for the dear life, in a town called Khartoum. There were columns of British troops in the desert, or in one of the many deserts; there were columns on the river; there were yet more columns waiting to embark on the river; there were fresh drafts waiting at Assioot and Assuan; there were lies and rumours running over the face of the hopeless land from Suakin to the Sixth Cataract, and men supposed generally that there must be some one in authority to direct the general scheme of the many movements. The duty of that particular river-column was to keep the whale-boats afloat in the water, to avoid trampling on the villagers' crops when the gangs "tracked" the boats with lines thrown from midstream, to get as much sleep and food as was possible, and, above all, to press on without delay in the teeth of the churning Nile.

With the soldiers sweated and toiled the correspondents of the newspapers, and they were almost as ignorant as their companions. But it was above all things necessary that England at breakfast should be amused and thrilled and interested, whether Gordon lived or died, or half the British army went to pieces in the sands. The Soudan campaign was a picturesque one, and lent itself to vivid word-painting. Now and again a "Special" managed to get slain,—which was not altogether a disadvantage to the paper that employed him,—and more often the hand-to-hand nature of the fighting allowed of miraculous escapes which were worth telegraphing home at eighteen-pence the word. There were many correspondents with many corps and columns,—from the veterans who had followed on the heels of the cavalry that occupied Cairo in '82, what time Arabi Pasha called himself king, who had seen the first miserable work round Suakin when the sentries were cut up nightly and the scrub swarmed with spears, to youngsters jerked into the business at the end of a telegraph-wire to take the place of their betters killed or invalided.

Among the seniors—those who knew every shift and change in the perplexing postal arrangements, the value of the seediest, weediest Egyptian garron offered for sale in Cairo or Alexandria, who could talk a telegraph-clerk into amiability and soothe the ruffled vanity of a newly appointed staff-officer when press regulations became burdensome—was the man in the flannel shirt, the black-browed Torpenhow. He represented the Central Southern Syndicate in the campaign, as he had represented it in the Egyptian war, and elsewhere. The syndicate did not concern itself greatly with criticisms of attack and the like. It supplied the masses, and all it demanded was picturesqueness and abundance of detail; for there is more joy in England over a soldier who insubordinately steps out of square to rescue a comrade than over twenty generals slaving even to baldness at the gross details of transport and commissariat.

He had met at Suakin a young man, sitting on the edge of a recently abandoned redoubt about the size of a hat-box, sketching a clump of shell-torn bodies on the gravel plain.

"What are you for?" said Torpenhow. The greeting of the correspondent is that of the commercial traveller on the road.

"My own hand," said the young man, without looking up. "Have you any tobacco?"

Torpenhow waited till the sketch was finished, and when he had looked at it said, "What's your business here?"

"Nothing; there was a row, so I came. I'm supposed to be doing something down at the painting-slips among the boats, or else I'm in charge of the condenser on one of the water-ships. I've forgotten which."

"You've cheek enough to build a redoubt with," said Torpenhow, and took stock of the new acquaintance. "Do you always draw like that?"

The young man produced more sketches. "Row on a Chinese pig-boat," said he sententiously, showing them one after another.—"Chief mate dirked by a comprador.—Junk sunk ashore off Hakodate.—Somali camp at Berbera.—Slave-dhow being chased round Tajurrah Bay.—Soldier lying dead in the moonlight outside Suakin,—throat cut by Fuzzies."

"H'm!" said Torpenhow, "can't say I care for Verestchagin-and-water myself, but there's no accounting for tastes. Doing anything now, are you?"

"No. I'm amusing myself here."

Torpenhow looked at the aching desolation of the place. "Faith, you've queer notions of amusement. Got any money?"

"Enough to go on with. Look here: do you want me to do war-work?"

"*I* don't. My syndicate may, though. You can draw more than a little, and I don't suppose you care much what you get, do you?"

"Not this time. I want my chance first."

Torpenhow looked at the sketches again, and nodded. "Yes, you're right to take your first chance when you can get it."

He rode away swiftly through the Gate of the Two War-Ships, rattled across the causeway into the town, and wired to his syndicate, "Got man here, picture-work. Good and cheap. Shall I arrange? Will do letterpress with sketches."

The man on the redoubt sat swinging his legs and murmuring, "I knew the chance would come, sooner or later. By Gad, they'll have to sweat for it if I come through this business alive!"

In the evening Torpenhow was able to announce to his friend that the Central Southern Agency was willing to take him on trial, paying expenses for three months. "And, by the way, what's your name?" said Torpenhow.

"Heldar. Do they give me a free hand?"

"They've taken you on chance. You must justify the choice. You'd better stick to me. I'm going up-country with a column, and I'll do what I can for you. Give me some of your sketches taken here, and I'll send 'em along." To himself he said, "That's the best bargain the Central Southern has ever made; and they got me cheaply enough."

So it came to pass that, after some purchase of horse-flesh and arrangements financial and political, Dick was made free of the New and Honourable Fraternity of war correspondents, who all possess the inalienable right of doing as much work as they can and getting as much for it as Providence and their owners shall please. To these things are added in time, if the brother be worthy, the power of glib speech that neither man nor woman can resist when a meal or a bed is in question, the eye of a horse-coper, the skill of a cook, the constitution of a bullock, the digestion of an ostrich, and an infinite adaptability to all circumstances. But many die before they attain to this degree, and the past-masters in the craft appear for the most part in dress-clothes when they are in England, and thus their glory is hidden from the multitude.

Dick followed Torpenhow wherever the latter's fancy chose to lead him, and between the two they managed to accomplish some work that almost satisfied themselves. It was not an easy life in any way, and under its influence the two were drawn very closely together, for they ate from the same dish, they shared the same water-bottle, and, most binding tie of all, their mails went off together. It was Dick who managed to make gloriously drunk a telegraph-clerk in a palm hut far beyond the Second Cataract, and, while the man lay in bliss on the floor, possessed himself of some laboriously acquired exclusive information, forwarded by a confiding correspondent of an opposition syndicate, made a careful duplicate of the matter, and brought the result to Torpenhow, who said that all was fair in love or war correspondence, and built an excellent descriptive article from his rival's riotous waste of words. It was Torpenhow who—but the tale of their adventures, together and apart, from Philæ to the waste wilderness of Herawi and Muella, would fill many books. They had been penned into a square side by side, in deadly fear of being shot by over-excited soldiers; they had fought with baggage-camels in the chill dawn; they had jogged along in silence under blinding sun on indefatigable little Egyptian horses; and they had floundered on the shallows of the Nile when the whale-boat in which they had found a berth chose to hit a hidden rock and rip out half her bottom-planks.

Now they were sitting on the sand-bank, and the whale-boats were bringing up the remainder of the column.

"Yes," said Torpenhow, as he put the last rude stitches into his over-long-neglected gear, "it has been a beautiful business."

"The patch or the campaign?" said Dick. "Don't think much of either, myself."

"You want the *Euryalus* brought up above the Third Cataract, don't you? and eighty-one-ton guns at Jakdul? Now, *I'm* quite satisfied with my breeches." He turned round gravely to exhibit himself, after the manner of a clown.

"It's very pretty. Specially the lettering on the sack. G. B. T. Government Bullock Train. That's a sack from India."

"It's my initials,—Gilbert Belling Torpenhow. I stole the cloth on purpose. What the mischief are the camel-corps doing yonder?" Torpenhow shaded his eyes and looked across the scrub-strewn gravel.

A bugle blew furiously, and the men on the bank hurried to their arms and accoutrements.

" 'Pisan soldiery surprised while bathing,' " remarked Dick, calmly. "D'you remember the picture? It's by Michael Angelo; all beginners copy it. That scrub's alive with enemy."

The camel-corps on the bank yelled to the infantry to come to them, and a hoarse shouting down the river showed that the remainder of the column had wind of the trouble and was hastening to take share in it. As swiftly as a reach of still water is crisped by the wind, the rock-strewn ridges and scrub-topped hills were troubled and alive with armed men. Mercifully, it occurred to these to stand far off for a time, to shout and gesticulate joyously. One man even delivered himself of a long story. The camel-corps did not fire. They were only too glad of a little breathing-space, until some sort of square could be formed. The men on the sand-bank ran to their side; and the whale-boats, as they toiled up within shouting distance, were thrust into the nearest bank and emptied of all save the sick and a few men to guard them. The Arab orator ceased his outcries, and his friends howled.

"They look like the Mahdi's men," said Torpenhow, elbowing himself into the crush of the square; "but what thousands of 'em there are! The tribes hereabouts aren't against us, I know."

"Then the Mahdi's taken another town," said Dick, "and set all these yelping devils free to chaw us up. Lend us your glass."

"Our scouts should have told us of this. We've been trapped," said a subaltern. "Aren't the camel-guns ever going to begin? Hurry up, you men!"

There was no need for any order. The men flung themselves panting against thc sides of the square, for they had good reason to know that whoso was left outside when the fighting began would very probably die in an extremely unpleasant fashion. The little hundred-and-fifty-pound camel-guns posted at one corner of the square opened the ball as the square moved forward by its right to get possession of a knoll of rising ground. All had fought in this manner many times before, and there was no novelty in the entertainment: always the same hot and stifling formation, the smell of dust and leather, the same boltlike rush of the enemy, the same pressure on the weakest side, the few minutes of hand-to-hand scuffle, and then the silence of the desert, broken only by the yells of those whom their handful of cavalry attempted to pursue. They had become careless. The camel-guns spoke at intervals, and the square slouched forward amid the protesting of the camels. Then came the attack of three thousand men who had not learned from books that it is impossible for troops in close order to attack against breech-loading fire. A few dropping shots heralded their approach, and a few horsemen led, but the bulk of the force was naked humanity, mad with rage, and armed with the spear and the sword. The instinct of the desert, where there is always much war, told them that the right flank of the square was the weakest, for they swung clear of the front. The camel-guns shelled them as they passed, and opened for an instant lanes through their midst, most like those quick-closing vistas in a Kentish hop-garden seen when the train races by at full speed; and the infantry fire, held till the opportune moment, dropped them in close-packed hundreds. No civilized troops in the world could have endured the hell through which they came, the living leaping high to avoid the dying who clutched at their heels, the wounded cursing and staggering forward, till they fell—a torrent black as the sliding water above a mill-dam—full on the right flank of the square. Then the line of the dusty troops and the faint blue desert sky overhead went out in rolling smoke, and the little stones on the heated ground and the tinder-dry clumps of scrub became matters of surpassing interest, for men measured their agonized retreat and recovery by these things, counting mechanically and hewing their way back to chosen pebble and branch. There was no semblance of any concerted fighting. For aught the men knew, the enemy might be attempting all four sides of the square at once. Their business was to destroy what lay in front of them, to bayonet in the back those who passed over them, and, dying, to drag down the slayer till he could be knocked on the head by some avenging gun-butt. Dick waited with Torpenhow and a young doctor till the stress grew unendurable. It was hopeless to attend to the wounded till the attack was repulsed, so the three moved forward gingerly towards the weakest side of the square. There was a rush from without, the short *hough-hough* of the stabbing spears, and a man on a horse, followed by thirty or forty others, dashed through, yelling and hacking.

The right flank of the square sucked in after them, and the other sides sent help. The wounded, who knew that they had but a few hours more to live, caught at the enemy's feet and brought them down, or, staggering to a discarded rifle, fired blindly into the scuffle that raged in the centre of the square. Dick was conscious that somebody had cut him violently across his helmet, that he had fired his revolver into a black, foam-flecked face which forthwith ceased to bear any resemblance to a face, and that Torpenhow had gone down under an Arab whom he had tried to "collar low," and was turning over and over with his captive, feeling for the man's eyes. The doctor jabbed at a venture with a bayonet, and a helmetless soldier fired over Dick's shoulder: the flying grains of powder stung his cheek. It was to Torpenhow that Dick turned by instinct. The representative of the Central Southern Syndicate had shaken himself clear of his enemy, and rose, wiping his thumb on his trousers. The Arab, both hands to his forehead, screamed aloud, then snatched up his spear and rushed at Torpenhow, who was panting under shelter of Dick's revolver. Dick fired twice, and the man dropped limply. His upturned face lacked one eye. The musketry-fire redoubled, but cheers mingled with it. The rush had failed and the enemy were flying. If the heart of the square were shambles, the ground beyond was a butcher's shop. Dick thrust his way forward between the maddened men. The remnant of the enemy were retiring, as the few—the very few—English cavalry rode down the laggards.

Beyond the lines of the dead, a broad blood-stained Arab spear cast aside in the retreat lay across a stump of scrub, and beyond this again the illimitable dark levels of the desert. The sun caught the steel and turned it into a red disc. Some one behind him was saying, "Ah, get away, you brute!" Dick raised his revolver and pointed towards the desert. His eye was held by the red splash in the distance, and the clamour about him seemed to die down to a very far-away whisper, like the whisper of a level sea. There was the revolver and the red light, . . . and the voice of some one scaring something away, exactly as had fallen somewhere before,—probably in a past life. Dick waited for what should happen afterwards. Something seemed to crack inside his head, and for an instant he stood in the dark,—a darkness that stung. He fired at random, and the bullet went out across the desert as he muttered, "Spoilt my aim. There aren't any more cartridges. We shall have to run home." He put his hand to his head and brought it away covered with blood.

"Old man, you're cut rather badly," said Torpenhow. "I owe you something for this business. Thanks. Stand up! I say, you can't be ill here."

Dick had fallen stiffly on Torpenhow's shoulder, and muttered something about aiming low and to the left. Then he sank to the ground and was silent. Torpenhow dragged him off to a doctor and sat down to work out an account of what he was pleased to call "a sanguinary battle, in which our arms had acquitted themselves," etc.

Throughout that night, when the troops were encamped by the whale-boats, a black figure danced in the strong moonlight on the sand-bar and shouted that Khartoum the accursed one was dead,—was dead,—was dead,—that two steamers were rock-staked on the Nile outside the city, and that of all their crews there remained not one; and Khartoum was dead,—was dead,—was dead!

But Torpenhow took no heed. He was watching Dick, who called aloud to the restless Nile for Maisie,—and again Maisie!

"Behold a phenomenon," said Torpenhow, rearranging the blanket. "Here is a man, presumably human, who mentions the name of one woman only. And I've seen a good deal of delirium, too.—Dick, here's some fizzy drink."

"Thank you, Maisie," said Dick.

CHAPTER III

So he thinks he shall take to the sea again
For one more cruise with his buccaneers,
To singe the beard of the King of Spain,
And capture another Dean of Jaen
And sell him in Algiers.

—A DUTCH PICTURE. LONGFELLOW

THE Soudan campaign and Dick's broken head had been some months ended and mended, and the Central Southern Syndicate had paid Dick a certain sum on account for work done, which work they were careful to assure him was not altogether up to their standard. Dick heaved the letter into the Nile at Cairo, cashed the draft in the same town, and bade a warm farewell to Torpenhow at the station.

"I am going to lie up for a while and rest," said Torpenhow. "I don't know where I shall live in London, but if God brings us to meet, we shall meet. Are you staying here on the off-chance of another row? There will be none till the Southern Soudan is reoccupied by our troops. Mark that. Good-bye; bless you; come back when your money's spent; and give me your address."

Dick loitered in Cairo, Alexandria, Ismaïlia, and Port Said, —especially Port Said. There is iniquity in many parts of the world, and vice in all, but the concentrated essence of all the iniquities and all the vices in all the continents finds itself at Port Said. And through the heart of that sand-bordered hell, where the mirage flickers day long above the Bitter Lakes, move, if you will only wait, most of the men and women you have known in this life. Dick established himself in quarters more riotous than respectable. He spent his evenings on the quay, and boarded many ships, and saw very many friends,— gracious Englishwomen with whom he had talked not too wisely in the veranda of Shepheard's Hotel, hurrying war correspondents, skippers of the contract troop-ships employed in the campaign, army officers by the score, and others of less reputable trades. He had choice of all the races of the East and West for studies, and the advantage of seeing his subjects under the influence of strong excitement, at the gaming-tables, saloons, dancing-hells, and elsewhere. For recreation there was the straight vista of the Canal, the blazing sands, the procession of shipping, and the white hospitals where the English soldiers lay. He strove to set down in black and white and colour all that Providence sent him, and when that supply was ended sought about for fresh material. It was a fascinating employment, but it ran away with his money, and he had drawn in advance the hundred and twenty pounds to which he was entitled yearly. "Now I shall have to work and starve!" thought he, and was addressing himself to this new fate when a mysterious telegram arrived from Torpenhow in England, which said, "Come back, quick: you have caught on. Come."

A large smile overspread his face. "So soon! that's good hearing," said he to himself. "There will be an orgy to-night. I'll stand or fall by my luck. Faith, it's time it came!" He deposited half of his funds in the hands of his well-known friends Monsieur and Madame Binat, and ordered himself a Zanzibar dance of the finest. Monsieur Binat was shaking with drink, but Madame smiled sympathetically—

"Monsieur needs a chair, of course, and of course Monsieur will sketch: Monsieur amuses himself strangely."

Binat raised a blue-white face from a cot in the inner room. "I understand," he quavered. "We all know Monsieur. Monsieur is an artist, as I have been." Dick nodded. "In the end," said Binat, with gravity, "Monsieur will descend alive into hell, as I have descended." And he laughed.

"You must come to the dance too," said Dick; "I shall want you."

"For my face? I knew it would be so. For my face? My God! and for my degradation so tremendous! I will not. Take him away. He is a devil. Or at least do thou, Cèleste, demand of him more." The excellent Binat began to kick and scream.

"All things are for sale in Port Said," said Madame. "If my husband comes it will be so much more. Eh, 'ow you call— 'alf a sovereign."

The money was paid, and the mad dance was held at night in a walled courtyard at the back of Madame Binat's house. The lady herself, in faded mauve silk always about to slide from her yellow shoulders, played the piano, and to the tin-pot music of a Western waltz the naked Zanzibari girls danced furiously by the light of kerosene lamps. Binat sat upon a chair and stared with eyes that saw nothing, till the whirl of the dance and the clang of the rattling piano stole into the drink that took the place of blood in his veins, and his face glistened. Dick took him by the chin brutally and turned that face to the light. Madame Binat looked over her shoulder and smiled with many teeth. Dick leaned against the wall and sketched for an hour, till the kerosene lamps began to smell, and the girls threw themselves panting on the hard-beaten ground. Then he shut his book with a snap and moved away, Binat plucking feebly at his elbow. "Show me," he whimpered. "I too was once an artist, even I!" Dick showed him the rough sketch. "Am I that?" he screamed. "Will you take that away with you and show all the world that it is I,—Binat?" He moaned and wept.

"Monsieur has paid for all," said Madame. "To the pleasure of seeing Monsieur again."

The courtyard gate shut, and Dick hurried up the sandy street to the nearest gambling-hell, where he was well known. "If the luck holds, it's an omen; if I lose, I must stay here." He placed his money picturesquely about the board, hardly daring to look at what he did. The luck held. Three turns of the wheel left him richer by twenty pounds, and he went down to the shipping to make friends with the captain of a decayed cargo-steamer, who landed him in London with fewer pounds in his pocket than he cared to think about.

A thin gray fog hung over the city, and the streets were very cold; for summer was in England.

"It's a cheerful wilderness, and it hasn't the knack of altering much," Dick thought, as he tramped from the Docks westward. "Now, what must I do?"

The packed houses gave no answer. Dick looked down the long lightless streets and at the appalling rush of traffic. "Oh, you rabbit-hutches!" said he, addressing a row of highly respectable semi-detached residences. "Do you know what you've got to do later on? You have to supply me with men-servants and maid-servants,"—here he smacked his lips,—"and the peculiar treasure of kings. Meantime I'll get clothes and boots, and presently I will return and trample on you." He stepped forward energetically; he saw that one of his shoes was burst at the side. As he stooped to make investigations, a man jostled him into the gutter. "All right," he said. "That's another nick in the score. I'll jostle you later on."

Good clothes and boots are not cheap, and Dick left his last shop with the certainty that he would be respectably arrayed for a time, but with only fifty shillings in his pocket. He returned to streets by the Docks, and lodged himself in one room, where the sheets on the bed were almost audibly marked in case of theft, and where nobody seemed to go to bed at all. When his clothes arrived he sought the Central Southern Syndicate for Torpenhow's address, and got it, with the intimation that there was still some money owing to him.

"How much?" said Dick, as one who habitually dealt in millions.

"Between thirty and forty pounds. If it would be any convenience to you, of course we could let you have it at once; but we usually settle accounts monthly."

"If I show that I want anything now, I'm lost," he said to himself. "All I need I'll take later on." Then, aloud, "It's hardly worth while; and I'm going into the country for a month, too. Wait till I come back, and I'll see about it."

"But we trust, Mr. Heldar, that you do not intend to sever your connection with us?"

Dick's business in life was the study of faces, and he watched the speaker keenly. "That man means something," he said. "I'll do no business till I've seen Torpenhow. There's a big deal coming." So he departed, making no promises, to his one little room by the Docks. And that day was the seventh of the month, and that month, he reckoned with awful distinctness, had thirty-one days in it!

It is not easy for a man of catholic tastes and healthy appetites to exist for twenty-four days on fifty shillings. Nor is it cheering to begin the experiment alone in all the loneliness of London. Dick paid seven shillings a week for his lodging, which left him rather less than a shilling a day for food and drink. Naturally, his first purchase was of the materials of his craft; he had been without them too long. Half a day's investigation and comparison brought him to the conclusion that sausages and mashed potatoes, twopence a plate, were the best food. Now, sausages once or twice a week for breakfast are not unpleasant. As lunch, even, with mashed potatoes, they become monotonous. As dinner they are impertinent. At the end of three days Dick loathed sausages, and, going forth, pawned his watch to revel on sheep's head, which is not as cheap as it looks, owing to the bones and the gravy. Then he returned to sausages and mashed potatoes. Then he confined himself entirely to mashed potatoes for a day, and was unhappy because of pain in his inside. Then he pawned his waistcoat and his tie, and thought regretfully of money thrown away in times past. There are few things more edifying unto Art than the actual belly-pinch of hunger, and Dick in his few walks abroad—he did not care for exercise; it raised desires that could not be satisfied—found himself dividing mankind into two classes,—those who looked as if they might give him something to eat, and those who looked otherwise. "I never knew what I had to learn about the human face before," he thought; and, as a reward for his humility, Providence caused a cab-driver at a sausage-shop where Dick fed that night to leave half eaten a great chunk of bread. Dick took it,—would have fought all the world for its possession,—and it cheered him.

The month dragged through at last, and, nearly prancing with impatience, he went to draw his money. Then he hastened to Torpenhow's address and smelt the smell of cooking meats all along the corridors of the chambers. Torpenhow was on the top floor, and Dick burst into his room, to be received with a hug which nearly cracked his ribs, as Torpenhow dragged him to the light and spoke of twenty different things in the same breath.

"But you're looking tucked up," he concluded.

"Got anything to eat?" said Dick, his eye roaming round the room.

"I shall be having breakfast in a minute. What do you say to sausages?"

"No, anything but sausages! Torp, I've been starving on that accursed horse-flesh for thirty days and thirty nights."

"Now, what lunacy has been your latest?"

Dick spoke of the last few weeks with unbridled speech. Then he opened his coat; there was no waistcoat below. "I ran it fine, awfully fine, but I've just scraped through."

"You haven't much sense, but you've got a backbone, anyhow. Eat, and talk afterwards." Dick fell upon eggs and bacon and gorged till he could gorge no more. Torpenhow handed him a filled pipe, and he smoked as men smoke who for three weeks have been deprived of good tobacco.

"Ouf!" said he. "That's heavenly! Well?"

"Why in the world didn't you come to me?"

"Couldn't; I owe you too much already, old man. Besides I had a sort of superstition that this temporary starvation—that's what it was, and it hurt—would bring me more luck later. It's over and done with now and none of the syndicate know how hard up I was. Fire away. What's the exact state of affairs as regards myself?"

"You had my wire? You've caught on here. People like your work immensely. I don't know why, but they do. They say you have a fresh touch and a new way of drawing things. And, because they're chiefly home-bred English, they say you have insight. You're wanted by half a dozen papers; you're wanted to illustrate books."

Dick grunted scornfully.

"You're wanted to work up your smaller sketches and sell them to the dealers. They seem to think the money sunk in you is a good investment. Good Lord! who can account for the fathomless folly of the public?"

"They're a remarkably sensible people."

"They are subject to fits, if that's what you mean; and you happen to be the object of the latest fit among those who are interested in what they call Art. Just now you're a fashion, a phenomenon, or whatever you please. I appeared to be the only person who knew anything about you here, and I have been showing the most useful men a few of the sketches you gave me from time to time. Those coming after your work on the Central Southern Syndicate appear to have done your business. You're in luck."

"Huh! call it luck! Do call it luck, when a man has been kicking about the world like a dog, waiting for it to come! I'll luck 'em later on. I want a place to work in first."

"Come here," said Torpenhow, crossing the landing. "This place is a big box room really, but it will do for you. There's your skylight, or your north light, or whatever window you call it, and plenty of room to thrash about in, and a bedroom beyond. What more do you need?"

"Good enough," said Dick, looking round the large room that took up a third of a top story in the rickety chambers overlooking the Thames. A pale yellow sun shone through the skylight and showed the much dirt of the place. Three steps led from the door to the landing, and three more to Torpenhow's room. The well of the staircase disappeared into darkness, pricked by tiny gas-jets, and there were sounds of men talking and doors slamming seven flights below, in the warm gloom.

"Do they give you a free hand here?" said Dick, cautiously. He was Ishmael enough to know the value of liberty.

"Anything you like: latch-keys and license unlimited. We are permanent tenants for the most part here. 'Tisn't a place I would recommend for a Young Men's Christian Association, but it will serve. I took these rooms for you when I wired."

"You're a great deal too kind, old man."

"You didn't suppose you were going away from me, did

you?" Torpenhow put his hand on Dick's shoulder, and the two walked up and down the room, henceforward to be called the studio, in sweet and silent communion. They heard rapping at Torpenhow's door. "That's some ruffian come up for a drink," said Torpenhow; and he raised his voice cheerily. There entered no one more ruffianly than a portly middle-aged gentleman in a satin-faced frockcoat. His lips were parted and pale, and there were deep pouches under the eyes.

"Weak heart," said Dick to himself, and, as he shook hands, "very weak heart. His pulse is shaking his fingers."

The man introduced himself as the head of the Central Southern Syndicate and "one of the most ardent admirers of your work, Mr. Heldar. I assure you, in the name of the syndicate, that we are immensely indebted to you; and I trust, Mr. Heldar, you won't forget that we were largely instrumental in bringing you before the public." He panted because of the seven flights of stairs.

Dick glanced at Torpenhow whose left eyelid lay for a moment dead on his cheek.

"I shan't forget," said Dick, every instinct of defence roused in him. "You've paid me so well that I couldn't, you know. By the way, when I am settled in this place I should like to send and get my sketches. There must be nearly a hundred and fifty of them with you."

"That is er—is what I came to speak about. I fear we can't allow it exactly, Mr. Heldar. In the absence of any specified agreement, the sketches are our property, of course."

"Do you mean to say that you are going to keep them?"

"Yes; and we hope to have your help, on your own terms, Mr. Heldar, to assist us in arranging a little exhibition, which, backed by our name and the influence we naturally command among the press, should be of material service to you. Sketches such as yours——"

"Belong to me. You engaged me by wire, you paid me the lowest rates you dared. You can't mean to keep them! Good God alive, man, they're all I've got in the world!"

Torpenhow watched Dick's face and whistled.

Dick walked up and down, thinking. He saw the whole

of his little stock in trade, the first weapon of his equipment, annexed at the outset of his campaign by an elderly gentleman whose name Dick had not caught aright, who said that he represented a syndicate, which was a thing for which Dick had not the least reverence. The injustice of the proceedings did not much move him; he had seen the strong hand prevail too often in other places to be squeamish over the moral aspects of right and wrong. But he ardently desired the blood of the gentleman in the frockcoat, and when he spoke again it was with a strained sweetness that Torpenhow knew well for the beginning of strife.

"Forgive me, sir, but you have no—no younger man who can arrange this business with me?"

"I speak for the syndicate. I see no reason for a third party to——"

"You will in a minute. Be good enough to give back my sketches."

The man stared blankly at Dick, and then at Torpenhow, who was leaning against the wall. He was not used to ex-employees who ordered him to be good enough to do things.

"Yes, it is rather a cold-blooded steal," said Torpenhow, critically; "but I'm afraid, I am very much afraid, you've struck the wrong man. Be careful, Dick: remember, this isn't the Soudan."

"Considering what services the syndicate have done you in putting your name before the world——"

This was not a fortunate remark; it reminded Dick of certain vagrant years lived out in loneliness and strife and unsatisfied desires. The memory did not contrast well with the prosperous gentleman who proposed to enjoy the fruit of those years.

"I don't know quite what to do with you," began Dick, meditatively. "Of course you're a thief, and you ought to be half killed, but in your case you'd probably die. I don't want you dead on this floor, and, besides, it's unlucky just as one's moving in. Don't hit, sir; you'll only excite yourself." He put one hand on the man's forearm and ran the other down the plump body beneath the coat. "My goodness!" said he to

Torpenhow, "and this gray oaf dares to be a thief! I have seen an Esneh camel-driver have the black hide taken off his body in strips for stealing half a pound of wet dates, and *he* was as tough as whipcord. This thing's soft all over—like a woman."

There are few things more poignantly humiliating than being handled by a man who does not intend to strike. The head of the syndicate began to breathe heavily. Dick walked round him, pawing him, as a cat paws a soft hearth-rug. Then he traced with his forefinger the leaden pouches underneath the eyes, and shook his head. "You were going to steal my things,—mine, mine, mine!—you, who don't know when you may die. Write a note to your office,—you say you're the head of it,—and order them to give Torpenhow my sketches,—every one of them. Wait a minute: your hand's shaking. Now!" He thrust a pocket-book before him. The note was written. Torpenhow took it and departed without a word, while Dick walked round and round the spellbound captive, giving him such advice as he conceived best for the welfare of his soul. When Torpenhow returned with a gigantic portfolio, he heard Dick say, almost soothingly, "Now, I hope this will be a lesson to you; and if you worry me when I have settled down to work with any nonsense about actions for assault, believe me, I'll catch you and manhandle you, and you'll die. You haven't very long to live, anyhow. Go! *Imshi, Vootsak,*—get out!" The man departed, staggering and dazed. Dick drew a long breath: "Phew! what a lawless lot these people are! The first thing a poor orphan meets is gang robbery, organized burglary! Think of the hideous blackness of that man's mind! Are my sketches all right, Torp?"

"Yes; one hundred and forty-seven of them. Well, I *must* say, Dick, you've begun well."

"He was interfering with me. It only meant a few pounds to him, but it was everything to me. I don't think he'll bring an action. I gave him some medical advice gratis about the state of his body. It was cheap at the little flurry it cost him. Now, let's look at my things."

Two minutes later Dick had thrown himself down on the

floor and was deep in the portfolio, chuckling lovingly as he turned the drawings over and thought of the price at which they had been bought.

The afternoon was well advanced when Torpenhow came to the door and saw Dick dancing a wild saraband under the skylight.

"I builded better than I knew, Torp," he said, without stopping the dance. "They're good! They're damned good! They'll go like flame! I shall have an exhibition of them on my own brazen hook. And that man would have cheated me out of it! Do you know that I'm sorry now that I didn't actually hit him?"

"Go out," said Torpenhow,—"go out and pray to be delivered from the sin of arrogance, which you never will be. Bring your things up from whatever place you're staying in, and we'll try to make this barn a little more shipshape."

"And then—oh, then," said Dick, still capering, "we will spoil the Egyptians!"

CHAPTER IV

The wolf-cub at even lay hid in the corn,
When the smoke of the cooking hung gray:
He knew where the doe made a couch for her fawn,
And he looked to his strength for his prey.
But the moon swept the smoke-wreaths away.
And he turned from his meal in the villager's close,
And he bayed to the moon as she rose.

—IN SEONEE

"WELL, and how does success taste?" said Torpenhow, some three months later. He had just returned to chambers after a holiday in the country.

"Good," said Dick, as he sat licking his lips before the easel in the studio. "I want more,—heaps more. The lean years have passed, and I approve of these fat ones."

"Be careful, old man. That way lies bad work."

Torpenhow was sprawling in a long chair with a small

fox-terrier asleep on his chest, while Dick was preparing a canvas. A dais, a background, and a lay-figure were the only fixed objects in the place. They rose from a wreck of oddments that began with felt-covered water-bottles, belts, and regimental badges, and ended with a small bale of second-hand uniforms and a stand of mixed arms. The mark of muddy feet on the dais showed that a military model had just gone away. The watery autumn sunlight was failing, and shadows sat in the corners of the studio.

"Yes," said Dick, deliberately, "I like the power; I like the fun; I like the fuss; and above all I like the money. I almost like the people who make the fuss and pay the money. Almost. But they're a queer gang,—an amazingly queer gang!"

"They have been good enough to you, at any rate. That tin-pot exhibition of your sketches must have paid. Did you see that the papers called it the 'Wild Work Show'?"

"Never mind. I sold every shred of canvas I wanted to; and, on my word, I believe it was because they believed I was a self-taught flagstone artist. I should have got better prices if I had worked my things on wool or scratched them on camel-bone instead of using mere black and white and colour. Verily, they are a queer gang, these people. Limited isn't the word to describe 'em. I met a fellow the other day who told me that it was impossible that shadows on white sand should be blue,—ultramarine,—as they are. I found out, later, that that man had been as far as Brighton beach; but he knew all about Art, confound him. He gave me a lecture on it, and recommended me to go to school to learn technique. I wonder what old Kami would have said to that."

"When were you under Kami, man of extraordinary beginnings?"

"I studied with him for two years in Paris. He taught by personal magnetism. All he ever said was, *'Continuez, mes enfants,'* and you had to make the best you could of that. He had a divine touch, and he knew something about colour. Kami used to dream colour; I swear he could never have seen the genuine article; but he evolved it; and it was good."

"Recollect some of those views in the Soudan?" said Torpenhow, with a provoking drawl.

Dick squirmed in his place. "Don't! It makes me want to get out there again. What colour that was! Opal and umber and amber and claret and brick-red and sulphur—cockatoo-crest sulphur—against brown, with a nigger-black rock sticking up in the middle of it all, and a decorative frieze of camels festooning in front of a pure pale turquoise sky." He began to walk up and down. "And yet, you know, if you try to give these people the thing as God gave it, keyed down to their comprehension and according to the powers He has given you——"

"Modest man! Go on!"

"Half a dozen epicene young pagans who haven't even been to Algiers will tell you, first, that your notion is borrowed, and, secondly, that it isn't Art."

"This comes of my leaving town for a month. Dickie, you've been promenading among the toy-shops and hearing people talk."

"I couldn't help it," said Dick, penitently. "You weren't here, and it was lonely these long evenings. A man can't work for ever."

"A man might have gone to a pub, and got decently drunk."

"I wish I had; but I forgathered with some men of sorts. They said they were artists, and I knew some of them could draw,—but they wouldn't draw. They gave me tea,—tea at five in the afternoon!—and talked about Art and the state of their souls. As if their souls mattered. I've heard more about Art and seen less of her in the last six months than in the whole of my life. Do you remember Cassavetti, who worked for some continental syndicate, out with the desert column? He was a regular Christmas-tree of contraptions when he took the field in full fig, with his water-bottle, lanyard, revolver, writing-case, housewife, gig-lamps, and the Lord knows what all. He used to fiddle about with 'em and show us how they worked; but he never seemed to do much except fudge his reports from the Nilghai. See?"

"Dear old Nilghai! He's in town, fatter than ever. He

ought to be up here this evening. I see the comparison perfectly. You should have kept clear of all that man-millinery. Serves you right; and I hope it will unsettle your mind."

"It won't. It has taught me what Art—holy sacred Art—means."

"You've learnt something while I've been away. What is Art?"

"Give 'em what they know, and when you've done it once do it again." Dick dragged forward a canvas laid face to the wall. "Here's a sample of real Art. It's going to be a facsimile reproduction for a weekly. I called it 'His Last Shot.' It's worked up from the little water-colour I made outside El Maghrib. Well, I lured my model, a beautiful rifleman, up here with drink; I drored him, and I redrored him, and I tredrored him, and I made him a flushed, dishevelled, bedevilled scallawag, with his helmet at the back of his head, and the living fear of death in his eye, and the blood oozing out of a cut over his ankle-bone. He wasn't pretty, but he was all soldier and very much man."

"Once more, modest child!"

Dick laughed. "Well, it's only to you I'm talking. I did him just as well as I knew how, making allowance for the slickness of oils. Then the art-manager of that abandoned paper said that his subscribers wouldn't like it. It was brutal and coarse and violent,—man being naturally gentle when he's fighting for his life. They wanted something more restful, with a little more colour. I could have said a good deal, but you might as well talk to a sheep as an art-manager. I took my 'Last Shot' back. Behold the result! I put him into a lovely red coat without a speck on it. That is Art. I polished his boots,—observe the high light on the toe. That is Art. I cleaned his rifle,—rifles are always clean on service,—because that is Art. I pipeclayed his helmet,—pipeclay is always used on active service, and is indispensable to Art. I shaved his chin, I washed his hands, and gave him an air of fatted peace. Result, military tailor's pattern-plate. Price, thank Heaven, twice as much as for the first sketch, which was moderately decent."

"And do you suppose you're going to give that thing out as your work?"

"Why not? I did it. Alone I did it, in the interests of sacred, home-bred Art and *Dickenson's Weekly*."

Torpenhow smoked in silence for a while. Then came the verdict, delivered from rolling clouds: "If you were only a mass of blathering vanity, Dick, I wouldn't mind,—I'd let you go to the deuce on your own mahl-stick; but when I consider what you are to me, and when I find that to vanity you add the twopenny-halfpenny pique of a twelve-year-old girl, then I bestir myself in your behalf. Thus!"

The canvas ripped as Torpenhow's booted foot shot through it, and the terrier jumped down, thinking rats were about.

"If you have any bad language to use, use it. You have not. I continue. You are an idiot, because no man born of woman is strong enough to take liberties with his public, even though they be—which they ain't—all you say they are."

"But they don't know any better. What can you expect from creatures born and bred in this light?" Dick pointed to the yellow fog. "If they want furniture-polish, let them have furniture-polish, so long as they pay for it. They are only men and women. You talk as though they were gods."

"That sounds very fine, but it has nothing to do with the case. They are the people you have to work for, whether you like it or not. They are your masters. Don't be deceived, Dickie, you aren't strong enough to trifle with them,—or with yourself, which is more important. Moreover,—Come back, Binkie: that red daub isn't going anywhere,—unless you take precious good care, you will fall under the damnation of the check-book, and that's worse than death. You will get drunk —you're half drunk already—on easily acquired money. For that money and your own infernal vanity you are willing to deliberately turn out bad work. You'll do quite enough bad work without knowing it. And, Dickie, as I love you and as I know you love me, I am not going to let you cut off your nose to spite your face for all the gold in England. That's settled. Now swear."

"Don't know," said Dick. "I've been trying to make myself angry, but I can't, you're so abominably reasonable. There will be a row on *Dickenson's Weekly,* I fancy."

"Why the Dickenson do you want to work on a weekly paper? It's slow bleeding of power."

"It brings in the very desirable dollars," said Dick, his hands in his pockets.

Torpenhow watched him with large contempt. "Why, I thought it was a man!" said he. "It's a child."

"No, it isn't," said Dick, wheeling quickly. "You've no notion what the certainty of cash means to a man who has always wanted it badly. Nothing will pay me for some of my life's joys; on that Chinese pig-boat, for instance, when we ate bread and jam for every meal, because Ho-Wang wouldn't allow us anything better, and it all tasted of pig,—Chinese pig. I've worked for this, I've sweated and I've starved for this, line on line and month after month. And now I've got it I am going to make the most of it while it lasts. Let them pay—they've no knowledge."

"What does Your Majesty please to want? You can't smoke more than you do; you won't drink; you're a gross feeder; and you dress in the dark, by the look of you. You wouldn't keep a horse the other day when I suggested, because, you said, it might fall lame, and whenever you cross the street you take a hansom. Even you are not foolish enough to suppose that theatres and all the live things you can buy thereabouts mean Life. What earthly need have you for money?"

"It's there, bless its golden heart," said Dick. "It's there all the time. Providence has sent me nuts while I have teeth to crack 'em with. I haven't yet found the nut I wish to crack, but I'm keeping my teeth filed. Perhaps some day you and I will go for a walk round the wide earth."

"With no work to do, nobody to worry us, and nobody to compete with? You would be unfit to speak to in a week. Besides, I shouldn't go. I don't care to profit by the price of a man's soul,—for that's what it would mean. Dick, it's no use arguing. You're a fool."

"Don't see it. When I was on that Chinese pig-boat, our

captain got credit for saving about twenty-five thousand very seasick little pigs, when our old tramp of a steamer fell foul of a timber-junk. Now, taking those pigs as a parallel——"

"Oh, confound your parallels! Whenever I try to improve your soul, you always drag in some anecdote from your very shady past. Pigs aren't the British public; and self-respect is self-respect the world over. Go out for a walk and try to catch some self-respect. And, I say, if the Nilghai comes up this evening can I show him your diggings?"

"Surely." And Dick departed, to take counsel with himself in the rapidly gathering London fog.

Half an hour after he had left, the Nilghai laboured up the staircase. He was the chiefest, as he was the hugest, of the war correspondents, and his experiences dated from the birth of the needle-gun. Saving only his ally, Keneu the Great War Eagle, there was no man higher in the craft than he, and he always opened his conversation with the news that there would be trouble in the Balkans in the spring. Torpenhow laughed as he entered.

"Never mind the trouble in the Balkans. Those little states are always screeching. You've heard about Dick's luck?"

"Yes; he has been called up to notoriety, hasn't he? I hope you keep him properly humble. He wants suppressing from time to time."

"He does. He's beginning to take liberties with what he thinks is his reputation."

"Already! By Jove, he *has* cheek! I don't know about his reputation, but he'll come a cropper if he tries that sort of thing."

"So I told him. I don't think he believes it."

"They never do when they first start off. What's that wreck on the ground there?"

"Specimen of his latest impertinence." Torpenhow thrust the torn edges of the canvas together and showed the well-groomed picture to the Nilghai, who looked at it for a moment and whistled.

"It's a chromo," said he,—"a chromo-litholeo-margarine fake! What possessed him to do it? And yet how thoroughly he has caught the note that catches a public who think with their boots and read with their elbows! The cold-blooded insolence of the work almost saves it; but he mustn't go on with this. Hasn't he been praised and cockered up too much? You know these people here have no sense of proportion. They'll call him a second Detaille and a third-hand Meissonier while his fashion lasts. It's windy diet for a colt."

"I don't think it affects Dick much. You might as well call a young wolf a lion and expect him to take the compliment in exchange for a shin-bone. Dick's soul is in the bank. He's working for cash."

"Now he has thrown up war work, I suppose he doesn't see that the obligations of the service are just the same, only the proprietors are changed."

"How should he know? He thinks he is his own master."

"Does he? I could undeceive him for his good, if there's any virtue in print. He wants the whip-lash."

"Lay it on with science, then. I'd flay him myself, but I like him too much."

"I've no scruples. He had the audacity to try to cut me out with a woman at Cairo once. I forgot that, but I remember now."

"*Did* he cut you out?"

"You'll see when I have dealt with him. But, after all, what's the good? Leave him alone and he'll come home, if he has any stuff in him, dragging or wagging his tail behind him. There's more in a week of life than in a lively weekly. None the less I'll slate him. I'll slate him ponderously in the *Cataclysm*."

"Good luck to you; but I fancy nothing short of a crow-bar would make Dick wince. His soul seems to have been fired before we came across him. He's intensely suspicious and utterly lawless."

"Matter of temper," said the Nilghai. "It's the same with horses. Some you wallop and they work, some you wallop and they jib, and some you wallop and they go out for a walk with their hands in their pockets."

"That's exactly what Dick has done," said Torpenhow.

"Wait till he comes back. In the meantime, you can begin your slating here. I'll show you some of his last and worst work in his studio."

Dick had instinctively sought running water for a comfort to his mood of mind. He was leaning over the Embankment wall, watching the rush of the Thames through the arches of Westminster Bridge. He began by thinking of Torpenhow's advice, but, as of custom, lost himself in the study of the faces flocking past. Some had death written on their features, and Dick marvelled that they could laugh. Others, clumsy and coarse-built for the most part, were alight with love; others were merely drawn and lined with work; but there was something, Dick knew, to be made out of them all. The poor at least should suffer that he might learn, and the rich should pay for the output of his learning. Thus his credit in the world and his cash balance at the bank would be increased. So much the better for him. He had suffered. Now he would take toll of the ills of others.

The fog was driven apart for a moment, and the sun shone, a blood-red wafer, on the water. Dick watched the spot till he heard the voice of the tide between the piers die down like the wash of the sea at low tide. A girl hard pressed by her lover shouted shamelessly, "Ah, get away, you beast!" and a shift of the same wind that had opened the fog drove across Dick's face the black smoke of a river-steamer at her berth below the wall. He was blinded for the moment, then spun round and found himself face to face with—Maisie.

There was no mistaking. The years had turned the child to a woman, but they had not altered the dark-gray eyes, the thin scarlet lips, or the firmly modelled mouth and chin; and, that all should be as it was of old, she wore a closely fitting gray dress.

Since the human soul is finite and not in the least under its own command, Dick, advancing, said, "Halloo!" after the manner of schoolboys, and Maisie answered, "Oh, Dick, is that you?" Then, against his will, and before the brain newly released from considerations of the cash balance had time to dictate to the nerves, every pulse of Dick's body throbbed furiously and his palate dried in his mouth. The fog shut down again, and Maisie's face was pearl-white through it. No word was spoken, but Dick fell into step at her side, and the two paced the Embankment together, keeping the step as perfectly as in their afternoon excursions to the mudflats. Then Dick, a little hoarsely—

"What has happened to Amomma?"

"He died, Dick. Not cartridges; over-eating. He was always greedy. Isn't it funny?"

"Yes. No. Do you mean Amomma?"

"Ye—es. No. This. Where have you come from?"

"Over there." He pointed eastward through the fog. "And you?"

"Oh, I'm in the north,—the black north, across all the Park. I am very busy."

"What do you do?"

"I paint a great deal. That's all I have to do."

"Why, what's happened? You had three hundred a year."

"I have that still. I am painting; that's all."

"Are you alone, then?"

"There's a girl living with me. Don't walk so fast, Dick; you're out of step."

"Then you noticed it too?"

"Of course I did. You're always out of step."

"So I am. I'm sorry. You went on with the painting?"

"Of course. I said I should. I was at the Slade, then at Merton's in St. John's Wood, the big studio, then I pepper-potted,—I mean I went to the National,—and now I'm working under Kami."

"But Kami is in Paris surely?"

"No; he has his teaching studio at Vitry-sur-Marne. I work with him in the summer, and I live in London in the winter. I'm a householder."

"Do you sell much?"

"Now and again, but not often. There is my 'bus. I must take it or lose half an hour. Good-bye, Dick."

"Good-bye, Maisie. Won't you tell me where you live? I

must see you again; and perhaps I could help you. I—I paint a little myself."

"I may be in the Park to-morrow, if there is no working light. I walk from the Marble Arch down and back again; that is my little excursion. But of course I shall see you again." She stepped into the omnibus and was swallowed up by the fog.

"Well—I—am—damned!" exclaimed Dick, and returned to the chambers.

Torpenhow and the Nilghai found him sitting on the steps to the studio door, repeating the phrase with an awful gravity.

"You'll be more damned when I'm done with you," said the Nilghai, upheaving his bulk from behind Torpenhow's shoulder and waving a sheaf of half-dry manuscript. "Dick, it is of common report that you are suffering from swelled head."

"Halloo, Nilghai. Back again? How are the Balkans and all the little Balkans? One side of your face is out of drawing, as usual."

"Never mind that. I am commissioned to smite you in print. Torpenhow refuses from false delicacy. I've been overhauling the pot-boilers in your studio. They are simply disgraceful."

"Oho! that's it, is it? If you think you can slate me, you're wrong. You can only describe, and you need as much room to turn in, on paper, as a P. and O. cargo-boat. But continue, and be swift. I'm going to bed."

"H'm! h'm h'm! The first part only deals with your pictures. Here's the peroration: 'For work done without conviction, for power wasted on trivialities, for labour expended with levity for the deliberate purpose of winning the easy applause of a fashion-driven public——' "

"That's 'His Last Shot,' second edition. Go on."

"——'public, there remains but one end,—the oblivion that is preceded by toleration and cenotaphed with contempt. From that fate Mr. Heldar has yet to prove himself out of danger.' "

"*Wow—wow—wow—wow—wow!*" said Dick, profanely.

"It's a clumsy ending and vile journalese, but it's quite true. And yet,"—he sprang to his feet and snatched at the manuscript,—"you scarred, deboshed, battered old gladiator! you're sent out when a war begins, to minister to the blind, brutal, British public's bestial thirst for blood. They have no arenas now, but they must have special correspondents. You're a fat gladiator who comes up through a trap-door and talks of what he's seen. You stand on precisely the same level as an energetic bishop, an affable actress, a devastating cyclone, or —mine own sweet self. And you presume to lecture me about my work! Nilghai, if it were worth while I'd caricature you in four papers!"

The Nilghai winced. He had not thought of this.

"As it is, I shall take this stuff and tear it small—so!" The manuscript fluttered in slips down the dark well of the staircase. "Go home, Nilghai," said Dick; "go home to your lonely little bed, and leave me in peace. I am about to turn in till to-morrow."

"Why, it isn't seven yet!" said Torpenhow, with amazement.

"It shall be two in the morning, if I choose," said Dick, backing to the studio door. "I go to grapple with a serious crisis, and I shan't want any dinner."

The door shut and was locked.

"What can you do with a man like that?" said the Nilghai.

"Leave him alone. He's as mad as a hatter."

At eleven there was a kicking on the studio door. "Is the Nilghai with you still?" said a voice from within. "Then tell him he might have condensed the whole of his lumbering nonsense into an epigram: 'Only the free are bond, and only the bond are free.' Tell him he's an idiot, Torp, and tell him I'm another."

"All right. Come out and have supper. You're smoking on an empty stomach."

There was no answer.

CHAPTER V

"I have a thousand men," said he,
"To wait upon my will,
And towers nine upon the Tyne,
And three upon the Till."

"And what care I for your men," said she,
"Or towers from Tyne to Till,
Sith you must go with me," she said,
"To wait upon my will?"

—SIR HOGGIE AND THE FAIRIES

NEXT morning Torpenhow found Dick sunk in deepest repose of tobacco.

"Well, madman, how d'you feel?"

"I don't know. I'm trying to find out."

"You had much better do some work."

"Maybe; but I'm in no hurry. I've made a discovery. Torp, there's too much Ego in my Cosmos."

"Not really! Is this revelation due to my lectures, or the Nilghai's?"

"It came to me suddenly, all on my own account. Much too much Ego; and now I'm going to work."

He turned over a few half-finished sketches, drummed on a new canvas, cleaned three brushes, set Binkie to bite the toes of the lay-figure, rattled through his collection of arms and accoutrements, and then went out abruptly, declaring that he had done enough for the day.

"This is positively indecent," said Torpenhow, "and the first time that Dick has ever broken up a light morning. Perhaps he has found out that he has a soul, or an artistic temperament, or something equally valuable. That comes of leaving him alone for a month. Perhaps he has been going out of evenings. I must look to this." He rang for the bald-headed old housekeeper, whom nothing could astonish or annoy.

"Beeton, did Mr. Heldar dine out at all while I was out of town?"

"Never laid 'is dress-clothes out once, sir, all the time. Mostly 'e dined in; but 'e brought some most remarkable fancy young gentlemen up 'ere after theatres once or twice. Remarkable fancy they was. You gentlemen on the top floor does very much as you likes, but it do seem to me, sir, droppin' a walkin'-stick down five flights o' stairs an' then goin' down four abreast to pick it up again at half-past two in the mornin', singin' 'Bring back the whiskey, Willie darlin','—not once or twice, but scores o' times,—isn't charity to the other tenants. What I say is, 'Do as you would be done by.' That's my motto."

"Of course! of course! I'm afraid the top floor isn't the quietest in the house."

"I make no complaints, sir. I have spoke to Mr. Heldar friendly, an' he laughed, an' did me a picture of the missis that is as good as a coloured print. It 'asn't the 'igh shine of a photograph, but what I say is, 'Never look a gift-horse in the mouth.' Mr. Heldar's dress-clothes 'aven't been on him for weeks."

"Then it's all right," said Torpenhow to himself. "Orgies are healthy, and Dick has a head of his own, but when it comes to women making eyes I'm not so certain,—Binkie, never you be a man, little dorglums. They're contrary brutes, and they do things without any reason."

Dick had turned northward across the Park, but he was walking in the spirit on the mud-flats with Maisie. He laughed aloud as he remembered the day when he had decked Amomma's horns with the ham-frills, and Maisie, white with rage, had cuffed him. How long those four years seemed in review, and how closely Maisie was connected with every hour of them! Storm across the sea, and Maisie in a gray dress on the beach, sweeping her drenched hair out of her eyes and laughing at the homeward race of the fishing-smacks; hot sunshine on the mud-flats, and Maisie sniffing scornfully, with her chin in the air; Maisie flying before the wind that threshed the foreshore and drove the sand like small shot about her ears; Maisie, very composed and independent, telling lies to Mrs. Jennett while Dick supported her with coarser perjuries; Maisie picking her way delicately from stone to stone, a pistol in her hand and her teeth firm-set; and Maisie in a gray dress sitting on the grass between the mouth of a cannon and a nodding yellow sea-poppy. The pictures passed before him one by one, and the last stayed the longest. Dick was perfectly happy with a quiet peace that was as new to his mind as it was foreign to his experience. It never occurred to him that there might be other calls upon his time than loafing across the Park in the forenoon.

"There's a good working light now," he said, watching his shadow placidly. "Some poor devil ought to be grateful for this. And there's Maisie."

She was walking towards him from the Marble Arch, and he saw that no mannerism of her gait had been changed. It was good to find her still Maisie, and, so to speak, his next-door neighbour. No greeting passed between them, because there had been none in the old days.

"What are you doing out of your studio at this hour?" said Dick, as one who was entitled to ask.

"Idling. Just idling. I got angry with a chin and scraped it out. Then I left it in a little heap of paint-chips and came away."

"I know what palette-knifing means. What was the piccy?"

"A fancy head that wouldn't come right,—horrid thing!"

"I don't like working over scraped paint when I'm doing flesh. The grain comes up woolly as the paint dries."

"Not if you scrape properly." Maisie waved her hand to illustrate her methods. There was a dab of paint on the white cuff. Dick laughed.

"You're as untidy as ever."

"That comes well from you. Look at your own cuff."

"By Jove, yes! It's worse than yours. I don't think we've much altered in anything. Let's see, though." He looked at Maisie critically. The pale blue haze of an autumn day crept between the tree-trunks of the Park and made a background for the gray dress, the black velvet toque above the black hair, and the resolute profile.

"No, there's nothing changed. How good it is! D'you remember when I fastened your hair into the snap of a handbag?"

Maisie nodded, with a twinkle in her eyes, and turned her full face to Dick.

"Wait a minute," said he. "That mouth is down at the corners a little. Who's been worrying you, Maisie?"

"No one but myself. I never seem to get on with my work, and yet I try hard enough, and Kami says——"

"'*Continuez, mesdemoiselles. Continuez toujours, mes enfants.*' Kami is depressing. I beg your pardon."

"Yes, that's what he says. He told me last summer that I was doing better and he'd let me exhibit this year."

"Not in this place, surely?"

"Of course not. The Salon."

"You fly high."

"I've been beating my wings long enough. Where do you exhibit, Dick?"

"I don't exhibit. I sell."

"What is your line, then?"

"Haven't you heard?" Dick's eyes opened. Was this thing possible? He cast about for some means of conviction. They were not far from the Marble Arch. "Come up Oxford Street a little and I'll show you."

A small knot of people stood round a print-shop that Dick knew well. "Some reproduction of my work inside," he said, with suppressed triumph. Never before had success tasted so sweet upon the tongue. "You see the sort of things I paint. D'you like it?"

Maisie looked at the wild whirling rush of a field-battery going into action under fire. Two artillerymen stood behind her in the crowd.

"They've chucked the off lead-'orse," said one to the other. "'E's tore up awful, but they're makin' good time with the others. That lead-driver drives better nor you, Tom. See 'ow cunnin' 'e's nursin' 'is 'orse."

"Number Three'll be off the limber, next jolt," was the answer.

"No, 'e won't. See 'ow 'is foot's braced against the iron? 'E's all right."

Dick watched Maisie's face and swelled with joy—fine, rank, vulgar triumph. She was more interested in the little crowd than in the picture. That was something that she could understand.

"And I wanted it so! Oh, I did want it so!" she said at last, under her breath.

"Me,—all me!" said Dick, placidly. "Look at their faces. It hits 'em. They don't know what makes their eyes and mouths open; but I know. And I know my work's right."

"Yes. I see. Oh, what a thing to have come to one!"

"Come to one, indeed! I had to go out and look for it. What do you think?"

"I call it success. Tell me how you got it."

They returned to the Park, and Dick delivered himself of the saga of his own doings, with all the arrogance of a young man speaking to a woman. From the beginning he told the tale, the I—I—I's flashing through the records as telegraph-poles fly past the traveller. Maisie listened and nodded her head. The histories of strife and privation did not move her a hair's-breadth. At the end of each canto he would conclude, "And *that* gave me some notion of handling colour," or light, or whatever it might be that he had set out to pursue and understand. He led her breathless across half the world, speaking as he had never spoken in his life before. And in the flood-tide of his exaltation there came upon him a great desire to pick up this maiden who nodded her head and said, "I understand. Go on,"—to pick her up and carry her away with him, because she was Maisie, and because she understood, and because she was his right, and a woman to be desired above all women.

Then he checked himself abruptly. "And so I took all I wanted," he said, "and I had to fight for it. Now you tell."

Maisie's tale was almost as gray as her dress. It covered years of patient toil backed by savage pride that would not be broken though dealers laughed, and fogs delayed work, and Kami was unkind and even sarcastic, and girls in other studios were painfully polite. It had a few bright spots, in pictures accepted at provincial exhibitions, but it wound up with the oft repeated wail, "And so you see, Dick, I had no success, though I worked so hard."

Then pity filled Dick. Even thus had Maisie spoken when she could not hit the breakwater, half an hour before she had kissed him. And that had happened yesterday.

"Never mind," he said. "I'll tell you something, if you'll believe it." The words were shaping themselves of their own accord. "The whole thing, lock, stock, and barrel, isn't worth one big yellow sea-poppy below Fort Keeling."

Maisie flushed a little. "It's all very well for you to talk, but you've had the success and I haven't."

"Let me talk, then. I know you'll understand. Maisie, dear, it sounds a bit absurd, but those ten years never existed, and I've come back again. It really is just the same. Can't you see? You're alone now and I'm alone. What's the use of worrying? Come to me instead, darling."

Maisie poked the gravel with her parasol. They were sitting on a bench. "I understand," she said slowly. "But I've got my work to do, and I must do it."

"Do it with me, then, dear. I won't interrupt."

"No, I couldn't. It's my work,—mine,—mine,—mine! I've been alone all my life in myself, and I'm not going to belong to anybody except myself. I remember things as well as you do, but that doesn't count. We were babies then, and we didn't know what was before us. Dick, don't be selfish. I think I see my way to a little success next year. Don't take it away from me."

"I beg your pardon, darling. It's my fault for speaking stupidly. I can't expect you to throw up all your life just because I'm back. I'll go to my own place and wait a little."

"But, Dick, I don't want you to—go—out of—my life, now you've just come back."

"I'm at your orders; forgive me." Dick devoured the troubled little face with his eyes. There was triumph in them, because he could not conceive that Maisie should refuse sooner or later to love him, since he loved her.

"It's wrong of me," said Maisie, more slowly than before; "it's wrong and selfish; but, oh, I've been so lonely! No, you misunderstand. Now I've seen you again,—it's absurd, but I want to keep you in my life."

"Naturally. We belong."

"We don't; but you always understood me, and there is so much in my work that you could help me in. You know things and the ways of doing things. You must."

"I do, I fancy, or else I don't know myself. Then you won't care to lose sight of me altogether, and—you want me to help you in your work?"

"Yes; but remember, Dick, nothing will ever come of it. That's why I feel so selfish. Can't things stay as they are? I do want your help."

"You shall have it. But let's consider. I must see your pics first, and overhaul your sketches, and find out about your tendencies. You should see what the papers say about my tendencies! Then I'll give you good advice, and you shall paint according. Isn't that it, Maisie?"

Again there was triumph in Dick's eye.

"It's too good for you,—much too good. Because you are consoling yourself with what will never happen, and I know that, and yet I want to keep you. Don't blame me later, please."

"I'm going into the matter with my eyes open. Moreover the Queen can do no wrong. It isn't your selfishness that impresses me. It's your audacity in proposing to make use of me."

"Pooh! You're only Dick,—and a print-shop."

"Very good: that's all I am. But, Maisie, you believe, don't you, that I love you? I don't want you to have any false notions about brothers and sisters."

Maisie looked up for a moment and dropped her eyes.

"It's absurd, but—I believe. I wish I could send you away before you get angry with me. But—but the girl that lives with me is red-haired, and an impressionist, and all our notions clash."

"So do ours, I think. Never mind. Three months from to-day we shall be laughing at this together."

Maisie shook her head mournfully. "I knew you wouldn't

understand, and it will only hurt you more when you find out. Look at my face, Dick, and tell me what you see."

They stood up and faced each other for a moment. The fog was gathering, and it stifled the roar of the traffic of London beyond the railings. Dick brought all his painfully acquired knowledge of faces to bear on the eyes, mouth, and chin underneath the black velvet toque.

"It's the same Maisie, and it's the same me," he said. "We've both nice little wills of our own, and one or other of us has to be broken. Now about the future. I must come and see your pictures some day,—I suppose when the red-haired girl is on the premises."

"Sundays are my best times. You must come on Sundays. There are such heaps of things I want to talk about and ask your advice about. Now I must get back to work."

"Try to find out before next Sunday what I am," said Dick. "Don't take my word for anything I've told you. Good-bye, darling, and bless you."

Maisie stole away like a little gray mouse. Dick watched her till she was out of sight, but he did not hear her say to herself, very soberly, "I'm a wretch,—a horrid, selfish wretch. But it's Dick, and Dick will understand."

No one has yet explained what actually happens when an irresistible force meets the immovable post, though many have thought deeply, even as Dick thought. He tried to assure himself that Maisie would be led in a few weeks by his mere presence and discourse to a better way of thinking. Then he remembered much too distinctly her face and all that was written on it.

"If I know anything of heads," he said, "there's everything in that face but love. I shall have to put that in myself; and that chin and mouth won't be won for nothing. But she's right. She knows what she wants, and she's going to get it. What insolence! Me! Of all the people in the wide world, to use me! But then she's Maisie. There's no getting over that fact; and it's good to see her again. This business must have been simmering at the back of my head for years. . . . She'll use me as I used Binat at Port Said. She's quite right. It will hurt a little. I shall have to see her every Sunday,—like a young man courting a housemaid. She's sure to come round; and yet—that mouth isn't a yielding mouth. I shall be wanting to kiss her all the time, and I shall have to look at her pictures,—I don't even know what sort of work she does yet,—and I shall have to talk about Art,—Woman's Art! Therefore, particularly and perpetually, damn all varieties of Art. It did me a good turn once, and now it's in my way. I'll go home and do some Art."

Half-way to the studio, Dick was smitten with a terrible thought. The figure of a solitary woman in the fog suggested it.

"She's all alone in London, with a red-haired impressionist girl, who probably has the digestion of an ostrich. Most red-haired people have. Maisie's a bilious little body. They'll eat like lone women,—meals at all hours, and tea with all meals. I remember how the students in Paris used to pig along. She may fall ill at any minute, and I shan't be able to help. Whew! this is ten times worse than owning a wife."

Torpenhow entered the studio at dusk, and looked at Dick with eyes full of the austere love that springs up between men who have tugged at the same oar together and are yoked by custom and use and the intimacies of toil. This is a good love, and, since it allows, and even encourages, strife, recrimination, and brutal sincerity, does not die, but grows, and is proof against any absence and evil conduct.

Dick was silent after he handed Torpenhow the filled pipe of council. He thought of Maisie and her possible needs. It was a new thing to think of anybody but Torpenhow, who could think for himself. Here at last was an outlet for that cash balance. He could adorn Maisie barbarically with jewellery,—a thick gold necklace round that little neck, bracelets upon the rounded arms, and rings of price upon her hands,—the cool, temperate, ringless hands that he had taken between his own. It was an absurd thought, for Maisie would not even allow him to put one ring on one finger, and she would laugh at golden trappings. It would be better to sit with her quietly in the dusk, his arm around her neck and her face on his shoulder, as befitted husband and wife. Torpenhow's boots creaked that night, and his strong face jarred. Dick's brows contracted and he murmured an evil word because he had taken all his success as a right and part payment for past discomfort, and now he was checked in his stride by a woman who admitted all the success and did not instantly care for him.

"I say, old man," said Torpenhow, who had made one or two vain attempts at conversation, "I haven't put your back up by anything I've said lately, have I?"

"You? No. How could you?"

"Liver out of order?"

"The truly healthy man doesn't know he has a liver. I'm only a bit worried about things in general. I suppose it's my soul."

"The truly healthy man doesn't know he has a soul. What business have you with luxuries of that kind?"

"It came of itself. Who's the man that says that we're all islands shouting lies to each other across seas of misunderstanding?"

"He's right, whoever he is,—except about the misunderstanding. I don't think we could misunderstand each other."

The blue smoke curled back from the ceiling in clouds. Then Torpenhow, insinuatingly—

"Dick, is it a woman?"

"Be hanged if it's anything remotely resembling a woman; and if you begin to talk like that, I'll hire a red-brick studio with white paint trimmings, and begonias and petunias and blue Hungarias to play among three-and-sixpenny pot-palms, and I'll mount all my pics in aniline-dye plush plasters, and I'll invite every woman who maunders over what her guide-books tell her is Art, and you shall receive 'em, Torp,—in a snuff-brown velvet coat with yellow trousers and an orange tie. You'll like that?"

"Too thin, Dick. A better man than you once denied with cursing and swearing. You've overdone it, just as he did. It's no business of mine, of course, but it's comforting to think that somewhere under the stars there's saving up for you a tremendous thrashing. Whether it'll come from heaven or earth, I don't know, but it's bound to come and break you up a little. You want hammering."

Dick shivered. "All right," said he. "When this island is disintegrated, it will call for you."

"I shall come round the corner and help to disintegrate it some more. We're talking nonsense. Come along to a theatre."

CHAPTER VI

"And you may lead a thousand men,
Nor ever draw the rein,
But ere ye lead the Faery Queen
'Twill burst your heart in twain."

He has slipped his foot from the stirrup-bar,
The bridle from his hand,
And he is bound by hand and foot
To the Queen o' Faery-land.

—SIR HOGGIE AND THE FAIRIES

SOME weeks later, on a very foggy Sunday, Dick was returning across the Park to his studio. "This," he said, "is evidently the thrashing that Torp meant. It hurts more than I expected; but the Queen can do no wrong; and she certainly has some notion of drawing."

He had just finished a Sunday visit to Maisie,—always under the green eyes of the red-haired impressionist girl, whom he learned to hate at sight,—and was tingling with a keen sense of shame. Sunday after Sunday, putting on his best clothes, he had walked over to the untidy house north of the Park, first to see Maisie's pictures, and then to criticize and advise upon them as he realized that they were productions on which advice would not be wasted. Sunday after Sunday, and his love grew with each visit, he had been compelled to cram his heart back from between his lips when it prompted him to kiss Maisie several times and very much indeed. Sunday after Sunday, the head above the heart had warned him that Maisie was not yet attainable, and that it would be better to talk as connectedly as possible upon the mysteries of the craft that was all in all to her. Therefore it was his fate to endure weekly torture in the studio built out over the clammy back-garden of a frail stuffy little villa where nothing was ever in its right place and nobody ever called,—to endure and to watch Maisie moving to and fro with the teacups. He abhorred tea, but, since it gave him a little longer time in her presence, he drank it devoutly, and the red-haired girl sat in an untidy heap and eyed him without speaking. She was always watching him. Once, and only once, when she had left the studio, Maisie showed him an album that held a few poor cuttings from provincial papers,—the briefest of hurried notes on some of her pictures sent to outlying exhibitions. Dick stooped and kissed the paint-smudged thumb on the open page. "Oh, my love, my love," he muttered, "do you value these things? Chuck 'em into the waste-paper basket!"

"Not till I get something better," said Maisie, shutting the book.

Then Dick, moved by no respect for his public and a very deep regard for the maiden, did deliberately propose, in order to secure more of these coveted cuttings, that he should paint a picture which Maisie should sign.

"That's childish," said Maisie, "and I didn't think it of you. It must be my work. Mine,—mine,—mine!"

"Go and design decorative medallions for rich brewers' houses. You are thoroughly good at that." Dick was sick and savage.

"Better things than medallions, Dick," was the answer, in tones that recalled a gray-eyed atom's fearless speech to Mrs. Jennett. Dick would have abased himself utterly, but that the other girl trailed in.

Next Sunday he laid at Maisie's feet small gifts of pencils that could almost draw of themselves and colours in whose permanence he believed, and he was ostentatiously attentive to the work in hand. It demanded, among other things, an exposition of the faith that was in him. Torpenhow's hair would have stood on end had he heard the fluency with which Dick preached his own gospel of Art.

A month before, Dick would have been equally astonished; but it was Maisie's will and pleasure, and he dragged his words together to make plain to her comprehension all that had been hidden to himself of the whys and wherefores of work. There is not the least difficulty in doing a thing if you only know how to do it; the trouble is to explain your method.

"I could put this right if I had a brush in my hand," said Dick, despairingly, over the modelling of a chin that Maisie complained would not "look flesh,"—it was the same chin that she had scraped out with the palette-knife,—"but I find it almost impossible to teach you. There's a queer grim Dutch touch about your painting that I like; but I've a notion that you're weak in drawing. You foreshorten as though you never used the model, and you've caught Kami's pasty way of dealing with flesh in shadow. Then, again, though you don't know it yourself, you shirk hard work. Suppose you spend some of your time on line alone. Line doesn't allow of shirking. Oils do, and three square inches of flashy, tricky stuff in the corner of a pic sometimes carry a bad thing off,—as I know. That's immoral. Do line-work for a little while, and then I can tell more about your powers, as old Kami used to say."

Maisie protested: she did not care for the pure line.

"I know," said Dick. "You want to do your fancy heads with a bunch of flowers at the base of the neck to hide bad modelling." The red-haired girl laughed a little. "You want to do landscapes with cattle knee-deep in grass to hide bad drawing. You want to do a great deal more than you can do. You have sense of colour, but you want form. Colour's a gift,—put it aside and think no more about it,—but form you can be drilled into. Now, all your fancy heads—and some of them are very good—will keep you exactly where you are. With line you must go forward or backward, and it will show up all your weaknesses."

"But other people——" began Maisie.

"You mustn't mind what other people do. If their souls were your soul, it would be different. You stand and fall by your own work, remember, and it's waste of time to think of any one else in this battle."

Dick paused, and the longing that had been so resolutely put away came back into his eyes. He looked at Maisie, and the look asked as plainly as words, Was it not time to leave all this barren wilderness of canvas and counsel and join hands with Life and Love?

Maisie assented to the new programme of schooling so adorably that Dick could hardly restrain himself from picking her up then and there and carrying her off to the nearest registrar's office. It was the implicit obedience to the spoken word and the blank indifference to the unspoken desire that baffled and buffeted his soul. He held authority in that house, —authority limited, indeed, to one-half of one afternoon in seven, but very real while it lasted. Maisie had learned to appeal to him on many subjects, from the proper packing of pictures to the condition of a smoky chimney. The red-haired girl never consulted him about anything. On the other hand, she accepted his appearances without protest, and watched him always. He discovered that the meals of the establishment were irregular and fragmentary. They depended chiefly on tea, pickles, and biscuit, as he had suspected from the beginning. The girls were supposed to market week and week about, but they lived, with the help of a charwoman, as casually as the young ravens. Maisie spent most of her income on models, and the other girl revelled in apparatus as refined as her work was rough. Armed with knowledge, dear-bought from the Docks, Dick warned Maisie that the end of semi-starvation meant the crippling of power to work, which was considerably worse than death. Maisie took the warning, and gave more thought to what she ate and drank. When his trouble returned upon him, as it generally did in the long winter twilights, the remembrance of that little act of domestic authority and his coercion with a hearth-brush of the smoky drawing-room chimney stung Dick like a whip-lash.

He conceived that this memory would be the extreme of his sufferings, till one Sunday the red-haired girl announced that she would make a study of Dick's head, and that he would be good enough to sit still, and—quite as an afterthought—look at Maisie. He sat, because he could not well refuse, and for the space of half an hour he reflected on all the people in the past whom he had laid open for the purposes of his own craft. He remembered Binat most distinctly,—that Binat who had once been an artist and talked about degradation.

It was the merest monochrome roughing in of a head, but it presented the dumb waiting, the longing, and, above all, the hopeless enslavement of the man, in a spirit of bitter mockery.

"I'll buy it," said Dick, promptly, "at your own price."

"My price is too high, but I dare say you'll be as grateful if——" The wet sketch fluttered from the girl's hand and fell into the ashes of the studio stove. When she picked it up it was hopelessly smudged.

"Oh, it's all spoiled!" said Maisie. "And I never saw it. Was it like?"

"Thank you," said Dick under his breath to the red-haired girl, and he removed himself swiftly.

"How that man hates me!" said the girl. "And how he loves you, Maisie!"

"What nonsense! I know Dick's very fond of me, but he has his work to do, and I have mine."

"Yes, he is fond of you, and I think he knows there is something in impressionism, after all. Maisie, can't you see?"

"See? See what?"

"Nothing; only, I know that if I could get any man to look at me as that man looks at you, I'd—I don't know what I'd do. But he hates me. Oh, how he hates me!"

She was not altogether correct. Dick's hatred was tempered with gratitude for a few moments, and then he forgot the girl entirely. Only the sense of shame remained, and he was nursing it across the Park in the fog. "There'll be an explosion one of these days," he said wrathfully. "But it isn't Maisie's fault; she's right, quite right, as far as she knows, and I can't blame her. This business has been going on for three months nearly. Three months!—and it cost me ten years' knocking about to get at the notion, the merest raw notion, of my work. That's true; but then I didn't have pins, drawing-pins, and palette-knives, stuck into me every Sunday. Oh, my little darling, if ever I break you, somebody will have a very bad time of it. No, she won't. I'd be as big a fool about her as I am now. I'll poison that red-haired girl on my wedding-day,—she's unwholesome,—and now I'll pass on these present bad times to Torp."

Torpenhow had been moved to lecture Dick more than once lately on the sin of levity, and Dick had listened and replied not a word. In the weeks between the first few Sundays of his discipline he had flung himself savagely into his work, resolved that Maisie should at least know the full stretch of his powers. Then he had taught Maisie that she must not pay the least attention to any work outside her own, and Maisie had obeyed him all too well. She took his counsels, but was not interested in his pictures.

"Your things smell of tobacco and blood," she said once. "Can't you do anything except soldiers?"

"I could do a head of you that would startle you," thought Dick,—this was before the red-haired girl had brought him under the guillotine,—but he only said, "I am very sorry," and harrowed Torpenhow's soul that evening with blasphemies against Art. Later, insensibly and to a large extent against his own will, he ceased to interest himself in his own work. For Maisie's sake, and to soothe the self-respect that it seemed to him he lost each Sunday, he would not consciously turn out bad stuff, but, since Maisie did not care even for his best, it were better not to do anything at all save wait and mark time between Sunday and Sunday. Torpenhow was disgusted as the weeks went by fruitless, and then attacked him one Sunday evening when Dick felt utterly exhausted after three hours' biting self-restraint in Maisie's presence. There was Language, and Torpenhow withdrew to consult the Nilghai, who had come in to talk continental politics.

"Bone-idle, is he? Careless, and touched in the temper?" said the Nilghai. "It isn't worth worrying over. Dick is probably playing the fool with a woman."

"Isn't that bad enough?"

"No. She may throw him out of gear and knock his work to pieces for a while. She may even turn up here some day and make a scene on the staircase: one never knows. But until

Dick speaks of his own accord you had better not touch him. He is no easy-tempered man to handle."

"No; I wish he were. He is such an aggressive, cock-sure, you-be-damned fellow."

"He'll get that knocked out of him in time. He must learn that he can't storm up and down the world with a box of moist tubes and a slick brush. You're fond of him?"

"I'd take any punishment that's in store for him if I could; but the worst of it is, no man can save his brother."

"No, and the worser of it is, there is no discharge in this war. Dick must learn his lesson like the rest of us. Talking of war, there'll be trouble in the Balkans in the spring."

"That trouble is long coming. I wonder if we could drag Dick out there when it comes off?"

Dick entered the room soon afterwards, and the question was put to him. "Not good enough," he said shortly. "I'm too comf'y where I am."

"Surely you aren't taking all the stuff in the papers seriously?" said the Nilghai. "Your vogue will be ended in less than six months,—the public will know your touch and go on to something new,—and where will you be then?"

"Here, in England."

"When you might be doing decent work among us out there? Nonsense! I shall go, the Keneu will be there, Torp will be there, Cassavetti will be there and the whole lot of us will be there, and we shall have as much as ever we can do, with unlimited fighting and the chance for you of seeing things that would make the reputation of three Verestchagins."

"Um!" said Dick, pulling at his pipe.

"You prefer to stay here and imagine that all the world is gaping at your pictures? Just think how full an average man's life is of his own pursuits and pleasures. When twenty thousand of him find time to look up between mouthfuls and grunt something about something they aren't the least interested in, the net result is called fame, reputation, or notoriety, according to the taste and fancy of the speller my lord."

"I know that as well as you do. Give me credit for a little gumption."

"Be hanged if I do!"

"*Be* hanged, then; you probably will be,—for a spy, by excited Turks. Heigh-ho! I'm weary, dead weary, and virtue has gone out of me." Dick dropped into a chair, and was fast asleep in a minute.

"That's a bad sign," said the Nilghai, in an undertone.

Torpenhow picked the pipe from the waistcoat where it was beginning to burn, and put a pillow behind the head. "We can't help; we can't help," he said. "It's a good ugly sort of old cocoanut, and I'm fond of it. There's the scar of the wipe he got when he was cut over in the square."

"Shouldn't wonder if that has made him a trifle mad."

"I should. He's a most businesslike madman."

Then Dick began to snore furiously.

"Oh, here, no affection can stand this sort of thing. Wake up, Dick, and go and sleep somewhere else, if you intend to make a noise about it."

"When a cat has been out on the tiles all night," said the Nilghai, in his beard, "I notice that she usually sleeps all day. This is natural history."

Dick staggered away rubbing his eyes and yawning. In the night-watches he was overtaken with an idea, so simple and so luminous that he wondered he had never conceived it before. It was full of craft. He would seek Maisie on a week-day,—would suggest an excursion, and would take her by train to Fort Keeling, over the very ground that they two had trodden together ten years ago.

"As a general rule," he explained to his chin-lathered reflection in the morning, "it isn't safe to cross an old trail twice. Things remind one of things, and a cold wind gets up, and you feel sad; but this is an exception to every rule that ever was. I'll go to Maisie at once."

Fortunately, the red-haired girl was out shopping when he arrived, and Maisie in a paint-spattered blouse was warring with her canvas. She was not pleased to see him; for week-day visits were a stretch of the bond; and it needed all his courage to explain his errand.

"I know you've been working too hard," he concluded,

with an air of authority. "If you do that, you'll break down. You had better come."

"Where?" said Maisie, wearily. She had been standing before her easel too long, and was very tired.

"Anywhere you please. We'll take a train to-morrow and see where it stops. We'll have lunch somewhere, and I'll bring you back in the evening."

"If there's a good working light to-morrow, I lose a day." Maisie balanced the heavy white chestnut palette irresolutely.

Dick bit back an oath that was hurrying to his lips. He had not yet learned patience with the maiden to whom her work was all in all.

"You'll lose ever so many more, dear, if you use every hour of working light. Overwork's only murderous idleness. Don't be unreasonable. I'll call for you to-morrow after breakfast early."

"But surely you are going to ask——"

"No, I am not. I want you and nobody else. Besides, she hates me as much as I hate her. She won't care to come. To-morrow, then; pray that we get sunshine."

Dick went away delighted, and by consequence did no work whatever. He strangled a wild desire to order a special train, but bought a great gray kangaroo cloak lined with glossy black marten, and then retired into himself to consider things.

"I'm going out for the day to-morrow with Dick," said Maisie to the red-haired girl when the latter returned, tired, from marketing in the Edgware Road.

"He deserves it. I shall have the studio floor thoroughly scrubbed while you're away. It's very dirty."

Maisie had enjoyed no sort of holiday for months and looked forward to the little excitement, but not without misgivings.

"There's nobody nicer than Dick when he talks sensibly," she thought, "but I'm sure he'll be silly and worry me, and I'm sure I can't tell him anything he'd like to hear. If he'd only be sensible, I should like him so much better."

Dick's eyes were full of joy when he made his appearance

next morning and saw Maisie, gray-ulstered and black-velvet-hatted, standing in the hallway. Palaces of marble, and not sordid imitation of grained wood, were surely the fittest background for such a divinity. The red-haired girl drew her into the studio for a moment and kissed her hurriedly. Maisie's eyebrows climbed to the top of her forehead; she was altogether unused to these demonstrations. "Mind my hat," she said, hurrying away, and ran down the steps to Dick waiting by the hansom.

"Are you quite warm enough? Are you sure you wouldn't like some more breakfast? Put this cloak over your knees."

"I'm quite comf'y, thanks. Where are we going, Dick? Oh, do stop singing like that. People will think we're mad."

"Let 'em think,—if the exertion doesn't kill them. They don't know who we are, and I'm sure I don't care who they are. My faith, Maisie, you're looking lovely!"

Maisie stared directly in front of her and did not reply. The wind of a keen clear winter morning had put colour into her cheeks. Overhead, the creamy-yellow smoke-clouds were thinning away one by one against a pale-blue sky, and the improvident sparrows broke off from water-spout committees and cab-rank cabals to clamour of the coming of spring.

"It will be lovely weather in the country," said Dick.

"But where are we going?"

"Wait and see."

They stopped at Victoria, and Dick sought tickets. For less than half the fraction of an instant it occurred to Maisie, comfortably settled by the waiting-room fire, that it was much more pleasant to send a man to the booking-office than to elbow one's way through the crowd. Dick put her into a Pullman,—solely on account of the warmth there; and she regarded the extravagance with grave scandalized eyes as the train moved out into the country.

"I wish I knew where we are going," she repeated for the twentieth time. The name of a well-remembered station flashed by, towards the end of the run, and Maisie was enlightened.

"Oh, Dick, you villain!"

"Well, I thought you might like to see the place again. You haven't been here since old times, have you?"

"No. I never cared to see Mrs. Jennett again; and she was all that was ever there."

"Not quite. Look out a minute. There's the windmill above the potato-fields; they haven't built villas there yet; d'you remember when I shut you up in it?"

"Yes. How she beat you for it! I never told it was you."

"She guessed. I jammed a stick under the door and told you that I was burying Amomma alive in the potatoes, and you believed me. You had a trusting nature in those days."

They laughed and leaned to look out, identifying ancient landmarks with many reminiscences. Dick fixed his weather eye on the curve of Maisie's cheek, very near his own, and watched the blood rise under the clear skin. He congratulated himself upon his cunning, and looked that the evening would bring him a great reward.

When the train stopped they went out to look at an old town with new eyes. First, but from a distance, they regarded the house of Mrs. Jennett.

"Suppose she should come out now, what would you do?" said Dick, with mock terror.

"I should make a face."

"Show, then," said Dick, dropping into the speech of childhood.

Maisie made that face in the direction of the mean little villa, and Dick laughed.

" 'This is disgraceful,' " said Maisie, mimicking Mrs. Jennett's tone. " 'Maisie, you run in at once, and learn the collect, gospel, and epistle for the next three Sundays. After all I've taught you, too, and three helps every Sunday at dinner! Dick's always leading you into mischief. If you aren't a gentleman, Dick, you might at least——' "

The sentence ended abruptly. Maisie remembered when it had last been used.

" 'Try to behave like one,' " said Dick, promptly. "Quite right. Now we'll get some lunch and go on to Fort Keeling,—unless you'd rather drive there?"

"We must walk, out of respect to the place. How little changed it all is!"

They turned in the direction of the sea through unaltered streets, and the influence of old things lay upon them. Presently they passed a confectioner's shop much considered in the days when their joint pocket-money amounted to a shilling a week.

"Dick, have you any pennies?" said Maisie, half to herself.

"Only three; and if you think you're going to have two of 'em to buy peppermints with, you're wrong. She says peppermints aren't ladylike."

Again they laughed, and again the colour came into Maisie's cheeks as the blood boiled through Dick's heart. After a large lunch they went down to the beach and to Fort Keeling across the waste, wind-bitten land that no builder had thought it worth his while to defile. The winter breeze came in from the sea and sang about their ears.

"Maisie," said Dick, "your nose is getting a crude Prussian blue at the tip. I'll race you as far as you please for as much as you please."

She looked round cautiously, and with a laugh set off, swiftly as the ulster allowed, till she was out of breath.

"We used to run miles," she panted. "It's absurd that we can't run now."

"Old age, dear. This it is to get fat and sleek in town. When I wished to pull your hair you generally ran for three miles, shrieking at the top of your voice. I ought to know, because those shrieks were meant to call up Mrs. Jennett with a cane and——"

"Dick, I never got you a beating on purpose in my life."

"No, of course you never did. Good heavens! Look at the sea."

"Why, it's the same as ever!" said Maisie.

Torpenhow had gathered from Mr. Beeton that Dick, properly dressed and shaved, had left the house at half-past eight in the morning with a travelling-rug over his arm. The Nilghai rolled in at mid-day for chess and polite conversation.

"It's worse than anything I imagined," said Torpenhow.

"Oh, the everlasting Dick, I suppose! You fuss over him like a hen with one chick. Let him run riot if he thinks it'll amuse him. You can whip a young pup off feather, but you can't whip a young man."

"It isn't a woman. It's one woman; and it's a girl."

"Where's your proof?"

"He got up and went out at eight this morning,—got up in the middle of the night, by Jove! a thing he never does except when he's on service. Even then, remember, we had to kick him out of his blankets before the fight began at El-Maghrib. It's disgusting."

"It looks odd; but maybe he's decided to buy a horse at last. He might get up for that, mightn't he?"

"Buy a blazing wheelbarrow! He'd have told us if there was a horse in the wind. It's a girl."

"Don't be certain. Perhaps it's only a married woman."

"Dick has some sense of humour, if you haven't. Who gets up in the gray dawn to call on another man's wife? It's a girl."

"Let it be a girl, then. She may teach him that there's somebody else in the world besides himself."

"She'll spoil his hand. She'll waste his time, and she'll marry him, and ruin his work for ever. He'll be a respectable married man before we can stop him, and—he'll never go on the long trail again."

"All quite possible, but the earth won't spin the other way when it happens. . . . Ho! ho! I'd give something to see Dick 'go wooing with the boys.' Don't worry about it. These things be with Allah, and we can only look on. Get the chessmen."

The red-haired girl was lying down in her own room, staring at the ceiling. The footsteps of people on the pavement sounded, as they grew indistinct in the distance, like a many-times-repeated kiss that was all one long kiss. Her hands were by her side, and they opened and shut savagely from time to time.

The charwoman in charge of the scrubbing of the studio

knocked at her door: "Beg y' pardon, miss, but in cleanin' of a floor there's two, not to say three, kind of soap, which is yaller, an' mottled, an' disinfectink. Now, jist before I took my pail into the passage I thought it would be pre'aps jest as well if I was to come up 'ere an' ask you what sort of soap you was wishful that I should use on them boards. The yaller soap, miss——"

There was nothing in the speech to have caused the paroxysm of fury that drove the red-haired girl into the middle of the room, almost shouting—

"Do you suppose *I* care what you use? Any kind will do!—*any* kind!"

The woman fled, and the red-haired girl looked at her own reflection in the glass for an instant and covered her face with her hands. It was as though she had shouted some shameless secret aloud.

CHAPTER VII

Roses red and roses white
Plucked I for my love's delight.
She would none of all my posies,—
Bade me gather her blue roses.

Half the world I wandered through,
Seeking where such flowers grew;
Half the world unto my quest
Answered with but laugh and jest.

It may be beyond the grave
She shall find what she would have.
Mine was but an idle quest,—
Roses white and red are best!

—BLUE ROSES

THE sea had not changed. Its waters were low on the mud-banks, and the Marazion Bell-buoy clanked and swung in the tide-way. On the white beach-sand dried stumps of sea-poppy shivered and chattered.

"I don't see the old breakwater," said Maisie, under her breath.

"Let's be thankful that we have as much as we have. I don't believe they've mounted a single new gun on the fort since we were here. Come and look."

They came to the glacis of Fort Keeling, and sat down in a nook sheltered from the wind under the tarred throat of a forty-pounder cannon.

"Now, if Amomma were only here!" said Maisie.

For a long time both were silent. Then Dick took Maisie's hand and called her by her name.

She shook her head and looked out to sea.

"Maisie, darling, doesn't it make any difference?"

"No!" between clenched teeth. "I'd—I'd tell you if it did; but it doesn't. Oh, Dick, please be sensible."

"Don't you think that it ever will?"

"No, I'm sure it won't."

"Why?"

Maisie rested her chin on her hand, and, still regarding the sea, spoke hurriedly—

"I know what you want perfectly well, but I can't give it you, Dick. It isn't my fault; indeed, it isn't. If I felt that I could care for any one—— But I don't feel that I care. I simply don't understand what the feeling means."

"Is that true, dear?"

"You've been very good to me, Dickie; and the only way I can pay you back is by speaking the truth. I daren't tell a fib. I despise myself quite enough as it is."

"What in the world for?"

"Because—because I take everything that you give me and I give you nothing in return. It's mean and selfish of me, and whenever I think of it it worries me."

"Understand once for all, then, that I can manage my own affairs, and if I choose to do anything you aren't to blame. You haven't a single thing to reproach yourself with, darling."

"Yes, I have, and talking only makes it worse."

"Then don't talk about it."

"How can I help myself? If you find me alone for a minute

you are always talking about it; and when you aren't you look it. You don't know how I despise myself sometimes."

"Great goodness!" said Dick, nearly jumping to his feet. "Speak the truth now, Maisie, if you never speak it again! Do I—does this worrying bore you?"

"No. It does not."

"You'd tell me if it did?"

"I should let you know, I think."

"Thank you. The other thing is fatal. But you must learn to forgive a man when he's in love. He's always a nuisance. You must have known that?"

Maisie did not consider the last question worth answering, and Dick was forced to repeat it.

"There were other men, of course. They always worried just when I was in the middle of my work, and wanted me to listen to them."

"Did you listen?"

"At first; and they couldn't understand why I didn't care. And they used to praise my pictures; and I thought they meant it. I used to be proud of the praise, and tell Kami, and—I shall never forget—once Kami laughed at me."

"You don't like being laughed at, Maisie, do you?"

"I hate it. I never laugh at other people unless—unless they do bad work. Dick, tell me honestly what you think of my pictures generally,—of everything of mine that you've seen."

"'Honest, honest, and honest over!'" quoted Dick from a catchword of long ago. "Tell me what Kami always says."

Maisie hesitated. "He—he says that there is feeling in them."

"How dare you tell me a fib like that? Remember, I was under Kami for two years. I know exactly what he says."

"It isn't a fib."

"It's worse; it's a half-truth. Kami says, when he puts his head on one side,—so,—*'Il y a du sentiment, mais il n'y a pas de parti pris.'*" He rolled the *r* threateningly, as Kami used to do.

"Yes, that is what he says; and I'm beginning to think that he is right."

"Certainly he is." Dick admitted that two people in the world could do and say no wrong. Kami was the man.

"And now you say the same thing. It's so disheartening."

"I'm sorry, but you asked me to speak the truth. Besides, I love you too much to pretend about your work. It's strong, it's patient sometimes,—not always,—and sometimes there's power in it, but there's no special reason why it should be done at all. At least, that's how it strikes me."

"There's no special reason why anything in the world should ever be done. You know that as well as I do. I only want success."

"You're going the wrong way to get it, then. Hasn't Kami ever told you so?"

"Don't quote Kami to me. I want to know what you think. My work's bad, to begin with."

"I didn't say that, and I don't think it."

"It's amateurish, then."

"That it most certainly is not. You're a work-woman, darling, to your boot-heels, and I respect you for that."

"You don't laugh at me behind my back?"

"No, dear. You see, you are more to me than any one else. Put this cloak thing round you, or you'll get chilled."

Maisie wrapped herself in the soft marten skins, turning the gray kangaroo fur to the outside.

"This is delicious," she said, rubbing her chin thoughtfully along the fur. "Well? Why am I wrong in trying to get a little success?"

"Just because you try. Don't you understand, darling? Good work has nothing to do with—doesn't belong to—the person who does it. It's put into him or her from outside."

"But how does that affect——"

"Wait a minute. All we can do is to learn how to do our work, to be masters of our materials instead of servants, and never to be afraid of anything."

"I understand that."

"Everything else comes from outside ourselves. Very good. If we sit down quietly to work out notions that are sent to us, we may or we may not do something that isn't bad. A great deal depends on being master of the bricks and mortar of the trade. But the instant we begin to think about success and the effect of our work—to play with one eye on the gallery—we lose power and touch and everything else. At least that's how I have found it. Instead of being quiet and giving every power you possess to your work, you're fretting over something which you can neither help nor hinder by a minute. See?"

"It's so easy for you to talk in that way. People like what you do. Don't you ever think about the gallery?"

"Much too often; but I'm always punished for it by loss of power. It's as simple as the Rule of Three. If we make light of our work by using it for our own ends, our work will make light of us, and, as we're the weaker, we shall suffer."

"I don't treat my work lightly. You know that it's everything to me."

"Of course; but, whether you realize it or not, you give two strokes for yourself to one for your work. It isn't your fault, darling. I do exactly the same thing, and know that I'm doing it. Most of the French schools, and all the schools here, drive the students to work for their own credit, and for the sake of their pride. I was told that all the world was interested in my work, and everybody at Kami's talked turpentine, and I honestly believed that the world needed elevating and influencing, and all manner of impertinences, by my brushes. By Jove, I actually believed that! When my little head was bursting with a notion that I couldn't handle because I hadn't sufficient knowledge of my craft, I used to run about wondering at my own magnificence and getting ready to astonish the world."

"But surely one can do that sometimes?"

"Very seldom with malice aforethought, darling. And when it's done it's such a tiny thing, and the world's so big, and all but a millionth part of it doesn't care. Maisie, come with me and I'll show you something of the size of the world. One can no more avoid working than eating,—that goes on by itself,—but try to see what you are working for. I know such little heavens that I could take you to,—islands tucked away under the Line. You sight them after weeks of crashing through water as black as black marble because it's so deep, and you sit in the fore-chains day after day and see the sun rise almost afraid because the sea's so lonely."

"Who is afraid?—you, or the sun?"

"The sun, of course. And there are noises under the sea, and sounds overhead in a clear sky. Then you find your island alive with hot moist orchids that make mouths at you and can do everything except talk. There's a waterfall in it three hundred feet high, just like a sliver of green jade laced with silver; and millions of wild bees live up in the rocks; and you hear the fat cocoanuts falling from the palms; and you order an ivory-white servant to sling you a long yellow hammock with tassels on it like ripe maize, and you put up your feet and hear the bees hum and the water fall till you go to sleep."

"Can one work there?"

"Certainly. One must do something always. You hang your canvas up in a palm tree and let the parrots criticize. When they scuffle you heave a ripe custard-apple at them, and it bursts in a lather of cream. There are hundreds of places. Come and see them."

"I don't quite like that place. It sounds lazy. Tell me another."

"What do you think of a big, red, dead city built of red sandstone, with raw green aloes growing between the stones, lying out neglected on honey-coloured sands? There are forty dead kings there, Maisie, each in a gorgeous tomb finer than all the others. You look at the palaces and streets and shops and tanks, and think that men must live there, till you find a wee gray squirrel rubbing its nose all alone in the market-place, and a jewelled peacock struts out of a carved doorway and spreads its tail against a marble screen as fine pierced as point-lace. Then a monkey—a little black monkey—walks through the main square to get a drink from a tank forty feet deep. He slides down the creepers to the water's edge, and a friend holds him by the tail, in case he should fall in."

"Is all that true?"

"I have been there and seen. Then evening comes, and the lights change till it's just as though you stood in the heart of a king-opal. A little before sundown, as punctually as clockwork, a big bristly wild boar, with all his family following, trots through the city gate, churning the foam on his tusks. You climb on the shoulder of a blind black stone god and watch that pig choose himself a palace for the night and stump in wagging his tail. Then the night-wind gets up, and the sands move, and you hear the desert outside the city singing, "Now I lay me down to sleep," and everything is dark till the moon rises. Maisie, darling, come with me and see what the world is really like. It's very lovely, and it's very horrible,—but I won't let you see anything horrid,—and it doesn't care your life or mine for pictures or anything else except doing its own work and making love. Come, and I'll show you how to brew sangaree, and sling a hammock, and—oh, thousands of things, and you'll see for yourself what colour means, and we'll find out together what love means, and then, maybe, we shall be allowed to do some good work. Come away!"

"Why?" said Maisie.

"How can you do anything until you have seen everything, or as much as you can? And besides, darling, I love you. Come along with me. You have no business here; you don't belong to this place; you're half a gipsy,—your face tells that; and I—even the smell of open water makes me restless. Come across the sea and be happy!"

He had risen to his feet, and stood in the shadow of the gun, looking down at the girl. The very short winter afternoon had worn away, and, before they knew, the winter moon was walking the untroubled sea. Long ruled lines of silver showed where a ripple of the rising tide was turning over the mud-banks. The wind had dropped, and in the intense stillness they could hear a donkey cropping the frosty grass many yards away. A faint beating, like that of a muffled drum, came out of the moon-haze.

"What's that?" said Maisie, quickly. "It sounds like a heart beating. Where is it?"

Dick was so angry at this sudden wrench to his pleadings that he could not trust himself to speak, and in this silence caught the sound. Maisie from her seat under the gun watched him with a certain amount of fear. She wished so much that he would be sensible and cease to worry her with over-sea emotion that she both could and could not understand. She was not prepared, however, for the change in his face as he listened.

"It's a steamer," he said,—"a twin-screw steamer, by the beat. I can't make her out, but she must be standing very close in-shore. Ah!" as the red of a rocket streaked the haze, "she's standing in to signal before she clears the Channel."

"Is it a wreck?" said Maisie, to whom these words were as Greek.

Dick's eyes were turned to the sea. "Wreck! What nonsense! She's only reporting herself. Red rocket forward—there's a green light aft now, and two red rockets from the bridge."

"What does it mean?"

"It's the signal of the Cross Keys Line running to Australia. I wonder which steamer it is." The note of his voice had changed; he seemed to be talking to himself, and Maisie did not approve of it. The moonlight broke the haze for a moment, touching the black sides of a long steamer working down Channel. "Four masts and three funnels—she's in deep draught, too. That must be the *Barralong,* or the *Bhutia.* No, the *Bhutia* has a clipper bow. It's the *Barralong,* to Australia. She'll lift the Southern Cross in a week,—lucky old tub!—oh, lucky old tub!"

He stared intently, and moved up the slope of the fort to get a better view, but the mist on the sea thickened again, and the beating of her screws grew fainter. Maisie called to him a little angrily, and he returned, still keeping his eyes seaward. "Have you ever seen the Southern Cross blazing right over your head?" he asked. "It's superb!"

"No," she said shortly, "and I don't want to. If you think it's so lovely, why don't you go and see it yourself?"

She raised her face from the soft blackness of the marten skins about her throat, and her eyes shone like diamonds. The moonlight on the gray kangaroo fur turned it to frosted silver of the coldest.

"By Jove, Maisie, you look like a little heathen idol tucked up there." The eyes showed that they did not appreciate the compliment. "I'm sorry," he continued. "The Southern Cross isn't worth looking at unless some one helps you to see. That steamer's out of hearing."

"Dick," she said quietly, "suppose I were to come to you now,—be quiet a minute,—just as I am, and caring for you just as much as I do."

"Not as a brother, though? You said you didn't—in the Park."

"I never had a brother. Suppose I said, 'Take me to those places, and in time, perhaps, I might really care for you,' what would you do?"

"Send you straight back to where you came from, in a cab. No, I wouldn't: I'd let you walk. But you couldn't do it, dear. And I wouldn't run the risk. You're worth waiting for till you can come without reservation."

"Do you honestly believe that?"

"I have a hazy sort of idea that I do. Has it never struck you in that light?"

"Ye—es. I feel so wicked about it."

"Wickeder than usual?"

"You don't know all I think. It's almost too awful to tell."

"Never mind. You promised to tell me the truth—at least."

"It's so ungrateful of me, but—but, though I know you care for me, and I like to have you with me, I'd—I'd even sacrifice you, if that would bring me what I want."

"My poor little darling! I know that state of mind. It doesn't lead to good work."

"You aren't angry? Remember, I do despise myself."

"I'm not exactly flattered,—I had guessed as much before,—but I'm not angry. I'm sorry for you. Surely you ought to have left a littleness like that behind you, years ago."

"You've no right to patronize me! I only want what I have worked for so long. It came to *you* without any trouble, and —and I don't think it's fair."

"What can I do? I'd give ten years of my life to get you what you want. But I can't help you; even I can't help."

A murmur of dissent from Maisie. He went on—

"And I know by what you have just said that you're on the

wrong road to success. It isn't got at by sacrificing other people,—I've had that much knocked into me; you must sacrifice yourself, and live under orders, and never think for yourself, and never have real satisfaction in your work except just at the beginning, when you're reaching out after a notion."

"How can you believe all that?"

"There's no question of belief or disbelief. That's the law, and you take it or refuse it as you please. I try to obey, but I can't, and then my work turns bad on my hands. Under any circumstances, remember, four-fifths of everybody's work must be bad. But the remnant is worth the trouble for its own sake."

"Isn't it nice to get credit even for bad work?"

"It's much too nice. But—— May I tell you something? It isn't a pretty tale, but you're so like a man that I forget when I'm talking to you."

"Tell me."

"Once when I was out in the Soudan I went over some ground that we had been fighting on for three days. There were twelve hundred dead; and we hadn't time to bury them."

"How ghastly!"

"I had been at work on a big double-sheet sketch, and I was wondering what people would think of it at home. The sight of that field taught me a good deal. It looked just like a bed of horrible toadstools in all colours, and—I'd never seen men in bulk go back to their beginnings before. So I began to understand that men and women were only material to work with, and that what they said or did was of no consequence. See? Strictly speaking, you might just as well put your ear down to the palette to catch what your colours are saying."

"Dick, that's disgraceful!"

"Wait a minute. I said, strictly speaking. Unfortunately, everybody must be either a man or a woman."

"I'm glad you allow that much."

"In your case I don't. You aren't a woman. But ordinary people, Maisie, must behave and work as such. That's what makes me so savage." He hurled a pebble towards the sea as he spoke. "I know that it is outside my business to care what people say; I can see that it spoils my output if I listen to 'em;

and yet, confound it all,"—another pebble flew seaward,—"I can't help purring when I'm rubbed the right way. Even when I can see on a man's forehead that he is lying his way through a clump of pretty speeches, those lies make me happy and play the mischief with my hand."

"And when he doesn't say pretty things?"

"Then, belovedest,"—Dick grinned,—"I forget that I am the steward of these gifts, and I want to make that man love and appreciate my work with a thick stick. It's too humiliating altogether; but I suppose even if one were an angel and painted humans altogether from outside, one would lose in touch what one gained in grip."

Maisie laughed at the idea of Dick as an angel.

"But you seem to think," she said, "that everything nice spoils your hand."

"I don't think. It's the law,—just the same as it was at Mrs. Jennett's. Everything that is nice does spoil your hand. I'm glad you see so clearly."

"I don't like the view."

"Nor I. But—have got orders: what can do? Are you strong enough to face it alone?"

"I suppose I must."

"Let me help, darling. We can hold each other very tight and try to walk straight. We shall blunder horribly, but it will be better than stumbling apart. Maisie, can't you see reason?"

"I don't think we should get on together. We should be two of a trade, so we should never agree."

"How I should like to meet the man who made that proverb! He lived in a cave and ate raw bear, I fancy. I'd make him chew his own arrow-heads. Well?"

"I should be only half married to you. I should worry and fuss about my work, as I do now. Four days out of seven I'm not fit to speak to."

"You talk as if no one else in the world had ever used a brush. D'you suppose that I don't know the feeling of worry and bother and can't-get-at-ness? You're lucky if you only have it four days out of the seven. What difference would that make?"

"A great deal—if you had it too."

"Yes, but I could respect it. Another man might not. He might laugh at you. But there's no use talking about it. If you can think in that way you can't care for me—yet."

The tide had nearly covered the mud-banks, and twenty little ripples broke on the beach before Maisie chose to speak.

"Dick," she said slowly, "I believe very much that you are better than I am."

"This doesn't seem to bear on the argument—but in what way?"

"I don't quite know, but in what you said about work and things; and then you're so patient. Yes, you're better than I am."

Dick considered rapidly the murkiness of an average man's life. There was nothing in the review to fill him with a sense of virtue. He lifted the hem of the cloak to his lips.

"Why," said Maisie, making as though she had not noticed, "can you see things that I can't? I don't believe what you believe; but you're right, I believe."

"If I've seen anything, God knows I couldn't have seen it but for you, and I know that I couldn't have said it except to you. You seemed to make everything clear for a minute; but I don't practise what I preach. You would help me. . . . There are only us two in the world for all purposes, and—and you like to have me with you?"

"Of course I do. I wonder if you can realize how utterly lonely I am!"

"Darling, I think I can."

"Two years ago, when I first took the little house, I used to walk up and down the back-garden trying to cry. I never can cry. Can you?"

"It's some time since I tried. What was the trouble? Overwork?"

"I don't know; but I used to dream that I had broken down, and had no money, and was starving in London. I thought about it all day, and it frightened me—oh, how it frightened me!"

"I know that fear. It's the most terrible of all. It wakes me up in the night sometimes. You oughtn't to know anything about it."

"How do *you* know?"

"Never mind. Is your three hundred a year safe?"

"It's in Consols."

"Very well. If any one comes to you and recommends a better investment,—even if I should come to you,—don't you listen. Never shift the money for a minute, and never lend a penny of it,—even to the red-haired girl."

"Don't scold me so! I'm not likely to be foolish."

"The earth is full of men who'd sell their souls for three hundred a year; and women come and talk, and borrow a five-pound note here and a ten-pound note there; and a woman has no conscience in a money debt. Stick to your money, Maisie; for there's nothing more ghastly in the world than poverty in London. It's scared me. By Jove, it put the fear into *me!* And one oughtn't to be afraid of anything."

To each man is appointed his particular dread,—the terror that, if he does not fight against it, must cow him even to the loss of his manhood. Dick's experience of the sordid misery of want had entered into the deeps of him, and, lest he might find virtue too easy, that memory stood behind him, tempting to shame, when dealers came to buy his wares. As the Nilghai quaked against his will at the still green water of a lake or a mill-dam, as Torpenhow flinched before any white arm that could cut or stab and loathed himself for flinching, Dick feared the poverty he had once tasted half in jest. His burden was heavier than the burdens of his companions.

Maisie watched the face working in the moonlight.

"You've plenty of pennies now," she said soothingly.

"I shall never get enough," he began, with vicious emphasis. Then, laughing, "I shall always be threepence short in my accounts."

"Why threepence?"

"I carried a man's bag once from Liverpool Street Station to Blackfriars Bridge. It was a sixpenny job,—you needn't laugh; indeed it was,—and I wanted the money desperately. He only gave me threepence; and he hadn't even the decency to pay in silver. Whatever money I make, I shall never get that odd threepence out of the world."

This was no language befitting the man who had preached of the sanctity of work. It jarred on Maisie, who preferred her payment in applause, which, since all men desire it, must be of the right. She hunted for her little purse and gravely took out a threepenny bit.

"There it is," she said. "I'll pay you, Dickie; and don't worry any more; it isn't worth while. Are you paid?"

"I am," said the very human apostle of fair craft, taking the coin. "I'm paid a thousand times, and we'll close that account. It shall live on my watch-chain; and you're an angel, Maisie."

"I'm very cramped, and I'm feeling a little cold. Good gracious! the cloak is all white, and so is your moustache! *I* never knew it was so chilly."

A light frost lay white on the shoulder of Dick's ulster. He, too, had forgotten the state of the weather. They laughed together, and with that laugh ended all serious discourse.

They ran inland across the waste to warm themselves, then turned to look at the glory of the full tide under the moonlight and the intense black shadows of the furze bushes. It was an additional joy to Dick that Maisie could see colour even as he saw it,—could see the blue in the white of the mist, the violet that is in gray palings, and all things else as they are,—not of one hue, but a thousand. And the moonlight came into Maisie's soul, so that she, usually reserved, chattered of herself and of the things she took interest in,—of Kami, wisest of teachers, and of the girls in the studio,—of the Poles, who will kill themselves with overwork if they are not checked; of the French, who talk at great length of much more than they will ever accomplish; of the slovenly English, who toil hopelessly and cannot understand that inclination does not imply power; of the Americans, whose rasping voices in the hush of a hot afternoon strain tense-drawn nerves to breaking-point, and whose suppers lead to indigestion; of tempestuous Russians, neither to hold nor to bind, who tell the girls ghost-stories till the girls shriek; of stolid Germans, who come to learn one thing, and, having mastered that much, stolidly go away and copy pictures for evermore. Dick listened enraptured because it was Maisie who spoke. He knew the old life.

"It hasn't changed much," he said. "Do they still steal colours at lunch-time?"

"Not steal. Attract is the word. Of course they do. I'm good —I only attract ultramarine; but there are students who'd attract flake-white."

"I've done it myself. You can't help it when the palettes are hung up. Every colour is common property once it runs down,—even though you do start it with a drop of oil. It teaches people not to waste their tubes."

"I should like to attract some of your colours, Dick. Perhaps I might catch your success with them."

"I mustn't say a bad word, but I should like to. What in the world, which you've just missed a lovely chance of seeing, does success or want of success, or a three-storied success, matter compared with—— No, I won't open that question again. It's time to go back to town."

"I'm sorry, Dick, but——"

"You're much more interested in that than you are in me."

"I don't know, I don't think I am."

"What will you give me if I tell you a sure short-cut to everything you want,—the trouble and the fuss and the tangle and all the rest? Will you promise to obey me?"

"Of course."

"In the first place, you must never forget a meal because you happen to be at work. You forgot your lunch twice last week," said Dick, at a venture, for he knew with whom he was dealing.

"No, no,—only once, really."

"That's bad enough. And you mustn't take a cup of tea and a biscuit in place of a regular dinner, because dinner happens to be a trouble."

"You're making fun of me!"

"I never was more in earnest in my life. Oh, my love, my love, hasn't it dawned on you yet what you are to me? Here's the whole earth in a conspiracy to give you a chill, or run over you, or drench you to the skin, or cheat you out of your money, or let you die of overwork and under feeding, and I haven't the mere right to look after you. Why, I don't even know if you have sense enough to put on warm things when the weather's cold."

"Dick, you're the most awful boy to talk to—really! How do you suppose I managed when you were away?"

"I wasn't here, and I didn't know. But now I'm back I'd give everything I have for the right of telling you to come in out of the rain."

"Your success too?"

This time it cost Dick a severe struggle to refrain from bad words.

"As Mrs. Jennett used to say, you're a trial, Maisie! You've been cooped up in the schools too long, and you think every one is looking at you. There aren't twelve hundred people in the world who understand pictures. The others pretend and don't care. Remember, I've seen twelve hundred men dead in toadstool-beds. It's only the voice of the tiniest little fraction of people that makes success. The real world doesn't care a tinker's—doesn't care a bit. For aught you or I know, every man in the world may be arguing with a Maisie of his own."

"Poor Maisie!"

"Poor Dick, I think. Do you believe while he's fighting for what's dearer than his life he wants to look at a picture? And even if he did, and if all the world did, and a thousand million people rose up and shouted hymns to my honour and glory, would that make up to me for the knowledge that you were out shopping in the Edgware Road on a rainy day without an umbrella? Now we'll go to the station."

"But you said on the beach——" persisted Maisie, with a certain fear.

Dick groaned aloud: "Yes, I know what I said. My work is everything I have, or am, or hope to be to me, and I believe I've learnt the law that governs it; but I've some lingering sense of fun left,—though you've nearly knocked it out of me. I can just see that it isn't everything to all the world. Do what I say, and not what I do."

Maisie was careful not to reopen debatable matters, and they returned to London joyously. The terminus stopped Dick in the midst of an eloquent harangue on the beauties of exercise. He would buy Maisie a horse,—such a horse as never yet bowed head to bit,—would stable it, with a companion, some twenty miles from London, and Maisie, solely for her health's sake, should ride with him twice or thrice a week.

"That's absurd," said she. "It wouldn't be proper."

"Now, who in all London to-night would have sufficient interest or audacity to call us two to account for anything we chose to do?"

Maisie looked at the lamps, the fog, and the hideous turmoil. Dick was right; but horseflesh did not make for Art as she understood it.

"You're very nice sometimes, but you're very foolish more times. I'm not going to let you give me horses, or take you out of your way to-night. I'll go home by myself. Only I want you to promise me something. You won't think any more about that extra threepence, will you? Remember, you've been paid; and I won't allow you to be spiteful and do bad work for a little thing like that. You can be so big that you mustn't be tiny."

This was turning the tables with a vengeance. There remained only to put Maisie into her hansom.

"Good-bye," she said simply. "You'll come on Sunday. It has been a beautiful day, Dick. Why can't it be like this always?"

"Because love's like line-work: you must go forward or backward; you can't stand still. By the way, go on with your line-work. Good-night, and, for my—for any sake, take care of yourself."

He turned to walk home, meditating. The day had brought him nothing that he hoped for, but—surely this was worth many days—it had brought him nearer to Maisie. The end was only a question of time now, and the prize well worth the waiting. By instinct, once more, he turned to the river.

"And she understood at once," he said, looking at the water. "She found out my pet besetting sin on the spot, and paid it off. My God, how she understood! And she said I was better than she was! Better than she was!" He laughed at the absurdity of the notion. "I wonder if girls guess at one-half a man's life. They can't, or—they wouldn't marry us." He took her gift out of his pocket, and considered it in the light of a miracle and a pledge of the comprehension that, one day, would lead to perfect happiness. Meantime, Maisie was alone in London, with none to save her from danger. And the packed wilderness was very full of danger.

Dick made his prayer to Fate disjointedly after the manner of the heathen as he threw the piece of silver into the river. If any evil were to befall, let him bear the burden and let Maisie go unscathed, since the threepenny piece was dearest to him of all his possessions. It was a small coin in itself, but Maisie had given it, and the Thames held it, and surely the Fates would be bribed for this once.

The drowning of the coin seemed to cut him free from thought of Maisie for the moment. He took himself off the bridge and went whistling to his chambers with a strong yearning for some man-talk and tobacco after his first experience of an entire day spent in the society of a woman. There was a stronger desire at his heart when there rose before him an unsolicited vision of the *Barralong* dipping deep and sailing free for the Southern Cross.

CHAPTER VIII

And these two, as I have told you,
Were the friends of Hiawatha,
Chibiabos, the musician,
And the very strong man, Kwasind.

—HIAWATHA

TORPENHOW was paging the last sheets of some manuscript, while the Nilghai, who had come for chess and remained to talk tactics, was reading through the first part commenting scornfully the while.

"It's picturesque enough and it's sketchy," said he, "but as a serious consideration of affairs in Eastern Europe, it's not worth much."

"It's off my hands at any rate. . . . Thirty-seven, thirty-eight, thirty-nine slips altogether, aren't there? That should make between eleven and twelve pages of valuable misinformation. Heigho!" Torpenhow shuffled the writing together and hummed—

Young lambs to sell, young lambs to sell,
If I'd as much money as I could tell,
I never would cry, Young lambs to sell!

Dick entered, self-conscious and a little defiant, but in the best of tempers with all the world.

"Back at last?" said Torpenhow.

"More or less. What have you been doing?"

"Work. Dickie, you behave as though the Bank of England were behind you. Here's Sunday, Monday, and Tuesday gone and you haven't done a line. It's scandalous."

"The notions come and go, my children—they come and go like our 'baccy," he answered, filling his pipe. "Moreover," he stooped to thrust a spill into the grate, "Apollo does not always stretch his—— Oh, confound your clumsy jests, Nilghai!"

"This is not the place to preach the theory of direct inspiration," said the Nilghai, returning Torpenhow's large and workmanlike bellows to their nail on the wall. "We believe in cobblers' wax. *La!*—where you sit down."

"If you weren't so big and fat," said Dick, looking round for a weapon, "I'd——"

"No skylarking in my rooms. You two smashed half my furniture last time you threw the cushions about. You might have the decency to say How d'you do? to Binkie. Look at him."

Binkie had jumped down from the sofa and was fawning round Dick's knee, and scratching at his boots.

"Dear man!" said Dick, snatching him up, and kissing him

on the black patch above his right eye. "Did ums was, Binks? Did that ugly Nilghai turn you off the sofa? Bite him, Mr. Binkle." He pitched him on the Nilghai's stomach, as the big man lay at ease, and Binkie pretended to destroy the Nilghai inch by inch, till a sofa cushion extinguished him, and panting he stuck out his tongue at the company.

"The Binkie-boy went for a walk this morning before you were up, Torp. I saw him making love to the butcher at the corner when the shutters were being taken down—just as if he hadn't enough to eat in his own proper house," said Dick.

"Binks, is that a true bill?" said Torpenhow, severely. The little dog retreated under the sofa cushion, and showed by the fat white back of him that he really had no further interest in the discussion.

"Strikes me that another disreputable dog went for a walk, too," said the Nilghai. "What made you get up so early? Torp said you might be buying a horse."

"He knows it would need three of us for a serious business like that. No, I felt lonesome and unhappy, so I went out to look at the sea, and watch the pretty ships go by."

"Where did you go?"

"Somewhere on the Channel. Progly or Snigly, or some watering-place was its name; I've forgotten; but it was only two hours' run from London and the ships went by."

"Did you see anything you knew?"

"Only the *Barralong* outwards to Australia, and an Odessa grain-boat loaded down by the head. It was a thick day, but the sea smelt good."

"Wherefore put on one's best trousers to see the *Barralong?*" said Torpenhow, pointing.

"Because I've nothing except these things and my painting duds. Besides, I wanted to do honour to the sea."

"Did She make you feel restless?" asked the Nilghai, keenly.

"Crazy. Don't speak of it. I'm sorry I went."

Torpenhow and the Nilghai exchanged a look as Dick, stooping, busied himself among the former's boots and trees.

"These will do," he said at last; "I can't say I think much

of your taste in slippers, but the fit's the thing." He slipped his feet into a pair of sock-like sambhur-skin foot coverings, found a long chair, and lay at length.

"They're my own pet pair," Torpenhow said. "I was just going to put them on myself."

"All your reprehensible selfishness. Just because you see me happy for a minute, you want to worry me and stir me up. Find another pair."

"Good for you that Dick can't wear your clothes, Torp. You two live communistically," said the Nilghai.

"Dick never has anything that I can wear. He's only useful to sponge upon."

"Confound you, have you been rummaging round among my caches, then?" said Dick. "I put a sovereign in the tobacco-jar yesterday. How do you expect a man to keep his accounts properly if you——"

Here the Nilghai began to laugh, and Torpenhow joined him.

"Hid a sovereign yesterday! You're no sort of a financier. You lent me a fiver about a month back. Do you remember?" Torpenhow said.

"Yes, of course."

"Do you remember that I paid it you ten days later, and you put it at the bottom of the tobacco?"

"By Jove, did I? I thought it was in one of my colour-boxes."

"You thought! About a week ago I went into your studio to get some 'baccy and found it."

"What did you do with it?"

"Took the Nilghai to a theatre and fed him."

"You couldn't feed the Nilghai under twice the money—not though you gave him Army beef. Well, I suppose I should have found it out sooner or later. What is there to laugh at?"

"You're a most amazing cuckoo in many directions," said the Nilghai, still chuckling over the thought of the dinner. "Never mind. We had both been working very hard, and it was your unearned increment we spent, and as you're only a loafer it didn't matter."

"That's pleasant—from the man who is bursting with my meat, too. I'll get that dinner back one of these days. Suppose we go to a theatre now."

"Put our boots on,—and dress,—*and* wash?" The Nilghai spoke very lazily.

"I withdraw the motion."

"Suppose, just for a change—as a startling variety, you know—we, that is to say *we,* get our charcoal and our canvas and go on with our work." Torpenhow spoke pointedly, but Dick only wriggled his toes inside the soft leather moccasins.

"What a one-ideaed clucker it is! If I had any unfinished figures on hand, I haven't any model; if I had my model, I haven't any spray, and I never leave charcoal unfixed overnight; and if I had my spray and twenty photographs of backgrounds, I couldn't do anything to-night. I don't feel that way."

"Binkie-dog, he's a lazy hog, isn't he?" said the Nilghai.

"Very good, I *will* do some work," said Dick, rising swiftly. "I'll fetch the Nungapunga Book, and we'll add another picture to the Nilghai Saga."

"Aren't you worrying him a little too much?" asked the Nilghai, when Dick had left the room.

"Perhaps, but I know what he can turn out if he likes. It makes me savage to hear him praised for past work when I know what he ought to do. You and I are arranged for——"

"By Kismet and our own powers, more's the pity. I have dreamed of a good deal."

"So have I, but we know our limitations now. I'm dashed if I know what Dick's may be when he gives himself to his work. That's what makes me so keen about him."

"And when all's said and done, you will be put aside—quite rightly—for a female girl."

"I wonder . . . Where do you think he has been to-day?"

"To the sea. Didn't you see the look in his eyes when he talked about her? He's as restless as a swallow in autumn."

"Yes; but did he go alone?"

"I don't know, and I don't care, but he has the beginnings of the go-fever upon him. He wants to up-stakes and move out.

There's no mistaking the signs. Whatever he may have said before, he has the call upon him now."

"It might be his salvation," Torpenhow said.

"Perhaps—if you care to take the responsibility of being a saviour."

Dick returned with the big clasped sketch-book that the Nilghai knew well and did not love too much. In it Dick had drawn all manner of moving incidents, experienced by himself or related to him by the others, of all the four corners of the earth. But the wider range of the Nilghai's body and life attracted him most. When truth failed he fell back on fiction of the wildest, and represented incidents in the Nilghai's career that were unseemly,—his marriages with many African princesses, his shameless betrayal, for Arab wives, of an army corps to the Mahdi, his tattooment by skilled operators in Burmah, his interview (and his fears) with the yellow headsman in the blood-stained execution-ground of Canton, and finally, the passings of his spirit into the bodies of whales, elephants, and toucans. Torpenhow from time to time had added rhymed descriptions, and the whole was a curious piece of art, because Dick decided, having regard to the name of the book which being interpreted means "naked," that it would be wrong to draw the Nilghai with any clothes on, under any circumstances. Consequently the last sketch, representing that much-enduring man calling on the War Office to press his claims to the Egyptian medal, was hardly delicate. He settled himself comfortably at Torpenhow's table and turned over the pages.

"What a fortune you would have been to Blake, Nilghai!" he said. "There's a succulent pinkness about some of these sketches that's more than lifelike. 'The Nilghai surrounded while bathing by the Mahdieh'—that was founded on fact, eh?"

"It was very nearly my last bath, you irreverent dauber. Has Binkie come into the Saga yet?"

"No; the Binkie-boy hasn't done anything except eat and kill cats. Let's see. Here you are as a stained-glass saint in a church. Deuced decorative lines about your anatomy; you ought to be grateful for being handed down to posterity in this way. Fifty years hence you'll exist in rare and curious facsimiles at ten guineas each. What shall I try this time? The domestic life of the Nilghai?"

"Hasn't got any."

"The undomestic life of the Nilghai, then. Of course. Mass-meeting of his wives in Trafalgar Square. That's it. They came from the ends of the earth to attend Nilghai's wedding to an English bride. This shall be in sepia. It's a sweet material to work with."

"It's a scandalous waste of time," said Torpenhow.

"Don't worry; it keeps one's hand in—specially when you begin without the pencil." He set to work rapidly. "That's Nelson's Column. Presently the Nilghai will appear shinning up it."

"Give him some clothes this time."

"Certainly—a veil and an orange-wreath, because he's been married."

"Gad, that's clever enough!" said Torpenhow over his shoulder, as Dick brought out of the paper with three twirls of the brush a very fat back and labouring shoulder pressed against the stone.

"Just imagine," Dick continued, "if we could publish a few of these dear little things every time the Nilghai subsidizes a man who can write, to give the public an honest opinion of my pictures."

"Well, you'll admit I always tell you when I have done anything of that kind. I know I can't hammer you as you ought to be hammered, so I give the job to another. Young Maclagan, for instance——"

"No-o—one half-minute, old man; stick your hand out against the dark of the wall-paper—you only burble and call me names. That left shoulder's out of drawing. I must literally throw a veil over that. Where's my penknife? Well, what about Maclagan?"

"I only gave him his riding-orders to—to lambast you on general principles for not producing work that will last."

"Whereupon that young fool,"—Dick threw back his head

and shut one eye as he shifted the page under his hand,—'being left alone with an ink-pot and what he conceived were his own notions, went and spilt them both over me in the papers. You might have engaged a grown man for the business, Nilghai. How do you think the bridal veil looks now, Torp?"

"How the deuce do three dabs and two scratches make the stuff stand away from the body as it does?" said Torpenhow, to whom Dick's methods were always new.

"It just depends on where you put 'em. If Maclagan had known that much about his business he might have done better."

"Why don't you put the damned dabs into something that will stay, then?" insisted the Nilghai, who had really taken considerable trouble in hiring for Dick's benefit the pen of a young gentleman who devoted most of his waking hours to an anxious consideration of the aims and ends of Art, which, he wrote, was one and indivisible.

"Wait a minute till I see how I am going to manage my procession of wives. You seem to have married extensively, and I must rough 'em in with the pencil—Medes, Parthians, Edomites. . . . Now, setting aside the weakness and the wickedness and—and the fat-headedness of deliberately trying to do work that will live as they call it, I'm content with the knowledge that I've done my best up to date, and I shan't do anything like it again for some hours at least—probably years. Most probably never."

"What! any stuff you have in stock your best work?" said Torpenhow.

"Anything you've sold?" said the Nilghai.

"Oh no. It isn't here and it isn't sold. Better than that, it can't be sold, and I don't think any one knows where it is. I'm sure I don't. . . . And yet more and more wives, on the north side of the square. Observe the virtuous horror of the lions!"

"You may as well explain," said Torpenhow, and Dick lifted his head from the paper.

"The sea reminded me of it," he said slowly. "I wish it

hadn't. It weighs some few thousand tons—unless you cut it out with a cold chisel."

"Don't be an idiot. You can't pose with us here," said the Nilghai.

"There's no pose in the matter at all. It's a fact. I was loafing from Lima to Auckland in a big, old, condemned passenger-ship turned into a cargo-boat and owned by a second-hand Italian firm. She was a crazy basket. We were cut down to fifteen ton of coal a day, and we thought ourselves lucky when we kicked seven knots an hour out of her. Then we used to stop and let the bearings cool down, and wonder whether the crack in the shaft was spreading."

"Were you a steward or a stoker in those days?"

"I was flush for the time being, so I was a passenger, or else I should have been a steward, I think," said Dick, with perfect gravity, returning to the procession of angry wives. "I was the only other passenger from Lima, and the ship was half empty, and full of rats and cockroaches and scorpions."

"But what has this to do with the picture?"

"Wait a minute. She had been in the China passenger trade and her lower decks had bunks for two thousand pigtails. Those were all taken down, and she was empty up to her nose, and the lights came through the portholes—most annoying lights to work in till you got used to them. I hadn't anything to do for weeks. The ship's charts were in pieces and our skipper daren't run south for fear of catching a storm. So he did his best to knock all the Society Islands out of the water one by one and I went into the lower deck, and did my picture on the port side as far forward in her as I could go. There was some brown paint and some green paint that they used for the boats, and some black paint for ironwork, and that was all I had."

"The passengers must have thought you mad."

"There was only one, and it was a woman; but it gave me the notion of my picture."

"What was she like?" said Torpenhow.

"She was a sort of Negroid-Jewess-Cuban; with morals to match. She couldn't read or write, and she didn't want to, but she used to come down and watch me paint, and the skipper didn't like it, because he was paying her passage and had to be on the bridge occasionally."

"I see. That must have been cheerful."

"It was the best time I ever had. To begin with, we didn't know whether we should go up or go down any minute when there was a sea on; and when it was calm it was paradise; and the woman used to mix the paints and talk broken English, and the skipper used to steal down every few minutes to the lower deck, because he said he was so afraid of fire. So, you see, we could never tell when we might be caught, and I had a splendid notion to work out in only three keys of colour."

"What was the notion?"

"Two lines in Poe—

Neither the angels in Heaven above nor the demons down under the sea,
Can ever dissever my soul from the soul of the beautiful Annabel Lee.

It came out of the sea—all by itself. I drew that fight, fought out in green water over the naked, choking soul, and the woman served as the model for the devils and the angels both—sea-devils and sea-angels, and the soul half drowned between them. It doesn't sound much, but when there was a good light on the lower deck it looked very fine and creepy. It was seven by fourteen feet, all done in shifting light for shifting light."

"Did the woman inspire you much?" said Torpenhow.

"She and the sea between them—immensely. There was a heap of bad drawing in that picture. I remember I went out of my way to foreshorten for sheer delight of doing it, and I foreshortened damnably, but for all that it's the best thing I've ever done; and now I suppose the ship's broken up or gone down. Whew! What a time that was!"

"What happened after all?"

"It all ended. They were loading her with wool when I left the ship, but even the stevedores kept the picture clear to the last. The eyes of the demons scared them, I honestly believe."

"And the woman?"

"She was scared too when it was finished. She used to cross herself before she went down to look at it. Just three colours and no chance of getting any more, and the sea outside and unlimited love-making inside, and the fear of death atop of everything else, O Lord!" He had ceased to look at the sketch, but was staring straight in front of him across the room.

"Why don't you try something of the same kind now?" said the Nilghai.

"Because those things come not by fasting and prayer. When I find a cargo-boat and a Jewess-Cuban and another notion and the same old life, I may."

"You won't find them here," said the Nilghai.

"No, I shall not." Dick shut the sketch-book with a bang. "This room's as hot as an oven. Open the window, some one."

He leaned into the darkness, watching the greater darkness of London below him. The chambers stood much higher than the other houses, commanding a hundred chimneys—crooked cowls that looked like sitting cats as they swung round, and other uncouth brick and zinc mysteries supported by iron stanchions and clamped by S-pieces. Northward the lights of Piccadilly Circus and Leicester Square threw a copper-coloured glare above the black roofs, and southward by all the orderly lights of the Thames. A train rolled out across one of the railway bridges, and its thunder drowned for a minute the dull roar of the streets. The Nilghai looked at his watch and said shortly, "That's the Paris night-mail. You can book from here to St. Petersburg if you choose."

Dick crammed head and shoulders out of the window and looked across the river. Torpenhow came to his side, while the Nilghai passed over quietly to the piano and opened it. Binkie, making himself as large as possible, spread out upon the sofa with the air of one who is not to be lightly disturbed.

"Well," said the Nilghai to the two pairs of shoulders, "have you never seen this place before?"

A steam-tug on the river hooted as she towed her barges to wharf. Then the boom of the traffic came into the room.

Torpenhow nudged Dick. "Good place to bank in—bad place to bunk in, Dickie, isn't it?"

Dick's chin was in his hand as he answered, in the words of a general not without fame, still looking out on the darkness —" 'My God, what a city to loot!' "

Binkie found the night air tickling his whiskers and sneezed plaintively.

"We shall give the Binkie-dog a cold," said Torpenhow. "Come in," and they withdrew their heads. "You'll be buried in Kensal Green, Dick, one of these days, if it isn't closed by the time you want to go there—buried within two feet of some one else, his wife and his family."

"Allah forbid! I shall get away before that time comes. Give a man room to stretch his legs, Mr. Binkle." Dick flung himself down on the sofa and tweaked Binkie's velvet ears, yawning heavily the while.

"You'll find that wardrobe-case very much out of tune," Torpenhow said to the Nilghai. "It's never touched except by you."

"A piece of gross extravagance," Dick grunted. "The Nilghai only comes when I'm out."

"That's because you're always out. Howl, Nilghai, and let him hear."

"The life of the Nilghai is fraud and slaughter,
His writings are watered Dickens and water;
But the voice of the Nilghai raised on high
Makes even the Mahdieh glad to die!"

Dick quoted from Torpenhow's letterpress in the Nunga-punga Book. "How do they call moose in Canada, Nilghai?"

The man laughed. Singing was his one polite accomplishment, as many Press-tents in far-off lands had known.

"What shall I sing?" said he, turning in the chair.

" 'Moll Roe in the Morning,' " said Torpenhow, at a venture.

"No," said Dick, sharply, and the Nilghai opened his eyes. The old chanty whereof he, among a very few, possessed all the words was not a pretty one, but Dick had heard it many times before without wincing. Without prelude he launched into that stately tune that calls together and troubles the hearts of the gipsies of the sea—

> *"Farewell and adieu to you, Spanish ladies,*
> *Farewell and adieu to you, ladies of Spain."*

Dick turned uneasily on the sofa, for he could hear the bows of the *Barralong* crashing into the green seas on her way to the Southern Cross. Then came the chorus—

> *"We'll rant and we'll roar like true British sailors,*
> *We'll rant and we'll roar across the salt seas,*
> *Until we take soundings in the Channel of Old England*
> *From Ushant to Scilly 'tis forty-five leagues."*

"Thirty-five—thirty-five," said Dick, petulantly. "Don't tamper with Holy Writ. Go on, Nilghai."

> *"The first land we made it was called the Deadman,"*

and they sang to the end very vigorously.

"That would be a better song if her head were turned the other way—to the Ushant light, for instance," said the Nilghai.

"Flinging its arms about like a mad windmill," said Torpenhow. "Give us something else, Nilghai. You're in fine fog-horn form to-night."

"Give us the 'Ganges Pilot': you sang that in the square the night before El-Maghrib. By the way, I wonder how many of the chorus are alive to-night," said Dick.

Torpenhow considered for a minute. "By Jove! I believe only you and I. Raynor, Vickery, and Deenes—all dead; Vincent caught smallpox in Cairo, carried it here and died of it. Yes, only you and I and the Nilghai."

"Umph! And yet the men here who've done their work in

a well-warmed studio all their lives, with a policeman at each corner, say that I charge too much for my pictures."

"They are buying your work, not your insurance policies, dear child," said the Nilghai.

"I gambled with one to get at the other. Don't preach. Go on with the Pilot. Where in the world did you get that song?"

"On a tombstone," said the Nilghai. "On a tombstone in a distant land. I made it an accompaniment with heaps of bass chords."

"Oh, Vanity! Begin." And the Nilghai began—

"I have slipped my cable, messmates, I'm drifting down with the tide,
I have my sailing orders, while ye at anchor ride.
And never on fair June morning have I put out to sea
With clearer conscience or better hope, or a heart more light and free.

"Shoulder to shoulder, Joe, my boy, into the crowd like a wedge.
Strike with the hangers, messmates, but do not cut with the edge.
Cries Charnock, 'Scatter the faggots, double that Brahmin in two,
The tall pale widow for me, Joe, the little brown girl for you!'

"Young Joe (you're nearing sixty), why is your hide so dark?
Katie has soft blue eyes, who blackened yours?—Why, hark!"

They were all singing now, Dick with the roar of the wind of the open sea about his ears as the deep bass voice let itself go.

"The morning gun—Ho, steady! the arquebuses to me!
I ha' sounded the Dutch High Admiral's heart as my lead doth sound the sea.

Sounding, sounding the Ganges, floating down with the tide,
Moor me close to Charnock, next to my nut-brown bride.
My blessing to Kate at Fairlight—Holwell, my thanks to
you;
Steady! We steer for heaven, through sand-drifts cold and
blue."

"Now what is there in that nonsense to make a man restless?" said Dick, hauling Binkie from his feet to his chest.

"It depends on the man," said Torpenhow.

"The man who has been down to look at the sea," said the Nilghai.

"I didn't know she was going to upset me in this fashion."

"That's what men say when they go to say good-bye to a woman. It's more easy though to get rid of three women than a piece of one's life and surroundings."

"But a woman can be——" began Dick, unguardedly.

"A piece of one's life," continued Torpenhow. "No, she can't." His face darkened for a moment. "She says she wants to sympathize with you and help you in your work, and everything else that clearly a man must do for himself. Then she sends round five notes a day to ask why the dickens you haven't been wasting your time with her."

"Don't generalize," said the Nilghai. "By the time you arrive at five notes a day you must have gone through a good deal and behaved accordingly. Shouldn't begin these things, my son."

"I shouldn't have gone down to the sea," said Dick, just a little anxious to change the conversation. "And you shouldn't have sung."

"The sea isn't sending you five notes a day," said the Nilghai.

"No, but I'm fatally compromised. She's an enduring old hag, and I'm sorry I ever met her. Why wasn't I born and bred and dead in a three-pair back?"

"Hear him blaspheming his first love! Why in the world shouldn't you listen to her?" said Torpenhow.

Before Dick could reply the Nilghai lifted up his voice

with a shout that shook the windows, in "The Men of the Sea," that begins, as all know, "The sea is a wicked old woman," and after racing through eight lines whose imagery is truthful, ends in a refrain, slow as the clacking of a capstan when the boat comes unwillingly up to the bars where the men sweat and tramp in the shingle.

> " '*Ye that bore us, O restore us!*
> *She is kinder than ye;*
> *For the call is on our heart-strings!*'
> *Said The Men of the Sea.*"

The Nilghai sang that verse twice, with simple cunning, intending that Dick should hear. But Dick was waiting for the farewell of the men to their wives.

> " '*Ye that love us, can ye move us?*
> *She is dearer than ye;*
> *And your sleep will be the sweeter,*'
> *Said The Men of the Sea.*"

The rough words beat like the blows of the waves on the bows of the rickety boat from Lima in the days when Dick was mixing paints, making love, drawing devils and angels in the half dark, and wondering whether the next minute would put the Italian captain's knife between his shoulder-blades. And the go-fever which is more real than many doctors' diseases, waked and raged, urging him who loved Maisie beyond anything in the world, to go away and taste the old hot, unregenerate life again,—to scuffle, swear, gamble, and love light loves with his fellows; to take ship and know the sea once more, and by her beget pictures; to talk to Binat among the sands of Port Said while Yellow 'Tina mixed the drinks; to hear the crackle of musketry, and see the smoke roll outward, thin and thicken again till the shining black faces came through, and in that hell every man was strictly responsible for his own head, and his own alone, and struck with an unfettered arm. It was impossible, utterly impossible, but—

"'*Oh, our fathers, in the churchyard,*
She is older than ye,
And our graves will be the greener,'
Said The Men of the Sea."

"What *is* there to hinder?" said Torpenhow, in the long hush that followed the song.

"You said a little time since that you wouldn't come for a walk round the world, Torp."

"That was months ago, and I only objected to your making money for travelling expenses. You've shot your bolt here and it has gone home. Go away and do some work, and see some things."

"Get some of the fat off you; you're disgracefully out of condition," said the Nilghai, making a plunge from the chair and grasping a handful of Dick generally over the right ribs. "Soft as putty—pure tallow born of over-feeding. Train it off, Dickie."

"We're all equally gross, Nilghai. Next time you have to take the field you'll sit down, wink your eyes, gasp, and die in a fit."

"Never mind. You go away on a ship. Go to Lima again, or to Brazil. There's always trouble in South America."

"Do you suppose I want to be told where to go? Great Heavens, the only difficulty is to know where I'm to stop. But I shall stay here, as I told you before."

"Then you'll be buried in Kensal Green and turn into adipocere with the others," said Torpenhow. "Are you thinking of commissions in hand? Pay forfeit and go. You've money enough to travel as a king if you please."

"You've the grisliest notions of amusement, Torp. I think I see myself shipping first class on a six-thousand-ton hotel, and asking the third engineer what makes the engines go round, and whether it isn't very warm in the stokehold. Ho! ho! I should ship as a loafer if ever I shipped at all, which I'm not going to do. I shall compromise, and go for a small trip to begin with."

"That's something at any rate. Where will you go?" said

Torpenhow. "It would do you all the good in the world, old man."

The Nilghai saw the twinkle in Dick's eye, and refrained from speech.

"I shall go in the first place to Rathray's stable, where I shall hire one horse, and take him very carefully as far as Richmond Hill. Then I shall walk him back again, in case he should accidentally burst into a lather and make Rathray angry. I shall do that to-morrow, for the sake of air and exercise."

"Bah!" Dick had barely time to throw up his arm and ward off the cushion that the disgusted Torpenhow heaved at his head.

"Air and exercise indeed," said the Nilghai, sitting down heavily on Dick. "Let's give him a little of both. Get the bellows, Torp."

At this point the conference broke up in disorder, because Dick would not open his mouth till the Nilghai held his nose fast, and there was some trouble in forcing the nozzle of the bellows between his teeth; and even when it was there he weakly tried to puff against the force of the blast, and his cheeks blew up with a great explosion; and the enemy becoming helpless with laughter he so beat them over the head with a soft sofa cushion that that became unsewn and distributed its feathers, and Binkie, interfering in Torpenhow's interests, was bundled into the half-empty bag and advised to scratch his way out, which he did after a while, travelling rapidly up and down the floor in the shape of an agitated green haggis, and when he came out looking for satisfaction, the three pillars of his world were picking feathers out of their hair.

"A prophet has no honour in his own country," said Dick, ruefully, dusting his knees. "This filthy fluff will never brush off my bags."

"It was all for your good," said the Nilghai. "Nothing like air and exercise."

"All for your good," said Torpenhow, not in the least with reference to past clowning. "It would let you focus things at their proper worth and prevent your becoming slack in this hothouse of a town. Indeed it would, old man. I shouldn't have spoken if I hadn't thought so. Only, you make a joke of everything."

"Before God I do no such thing," said Dick, quickly and earnestly. "You don't know me if you think that."

"*I* don't think it," said the Nilghai.

"How can fellows like ourselves, who know what life and death really mean, dare to make a joke of anything? I know we pretend it, to save ourselves from breaking down or going to the other extreme. Can't I see, old man, how you're always anxious about me, and try to advise me to make my work better? Do you suppose I don't think about that myself? But you can't help me—you can't help me—not even you. I must play my own hand alone in my own way."

"Hear, hear," from the Nilghai.

"What's the one thing in the Nilghai Saga that I've never drawn in the Nungapunga Book?" Dick continued to Torpenhow, who was a little astonished at the outburst.

Now there was one blank page in the book given over to the sketch that Dick had not drawn of the crowning exploit in the Nilghai's life; when that man, being young, and forgetting that his body and bones belonged to the paper that employed him, had ridden over sunburned slippery grass in the rear of Bredow's brigade on the day that the troopers flung themselves at Canrobert's artillery, and for aught they knew twenty battalions in front, to save the battered 24th German Infantry, to give time to decide the fate of Vionville, and to learn ere their remnant came back to Flavigay that cavalry can attack and crumple and break unshaken infantry. Whenever he was inclined to think over a life that might have been better, an income that might have been larger, and a soul that might have been considerably cleaner, the Nilghai would comfort himself with the thought, "I rode with Bredow's brigade at Vionville," and take heart for any lesser battle the next day might bring.

"I know," he said very gravely. "I was always glad that you left it out."

"I left it out because Nilghai taught me what the German

army learned then, and what Schmidt taught their cavalry. I don't know German. What is it? 'Take care of the time and the dressing will take care of itself.' I must ride my own line to my own beat, old man."

"*Tempo ist richtung.* You've learned your lesson well," said the Nilghai. "He must go alone. He speaks truth, Torp."

"Maybe I'm as wrong as I can be—hideously wrong. I must find that out for myself, as I have to think things out for myself, but I daren't turn my head to dress by the next man. It hurts me a great deal more than you know not to be able to go, but I cannot, that's all. I must do my own work and live my own life in my own way, because I'm responsible for both. Only don't think I frivol about it, Torp. I have my own matches and sulphur, and I'll make my own hell, thanks."

There was an uncomfortable pause. Then Torpenhow said blandly, "What did the Governor of North Carolina say to the Governor of South Carolina?"

"Excellent notion. It *is* a long time between drinks. There are the makings of a very fine prig in you, Dick," said the Nilghai.

"I've liberated my mind, estimable Binkie, with the feathers in his mouth." Dick picked up the still indignant one and shook him tenderly. "You're tied up in a sack and made to run about blind, Binkie-wee, without any reason, and it has hurt your little feelings. Never mind. *Sic volo, sic jubeo, stet pro ratione voluntas,* and don't sneeze in my eye because I talk Latin. Good-night."

He went out of the room.

"That's distinctly one for you," said the Nilghai. "I told you it was hopeless to meddle with him. He's not pleased."

"He'd swear at me if he weren't. I can't make it out. He has the go-fever upon him and he won't go. I only hope that he mayn't have to go some day when he doesn't want to," said Torpenhow.

. . . .

In his own room Dick was settling a question with himself —and the question was whether all the world, and all that was therein, and a burning desire to exploit both, was worth one threepenny piece thrown into the Thames.

"It came of seeing the sea, and I'm a cur to think about it," he decided. "After all, the honeymoon will be that tour—with reservations; only . . . only I didn't realize that the sea was so strong. I didn't feel it so much when I was with Maisie. These damnable songs did it. He's beginning again."

But it was only Herrick's Nightpiece to Julia that the Nilghai sang, and before it was ended Dick reappeared on the threshold, not altogether clothed indeed, but in his right mind, thirsty and at peace.

The mood had come and gone with the rising and the falling of the tide by Fort Keeling.

CHAPTER IX

"If I have taken the common clay
And wrought it cunningly
In the shape of a god that was digged a clod,
The greater honour to me."

"If thou hast taken the common clay,
And thy hands be not free
From the taint of the soil, thou hast made thy spoil
The greater shame to thee."

—THE TWO POTTERS

HE DID no work of any kind for the rest of the week. Then came another Sunday. He dreaded and longed for the day always, but since the red-haired girl had sketched him there was rather more dread than desire in his mind.

He found that Maisie had entirely neglected his suggestions about line-work. She had gone off at score filled with some absurd notion for a "fancy head." It cost Dick something to command his temper.

"What's the good of suggesting anything?" he said pointedly.

"Ah, but this will be a picture,—a real picture; and I know

that Kami will let me send it to the Salon. You don't mind, do you?"

"I suppose not. But you won't have time for the Salon."

Maisie hesitated a little. She even felt uncomfortable.

"We're going over to France a month sooner because of it. I shall get the idea sketched out here and work it up at Kami's."

Dick's heart stood still, and he came very near to being disgusted with his queen who could do no wrong. "Just when I thought I had made some headway, she goes off chasing butterflies. It's too maddening!"

There was no possibility of arguing, for the red-haired girl was in the studio. Dick could only look unutterable reproach.

"I'm sorry," he said, "and I think you make a mistake. But what's the idea of your new picture?"

"I took it from a book."

"That's bad, to begin with. Books aren't the place for pictures. And——"

"It's this," said the red-haired girl behind him. "I was reading it to Maisie the other day from *The City of Dreadful Night*. D'you know the book?"

"A little. I am sorry I spoke. There are pictures in it. What has taken her fancy?"

"The description of the Melancolia—

"Her folded wings as of a mighty eagle,
But all too impotent to lift the regal
Robustness of her earth-born strength and pride.

And here again. (Maisie, get the tea, dear.)

"The forehead charged with baleful thoughts and dreams.
The household bunch of keys, the housewife's gown,
Voluminous indented, and yet rigid
As though a shell of burnished metal frigid,
Her feet thick-shod to tread all weakness down."

There was no attempt to conceal the scorn of the lazy voice. Dick winced.

"But that has been done already by an obscure artist by the name of Dürer," said he. "How does the poem run?—

"Three centuries and threescore years ago,
With phantasies of his peculiar thought.

You might as well try to rewrite *Hamlet*. It will be waste of time."

"No, it won't," said Maisie, putting down the teacups with a clatter to reassure herself. "And I mean to do it. Can't you see what a beautiful thing it would make?"

"How in perdition can one do work when one hasn't had the proper training? Any fool can get a notion. It needs training to drive the thing through,—training and conviction; not rushing after the first fancy." Dick spoke between his teeth.

"You don't understand," said Maisie. "I think I can do it."

Again the voice of the girl behind him—

"Baffled and beaten back, she works on still;
Weary and sick of soul, she works the more.
Sustained by her indomitable will,
The hands shall fashion, and the brain shall pore,
And all her sorrow shall be turned to labour——

I fancy Maisie means to embody herself in the picture."

"Sitting on a throne of rejected pictures? No, I shan't, dear. The notion in itself has fascinated me.—Of course you don't care for fancy heads, Dick. I don't think you could do them. You like blood and bones."

"That's a direct challenge. If you can do a Melancolia that isn't merely a sorrowful female head, I can do a better one; and I will, too. What d'you know about Melancolias?" Dick firmly believed that he was even then tasting three-quarters of all the sorrow in the world.

"She was a woman," said Maisie, "and she suffered a great deal,—till she could suffer no more. Then she began to laugh at it all, and then I painted her and sent her to the Salon."

The red-haired girl rose up and left the room, laughing.

Dick looked at Maisie humbly and hopelessly.

"Never mind about the picture," he said. "Are you really going back to Kami's a month before your time?"

"I must, if I want to get the picture done."

"And that's all you want?"

"Of course. Don't be stupid, Dick."

"You haven't the power. You have only the ideas—the ideas and the little cheap impulses. How you could have kept at your work for ten years steadily is a mystery to me. So you are really going,—a month before you need?"

"I must do my work."

"Your work—bah! . . . No, I didn't mean that. It's all right, dear. Of course you must do your work, and—I think I'll say good-bye for this week."

"Won't you even stay for tea?"

"No, thank you. Have I your leave to go, dear? There's nothing more you particularly want me to do, and the line-work doesn't matter."

"I wish you could stay, and then we could talk over my picture. If only one single picture's a success, it draws attention to all the others. I know some of my work is good, if only people could see. And you needn't have been so rude about it."

"I'm sorry. We'll talk the Melancolia over some one of the other Sundays. There are four more—yes, one, two, three, four—before you go. Good-bye, Maisie."

Maisie stood by the studio window, thinking, till the red-haired girl returned, a little white at the corners of her lips.

"Dick's gone off," said Maisie. "Just when I wanted to talk about the picture. Isn't it selfish of him?"

Her companion opened her lips as if to speak, shut them again, and went on reading *The City of Dreadful Night.*

Dick was in the Park, walking round and round a tree that he had chosen as his confidante for many Sundays past. He was swearing audibly, and when he found that the infirmities of the English tongue hemmed in his rage, he sought consolation in Arabic, which is expressly designed for the use of the afflicted. He was not pleased with the reward of his patient service; nor was he pleased with himself; and it was long before he arrived at the proposition that the queen could do no wrong.

"It's a losing game," he said. "I'm worth nothing when a whim of hers is in question. But in a losing game at Port Said we used to double the stakes and go on. She do a Melancolia! She hasn't the power, or the insight, or the training. Only the desire. She's cursed with the curse of Reuben. She won't do line-work, because it means real work; and yet she's stronger than I am. I'll make her understand that I can beat her on her own Melancolia. Even then she wouldn't care. She says I can only do blood and bones. I don't believe she has blood in her veins. All the same I love her; and I must go on loving her; and if I can humble her inordinate vanity I will. I'll do a Melancolia that shall be something like a Melancolia—'the Melancolia that transcends all wit.' I'll do it at once, con—bless her."

He discovered that the notion would not come to order, and that he could not free his mind for an hour from the thought of Maisie's departure. He took very small interest in her rough studies for the Melancolia when she showed them next week. The Sundays were racing past, and the time was at hand when all the church bells in London could not ring Maisie back to him. Once or twice he said something to Binkie about "hermaphroditic futilities," but the little dog received so many confidences both from Torpenhow and Dick that he did not trouble his tulip-ears to listen.

Dick was permitted to see the girls off. They were going by the Dover night-boat; and they hoped to return in August. It was then February, and Dick felt that he was being hardly used. Maisie was so busy stripping the small house across the Park, and packing her canvases, that she had no time for thought. Dick went down to Dover and wasted a day there fretting over a wonderful possibility. Would Maisie at the very last allow him one small kiss? He reflected that he might capture her by the strong arm, as he had seen women captured in the Southern Soudan, and lead her away; but Maisie would never be led. She would turn her gray eyes upon him and say,

"Dick, how selfish you are!" Then his courage would fail him. It would be better, after all, to beg for that kiss.

Maisie looked more than usually kissable as she stepped from the night-mail on to the windy pier, in a gray waterproof and a little gray cloth travelling-cap. The red-haired girl was not so lovely. Her green eyes were hollow and her lips were dry. Dick saw the trunks aboard, and went to Maisie's side in the darkness under the bridge. The mail-bags were thundering into the forehold, and the red-haired girl was watching them.

"You'll have a rough passage to-night," said Dick. "It's blowing outside. I suppose I may come over and see you if I'm good?"

"You mustn't. I shall be busy. At least, if I want you I'll send for you. But I shall write from Vitry-sur-Marne. I shall have heaps of things to consult you about. Oh, Dick, you have been so good to me!—so good to me!"

"Thank you for that, dear. It hasn't made any difference, has it?"

"I can't tell a fib. It hasn't—in that way. But don't think I'm not grateful."

"Damn the gratitude!" said Dick, huskily, to the paddle-box.

"What's the use of worrying? You know I should ruin your life, and you'd ruin mine, as things are now. You remember what you said when you were so angry that day in the Park? One of us has to be broken. Can't you wait till that day comes?"

"No, love. I want you unbroken—all to myself."

Maisie shook her head. "My poor Dick, what can I say!"

"Don't say anything. Give me a kiss. Only one kiss, Maisie. I'll swear I won't take any more. You might as well, and then I can be sure you're grateful."

Maisie put her cheek forward, and Dick took his reward in the darkness. It was only one kiss, but, since there was no time-limit specified, it was a long one. Maisie wrenched herself free angrily, and Dick stood abashed and tingling from head to heel.

"Good-bye, darling. I didn't mean to scare you. I'm sorry. Only—keep well and do good work,—specially the Melancolia. I'm going to do one, too. Remember me to Kami, and be careful what you drink. Country drinking-water is bad everywhere, but it's worse in France. Write to me if you want anything, and good-bye. Say good-bye to the what-you-call-um girl, and—can't I have another kiss? No. You're quite right. Good-bye."

A shout told him that it was not seemly to charge up the mail-bag incline. He reached the pier as the steamer began to move off, and he followed her with his heart.

"And there's nothing—nothing in the wide world—to keep us apart except her obstinacy. These Calais night-boats are much too small. I'll get Torp to write to the papers about it. She's beginning to pitch already."

Maisie stood where Dick had left her till she heard a little gasping cough at her elbow. The red-haired girl's eyes were alight with cold flame.

"He kissed you!" she said. "How could you let him, when he wasn't anything to you? How dared you take a kiss from him? Oh, Maisie, let's go to the ladies' cabin. I'm sick,—deadly sick."

"We aren't into open water yet. Go down, dear, and I'll stay here. I don't like the smell of the engines. . . . Poor Dick! He deserved one,—only one. But I didn't think he'd frighten me so."

Dick returned to town next day just in time for lunch, for which he had telegraphed. To his disgust, there were only empty plates in the studio. He lifted up his voice like the bears in the fairy-tale, and Torpenhow entered, looking guilty.

"H'sh!" said he. "Don't make such a noise. I took it. Come into my rooms, and I'll show you why."

Dick paused amazed at the threshold, for on Torpenhow's sofa lay a girl asleep and breathing heavily. The little cheap sailor-hat, the blue-and-white dress, fitter for June than for February, dabbled with mud at the skirts, the jacket trimmed with imitation Astrakhan and ripped at the shoulder-seams, the one-and-elevenpenny umbrella, and, above all, the disgraceful condition of the kid-topped boots, declared all things.

"Oh, I say, old man, this is too bad! You mustn't bring this sort up here. They steal things from the rooms."

"It looks bad, I admit, but I was coming in after lunch, and she staggered into the hall. I thought she was drunk at first, but it was collapse. I couldn't leave her as she was, so I brought her up here and gave her your lunch. She was fainting from want of food. She went fast asleep the minute she had finished."

"I know something of that complaint. She's been living on sausages, I suppose. Torp, you should have handed her over to a policeman for presuming to faint in a respectable house. Poor little wretch! Look at that face! There isn't an ounce of immorality in it. Only folly,—slack, fatuous, feeble, futile folly. It's a typical head. D'you notice how the skull begins to show through the flesh padding on the face and cheekbone?"

"What a cold-blooded barbarian it is! Don't hit a woman when she's down. Can't we do anything? She was simply dropping with starvation. She almost fell into my arms, and when she got to the food she ate like a wild beast. It was horrible."

"I can give her money, which she would probably spend in drinks. Is she going to sleep for ever?"

The girl opened her eyes and glared at the men between terror and effrontery.

"Feeling better?" said Torpenhow.

"Yes. Thank you. There aren't many gentlemen that are as kind as you are. Thank you."

"When did you leave service?" said Dick, who had been watching the scarred and chapped hands.

"How did you know I was in service? I was. General servant. I didn't like it."

"And how do you like being your own mistress?"

"Do I look as if I liked it?"

"I suppose not. One moment. Would you be good enough to turn your face to the window?"

The girl obeyed, and Dick watched her face keenly,—so keenly that she made as if to hide behind Torpenhow.

"The eyes have it," said Dick, walking up and down. "They are superb eyes for my business. And, after all, every head depends on the eyes. This has been sent from heaven to make up for—what was taken away. Now the weekly strain's off my shoulders, I can get to work in earnest. Evidently sent from heaven. Yes. Raise your chin a little, please."

"Gently, old man, gently. You're scaring somebody out of her wits," said Torpenhow, who could see the girl trembling.

"Don't let him hit me! Oh, please don't let him hit me. I've been hit cruel to-day because I spoke to a man. Don't let him look at me like that! He's reg'lar wicked, that one. Don't let him look at me like that, neither! Oh, I feel as if I hadn't nothing on when he looks at me like that!"

The overstrained nerves in the frail body gave way, and the girl wept like a little child and began to scream. Dick threw open the window, and Torpenhow flung the door back.

"There you are," said Dick, soothingly. "My friend here can call for a policeman, and you can run through that door. Nobody is going to hurt you."

The girl sobbed convulsively for a few minutes, and then tried to laugh.

"Nothing in the world to hurt you. Now listen to me for a minute. I'm what they call an artist by profession. You know what artists do?"

"They draw the things in red and black ink on the pop-shop labels."

"I dare say. I haven't risen to pop-shop labels yet. Those are done by the Academicians. I want to draw your head."

"What for?"

"Because it's pretty. That is why you will come to the room across the landing three times a week at eleven in the morning, and I'll give you three quid a week just for sitting still and being drawn. And there's a quid on account."

"For nothing? Oh, my!" The girl turned the sovereign in her hand, and with more foolish tears, "Ain't neither o' you two gentlemen afraid of my bilking you?"

"No. Only ugly girls do that. Try and remember this place. And, by the way, what's your name?"

"I'm Bessie,—Bessie—— It's no use giving the rest. Bessie Broke,—Stone-broke, if you like. What's your names? But there,—no one ever gives the real ones."

Dick consulted Torpenhow with his eyes.

"My name's Heldar, and my friend's called Torpenhow; and you must be sure to come here. Where do you live?"

"South-the-water,—one room,—five and sixpence a week. Aren't you making fun of me about that three quid?"

"You'll see later on. And, Bessie, next time you come, remember, you needn't wear that paint. It's bad for the skin, and I have all the colours you'll be likely to need."

Bessie withdrew, scrubbing her cheek with a ragged pocket-handkerchief. The two men looked at each other.

"You're a man," said Torpenhow.

"I'm afraid I've been a fool. It isn't our business to run about the earth reforming Bessie Brokes. And a woman of any kind has no right on this landing."

"Perhaps she won't come back."

"She will if she thinks she can get food and warmth here. I know she will, worse luck. But remember, old man, she isn't a woman: she's my model; and be careful."

"The idea! She's a dissolute little scarecrow,—a gutter-snippet and nothing more."

"So you think. Wait till she has been fed a little and freed from fear. That fair type recovers itself very quickly. You won't know her in a week or two, when that abject fear has died out of her eyes. She'll be too happy and smiling for my purposes."

"But surely you're taking her out of charity?—to please me?"

"I'm not in the habit of playing with hot coals to please anybody. She has been sent from heaven, as I may have remarked before, to help me with my Melancolia."

"Never heard a word about the lady before."

"What's the use of having a friend, if you must sling your notions at him in words? You ought to know what I'm thinking about. You've heard me grunt lately?"

"Even so; but grunts mean anything in your language, from

bad 'baccy to wicked dealers. And I don't think I've been much in your confidence for some time."

"It was a high and soulful grunt. You ought to have understood that it meant the Melancolia." Dick walked Torpenhow up and down the room, keeping silence. Then he smote him in the ribs. "*Now* don't you see it? Bessie's abject futility, and the terror in her eyes, welded on to one or two details in the way of sorrow that have come under my experience lately. Likewise some orange and black,—two keys of each. But I can't explain on an empty stomach."

"It sounds mad enough. You'd better stick to your soldiers, Dick, instead of maundering about heads and eyes and experiences."

"Think so?" Dick began to dance on his heels, singing—

"They're as proud as a turkey when they hold the ready cash,
You ought to 'ear the way they laugh an' joke;
They are tricky an' they're funny when they've got the ready money,—
Ow! but see' em when they're all stone-broke."

Then he sat down to pour out his heart to Maisie in a four-sheet letter of counsel and encouragement, and registered an oath that he would get to work with an undivided heart as soon as Bessie should reappear.

The girl kept her appointment unpainted and unadorned, afraid and overbold by turns. When she found that she was merely expected to sit still, she grew calmer, and criticized the appointments of the studio with freedom and some point. She liked the warmth and the comfort and the release from fear of physical pain. Dick made two or three studies of her head in monochrome, but the actual notion of the Melancolia would not arrive.

"What a mess you keep your things in!" said Bessie, some days later, when she felt herself thoroughly at home. "I s'pose your clothes are just as bad. Gentlemen never think what buttons and tape are made for."

"I buy things to wear, and wear 'em till they go to pieces. I don't know what Torpenhow does."

Bessie made diligent inquiry in the latter's room, and unearthed a bale of disreputable socks. "Some of these I'll mend now," she said, "and some I'll take home. D'you know, I sit all day long at home doing nothing, just like a lady, and no more noticing them other girls in the house than if they was so many flies. I don't have any unnecessary words, but I put 'em down quick, I can tell you, when they talk to me. No; it's quite nice these days. I lock my door, and they can only call me names through the keyhole, and I sit inside, just like a lady, mending socks. Mr. Torpenhow wears his socks out both ends at once."

"Three quid a week from me, and the delights of my society. No socks mended. Nothing from Torp except a nod on the landing now and again, and all his socks mended. Bessie is very much a woman," thought Dick; and he looked at her between half-shut eyes. Food and rest had transformed the girl, as Dick knew they would.

"What are you looking at me like that for?" she said quickly. "Don't. You look reg'lar bad when you look that way. You don't think much o' me, do you?"

"That depends on how you behave."

Bessie behaved beautifully. Only it was difficult at the end of a sitting to bid her go out into the gray streets. She very much preferred the studio and a big chair by the stove, with some socks in her lap as an excuse for delay. Then Torpenhow would come in, and Bessie would be moved to tell strange and wonderful stories of her past, and still stranger ones of her present improved circumstances. She would make them tea as though she had a right to make it; and once or twice on these occasions Dick caught Torpenhow's eyes fixed on the trim little figure, and because Bessie's flittings about the room made Dick ardently long for Maisie, he realized whither Torpenhow's thoughts were tending. And Bessie was exceedingly careful of the condition of Torpenhow's linen. She spoke very little to him, but sometimes they talked together on the landing.

"I was a great fool," Dick said to himself. "I know what red firelight looks like when a man's tramping through a strange town; and ours is a lonely, selfish sort of life at the best. I wonder Maisie doesn't feel that sometimes. But I can't order Bessie away. That's the worst of beginning things. One never knows where they stop."

One evening, after a sitting prolonged to the last limit of the light, Dick was roused from a nap by a broken voice in Torpenhow's room. He jumped to his feet. "Now what ought I to do? It looks foolish to go in.—Oh, bless you, Binkie!" The little terrier thrust Torpenhow's door open with his nose and came out to take possession of Dick's chair. The door swung wide unheeded, and Dick across the landing could see Bessie in the half light making her little supplication to Torpenhow. She was kneeling by his side, and her hands were clasped across his knee.

"I know,—I know," she said thickly. " 'Tisn't right o' me to do this, but I can't help it; and you were so kind,—so kind; and you never took any notice o' me. And I've mended all your things so carefully,—I did. Oh, please, 'tisn't as if I was asking you to marry me. I wouldn't think of it. But cou—couldn't you take and live with me till Miss Right comes along? I'm only Miss Wrong, I know, but I'd work my hands to the bare bone for you. And I'm not ugly to look at. Say you will!"

Dick hardly recognized Torpenhow's voice in reply—

"But look here. It's no use. I'm liable to be ordered off anywhere at a minute's notice if a war breaks out. At a minute's notice—dear."

"What does that matter? Until you go, then. Until you go. 'Tisn't much I'm asking, and—you don't know how good I can cook." She had put an arm round his neck and was drawing his head down.

"Until—I—go, then."

"Torp," said Dick, across the landing. He could hardly steady his voice. "Come here a minute, old man. I'm in trouble."—"Heaven send he'll listen to me!" There was something very like an oath from Bessie's lips. She was afraid of

Dick, and disappeared down the staircase in panic, but it seemed an age before Torpenhow entered the studio. He went to the mantelpiece, buried his head on his arms, and groaned like a wounded bull.

"What the devil right have you to interfere?" he said, at last.

"Who's interfering with which? Your own sense told you long ago you couldn't be such a fool. It was a tough rack, St. Anthony, but you're all right now."

"I oughtn't to have seen her moving about these rooms as if they belonged to her. That's what upset me. It gives a lonely man a sort of hankering, doesn't it?" said Torpenhow, piteously.

"Now you talk sense. It does. But, since you aren't in a condition to discuss the disadvantages of double housekeeping, do you know what you're going to do?"

"I don't. I wish I did."

"You're going away for a season on a brilliant tour to regain tone. You're going to Brighton, or Scarborough, or Prawle Point, to see the ships go by. And you're going at once. Isn't it odd? I'll take care of Binkie, but out you go immediately. Never resist the devil. He holds the bank. Fly from him. Pack your things and go."

"I believe you're right. Where shall I go?"

"And you call yourself a special correspondent! Pack first and inquire afterwards."

An hour later Torpenhow was despatched into the night in a hansom. "You'll probably think of some place to go to while you're moving," said Dick. "Go to Euston, to begin with, and—oh yes—get drunk to-night."

He returned to the studio, and lighted more candles, for he found the room very dark.

"Oh, you Jezebel! you futile little Jezebel! Won't you hate me to-morrow!—Binkie, come here."

Binkie turned over on his back on the hearthrug, and Dick stirred him with a meditative foot.

"I said she was not immoral. I was wrong. She said she could cook. That showed premeditated sin. Oh, Binkie, if you are a man you will go to perdition; but if you are a woman, and say that you can cook, you will go to a much worse place."

CHAPTER X

What's yon that follows at my side?—
The foe that ye must fight, my lord.—
That hirples swift as I can ride?—
The shadow of the night, my lord.—
Then wheel my horse against the foe!—
He's down and overpast, my lord.
Ye war against the sunset glow:
The darkness gathers fast, my lord.

—THE FIGHT OF HERIOT'S FORD

"THIS is a cheerful life," said Dick, some days later. "Torp's away; Bessie hates me; I can't get at the notion of the Melancolia; Maisie's letters are scrappy; and I believe I have indigestion. What gives a man pains across his head and spots before his eyes, Binkie? Shall us take some liver pills?"

Dick had just gone through a lively scene with Bessie. She had for the fiftieth time reproached him for sending Torpenhow away. She explained her enduring hatred for Dick, and made it clear to him that she only sat for the sake of his money. "And Mr. Torpenhow's ten times a better man than you," she concluded.

"He is. That's why he went away. *I* should have stayed and made love to you."

The girl sat with her chin on her hand, scowling. "To me! I'd like to catch you! If I wasn't afraid o' being hung I'd kill you. That's what I'd do. D'you believe me?"

Dick smiled wearily. It is not pleasant to live in the company of a notion that will not work out, a fox-terrier that cannot talk, and a woman who talks too much. He would have answered, but at that moment there unrolled itself from one corner of the studio a veil, as it were, of the filmiest gauze. He rubbed his eyes, but the gray haze would not go.

"This is disgraceful indigestion. Binkie, we will go to a medicine-man. We can't have our eyes interfered with, for by these we get our bread; also mutton-chop bones for little dogs."

The doctor was an affable local practitioner with white hair, and he said nothing till Dick began to describe the gray film in the studio.

"We all want a little patching and repairing from time to time," he chirped. "Like a ship, my dear sir,—exactly like a ship. Sometimes the hull is out of order, and we consult the surgeon; sometimes the rigging, and then I advise; sometimes the engines, and we go to the brain-specialist; sometimes the look-out on the bridge is tired, and then we see an oculist. I should recommend you to see an oculist. A little patching and repairing from time to time is all we want. An oculist, by all means."

Dick sought an oculist,—the best in London. He was certain that the local practitioner did not know anything about his trade, and more certain that Maisie would laugh at him if he were forced to wear spectacles.

"I've neglected the warnings of my lord the stomach too long. Hence these spots before the eyes, Binkie. I can see as well as I ever could."

As he entered the dark hall that led to the consulting-room a man cannoned against him. Dick saw the face as it hurried out into the street.

"That's the writer-type. He has the same modelling of the forehead as Torp. He looks very sick. Probably heard something he didn't like."

Even as he thought, a great fear came upon Dick, a fear that made him hold his breath as he walked into the oculist's waiting room, with the heavy carved furniture, the dark-green paper, and the sober-hued prints on the wall. He recognized a reproduction of one of his own sketches.

Many people were waiting their turn before him. His eye was caught by a flaming red-and-gold Christmas-carol book. Little children came to that eye-doctor, and they needed large-type amusement.

"That's idolatrous bad Art," he said, drawing the book towards himself. "From the anatomy of the angels, it has been made in Germany." He opened it mechanically, and there leaped to his eyes a verse printed in red ink—

The next good joy that Mary had,
It was the joy of three,
To see her good Son Jesus Christ
Making the blind to see:
Making the blind to see, good Lord,
And happy may we be.
Praise Father, Son, and Holy Ghost
To all eternity!

Dick read and re-read the verse till his turn came, and the doctor was bending above him seated in an arm-chair. The blaze of the gas-microscope in his eyes made him wince. The doctor's hand touched the scar of the sword-cut on Dick's head, and Dick explained briefly how he had come by it. When the flame was removed, Dick saw the doctor's face, and the fear came upon him again. The doctor wrapped himself in a mist of words. Dick caught allusions to "scar," "frontal bone," "optic nerve," "extreme caution," and the "avoidance of mental anxiety."

"Verdict?" he said faintly. "My business is painting, and I daren't waste time. What do you make of it?"

Again the whirl of words, but this time they conveyed a meaning.

"Can you give me anything to drink?"

Many sentences were pronounced in that darkened room, and the prisoners often needed cheering. Dick found a glass of liqueur brandy in his hand.

"As far as I can gather," he said, coughing above the spirit, "you call it decay of the optic nerve, or something, and therefore hopeless. What is my time-limit, avoiding all strain and worry?"

"Perhaps one year."

"My God! And if I do not take care of myself?"

"I really could not say. One cannot ascertain the exact amount of injury inflicted by the sword-cut. The scar is an old one, and—exposure to the strong light of the desert, did you say?—with excessive application to fine work? I really could not say."

"I beg your pardon, but it has come without any warning. If you will let me, I'll sit here for a minute, and then I'll go. You have been very good in telling me the truth. Without any warning; without any warning. Thanks."

Dick went into the street, and was rapturously received by Binkie. "We've got it very badly, little dog! Just as badly as we can get it. We'll go to the Park to think it out."

They headed for a certain tree that Dick knew well, and they sat down to think, because his legs were trembling under him and there was cold fear at the pit of his stomach.

"How could it have come without any warning? It's as sudden as being shot. It's the living death, Binkie. We're to be shut up in the dark in one year if we're careful, and we shan't see anybody, and we shall never have anything we want, not though we live to be a hundred." Binkie wagged his tail joyously. "Binkie, we must think. Let's see how it feels to be blind." Dick shut his eyes, and flaming commas and Catherine-wheels floated inside the lids. Yet when he looked across the Park the scope of his vision was not contracted. He could see perfectly, until a procession of slow-wheeling fireworks defiled across his eyeballs.

"Little dorglums, we aren't at all well. Let's go home. If only Torp were back, now!"

But Torpenhow was in the south of England, inspecting dockyards in the company of the Nilghai. His letters were brief and full of mystery.

Dick had never asked anybody to help him in his joys or his sorrows. He argued, in the loneliness of the studio, henceforward to be decorated with a film of gray gauze in one corner, that, if his fate were blindness, all the Torpenhows in the world could not save him. "I can't call him off his trip to sit down and sympathize with me. I must pull through the business alone," he said. He was lying on the sofa, eating his moustache and wondering what the darkness of the night would be like. Then came to his mind the memory of a quaint scene in the Soudan. A soldier had been nearly hacked in two by a broad-bladed Arab spear. For one instant the man felt no pain. Looking down, he saw that his life-blood was going from him. The stupid bewilderment on his face was so intensely comic that both Dick and Torpenhow, still panting and unstrung from a fight for life, had roared with laughter, in which the man seemed as if he would join, but, as his lips parted in a sheepish grin, the agony of death came upon him, and he pitched grunting at their feet. Dick laughed again, remembering the horror. It seemed so exactly like his own case. "But I have a little more time allowed me," he said. He paced up and down the room, quietly at first, but afterwards with the hurried feet of fear. It was as though a black shadow stood at his elbow and urged him to go forward; and there were only weaving circles and floating pin-dots before his eyes.

"We must be calm, Binkie; we must be calm." He talked aloud for the sake of distraction. "This isn't nice at all. What shall we do? We must do something. Our time is short. I shouldn't have believed that this morning; but now things are different. Binkie, where was Moses when the light went out?"

Binkie smiled from ear to ear, as a well-bred terrier should, but made no suggestion.

" 'Were there but world enough and time, This coyness, Binkie, were no crime. . . . But at my back I always hear ——' " He wiped his forehead, which was unpleasantly damp. "What can I do? What can I do? I haven't any notions left, and I can't think connectedly, but I must do something, or I shall go off my head."

The hurried walk recommenced, Dick stopping every now and again to drag forth long-neglected canvases and old note-books; for he turned to his work by instinct, as a thing that could not fail. "You won't do, and you won't do," he said, at each inspection. "No more soldiers. I couldn't paint 'em. Sudden death comes home too nearly, and this is battle and murder both for me."

The day was failing, and Dick thought for a moment that

the twilight of the blind had come upon him unawares. "Allah Almighty!" he cried despairingly, "help me through the time of waiting, and I won't whine when my punishment comes. What can I do now, before the light goes?"

There was no answer. Dick waited till he could regain some sort of control over himself. His hands were shaking, and he prided himself on their steadiness; he could feel that his lips were quivering, and the sweat was running down his face. He was lashed by fear, driven forward by the desire to get to work at once and accomplish something, and maddened by the refusal of his brain to do more than repeat the news that he was about to go blind. "It's a humiliating exhibition," he thought, "and I'm glad Torp isn't here to see. The doctor said I was to avoid mental worry. Come here and let me pet you, Binkie."

The little dog yelped because Dick nearly squeezed the bark out of him. Then he heard the man speaking in the twilight, and, doglike, understood that his trouble stood off from him—

"Allah is good, Binkie. Not quite so gentle as we could wish, but we'll discuss that later. I think I see my way to it now. All those studies of Bessie's head were nonsense, and they nearly brought your master into a scrape. I hold the notion now as clear as crystal,—'the Melancolia that transcends all wit.' There shall be Maisie in that head, because I shall never get Maisie; and Bess, of course, because she knows all about Melancolia, though she doesn't know she knows; and there shall be some drawing in it, and it shall all end up with a laugh. That's for myself. Shall she giggle or grin? No, she shall laugh right out of the canvas, and every man and woman that ever had a sorrow of their own shall—what is it the poem says?—

"Understand the speech and feel a stir
Of fellowship in all disastrous fight.

'In all disastrous fight'? That's better than painting the thing merely to pique Maisie. I can do it now because I have it inside me. Binkie, I'm going to hold you up by your tail. You're an omen. Come here."

Binkie swung head downward for a moment without speaking.

"Rather like holding a guinea-pig; but you're a brave little dog, and you don't yelp when you're hung up. It is an omen."

Binkie went to his own chair, and as often as he looked saw Dick walking up and down, rubbing his hands and chuckling. That night Dick wrote a letter to Maisie full of the tenderest regard for her health, but saying very little about his own, and dreamed of the Melancolia to be born. Not till morning did he remember that something might happen to him in the future.

He fell to work, whistling softly, and was swallowed up in the clean, clear joy of creation, which does not come to man too often, lest he should consider himself the equal of his God, and so refuse to die at the appointed time. He forgot Maisie, Torpenhow, and Binkie at his feet, but remembered to stir Bessie, who needed very little stirring, into a tremendous rage, that he might watch the smouldering lights in her eyes. He threw himself without reservation into his work, and did not think of the doom that was to overtake him, for he was possessed with his notion, and the things of this world had no power upon him.

"You're pleased to-day," said Bessie.

Dick waved his mahl-stick in mystic circles and went to the sideboard for a drink. In the evening, when the exaltation of the day had died down, he went to the sideboard again, and after some visits became convinced that the eye-doctor was a liar, since he could still see everything very clearly. He was of opinion that he would even make a home for Maisie, and that whether she liked it or not she should be his wife. The mood passed next morning, but the sideboard and all upon it remained for his comfort. Again he set to work, and his eyes troubled him with spots and dashes and blurs till he had taken counsel with the sideboard, and the Melancolia both on the canvas and in his own mind appeared lovelier than ever. There was a delightful sense of irresponsibility upon him, such as they feel who walking among their fellow-men know that the death-sentence of disease is upon them, and, seeing that fear is but waste of the little time left, are riotously happy. The days passed without event. Bessie arrived punctually always, and, though her voice seemed to Dick to come from a distance, her face was always very near. The Melancolia began to flame on the canvas, in the likeness of a woman who had known all the sorrow in the world and was laughing at it. It was true that the corners of the studio draped themselves in gray film and retired into the darkness, that the spots in his eyes and the pains across his head were very troublesome, and that Maisie's letters were hard to read and harder still to answer. He could not tell her of his trouble, and he could not laugh at her accounts of her own Melancolia which was always going to be finished. But the furious days of toil and the nights of wild dreams made amends for all, and the sideboard was his best friend on earth. Bessie was singularly dull. She used to shriek with rage when Dick stared at her between half-closed eyes. Now she sulked, or watched him with disgust, saying very little.

Torpenhow had been absent for six weeks. An incoherent note heralded his return. "News! great news!" he wrote. "The Nilghai knows, and so does the Keneu. We're all back on Thursday. Get lunch and clean your accoutrements."

Dick showed Bessie the letter, and she abused him for that he had ever sent Torpenhow away and ruined her life.

"Well," said Dick, brutally, "you're better as you are, instead of making love to some drunken beast in the street." He felt that he had rescued Torpenhow from great temptation.

"I don't know if that's any worse than sitting to a drunken beast in a studio. *You* haven't been sober for three weeks. You've been soaking the whole time; and yet you pretend you're better than me!"

"What d'you mean?" said Dick.

"Mean! You'll see when Mr. Torpenhow comes back."

It was not long to wait. Torpenhow met Bessie on the staircase without a sign of feeling. He had news that was more to him than many Bessies, and the Keneu and the Nilghai were trampling behind him, calling for Dick.

"Drinking like a fish," Bessie whispered. "He's been at it for nearly a month." She followed the men stealthily to hear judgment done.

They came into the studio, rejoicing, to be welcomed over effusively by a drawn, lined, shrunken, haggard wreck,—unshaven, blue-white about the nostrils, stooping in the shoulders, and peering under his eyebrows nervously. The drink had been at work as steadily as Dick.

"Is this you?" said Torpenhow.

"All that's left of me. Sit down. Binkie's quite well, and I've been doing some good work." He reeled where he stood.

"You've done some of the worst work you've ever done in your life. Man alive, you're——"

Torpenhow turned to his companions appealingly, and they left the room to find lunch elsewhere. Then he spoke; but, since the reproof of a friend is much too sacred and intimate a thing to be printed, and since Torpenhow used figures and metaphors which were unseemly, and contempt untranslatable, it will never be known what was actually said to Dick, who blinked and winked and picked at his hands. After a time the culprit began to feel the need of a little self-respect. He was quite sure that he had not in any way departed from virtue, and there were reasons, too, of which Torpenhow knew nothing. He would explain.

He rose, tried to straighten his shoulders, and spoke to the face he could hardly see.

"You are right," he said. "But I am right, too. After you went away I had some trouble with my eyes. So I went to an oculist, and he turned a gasogene—I mean a gas-engine—into my eye. That was very long ago. He said, 'Scar on the head,—sword-cut and optic nerve.' Make a note of that. So I am going blind. I have some work to do before I go blind, and I suppose that I must do it. I cannot see much now, but I can see best when I am drunk. I did not know I was drunk till I was told, but I must go on with my work. If you want to see it, there it is." He pointed to the all but finished Melancolia and looked for applause.

Torpenhow said nothing, and Dick began to whimper feebly, for joy at seeing Torpenhow again, for grief at misdeeds—if indeed they were misdeeds—that made Torpenhow remote and unsympathetic, and for childish vanity hurt, since Torpenhow had not given a word of praise to his wonderful picture.

Bessie looked through the keyhole after a long pause, and saw the two walking up and down as usual, Torpenhow's hand on Dick's shoulder. Hereat she said something so improper that it shocked even Binkie, who was dribbling patiently on the landing with the hope of seeing his master again.

CHAPTER XI

The lark will make her hymn to God,
The partridge call her brood,
While I forget the heath I trod,
The fields wherein I stood.
'Tis dule to know not night from morn,
But deeper dule to know
I can but hear the hunter's horn
That once I used to blow.

—THE ONLY SON

IT WAS the third day after Torpenhow's return, and his heart was heavy.

"Do you mean to tell me that you can't see to work without whiskey? It's generally the other way about."

"Can a drunkard swear on his honour?" said Dick.

"Yes, if he has been as good a man as you."

"Then I give you my word of honour," said Dick, speaking hurriedly through parched lips. "Old man, I can hardly see your face now. You've kept me sober for two days,—if I ever was drunk,—and I've done no work. Don't keep me back any more. I don't know when my eyes may give out. The spots and dots and the pains and things are crowding worse than ever. I swear I can see all right when I'm—when I'm moderately screwed, as you say. Give me three more sittings from Bessie and all the—stuff I want, and the picture will be done. I can't kill myself in three days. It only means a touch of D. T. at the worst."

"If I give you three days more will you promise me to stop work and—the other thing, whether the picture's finished or not?"

"I can't. You don't know what that picture means to me. But surely you could get the Nilghai to help you, and knock me down and tie me up. I shouldn't fight for the whiskey, but I should for the work."

"Go on, then. I give you three days; but you're nearly breaking my heart."

Dick returned to his work, toiling as one possessed; and the yellow devil of whiskey stood by him and chased away the spots in his eyes. The Melancolia was nearly finished, and was all or nearly all that he had hoped she would be. Dick jested with Bessie, who reminded him that he was "a drunken beast"; but the reproof did not move him.

"You can't understand, Bess. We are in sight of land now, and soon we shall lie back and think about what we've done. I'll give you three months' pay when the picture's finished, and next time I have any more work in hand—but that doesn't matter. Won't three months' pay make you hate me less?"

"No, it won't! I hate you, and I'll go on hating you. Mr. Torpenhow won't speak to me any more. He's always looking at maps."

Bessie did not say that she had again laid siege to Torpenhow, or that at the end of her passionate pleading he had picked her up, given her a kiss, and put her outside the door with the recommendation not to be a little fool. He spent most of his time in the company of the Nilghai, and their talk was of war in the near future, the hiring of transports, and secret preparations among the dockyards. He did not wish to see Dick till the picture was finished.

"He's doing first-class work," he said to the Nilghai, "and

it's quite out of his regular line. But, for the matter of that, so's his infernal soaking."

"Never mind. Leave him alone. When he has come to his senses again we'll carry him off from this place and let him breathe clean air. Poor Dick! I don't envy you, Torp, when his eyes fail."

"Yes, it will be a case of 'God help the man who's chained to our Davie.' The worst is that we don't know when it will happen; and I believe the uncertainty and the waiting have sent Dick to the whiskey more than anything else."

"How the Arab who cut his head open would grin if he knew!"

"He's at perfect liberty to grin if he can. He's dead. That's poor consolation now."

In the afternoon of the third day Torpenhow heard Dick calling for him. "All finished!" he shouted. "I've done it! Come in! Isn't she a beauty? Isn't she a darling? I've been down to hell to get her; but isn't she worth it?"

Torpenhow looked at the head of a woman who laughed,—a full-lipped, hollow-eyed woman who laughed from out of the canvas as Dick had intended she should.

"Who taught you how to do it?" said Torpenhow. "The touch and notion have nothing to do with your regular work. What a face it is! What eyes, and what insolence!" Unconsciously he threw back his head and laughed with her. "She's seen the game played out,—I don't think she had a good time of it,—and now she doesn't care. Isn't that the idea?"

"Exactly."

"Where did you get the mouth and chin from? They don't belong to Bess."

"They're—some one else's. But isn't it good? Isn't it thundering good? Wasn't it worth the whiskey? I did it. Alone I did it, and it's the best I can do." He drew his breath sharply, and whispered, "Just God! what could I not do ten years hence, if I can do this now!—By the way, what do you think of it, Bess?"

The girl was biting her lips. She loathed Torpenhow because he had taken no notice of her.

"I think it's just the horridest, beastliest thing I ever saw," she answered, and turned away.

"More than you will be of that way of thinking, young woman.—Dick, there's a sort of murderous, viperine suggestion in the poise of the head that I don't understand," said Torpenhow.

"That's trick-work," said Dick, chuckling with delight at being completely understood. "I couldn't resist one little bit of sheer swagger. It's a French trick, and you wouldn't understand; but it's got at by slewing round the head a trifle, and a tiny, tiny foreshortening of one side of the face from the angle of the chin to the top of the left ear. That, and deepening the shadow under the lobe of the ear. It was flagrant trick-work; but, having the notion fixed, I felt entitled to play with it.—Oh, you beauty!"

"Amen! She is a beauty. I can feel it."

"So will every man who has any sorrow of his own," said Dick, slapping his thigh. "He shall see his trouble there, and, by the Lord Harry, just when he's feeling properly sorry for himself he shall throw back his head and laugh,—as she is laughing. I've put the life of my heart and the light of my eyes into her, and I don't care what comes. . . . I'm tired,—awfully tired. I think I'll get to sleep. Take away the whiskey, it has served its turn, and give Bessie thirty-six quid, and three over for luck. Cover the picture."

He dropped asleep in the long chair, his face white and haggard, almost before he had finished the sentence. Bessie tried to take Torpenhow's hand. "Aren't you never going to speak to me any more?" she said; but Torpenhow was looking at Dick.

"What a stock of vanity the man has! I'll take him in hand to-morrow and make much of him. He deserves it.—Eh! what was that, Bess?"

"Nothing. I'll put things tidy here a little, and then I'll go. You couldn't give me that three months' pay now, could you? He said you were to."

Torpenhow gave her a check and went to his own rooms. Bessie faithfully tidied up the studio, set the door ajar for flight, emptied half a bottle of turpentine on a duster, and began to scrub the face of the Melancolia viciously. The paint did not smudge quickly enough. She took a palette-knife and scraped, following each stroke with the wet duster. In five minutes the picture was a formless, scarred muddle of colours. She threw the paint-stained duster into the studio stove, stuck out her tongue at the sleeper, and whispered, "Bilked!" as she turned to run down the staircase. She would never see Torpenhow any more, but she had at least done harm to the man who had come between her and her desire and who used to make fun of her. Cashing the check was the very cream of the jest to Bessie. Then the little privateer sailed across the Thames, to be swallowed up in the gray wilderness of South-the-water.

Dick slept till late into the evening, when Torpenhow dragged him off to bed. His eyes were as bright as his voice was hoarse. "Let's have another look at the picture," he said, insistently as a child.

"You—go—to—bed," said Torpenhow. "You aren't at all well, though you mayn't know it. You're as jumpy as a cat."

"I reform to-morrow. Good-night."

As he repassed through the studio, Torpenhow lifted the cloth above the picture, and almost betrayed himself by outcries: "Wiped out!—scraped out and turped out! If Dick knows this to-night he'll go perfectly mad. He's on the verge of jumps as it is. That's Bess,—the little fiend! Only a woman could have done that!—with the ink not dry on the check, too! Dick will be raving mad to-morrow. It was all my fault for trying to help gutter-devils. Oh, my poor Dick, the Lord is hitting you very hard!"

Dick could not sleep that night, partly for pure joy, and partly because the well-known Catherine-wheels inside his eyes had given place to crackling volcanoes of many-coloured fire. "Spout away," he said aloud. "I've done my work, and now you can do what you please." He lay still, staring at the ceiling, the long-pent-up delirium of drink in his veins, his brain on fire with racing thoughts that would not stay to be considered, and his hands crisped and dry. He had just discovered that he was painting the face of the Melancolia on a revolving dome ribbed with millions of lights, and that all his wondrous thoughts stood embodied hundreds of feet below his tiny swinging plank, shouting together in his honour, when something cracked inside his temples like an overstrained bowstring, the glittering dome broke inward, and he was alone in the thick night.

"I'll go to sleep. The room's very dark. Let's light a lamp and see how the Melancolia looks. There ought to have been a moon."

It was then that Torpenhow heard his name called by a voice that he did not know,—in the rattling accents of deadly fear. "He's looked at the picture," was his first thought, as he hurried into the bedroom and found Dick sitting up and beating the air with his hands.

"Torp! Torp! where are you? For pity's sake, come to me!"

"What's the matter?"

Dick clutched at his shoulder. "Matter! I've been lying here for hours in the dark, and you never heard me. Torp, old man, don't go away. I'm all in the dark. In the dark, I tell you!"

Torpenhow held the candle within a foot of Dick's eyes, but there was no light in those eyes. He lit the gas, and Dick heard the flame catch. The grip of his fingers on Torpenhow's shoulder made Torpenhow wince.

"Don't leave me. You wouldn't leave me alone now, would you? I can't see. D'you understand? It's black,—quite black,—and I feel as if I was falling through it all."

"Steady does it." Torpenhow put his arm round Dick and began to rock him gently to and fro.

"That's good. Now don't talk. If I keep very quiet for a while, this darkness will lift. It seems just on the point of breaking. H'sh!" Dick knit his brows and stared desperately in front of him. The night air was chilling Torpenhow's toes.

"Can you stay like that a minute?" he said. "I'll get my dressing-gown and some slippers."

Dick clutched the bed-head with both hands and waited

for the darkness to clear away. "What a time you've been!" he cried, when Torpenhow returned. "It's as black as ever. What are you banging about in the doorway?"

"Long chair,—horse-blanket,—pillow. Going to sleep by you. Lie down now; you'll be better in the morning."

"I shan't!" The voice rose to a wail. "My God! I'm blind! I'm blind, and the darkness will never go away." He made as if to leap from the bed, but Torpenhow's arms were round him, and Torpenhow's chin was on his shoulder, and his breath was squeezed out of him. He could only gasp, "Blind!" and wriggle feebly.

"Steady, Dickie, steady!" said the deep voice in his ear, and the grip tightened. "Bite on the bullet, old man, and don't let them think you're afraid." The grip could draw no closer. Both men were breathing heavily. Dick threw his head from side to side and groaned.

"Let me go," he panted. "You're cracking my ribs. We—we mustn't let them think we're afraid, must we,—all the powers of darkness and that lot?"

"Lie down. It's all over now."

"Yes," said Dick, obediently. "But would you mind letting me hold your hand? I feel as if I wanted something to hold on to. One drops through the dark so."

Torpenhow thrust out a large and hairy paw from the long chair. Dick clutched it tightly, and in half an hour had fallen asleep. Torpenhow withdrew his hand, and, stooping over Dick, kissed him lightly on the forehead, as men do sometimes kiss a wounded comrade in the hour of death, to ease his departure.

In the gray dawn Torpenhow heard Dick talking to himself. He was adrift on the shoreless tides of delirium, speaking very quickly—

"It's a pity,—a great pity; but it's helped, and it must be eaten, Master George. Sufficient unto the day is the blindness thereof, and, further, putting aside all Melancolias and false humours, it is of obvious notoriety—such as mine was—that the queen can do no wrong. Torp doesn't know that. I'll tell him when we're a little farther into the desert. What a bungle those boatmen are making of the steamer-ropes! They'll have that four-inch hawser chafed through in a minute. I told you so—there she goes! White foam on green water, and the steamer slewing round. How good that looks! I'll sketch it. No, I can't. I'm afflicted with ophthalmia. That was one of the ten plagues of Egypt, and it extends up the Nile in the shape of cataract. Ha! that's a joke, Torp. Laugh, you graven image, and stand clear of the hawser. . . . It'll knock you into the water and make your dress all dirty, Maisie dear."

"Oh!" said Torpenhow. "This happened before. That night on the river."

"She'll be sure to say it's my fault if you get muddy, and you're quite near enough to the breakwater. Maisie, that's not fair. Ah! I knew you'd miss. Low and to the left, dear. But you've no conviction. Everything in the world except conviction. Don't be angry, darling. I'd cut my hand off if it would give you anything more than obstinacy. My right hand, if it would serve."

"Now we mustn't listen. Here's an island shouting across seas of misunderstanding with a vengeance. But it's shouting truth, I fancy," said Torpenhow.

The babble continued. It all bore upon Maisie. Sometimes Dick lectured at length on his craft, then he cursed himself for his folly in being enslaved. He pleaded to Maisie for a kiss—only one kiss—before she went away, and called to her to come back from Vitry-sur-Marne, if she would; but through all his ravings he bade heaven and earth witness that the queen could do no wrong.

Torpenhow listened attentively, and learned every detail of Dick's life that had been hidden from him. For three days Dick raved through his past, and then slept a natural sleep. "What a strain he has been running under, poor chap!" said Torpenhow. "Dick, of all men, handing himself over like a dog! And I was lecturing him on arrogance! I ought to have known that it was no use to judge a man. But I did it. What a demon that girl must be! Dick's given her his life,—confound him!—and she's given him one kiss apparently."

"Torp," said Dick, from the bed, "go out for a walk.

You've been here too long. I'll get up. Hi! This is annoying. I can't dress myself. Oh, it's too absurd!"

Torpenhow helped him into his clothes and led him to the big chair in the studio. He sat quietly waiting under strained nerves for the darkness to lift. It did not lift that day, nor the next. Dick adventured on a voyage round the walls. He hit his shins against the stove, and this suggested to him that it would be better to crawl on all fours, one hand in front of him. Torpenhow found him on the floor.

"I'm trying to get the geography of my new possessions," said he. "D'you remember that nigger you gouged in the square? Pity you didn't keep the odd eye. It would have been useful. Any letters for me? Give me all the ones in fat gray envelopes with a sort of crown thing outside. They're of no importance."

Torpenhow gave him a letter with a black M. on the envelope flap. Dick put it into his pocket. There was nothing in it that Torpenhow might not have read, but it belonged to himself and to Maisie, who would never belong to him.

"When she finds that I don't write, she'll stop writing. It's better so. I couldn't be any use to her now," Dick argued, and the tempter suggested that he should make known his condition. Every nerve in him revolted. "I have fallen low enough already. I'm not going to beg for pity. Besides, it would be cruel to her." He strove to put Maisie out of his thoughts; but the blind have many opportunities for thinking, and as the tides of his strength came back to him in the long employless days of dead darkness, Dick's soul was troubled to the core. Another letter, and another, came from Maisie. Then there was silence, and Dick sat by the window, the pulse of summer in the air, and pictured her being won by another man, stronger than himself. His imagination, the keener for the dark background it worked against, spared him no single detail that might send him raging up and down the studio, to stumble over the stove that seemed to be in four places at once. Worst of all, tobacco would not taste in the darkness. The arrogance of the man had disappeared, and in its place were settled despair that Torpenhow knew, and blind passion that Dick confided to his pillow at night. The intervals between the paroxysms were filled with intolerable waiting and the weight of intolerable darkness.

"Come out into the Park," said Torpenhow. "You haven't stirred out since the beginning of things."

"What's the use? There's no movement in the dark; and, besides,"—he paused irresolutely at the head of the stairs,—"something will run over me."

"Not if I'm with you. Proceed gingerly."

The roar of the streets filled Dick with nervous terror, and he clung to Torpenhow's arm. "Fancy having to feel for a gutter with your foot!" he said petulantly, as he turned into the Park. "Let's curse God and die."

"Sentries are forbidden to pay unauthorized compliments. By Jove, there are the Guards!"

Dick's figure straightened. "Let's get near 'em. Let's go in and look. Let's get on the grass and run. I can smell the trees."

"Mind the low railing. That's all right!" Torpenhow kicked out a tuft of grass with his heel. "Smell that," he said. "Isn't it good?" Dick sniffed luxuriously. "Now pick up your feet and run." They approached as near to the regiment as was possible. The clank of bayonets being unfixed made Dick's nostrils quiver.

"Let's get nearer. They're in column, aren't they?"

"Yes. How did you know?"

"Felt it. Oh, my men!—my beautiful men!" He edged forward as though he could see. "I could draw those chaps once. Who'll draw 'em now?"

"They'll move off in a minute. Don't jump when the band begins."

"Huh! I'm not a new charger. It's the silences that hurt. Nearer, Torp!—nearer! Oh, my God, what wouldn't I give to see 'em for a minute!—one half-minute!"

He could hear the armed life almost within reach of him, could hear the slings tighten across the bandsman's chest as he heaved the big drum from the ground.

"Sticks crossed above his head," whispered Torpenhow.

"I know. *I* know! Who should know if I don't? H'sh!"

The drum-sticks fell with a boom, and the men swung forward to the crash of the band. Dick felt the wind of the massed movement in his face, heard the maddening tramp of feet and the friction of the pouches on the belts. The big drum pounded out the tune. It was a music-hall refrain that made a perfect quickstep—

He must be a man of decent height,
He must be a man of weight,
He must come home on a Saturday night
In a thoroughly sober state;
He must know how to love me,
And he must know how to kiss;
And if he's enough to keep us both
I can't refuse him bliss.

"What's the matter?" said Torpenhow, as he saw Dick's head fall when the last of the regiment had departed.

"Nothing. I feel a little bit out of the running,—that's all. Torp, take me back. Why did you bring me out?"

CHAPTER XII

There were three friends that buried the fourth,
The mould in his mouth and the dust in his eyes;
And they went south and east, and north,—
The strong man fights, but the sick man dies.

There were three friends that spoke of the dead,—
The strong man fights, but the sick man dies.—
"And would he were here with us now," they said,
"The sun in our face and the wind in our eyes."

—BALLAD

THE Nilghai was angry with Torpenhow. Dick had been sent to bed,—blind men are ever under the orders of those who can see,—and since he had returned from the Park had fluently sworn at Torpenhow because he was alive, and all the world because it was alive and could see, while he, Dick, was dead in the death of the blind, who, at the best, are only burdens upon their associates. Torpenhow had said something about a Mrs. Gummidge, and Dick had retired in a black fury to handle and re-handle three unopened letters from Maisie.

The Nilghai, fat, burly, and aggressive, was in Torpenhow's rooms. Behind him sat the Keneu, the Great War Eagle, and between them lay a large map embellished with black-and-white-headed pins.

"I was wrong about the Balkans," said the Nilghai. "But I'm not wrong about this business. The whole of our work in the Southern Soudan must be done over again. The public doesn't care, of course, but the government does, and they are making their arrangements quietly. You know that as well as I do."

"I remember how the people cursed us when our troops withdrew from Omdurman. It was bound to crop up sooner or later. But I can't go," said Torpenhow. He pointed through the open door; it was a hot night. "Can you blame me?"

The Keneu purred above his pipe like a large and very happy cat—

"Don't blame you in the least. It's uncommonly good of you, and all the rest of it, but every man—even you, Torp—must consider his work. I know it sounds brutal, but Dick's out of the race,—down,—*gastados,* expended, finished, done for. He has a little money of his own. He won't starve, and you can't pull out of your slide for his sake. Think of your own reputation."

"Dick's was five times bigger than mine and yours put together."

"That was because he signed his name to everything he did. It's all ended now. You just hold yourself in readiness to move out. You can command your own prices, and you do better work than any three of us."

"Don't tell me how tempting it is. I'll stay here to look after Dick for a while. He's as cheerful as a bear with a sore head, but I think he likes to have me near him."

The Nilghai said something uncomplimentary about soft-headed fools who throw away their careers for other fools. Torpenhow flushed angrily. The constant strain of attendance on Dick had worn his nerves thin.

"There remains a third fate," said the Keneu, thoughtfully. "Consider this, and be not larger fools than is necessary. Dick is—or rather was—an able-bodied man of moderate attractions and a certain amount of audacity."

"Oho!" said the Nilghai, who remembered an affair at Cairo. "I begin to see.—Torp, I'm sorry."

Torpenhow nodded forgiveness: "You were more sorry when he cut you out, though.—Go on, Keneu."

"I've often thought, when I've seen men die out in the desert, that if the news could be sent through the world, and the means of transport were quick enough, there would be one woman at least at each man's bedside."

"There would be some mighty quaint revelations. Let us be grateful things are as they are," said the Nilghai.

"Let us rather reverently consider whether Torp's three-cornered ministrations are exactly what Dick needs just now.—What do you think yourself, Torp?"

"I know they aren't. But what can I do?"

"Lay the matter before the board. We are all Dick's friends here. You've been most in his life."

"But I picked it up when he was off his head."

"The greater chance of its being true. I thought we should arrive. Who is she?"

Then Torpenhow told a tale in plain words, as a special correspondent who knows how to make a verbal *précis* should tell it. The men listened without interruption.

"Is it possible that a man can come back across the years to his calf-love?" said the Keneu. "Is it possible?"

"I give the facts. He says nothing about it now, but he sits fumbling three letters from her when he thinks I'm not looking. What am I to do?"

"Speak to him," said the Nilghai.

"Oh yes! Write to her,—I don't know her full name, remember,—and ask her to accept him out of pity. I believe you once told Dick you were sorry for him, Nilghai. You remember what happened, eh? Go into the bedroom and suggest full confession and an appeal to this Maisie girl, whoever she is. I honestly believe he'd try to kill you; and the blindness has made him rather muscular."

"Torpenhow's course is perfectly clear," said the Keneu. "He will go to Vitry-sur-Marne, which is on the Bézières-Landes Railway,—single track from Tourgas. The Prussians shelled it out in '70 because there was a poplar on the top of a hill eighteen hundred yards from the church spire. There's a squadron of cavalry quartered there,—or ought to be. Where this studio Torp spoke about may be I cannot tell. That is Torp's business. I have given him his route. He will dispassionately explain the situation to the girl, and she will come back to Dick,—the more especially because, to use Dick's words, 'there is nothing but her damned obstinacy to keep them apart.'"

"And they have four hundred and twenty pounds a year between 'em. Dick never lost his head for figures, even in his delirium. You haven't the shadow of an excuse for not going," said the Nilghai.

Torpenhow looked very uncomfortable. "But it's absurd and impossible. I can't drag her back by the hair."

"Our business—the business for which we draw our money—is to do absurd and impossible things,—generally with no reason whatever except to amuse the public. Here we have a reason. The rest doesn't matter. I shall share these rooms with the Nilghai till Torpenhow returns. There will be a batch of unbridled 'specials' coming to town in a little while, and these will serve as their headquarters. Another reason for sending Torpenhow away. Thus Providence helps those who help others, and"—here the Keneu dropped his measured speech—"we can't have you tied by the leg to Dick when the trouble begins. It's your only chance of getting away; and Dick will be grateful."

"He will,—worse luck! I can but go and try. I can't conceive a woman in her senses refusing Dick."

"Talk that out with the girl. I have seen you wheedle an angry Mahdieh woman into giving you dates. This won't be a tithe as difficult. You had better not be here to-morrow afternoon, because the Nilghai and I will be in possession. It is an order. Obey."

"Dick," said Torpenhow, next morning, "can I do anything for you?"

"No! Leave me alone. How often must I remind you that I'm blind?"

"Nothing I could go for to fetch for to carry for to bring?"

"No. Take those infernal creaking boots of yours away."

"Poor chap!" said Torpenhow to himself. "I must have been sitting on his nerves lately. He wants a lighter step." Then, aloud, "Very well. Since you're so independent, I'm going off for four or five days. Say good-bye at least. The housekeeper will look after you, and Keneu has my rooms."

Dick's face fell. "You won't be longer than a week at the outside? I know I'm touched in the temper, but I can't get on without you."

"Can't you? You'll have to do without me in a little time, and you'll be glad I'm gone."

Dick felt his way back to the big chair, and wondered what these things might mean. He did not wish to be tended by the housekeeper, and yet Torpenhow's constant tendernesses jarred on him. He did not exactly know what he wanted. The darkness would not lift, and Maisie's unopened letters felt worn and old from much handling. He could never read them for himself as long as life endured; but Maisie might have sent him some fresh ones to play with. The Nilghai entered with a gift,—a piece of red modelling-wax. He fancied that Dick might find interest in using his hands. Dick poked and patted the stuff for a few minutes, and, "Is it like anything in the world?" he said drearily. "Take it away. I may get the touch of the blind in fifty years. Do you know where Torpenhow has gone?"

The Nilghai knew nothing. "We're staying in his rooms till he comes back. Can we do anything for you?"

"I'd like to be left alone, please. Don't think I'm ungrateful; but I'm best alone."

The Nilghai chuckled, and Dick resumed his drowsy brooding and sullen rebellion against fate. He had long since ceased to think about the work he had done in the old days, and the desire to do more work had departed from him. He was exceedingly sorry for himself, and the completeness of his tender grief soothed him. But his soul and his body cried for Maisie—Maisie who would understand. His mind pointed out that Maisie, having her own work to do, would not care. His experience had taught him that when money was exhausted women went away, and that when a man was knocked out of the race the others trampled on him. "Then at the least," said Dick, in reply, "she could use me as I used Binat,—for some sort of a study. I wouldn't ask more than to be near her again, even though I knew that another man was making love to her. Ugh! what a dog I am!"

A voice on the staircase began to sing joyfully—

"When we go—go—go away from here,
Our creditors will weep and they will wail,
Our absence much regretting when they find that we've been getting
Out of England by next Tuesday's Indian mail."

Following the trampling of feet, slamming of Torpenhow's door, and the sound of voices in strenuous debate, some one squeaked, "And see, you good fellows, I have found a new water-bottle,—firs'-class patent—eh, how you say? Open himself inside out."

Dick sprang to his feet. He knew the voice well. "That's Cassavetti, come back from the Continent. Now I know why Torp went away. There's a row somewhere, and—I'm out of it!"

The Nilghai commanded silence in vain. "That's for my sake," Dick said bitterly. "The birds are getting ready to fly, and they wouldn't tell me. I can hear Morten-Sutherland and Mackaye. Half the War Correspondents in London are there:—and I'm out of it."

He stumbled across the landing and plunged into Torpenhow's room. He could feel that it was full of men. "Where's the trouble?" said he. "In the Balkans at last? Why didn't some one tell me?"

"We thought you wouldn't be interested," said the Nilghai, shamefacedly. "It's in the Soudan, as usual."

"You lucky dogs! Let me sit here while you talk. I shan't be a skeleton at the feast.—Cassavetti, where are you? Your English is as bad as ever."

Dick was led into a chair. He heard the rustle of the maps, and the talk swept forward, carrying him with it. Everybody spoke at once, discussing press censorships, railway-routes, transport, water-supply, the capacities of generals,—these in language that would have horrified a trusting public,—ranting, asserting, denouncing, and laughing at the top of their voices. There was the glorious certainty of war in the Soudan at any moment. The Nilghai said so, and it was well to be in readiness. The Keneu had telegraphed to Cairo for horses; Cassavetti had stolen a perfectly inaccurate list of troops that would be ordered forward, and was reading it out amid profane interruptions, and the Keneu introduced to Dick some man unknown who would be employed as war artist by the Central Southern Syndicate. "It's his first outing," said the Keneu. "Give him some tips—about riding camels."

"Oh, those camels!" groaned Cassavetti. "I shall learn to ride him again, and now I am so much all soft! Listen, you good fellows. I know your military arrangement very well. There will go the Royal Argalshire Sutherlanders. So it was read to me upon best authority."

A roar of laughter interrupted him.

"Sit down," said the Nilghai. "The lists aren't even made out in the War Office."

"Will there be any force at Suakin?" said a voice.

Then the outcries redoubled, and grew mixed, thus: "How many Egyptian troops will they use?——God help the Fellaheen!——There's a railway in Plumstead marshes doing duty as a fives-court.——We shall have the Suakin-Berber line built at last.——Canadian voyageurs are too careful. Give me a half-drunk Krooman in a whale-boat.——Who commands the Desert column?——No, they never blew up the big rock in the Ghineh bend. We shall have to be hauled up, as usual.——Somebody tell me if there's an Indian contingent, or I'll break everybody's head.——Don't tear the map in two.——It's a war of occupation, I tell you, to connect with the African companies in the South.——There's Guinea-worm in most of the wells on that route." Then the Nilghai, despairing of peace, bellowed like a fog-horn and beat upon the table with both hands.

"But what becomes of Torpenhow?" said Dick, in the silence that followed.

"Torp's in abeyance just now. He's off love-making somewhere, I suppose," said the Nilghai.

"He said he was going to stay at home," said the Keneu.

"Is he?" said Dick, with an oath. "He won't. I'm not much good now, but if you and the Nilghai hold him down I'll engage to trample on him till he sees reason. He stay behind, indeed! He's the best of you all. There'll be some tough work by Omdurman. We shall come there to stay, this time. But I forgot. I wish I were going with you."

"So do we all, Dickie," said the Keneu.

"And I most of all," said the new artist of the Central Southern Syndicate. "Could you tell me——"

"I'll give you one piece of advice," Dick answered, moving towards the door. "If you happen to be cut over the head in a scrimmage, don't guard. Tell the man to go on cutting. You'll find it cheapest in the end. Thanks for letting me look in."

"There's grit in Dick," said the Nilghai, an hour later, when the room was emptied of all save the Keneu.

"It was the sacred call of the war-trumpet. Did you notice how he answered to it? Poor fellow! Let's look at him," said the Keneu.

The excitement of the talk had died away. Dick was sitting by the studio table, with his head on his arms, when the men came in. He did not change his position.

"It hurts," he moaned. "God forgive me, but it hurts

cruelly; and yet, y'know, the world has a knack of spinning round all by itself. Shall I see Torp before he goes?"

"Oh, yes. You'll see him," said the Nilghai.

CHAPTER XIII

The sun went down an hour ago,
I wonder if I face towards home;
If I lost my way in the light of day
How shall I find it now night is come?

—OLD SONG

"MAISIE, come to bed."

"It's so hot I can't sleep. Don't worry."

Maisie put her elbows on the window-sill and looked at the moonlight on the straight, poplar-flanked road. Summer had come upon Vitry-sur-Marne and parched it to the bone. The grass was dry-burnt in the meadows, the clay by the bank of the river was caked to brick, the roadside flowers were long since dead, and the roses in the garden hung withered on their stalks. The heat in the little low bedroom under the eaves was almost intolerable. The very moonlight on the wall of Kami's studio across the road seemed to make the night hotter, and the shadow of the big bell-handle by the closed gate cast a bar of inky black that caught Maisie's eye and annoyed her.

"Horrid thing! It should be all white," she murmured. "And the gate isn't in the middle of the wall, either. I never noticed that before."

Maisie was hard to please at that hour. First, the heat of the past few weeks had worn her down; secondly, her work, and particularly the study of a female head intended to represent the Melancolia and not finished in time for the Salon, was unsatisfactory; thirdly, Kami had said as much two days before; fourthly,—but so completely fourthly that it was hardly worth thinking about,—Dick, her property, had not written to her for more than six weeks. She was angry with the heat, with Kami, and with her work, but she was exceedingly angry with Dick.

She had written to him three times,—each time proposing a fresh treatment of her Melancolia. Dick had taken no notice of these communications. She had resolved to write no more. When she returned to England in the autumn—for her pride's sake she could not return earlier—she would speak to him. She missed the Sunday afternoon conferences more than she cared to admit. All that Kami said was, *"Continuez, mademoiselle, continuez, toujours,"* and he had been repeating his wearisome counsel through the hot summer, exactly like a cicala,—an old gray cicala in a black alpaca coat, white trousers, and a huge felt hat. But Dick had tramped masterfully up and down her little studio north of the cool green London park, and had said things ten times worse than *continuez,* before he snatched the brush out of her hand and showed her where her error lay. His last letter, Maisie remembered, contained some trivial advice about not sketching in the sun or drinking water at wayside farmhouses; and he had said that not once, but three times,—as if he did not know that Maisie could take care of herself.

But what was he doing, that he could not trouble to write? A murmur of voices in the road made her lean from the window. A cavalryman of the little garrison in the town was talking to Kami's cook. The moonlight glittered on the scabbard of his sabre, which he was holding in his hand lest it should clank inopportunely. The cook's cap cast deep shadows on her face, which was close to the conscript's. He slid his arm round her waist, and there followed the sound of a kiss.

"Faugh!" said Maisie, stepping back.

"What's that?" said the red-haired girl, who was tossing uneasily outside her bed.

"Only a conscript kissing the cook," said Maisie.

"They've gone away now." She leaned out of the window again, and put a shawl over her nightgown to guard against chills. There was a very small night-breeze abroad, and a sunbaked rose below nodded its head as one who knew unutterable secrets. Was it possible that Dick should turn his thoughts from her work and his own and descend to the degradation of Suzanne and the conscript? He could not! The rose nodded its head and one leaf therewith. It looked like a naughty little devil scratching its ear. Dick could not, "because," thought Maisie, "he is mine,—mine,—mine. He said he was. I'm sure I don't care what he does. It will only spoil his work if he does; and it will spoil mine too."

The rose continued to nod in the futile way peculiar to flowers. There was no earthly reason why Dick should not disport himself as he chose, except that he was called by Providence, which was Maisie, to assist Maisie in her work. And her work was the preparation of pictures that went sometimes to English provincial exhibitions, as the notices in the scrap-book proved, and that were invariably rejected by the Salon when Kami was plagued into allowing her to send them up. Her work in the future, it seemed, would be the preparation of pictures on exactly similar lines which would be rejected in exactly the same way——

The red-haired girl threshed distressfully across the sheets. "It's too hot to sleep," she moaned; and the interruption jarred.

Exactly the same way. Then she would divide her years between the little studio in England and Kami's big studio at Vitry-sur-Marne. No, she would go to another master, who should force her into the success that was her right, if patient toil and desperate endeavour gave one a right to anything. Dick had told her that he had worked ten years to understand his craft. She had worked ten years, and ten years were nothing. Dick had said that ten years were nothing,—but that was in regard to herself only. He had said—this very man who could not find time to write—that he would wait ten years for her, and that she was bound to come back to him sooner or later. He had said this in the absurd letter about sunstroke and diphtheria; and then he had stopped writing. He was wandering up and down moonlit streets, kissing cooks. She would like to lecture him now,—not in her nightgown, of course, but properly dressed, severely and from a height. Yet if he was kissing other girls he certainly would not care whether she lectured him or not. He would laugh at her. Very good. She would go back to her studio and prepare pictures that went, etc., etc. The mill-wheel of thought swung round slowly, that no section of it might be slurred over, and the red-haired girl tossed and turned behind her.

Maisie put her chin in her hands and decided that there could be no doubt whatever of the villainy of Dick. To justify herself, she began, unwomanly, to weigh the evidence. There was a boy, and he had said he loved her. And he kissed her,—kissed her on the cheek,—by a yellow sea-poppy that nodded its head exactly like the maddening dry rose in the garden. Then there was an interval, and men had told her that they loved her—just when she was busiest with her work. Then the boy came back, and at their very second meeting had told her that he loved her. Then he had—— But there was no end to the things he had done. He had given her his time and his powers. He had spoken to her of Art, housekeeping, technique, tea-cups, the abuse of pickles as a stimulant,—that was rude,—sable hair-brushes,—he had given her the best in her stock,—she used them daily; he had given her advice that she profited by, and now and again—a look. Such a look! The look of a beaten hound waiting for the word to crawl to his mistress's feet. In return she had given him nothing whatever, except—here she brushed her mouth against the open-work sleeve of her nightgown—the privilege of kissing her once. And on the mouth, too. Disgraceful! Was that not enough, and more than enough? and if it was not, had he not cancelled the debt by not writing and—probably kissing other girls?

"Maisie, you'll catch a chill. Do go and lie down," said the wearied voice of her companion. "I can't sleep a wink with you at the window."

Maisie shrugged her shoulders and did not answer. She was reflecting on the meannesses of Dick, and on other meannesses with which he had nothing to do. The moonlight would not let her sleep. It lay on the skylight of the studio across the road in cold silver; she stared at it intently and her thoughts began to slide one into the other. The shadow of the big bell-handle in the wall grew short, lengthened again, and faded out as the moon went down behind the pasture and a hare came limping home across the road. Then the dawn-wind washed through the upland grasses, and brought coolness with it, and the cattle lowed by the drought-shrunk river. Maisie's head fell forward on the window-sill, and the tangle of black hair covered her arms.

"Maisie, wake up. You'll catch a chill."

"Yes, dear; yes, dear." She staggered to her bed like a wearied child, and as she buried her face in the pillows she muttered, "I think—I think. . . . But he ought to have written."

Day brought the routine of the studio, the smell of paint and turpentine, and the monotonous wisdom of Kami, who was a leaden artist, but a golden teacher if the pupil were only in sympathy with him. Maisie was not in sympathy that day, and she waited impatiently for the end of the work. She knew when it was coming; for Kami would gather his black alpaca coat into a bunch behind him, and, with faded blue eyes that saw neither pupils nor canvas, look back into the past to recall the history of one Binat. "You have all done not so badly," he would say. "But you shall remember that it is not enough to have the method, and the art, and the power, nor even that which is touch, but you shall have also the conviction that nails the work to the wall. Of the so many I have taught,"—here the students would begin to unfix drawing-pins or get their tubes together,—"the very so many that I have taught, the best was Binat. All that comes of the study and the work and the knowledge was to him even when he came. After he left me he should have done all that could be done with the colour, the form, and the knowledge. Only, he had not the conviction. So to-day I hear no more of Binat,—the best of my pupils,—and that is long ago. So to-day, too, you will be glad to hear no more of me. *Continuez, mesdemoiselles,* and, above all, with conviction."

He went into the garden to smoke and mourn over the lost Binat as the pupils dispersed to their several cottages or loitered in the studio to make plans for the cool of the afternoon.

Maisie looked at her very unhappy Melancolia, restrained a desire to grimace before it, and was hurrying across the road to write a letter to Dick, when she was aware of a large man on a white troop-horse. How Torpenhow had managed in the course of twenty hours to find his way to the hearts of the cavalry officers in quarters at Vitry-sur-Marne, to discuss with them the certainty of a glorious revenge for France, to reduce the colonel to tears of pure affability, and to borrow the best horse in the squadron for the journey to Kami's studio, is a mystery that only special correspondents can unravel.

"I beg your pardon," said he. "It seems an absurd question to ask, but the fact is that I don't know her by any other name: Is there any young lady here that is called Maisie?"

"I am Maisie," was the answer from the depths of a great sun-hat.

"I ought to introduce myself," he said, as the horse capered in the blinding white dust. "My name is Torpenhow. Dick Heldar is my best friend, and—and—the fact is that he has gone blind."

"Blind!" said Maisie, stupidly. "He can't be blind."

"He has been stone-blind for nearly two months."

Maisie lifted up her face, and it was pearly white. "No! No! Not blind! I won't have him blind!"

"Would you care to see for yourself?" said Torpenhow.

"Now,—at once?"

"Oh no! The Paris train doesn't go through this place till eight to-night. There will be ample time."

"Did Mr. Heldar send you to me?"

"Certainly not. Dick wouldn't do that sort of thing. He's sitting in his studio, turning over some letters that he can't read because he's blind."

There was a sound of choking from the sun-hat. Maisie bowed her head and went into the cottage, where the red-haired girl was on a sofa, complaining of a headache.

"Dick's blind!" said Maisie, taking her breath quickly as she steadied herself against a chair-back. "My Dick's blind!"

"What?" The girl was on the sofa no longer.

"A man has come from England to tell me. He hasn't written to me for six weeks."

"Are you going to him?"

"I must think."

"Think! *I* should go back to London and see him, and I should kiss his eyes and kiss them and kiss them until they got well again! If you don't go I shall. Oh, what am I talking about? You wicked little idiot! Go to him at once. Go!"

Torpenhow's neck was blistering, but he preserved a smile of infinite patience as Maisie appeared bare-headed in the sunshine.

"I am coming," said she, her eyes on the ground.

"You will be at Vitry Station, then, at seven this evening." This was an order delivered by one who was used to being obeyed. Maisie said nothing, but she felt grateful that there was no chance of disputing with this big man who took everything for granted and managed a squealing horse with one hand. She returned to the red-haired girl, who was weeping bitterly, and between tears, kisses,—very few of those,—menthol, packing, and an interview with Kami, the sultry afternoon wore away. Thought might come afterwards. Her present duty was to go to Dick,—Dick who owned the wondrous friend and sat in the dark playing with her unopened letters.

"But what will you do?" she said to her companion.

"I? Oh, I shall stay here and—finish your Melancolia," she said, smiling pitifully. "Write to me afterwards."

That night there ran a legend through Vitry-sur-Marne of a mad Englishman, doubtless suffering from sunstroke, who had drunk all the officers of the garrison under the table, had borrowed a horse from the lines, and had then and there eloped, after the English custom, with one of those more than mad English girls who drew pictures down there under the care of that good Monsieur Kami.

"They are very droll," said Suzanne to the conscript in the moonlight by the studio wall. "She walked always with those big eyes that saw nothing, and yet she kisses me on both cheeks as though she were my sister, and gives me—see—ten francs!"

The conscript levied a contribution on both gifts; for he prided himself on being a good soldier.

Torpenhow spoke very little to Maisie during the journey to Calais; but he was careful to attend to all her wants, to get her a compartment entirely to herself, and to leave her alone. He was amazed at the ease with which the matter had been accomplished.

"The safest thing would be to let her think things out. By Dick's showing,—when he was off his head,—she must have ordered him about very thoroughly. Wonder how she likes being under orders."

Maisie never told. She sat in the empty compartment often with her eyes shut, that she might realize the sensation of blindness. It was an order that she should return to London swiftly, and she found herself at last almost beginning to enjoy the situation. This was better than looking after luggage and a red-haired friend who never took any interest in her surroundings. But there appeared to be a feeling in the air that she, Maisie,—of all people,—was in disgrace. Therefore she justified her conduct to herself with great success, till Torpenhow came up to her on the steamer and without preface began to tell the story of Dick's blindness, suppressing a few details, but dwelling at length on the miseries of delirium. He stopped before he reached the end, as though he had lost interest in the subject, and went forward to smoke. Maisie was furious with him and with herself.

She was hurried on from Dover to London almost before she could ask for breakfast, and—she was past any feeling of indignation now—was bidden curtly to wait in a hall at the foot of some lead-covered stairs while Torpenhow went up to make inquiries. Again the knowledge that she was being treated like a naughty little girl made her pale cheeks flame. It was all Dick's fault for being so stupid as to go blind.

Torpenhow led her up to a shut door, which he opened very softly. Dick was sitting by the window, with his chin on his chest. There were three envelopes in his hand, and he turned them over and over. The big man who gave orders was no longer by her side, and the studio door snapped behind her.

Dick thrust the letters into his pocket as he heard the sound. "Hullo, Torp! Is that you? I've been so lonely."

His voice had taken the peculiar flatness of the blind. Maisie pressed herself up into a corner of the room. Her heart was beating furiously, and she put one hand on her breast to keep it quiet. Dick was staring directly at her, and she realized for the first time that he was blind. Shutting her eyes in a railway-carriage to open them when she pleased was child's play. This man was blind though his eyes were wide open.

"Torp, is that you? They said you were coming." Dick looked puzzled and a little irritated at the silence.

"No: it's only me," was the answer, in a strained little whisper. Maisie could hardly move her lips.

"H'm!" said Dick, composedly, without moving. "This is a new phenomenon. Darkness I'm getting used to; but I object to hearing voices."

Was he mad, then, as well as blind, that he talked to himself? Maisie's heart beat more wildly, and she breathed in gasps. Dick rose and began to feel his way across the room, touching each table and chair as he passed. Once he caught his foot on a rug, and swore, dropping on his knees to feel what the obstruction might be. Maisie remembered him walking in the Park as though all the earth belonged to him, tramping up and down her studio two months ago, and flying up the gangway of the Channel steamer. The beating of her heart was making her sick, and Dick was coming nearer, guided by the sound of her breathing. She put out a hand mechanically to ward him off or to draw him to herself, she did not know which. It touched his chest, and he stepped back as though he had been shot.

"It's Maisie!" said he, with a dry sob. "What are you doing here?"

"I came—I came—to see you, please."

Dick's lips closed firmly.

"Won't you sit down, then? You see, I've had some bother with my eyes, and——"

"I know. I know. Why didn't you tell me?"

"I couldn't write."

"You might have told Mr. Torpenhow."

"What has he to do with my affairs?"

"He—he brought me from Vitry-sur-Marne. He thought I ought to see you."

"Why, what has happened? Can I do anything for you? No, I can't. I forgot."

"Oh, Dick, I'm so sorry! I've come to tell you, and—— Let me take you back to your chair."

"Don't! I'm not a child. You only do that out of pity. I never meant to tell you anything about it. I'm no good now. I'm down and done for. Let me alone!"

He groped back to his chair, his chest labouring as he sat down.

Maisie watched him, and the fear went out of her heart, to be followed by a very bitter shame. He had spoken a truth that had been hidden from the girl through every step of the impetuous flight to London; for he was, indeed, down and done for—masterful no longer but rather a little abject; neither an artist stronger than she, nor a man to be looked up to—only some blind one that sat in a chair and seemed on the point of crying. She was immensely and unfeignedly sorry for him—more sorry than she had ever been for any one in her life, but not sorry enough to deny his words. So she stood still and felt ashamed and a little hurt, because she had honestly intended that her journey should end triumphantly; and now she was only filled with pity most startlingly distinct from love.

"Well?" said Dick, his face steadily turned away. "I never meant to worry you any more. What's the matter?"

He was conscious that Maisie was catching her breath, but was as unprepared as herself for the torrent of emotion that followed. She had dropped into a chair and was sobbing with her face hidden in her hands.

"I can't—I can't!" she cried desperately. "Indeed, I can't. It isn't my fault. I'm so sorry. Oh, Dickie, I'm so sorry."

Dick's shoulders straightened again, for the words lashed like a whip. Still the sobbing continued. It is not good to realize that you have failed in the hour of trial or flinched before the mere possibility of making sacrifices.

"I do despise myself—indeed I do. But I can't. Oh, Dickie, you wouldn't ask me—would you?" wailed Maisie.

She looked up for a minute, and by chance it happened that Dick's eyes fell on hers. The unshaven face was very white and set, and the lips were trying to force themselves into a smile. But it was the worn-out eyes that Maisie feared. Her Dick had gone blind and left in his place some one that she could hardly recognize till he spoke.

"Who is asking you to do anything, Maisie? I told you how it would be. What's the use of worrying? For pity's sake don't cry like that; it isn't worth it."

"You don't know how I hate myself. Oh, Dick, help me—help me!" The passion of tears had grown beyond her control and was beginning to alarm the man. He stumbled forward and put his arm round her, and her head fell on his shoulder.

"Hush, dear, hush! Don't cry. You're quite right, and you've nothing to reproach yourself with—you never had. You're only a little upset by the journey, and I don't suppose you've had any breakfast. What a brute Torp was to bring you over."

"I wanted to come. I did indeed," she protested.

"Very well. And now you've come and seen, and I'm—immensely grateful. When you're better you shall go away and get something to eat. What sort of a passage did you have coming over?"

Maisie was crying more subduedly, for the first time in her life glad that she had something to lean against. Dick patted her on the shoulder tenderly but clumsily, for he was not quite sure where her shoulder might be.

She drew herself out of his arms at last and waited, trembling and most unhappy. He had felt his way to the window to put the width of the room between them, and to quiet a little the tumult in his heart.

"Are you better now?" he said.

"Yes, but—don't you hate me?"

"I hate you? My God! I?"

"Isn't—isn't there anything I could do for you, then? I'll stay here in England to do it, if you like. Perhaps I could come and see you sometimes."

"I think not, dear. It would be kindest not to see me any more, please. I don't want to seem rude, but—don't you think—perhaps you had almost better go now."

He was conscious that he could not bear himself as a man if the strain continued much longer.

"I don't deserve anything else. I'll go, Dick. Oh, I'm so miserable."

"Nonsense. You've nothing to worry about; I'd tell you if you had. Wait a moment, dear. I've got something to give you first. I meant it for you ever since this little trouble began. It's my Melancolia; she was a beauty when I last saw her. You can keep her for me, and if ever you're poor you can sell her. She's worth a few hundreds at any state of the market." He groped among his canvases. "She's framed in black. Is this a black frame that I have my hand on? There she is. What do you think of her?"

He turned a scarred formless muddle of paint towards Maisie, and the eyes strained as though they would catch her wonder and surprise. One thing and one thing only could she do for him.

"Well?"

The voice was fuller and more rounded, because the man knew he was speaking of his best work. Maisie looked at the blur, and a lunatic desire to laugh caught her by the throat. But for Dick's sake—whatever this mad blankness might mean—she must make no sign. Her voice choked with hard-held tears as she answered, still gazing at the wreck—

"Oh, Dick, it *is* good!"

He heard the little hysterical gulp and took it for tribute. "Won't you have it, then? I'll send it over to your house if you will."

"I? Oh yes—thank you. Ha! ha!" If she did not fly at once the laughter that was worse than tears would kill her. She turned and ran, choking and blinded, down the staircases that were empty of life to take refuge in a cab and go to her house across the Parks. There she sat down in the dismantled drawing-room and thought of Dick in his blindness, useless till the end of life, and of herself in her own eyes. Behind the sorrow, the shame, and the humiliation, lay fear of the cold wrath of the red-haired girl when Maisie should return. Maisie had never feared her companion before. Not until she found herself saying, "Well, he never asked me," did she realize her scorn of herself.

And that is the end of Maisie.

. . . .

For Dick was reserved more searching torment. He could not realize at first that Maisie, whom he had ordered to go had left him without a word of farewell. He was savagely angry against Torpenhow, who had brought upon him this humiliation and troubled his miserable peace. Then his dark hour came and he was alone with himself and his desires to get what help he could from the darkness. The queen could do no wrong, but in following the right, so far as it served her work, she had wounded her one subject more than his own brain would let him know.

"It's all I had and I've lost it," he said, as soon as the misery permitted clear thinking. "And Torp will think that he has been so infernally clever that I shan't have the heart to tell him. I must think this out quietly."

"Hullo!" said Torpenhow, entering the studio after Dick had enjoyed two hours of thought. "I'm back. Are you feeling any better?"

"Torp, I don't know what to say. Come here." Dick coughed huskily, wondering, indeed, what he should say, and how to say it temperately.

"What's the need for saying anything? Get up and tramp." Torpenhow was perfectly satisfied.

They walked up and down as of custom, Torpenhow's hand on Dick's shoulder, and Dick buried in his own thoughts.

"How in the world did you find it all out?" said Dick, at last.

"You shouldn't go off your head if you want to keep secrets, Dickie. It was absolutely impertinent on my part; but if you'd seen me rocketing about on a half-trained French troop-horse under a blazing sun you'd have laughed. There will be a charivari in my rooms to-night. Seven other devils——"

"I know—the row in the Southern Soudan. I surprised their councils the other day, and it made me unhappy. Have you fixed your flint to go? Who d'you work for?"

"Haven't signed any contracts yet. I wanted to see how your business would turn out."

"Would you have stayed with me, then, if—things had gone wrong?" He put his question cautiously.

"Don't ask me too much. I'm only a man."

"You've tried to be an angel very successfully."

"Oh ye—es! . . . Well, do you attend the function to-night? We shall be half screwed before the morning. All the men believe the war's a certainty."

"I don't think I will, old man, if it's all the same to you. I'll stay quiet here."

"And meditate? I don't blame you. You deserve a good time if ever a man did."

That night there was a tumult on the stairs. The correspondents poured in from theatre, dinner, and music-hall to Torpenhow's room that they might discuss their plan of campaign in the event of military operations being a certainty. Torpenhow, the Keneu, and the Nilghai had bidden all the men they had worked with to the orgy; and Mr. Beeton, the housekeeper, declared that never before in his checkered experience had he seen quite such a fancy lot of gentlemen. They waked the chambers with shoutings and song; and the elder men were quite as bad as the younger. For the chances of war were in front of them, and all knew what those meant.

Sitting in his own room a little perplexed by the noise across the landing, Dick suddenly began to laugh to himself.

"When one comes to think of it the situation is intensely

comic. Maisie's quite right—poor little thing. I didn't know she could cry like that before; but now I know what Torp thinks, I'm sure he'd be quite fool enough to stay at home and try to console me—if he knew. Besides, it isn't nice to own that you've been thrown over like a broken chair. I must carry this business through alone—as usual. If there isn't a war, and Torp finds out, I shall look foolish, that's all. If there is a war I mustn't interfere with another man's chances. Business is business, and I want to be alone—I want to be alone. What a row they're making!"

Somebody hammered at the studio door.

"Come out and frolic, Dickie," said the Nilghai.

"I should like to, but I can't. I'm not feeling frolicsome."

"Then, I'll tell the boys and they'll draw you like a badger."

"Please not, old man. On my word, I'd sooner be left alone just now."

"Very good. Can we send anything in to you? Fizz, for instance. Cassavetti is beginning to sing songs of the Sunny South already."

For one minute Dick considered the proposition seriously.

"No, thanks, I've a headache already."

"Virtuous child. That's the effect of emotion on the young. All my congratulations, Dick. I also was concerned in the conspiracy for your welfare."

"Go to the devil and—oh, send Binkie in here."

The little dog entered on elastic feet, riotous from having been made much of all the evening. He had helped to sing the choruses; but scarcely inside the studio he realized that this was no place for tail-wagging, and settled himself on Dick's lap till it was bedtime. Then he went to bed with Dick, who counted every hour as it struck, and rose in the morning with a painfully clear head to receive Torpenhow's more formal congratulations and a particular account of the last night's revels.

"You aren't looking very happy for a newly accepted man," said Torpenhow.

"Never mind that—it's my own affair, and I'm all right. Do you really go?"

"Yes. With the old Central Southern as usual. They wired, and I accepted on better terms than before."

"When do you start?"

"The day after to-morrow—for Brindisi."

"Thank God." Dick spoke from the bottom of his heart.

"Well, that's not a pretty way of saying you're glad to get rid of me. But men in your condition are allowed to be selfish."

"I didn't mean that. Will you get a hundred pounds cashed for me before you leave?"

"That's a slender amount for housekeeping, isn't it?"

"Oh, it's only for—marriage expenses."

Torpenhow brought him the money, counted it out in fives and tens, and carefully put it away in the writing table.

"Now I suppose I'll have to listen to his ravings about his girl until I go. Heaven send us patience with a man in love!" said he to himself.

But never a word did Dick say of Maisie or marriage. He hung in the doorway of Torpenhow's room when the latter was packing and asked innumerable questions about the coming campaign, till Torpenhow began to feel annoyed.

"You're a secretive animal, Dickie, and you consume your own smoke, don't you?" he said on the last evening.

"I—I suppose so. By the way, how long do you think this war will last?"

"Days, weeks, or months. One can never tell. It may go on for years."

"I wish I were going."

"Good heavens! You're the most unaccountable creature! Hasn't it occurred to you that you're going to be married—thanks to me?"

"Of course, yes. I'm going to be married—so I am. Going to be married. I'm awfully grateful to you. Haven't I told you that?"

"You might be going to be hanged by the look of you," said Torpenhow.

And the next day Torpenhow bade him good-bye and left him to the loneliness he had so much desired.

CHAPTER XIV

Yet at the last, ere our spearmen had found him,
Yet at the last, ere a sword-thrust could save,
Yet at the last, with his masters around him,
He of the Faith spoke as master to slave;
Yet at the last, tho' the Kafirs had maimed him,
Broken by bondage and wrecked by the reiver,—
Yet at the last, tho' the darkness had claimed him,
He called upon Allah and died a believer.

—KIZZILBASHI

"BEG your pardon, Mr. Heldar, but—but isn't nothin' going to happen?" said Mr. Beeton.

"No!" Dick had just waked to another morning of blank despair and his temper was of the shortest.

"'Tain't my regular business, o' course, sir; and what I say is, 'Mind your own business and let other people mind theirs;' but just before Mr. Torpenhow went away he give me to understand, like, that you might be moving into a house of your own, so to speak—a sort of house with rooms upstairs and downstairs where you'd be better attended to, though I try to act just by all our tenants. Don't I?"

"Ah! That must have been a mad-house. I shan't trouble you to take me there yet. Get me my breakfast, please, and leave me alone."

"I hope I haven't done anything wrong, sir, but you know I hope that as far as a man can I tries to do the proper thing by all the gentlemen in chambers—and more particular those whose lot is hard—such as you, for instance, Mr. Heldar. You likes soft-roe bloater, don't you? Soft-roe bloaters is scarcer than hard-roe, but what I says is, 'Never mind a little extra trouble so long as you gives satisfaction to the tenants.'"

Mr. Beeton withdrew and left Dick to himself. Torpenhow had been long away; there was no more rioting in the chambers, and Dick had settled down to his new life, which he was weak enough to consider nothing better than death.

It is hard to live alone in the dark, confusing the day and

night; dropping to sleep through sheer weariness at mid-day, and rising restless in the chill of the dawn. At first Dick, on his awakenings, would grope along the corridors of the chambers till he heard some one snore. Then he would know that the day had not yet come, and return wearily to his bed-room. Later he learned not to stir till there was a noise and movement in the house and Mr. Beeton advised him to get up. Once dressed—and dressing, now that Torpenhow was away, was a lengthy business, because collars, ties, and the like hid themselves in far corners of the room, and search meant head-beating against chairs and trunks—once dressed, there was nothing whatever to do except to sit still and brood till the three daily meals came. Centuries separated breakfast from lunch and lunch from dinner, and though a man prayed for hundreds of years that his mind might be taken from him, God would never hear. Rather the mind was quickened and the revolving thoughts ground against each other as millstones grind when there is no corn between; and yet the brain would not wear out and give him rest. It continued to think, at length, with imagery and all manner of reminiscences. It re-called Maisie and past success, reckless travels by land and sea, the glory of doing work and feeling that it was good, and suggested all that might have happened had the eyes only been faithful to their duty. When thinking ceased through sheer weariness, there poured into Dick's soul tide on tide of overwhelming, purposeless fear—dread of starvation always, terror lest the unseen ceiling should crush down upon him, fear of fire in the chambers and a louse's death in red flame, and agonies of fiercer horror that had nothing to do with any fear of death. Then Dick bowed his head, and clutching the arms of his chair fought with his sweating self till the tinkle of plates told him that something to eat was being set before him.

Mr. Beeton would bring the meal when he had time to spare, and Dick learned to hang upon his speech, which dealt with badly fitted gas-plugs, waste-pipes out of repair, little tricks for driving picture-nails into walls, and the sins of the charwoman or the housemaids. In the lack of better things the small gossip of a servant's hall becomes immensely interesting, and the screwing of a washer on a tap an event to be talked over for days.

Once or twice a week, too, Mr. Beeton would take Dick out with him when he went marketing in the morning to haggle with tradesmen over fish, lamp-wicks, mustard, tapioca, and so forth, while Dick rested his weight first on one foot and then on the other and played aimlessly with the tins and string-ball on the counter. Then they would perhaps meet one of Mr. Beeton's friends, and Dick, standing aside a little, would hold his peace till Mr. Beeton was willing to go on again.

The life did not increase his self-respect. He abandoned shaving as a dangerous exercise, and being shaved in a barber's shop meant exposure of his infirmity. He could not see that his clothes were properly brushed, and since he had never taken any care of his personal appearance he became every known variety of sloven. A blind man cannot eat with cleanliness till he has been some months used to the darkness. If he demand attendance and grow angry at the want of it, he must assert himself and stand upright. Then the meanest menial can see that he is blind and, therefore, of no consequence. A wise man will keep his eyes on the floor and sit still. For amusement he may pick coal lump by lump out of the scuttle with the tongs and pile it in a little heap in the fender, keeping count of the lumps, which must all be put back again, one by one and very carefully. He may set himself sums if he cares to work them out; he may talk to himself or to the cat if she chooses to visit him; and if his trade has been that of an artist, he may sketch in the air with his forefinger; but that is too much like drawing a pig with the eyes shut. He may go to his bookshelves and count his books, ranging them in order of their size; or to his wardrobe and count his shirts, laying them in piles of two or three on the bed, as they suffer from frayed cuffs or lost buttons. Even this entertainment wearies after a time; and all the times are very, very long.

Dick was allowed to sort a tool-chest where Mr. Beeton kept hammers, taps and nuts, lengths of gas-pipes, oil-bottles, and string.

"If I don't have everything just where I know where to look for it, why, then, I can't find anything when I do want it. You've no idea, sir, the amount of little things that these chambers uses up," said Mr. Beeton. Fumbling at the handle of the door as he went out: "It's hard on you, sir, I *do* think it's hard on you. Ain't you going to do anything, sir?"

"I'll pay my rent and messing. Isn't that enough?"

"I wasn't doubting for a moment that you couldn't pay your way, sir; but I 'ave often said to my wife, 'It's 'ard on 'im because it isn't as if he was an old man, nor yet a middle-aged one, but quite a young gentleman. *That's* where it comes so 'ard.' "

"I suppose so," said Dick, absently. This particular nerve through long battering had ceased to feel—much.

"I was thinking," continued Mr. Beeton, still making as if to go, "that you might like to hear my boy Alf read you the papers sometimes of an evening. He do read beautiful, seeing he's only nine."

"I should be very grateful," said Dick. "Only let me make it worth his while."

"We wasn't thinking of *that,* sir, but of course it's in your own 'ands; but only to 'ear Alf sing 'A Boy's best Friend is 'is Mother!' Ah!"

"I'll hear him sing that too. Let him come in this evening with the newspapers."

Alf was not a nice child, being puffed up with many school-board certificates for good conduct, and inordinately proud of his singing. Mr. Beeton remained, beaming, while the child wailed his way through a song of some eight eight-line verses in the usual whine of the young Cockney, and, after compliments, left him to read Dick the foreign telegrams. Ten minutes later Alf returned to his parents rather pale and scared.

" 'E said 'e couldn't stand it no more," he explained.

"He never said you read badly, Alf?" Mrs. Beeton spoke.

"No. 'E said I read beautiful. Said 'e never 'eard any one read like that, but 'e said 'e couldn't abide the stuff in the papers."

"P'raps he's lost some money in the Stocks. Were you readin' him about Stocks, Alf?"

"No; it was all about fightin' out there where the soldiers is gone—a great long piece with all the lines close together and very hard words in it. 'E give me 'arf a crown because I read so well. And 'e says the next time there's anything 'e wants read 'e'll send for me."

"That's good hearing, but I do think for all the half-crown—put it into the kicking-donkey money-box, Alf, and let me see you do it—he might have kept you longer. Why, he couldn't have begun to understand how beautiful you read."

"He's best left to hisself—gentlemen always are when they're downhearted," said Mr. Beeton.

Alf's rigorously limited powers of comprehending Torpenhow's special correspondence had waked the devil of unrest in Dick. He could hear, through the boy's nasal chant, the camels grunting in the squares behind the soldiers outside Suakin; could hear the men swearing and chaffing across the cooking pots, and could smell the acrid wood-smoke as it drifted over the camp before the wind of the desert.

That night he prayed to God that his mind might be taken from him, offering for proof that he was worthy of this favour the fact that he had not shot himself long ago. That prayer was not answered, and indeed Dick knew in his heart of hearts that only a lingering sense of humour and no special virtue had kept him alive. Suicide, he had persuaded himself, would be ludicrous insult to the gravity of the situation as well as a weak-kneed confession of fear.

"Just for the fun of the thing," he said to the cat, who had taken Binkie's place in his establishment, "I should like to know how long this is going to last. I can live for a year on the hundred pounds Torp cashed for me. I must have two or three thousand at least at the Bank—twenty or thirty years more provided for, that is to say. Then I fall back on my hundred and twenty a year, which will be more by that time. Let's consider. Twenty-five—thirty-five—a man's in his prime then, they say—forty-five—a middle-aged man just entering politics—fifty-five—'died at the comparatively early age of fifty-five,' according to the newspapers. Bah! How these Christians funk death! Sixty-five—we're only getting on in years. Seventy-five is just possible, though. Great hell, cat O! fifty years more of solitary confinement in the dark! You'll die, and Beeton will die, and Torp will die, and Mai—everybody else will die, but I shall be alive and kicking with nothing to do. I'm very sorry for myself. I should like some one else to be sorry for me. Evidently I'm not going mad before I die, but the pain's just as bad as ever. Some day when you're vivisected, cat O! they'll tie you down on a little table and cut you open—but don't be afraid; they'll take precious good care that you don't die. You'll live, and you'll be very sorry then that you weren't sorry for me. Perhaps Torp will come back or . . . I wish I could go to Torp and the Nilghai, even though I were in their way."

Pussy left the room before the speech was ended, and Alf, as he entered, found Dick addressing the empty hearth-rug.

"There's a letter for you, sir," he said. "Perhaps you'd like me to read it."

"Lend it to me for a minute and I'll tell you."

The outstretched hand shook just a little and the voice was not over-steady. It was within the limits of human possibility that—that was no letter from Maisie. He knew the heft of three closed envelopes only too well. It was a foolish hope that the girl should write to him, for he did not realize that there is a wrong which admits of no reparation though the evildoer may with tears and the heart's best love strive to mend all. It is best to forget that wrong whether it be caused or endured, since it is as remediless as bad work once put forward.

"Read it, then," said Dick, and Alf began intoning according to the rules of the Board School—

"'*I could have given you love, I could have given you loyalty, such as you never dreamed of. Do you suppose I cared* what *you were? But you chose to whistle everything down the wind for nothing. My only excuse for you is that you are so young.*'

"That's all," he said, returning the paper to be dropped into the fire.

"What was in the letter?" asked Mrs. Beeton, when Alf returned.

"I don't know. I think it was a circular or a tract about not whistlin' at everything when you're young."

"I must have stepped on something when I was alive and walking about and it has bounced up and hit me. God help it, whatever it is—unless it was all a joke. But I don't know any one who'd take the trouble to play a joke on me. . . . Love and loyalty for nothing. It sounds tempting enough. I wonder whether I have lost anything really?"

Dick considered for a long time but could not remember when or how he had put himself in the way of winning these trifles at a woman's hands.

Still, the letter as touching on matters that he preferred not to think about stung him into a fit of frenzy that lasted for a day and night. When his heart was so full of despair that it would hold no more, body and soul together seemed to be dropping without check through the darkness. Then came fear of darkness and desperate attempts to reach the light again. But there was no light to be reached. When that agony had left him sweating and breathless, the downward flight would recommence till the gathering torture of it spurred him into another fight as hopeless as the first. Followed some few minutes of sleep in which he dreamed that he saw. Then the procession of events would repeat itself till he was utterly worn out and the brain took up its everlasting consideration of Maisie and might-have-beens.

At the end of everything Mr. Beeton came to his room and volunteered to take him out. "Not marketing this time, but we'll go into the Parks if you like."

"Be damned if I do," quoth Dick. "Keep to the streets and walk up and down. I like to hear the people round me."

This was not altogether true. The blind in the first stages of their infirmity dislike those who can move with a free stride and unlifted arms—but Dick had no earthly desire to go to the Parks. Once and only once since Maisie had shut the door he had gone there under Alf's charge. Alf forgot him and fished for minnows in the Serpentine with some companions. After half an hour's waiting, Dick, almost weeping with rage and wrath, caught a passer-by, who introduced him to a friendly policeman, who led him to a four-wheeler opposite the Albert Hall. He never told Mr. Beeton of Alf's forgetfulness, but . . . this was not the manner in which he was used to walk the Parks aforetime.

"What streets would you like to walk down, then?" said Mr. Beeton, sympathetically. His own ideas of a riotous holiday meant picnicking on the grass of the Green Park with his family, and half a dozen paper bags full of food.

"Keep to the river," said Dick, and they kept to the river, and the rush of it was in his ears till they came to Blackfriars Bridge and struck thence on to the Waterloo Road, Mr. Beeton explaining the beauties of the scenery as he went on.

"And walking on the other side of the pavement," said he, "unless I'm much mistaken, is the young woman that used to come to your rooms to be drawed. I never forgets a face and I never remembers a name, except paying tenants, o' course!"

"Stop her," said Dick. "It's Bessie Broke. Tell her I'd like to speak to her again. Quick, man!"

Mr. Beeton crossed the road under the noses of the omnibuses and arrested Bessie then on her way northward. She recognized him as the man in authority who used to glare at her when she passed up Dick's staircase, and her first impulse was to run.

"Wasn't you Mr. Heldar's model?" said Mr. Beeton, planting himself in front of her. "You was. He's on the other side of the road and he'd like to see you."

"Why?" said Bessie, faintly. She remembered—indeed had never for long forgotten—an affair connected with a newly finished picture.

"Because he has asked me to do so, and because he's most particular blind."

"Drunk?"

"No. 'Orspital blind. He can't see. That's him over there."

Dick was leaning against the parapet of the bridge as

Mr. Beeton pointed him out—a stub-bearded, bowed creature wearing a dirty magenta-coloured neckcloth outside an unbrushed coat. There was nothing to fear from such an one. Even if he chased her, Bessie thought, he could not follow far. She crossed over, and Dick's face lighted up. It was long since a woman of any kind had taken the trouble to speak to him.

"I hope you're well, Mr. Heldar?" said Bessie, a little puzzled. Mr. Beeton stood by with the air of an ambassador and breathed responsibly.

"I'm very well indeed, and, by Jove! I'm glad to see—hear you, I mean, Bess. You never thought it worth while to turn up and see us again after you got your money. I don't know why you should. Are you going anywhere in particular just now?"

"I was going for a walk," said Bessie.

"Not the old business?" Dick spoke under his breath.

"Lor, no! I paid my premium"—Bessie was very proud of that word—"for a barmaid, sleeping in, and I'm at the bar now quite respectable. Indeed I am."

Mr. Beeton had no special reason to believe in the loftiness of human nature. Therefore he dissolved himself like a mist and returned to his gas-plugs without a word of apology. Bessie watched the flight with a certain uneasiness; but so long as Dick appeared to be ignorant of the harm that had been done to him . . .

"It's hard work pulling the beer-handles," she went on, "and they've got one of them penny-in-the-slot cash-machines, so if you get wrong by a penny at the end of the day—but then I don't believe the machinery is right. Do you?"

"I've only seen it work. Mr. Beeton."

"He's gone."

"I'm afraid I must ask you to help me home, then. I'll make it worth your while. You see." The sightless eyes turned towards her and Bessie saw.

"It isn't taking you out of your way?" he said hesitatingly. "I can ask a policeman if it is."

"Not at all. I come on at seven and I'm off at four. That's easy hours."

"Good God!—but I'm on all the time. I wish I had some work to do too. Let's go home, Bess."

He turned and cannoned into a man on the sidewalk, recoiling with an oath. Bessie took his arm and said nothing—as she had said nothing when he had ordered her to turn her face a little more to the light. They walked for some time in silence, the girl steering him deftly through the crowd.

"And where's—where's Mr. Torpenhow?" she inquired at last.

"He has gone away to the desert."

"Where's that?"

Dick pointed to the right. "East—out of the mouth of the river," said he. "Then west, then south, and then east again, all along the under-side of Europe. Then south again, God knows how far." The explanation did not enlighten Bessie in the least, but she held her tongue and looked to Dick's path till they came to the chambers.

"We'll have tea and muffins," he said joyously. "I can't tell you, Bessie, how glad I am to find you again. What made you go away so suddenly?"

"I didn't think you'd want me any more," she said, emboldened by his ignorance.

"I didn't, as a matter of fact—but afterwards—At any rate I'm glad you've come. You know the stairs."

So Bessie led him home to his own place—there was no one to hinder—and shut the door of the studio.

"What a mess!" was her first word. "All these things haven't been looked after for months and months."

"No, only weeks, Bess. You can't expect them to care."

"I don't know what you expect them to do. They ought to know what you've paid them for. The dust's just awful. It's all over the easel."

"I don't use it much now."

"All over the pictures and the floor, and all over your coat. I'd like to speak to them housemaids."

"Ring for tea, then." Dick felt his way to the one chair he used by custom.

Bessie saw the action and, as far as in her lay, was touched.

But there remained always a keen sense of new-found superiority, and it was in her voice when she spoke.

"How long have you been like this?" she said wrathfully, as though the blindness were some fault of the housemaids.

"How?"

"As you are."

"The day after you went away with the check, almost as soon as my picture was finished; I hardly saw her alive."

"Then they've been cheating you ever since, that's all. I know their nice little ways."

A woman may love one man and despise another, but on general feminine principles she will do her best to save the man she despises from being defrauded. Her loved one can look to himself, but the other man, being obviously an idiot, needs protection.

"I don't think Mr. Beeton cheats much," said Dick. Bessie was flouncing up and down the room, and he was conscious of a keen sense of enjoyment as he heard the swish of her skirts and the light step between.

"Tea *and* muffins," she said shortly, when the ring at the bell was answered; "two teaspoonfuls and one over for the pot. I don't want the old teapot that was here when I used to come. It don't draw. Get another."

The housemaid went away scandalized, and Dick chuckled. Then he began to cough as Bessie banged up and down the studio disturbing the dust.

"What are you trying to do?"

"Put things straight. This is like unfurnished lodgings. How could you let it go so?"

"How could I help it? Dust away."

She dusted furiously, and in the midst of all the pother entered Mrs. Beeton. Her husband on his return had explained the situation, winding up with the peculiarly felicitous proverb, "Do unto others as you would be done by." She had descended to put into her place the person who demanded muffins and an uncracked teapot as though she had a right to both.

"Muffins ready yet?" said Bess, still dusting. She was no

longer a drab of the streets but a young lady who, thanks to Dick's check, had paid her premium and was entitled to pull beer-handles with the best. Being neatly dressed in black she did not hesitate to face Mrs. Beeton, and there passed between the two women certain regards that Dick would have appreciated. The situation adjusted itself by eye. Bessie had won, and Mrs. Beeton returned to cook muffins and make scathing remarks about models, hussies, trollops, and the like, to her husband.

"There's nothing to be got of interfering with him, Liza," he said. "Alf, you go along into the street to play. When he isn't crossed he's as kindly as kind, but when he's crossed he's the devil and all. We took too many little things out of his rooms since he was blind to be that particular about what he does. They ain't no objects to a blind man, of course, but if it was to come into court we'd get the sack. Yes, I did introduce him to that girl because I'm a feelin' man myself."

"Much too feelin'!" Mrs. Beeton slapped the muffins into the dish, and thought of comely housemaids long since dismissed on suspicion.

"I ain't ashamed of it, and it isn't for us to judge him hard so long as he pays quiet and regular as he do. I know how to manage young gentlemen, you know how to cook for them, and what I says is, let each stick to his own business and then there won't be any trouble. Take them muffins down, Liza, and be sure you have no words with that young woman. His lot is cruel hard, and if he's crossed he do swear worse than any one I've ever served."

"That's a little better," said Bessie, sitting down to the tea. "You needn't wait, thank you, Mrs. Beeton."

"I had no intention of doing such, I do assure you."

Bessie made no answer whatever. This, she knew, was the way in which real ladies routed their foes, and when one is a barmaid at a first-class public-house one may become a real lady at ten minutes' notice.

Her eyes fell on Dick opposite her and she was both shocked and displeased. There were droppings of food all down the front of his coat; the mouth under the ragged ill-grown beard drooped sullenly; the forehead was lined and contracted; and on the lean temples the hair was a dusty indeterminate colour that might or might not have been called gray. The utter misery and self-abandonment of the man appealed to her, and at the bottom of her heart lay the wicked feeling that he was humbled and brought low who had once humbled her.

"Oh! it *is* good to hear you moving about," said Dick, rubbing his hands. "Tell us all about your bar successes, Bessie, and the way you live now."

"Never mind that. I'm quite respectable, as you'd see by looking at me. *You* don't seem to live too well. What made you go blind that sudden? Why isn't there any one to look after you?"

Dick was too thankful for the sound of her voice to resent the tone of it.

"I was cut across the head a long time ago, and that ruined my eyes. I don't suppose anybody thinks it worth while to look after me any more. Why should they?—and Mr. Beeton really does everything I want."

"Don't you know any gentlemen and ladies, then, while you was—well?"

"A few, but I don't care to have them looking at me."

"I suppose that's why you've growed a beard. Take it off, it don't become you."

"Good gracious, child, do you imagine that I think of what becomes me these days?"

"You ought. Get that taken off before I come here again. I suppose I can come, can't I?"

"I'd be only too grateful if you did. I don't think I treated you very well in the old days. I used to make you angry."

"Very angry, you did."

"I'm sorry for it, then. Come and see me when you can and as often as you can. God knows, there isn't a soul in the world to take that trouble except you and Mr. Beeton."

"A lot of trouble *he's* taking and *she* too." This with a toss of the head. "They've let you do anyhow and they haven't done anything for you. I've only to look to see that much. I'll come, and I'll be glad to come, but you must go and be shaved, and you must get some other clothes—those ones aren't fit to be seen."

"I have heaps somewhere," he said helplessly.

"I know you have. Tell Mr. Beeton to give you a new suit and I'll brush it and keep it clean. You may be as blind as a barn-door, Mr. Heldar, but it doesn't excuse you looking like a sweep."

"Do I look like a sweep, then?"

"Oh, I'm sorry for you. I'm that sorry for you!" she cried impulsively, and took Dick's hands. Mechanically, he lowered his head as if to kiss—she was the only woman who had taken pity on him, and he was not too proud for a little pity now. She stood up to go.

"Nothing o' that kind till you look more like a gentleman. It's quite easy when you get shaved, and some clothes."

He could hear her drawing on her gloves and rose to say good-bye. She passed behind him, kissed him audaciously on the back of the neck, and ran away as swiftly as on the day when she had destroyed the Melancolia.

"To think of me kissing Mr. Heldar," she said to herself, "after all he's done to me and all! Well, I'm sorry for him, and if he was shaved he wouldn't be so bad to look at, but . . . Oh them Beetons, how shameful they've treated him! I know Beeton's wearing his shirt on his back to-day just as well as if I'd aired it. To-morrow, I'll see . . . I wonder if he has much of his own. It might be worth more than the bar—I wouldn't have to do any work—and just as respectable if no one knew."

Dick was not grateful to Bessie for her parting gift. He was acutely conscious of it in the nape of his neck throughout the night, but it seemed, among very many other things, to enforce the wisdom of getting shaved. He was shaved accordingly in the morning, and felt the better for it. A fresh suit of clothes, white linen, and the knowledge that some one in the world said that she took an interest in his personal appearance made him carry himself almost upright; for the brain was relieved for a while from thinking of Maisie, who, under other circumstances, might have given that kiss and a million others.

"Let us consider," said he, after lunch. "The girl can't care, and it's a toss-up whether she comes again or not, but if money can buy her to look after me she shall be bought. Nobody else in the world would take the trouble, and I can make it worth her while. She's a child of the gutter holding brevet rank as a barmaid; so she shall have everything she wants if she'll only come and talk and look after me." He rubbed his newly shorn chin and began to perplex himself with the thought of her not coming. "I suppose I did look rather a sweep," he went on. "I had no reason to look otherwise. I knew things dropped on my clothes, but it didn't matter. It would be cruel if she didn't come. She must. Maisie came once, and that was enough for her. She was quite right. She had something to work for. This creature has only beer-handles to pull, unless she has deluded some young man into keeping company with her. Fancy being cheated for the sake of a counter-jumper! We're falling pretty low."

Something cried aloud within him:—This will hurt more than anything that has gone before. It will recall and remind and suggest and tantalize, and in the end drive you mad.

"I know it, I know it!" Dick cried, clenching his hands despairingly; "but, good heavens! is a poor blind beggar never to get anything out of his life except three meals a day and a greasy waistcoat? I wish she'd come."

Early in the afternoon time she came, because there was no young man in her life just then, and she thought of material advantages which would allow her to be idle for the rest of her days.

"I shouldn't have known you," she said approvingly. "You look as you used to look—a gentleman that was proud of himself."

"Don't you think I deserve another kiss, then?" said Dick, flushing a little.

"Maybe—but you won't get it yet. Sit down and let's see what I can do for you. I'm certain sure Mr. Beeton cheats you, now that you can't go through the housekeeping books every month. Isn't that true?"

"You'd better come and housekeep for me then, Bessie."

"Couldn't do it in these chambers—you know that as well as I do."

"I know, but we might go somewhere else, if you thought it worth your while."

"I'd try to look after you, anyhow; but I shouldn't care to have to work for both of us." This was tentative.

Dick laughed.

"Do you remember where I used to keep my bank-book?" said he. "Torp took it to be balanced just before he went away. Look and see."

"It was generally under the tobacco-jar. Ah!"

"Well?"

"Oh! Four thousand two hundred and ten pounds nine shillings and a penny! Oh my!"

"You can have the penny. That's not bad for one year's work. Is that and a hundred and twenty pounds a year good enough?"

The idleness and the pretty clothes were almost within her reach now, but she must, by being housewifely, show that she deserved them.

"Yes; but you'd have to move, and if we took an inventory, I think we'd find that Mr. Beeton has been prigging little things out of the rooms here and there. They don't look as full as they used."

"Never mind, we'll let him have them. The only thing I'm particularly anxious to take away is that picture I used you for—when you used to swear at me. We'll pull out of this place, Bess, and get away as far as ever we can."

"Oh yes," she said uneasily.

"I don't know where I can go to get away from myself, but I'll try, and you shall have all the pretty frocks that you care for. You'll like that. Give me that kiss now, Bess. Ye gods! it's good to put one's arm round a woman's waist again."

Then came the fulfilment of the prophecy within the brain.

If his arm were thus round Maisie's waist and a kiss had just been given and taken between them,—why then . . . He pressed the girl more closely to himself because the pain whipped him. She was wondering how to explain a little accident to the Melancolia. At any rate, if this man really desired the solace of her company—and certainly he would relapse into his original slough if she withdrew it—he would not be more than just a little vexed. It would be delightful at least to see what would happen, and by her teachings it was good for a man to stand in certain awe of his companion.

She laughed nervously, and slipped out of his reach.

"I shouldn't worrit about that picture if I was you," she began, in the hope of turning his attention.

"It's at the back of all my canvases somewhere. Find it, Bess; you know it as well as I do."

"I know—but——"

"But what? You've wit enough to manage the sale of it to a dealer. Women haggle much better than men. It might be a matter of eight or nine hundred pounds to—to us. I simply didn't like to think about it for a long time. It was mixed up with my life so.—But we'll cover up our tracks and get rid of everything, eh? Make a fresh start from the beginning, Bess."

Then she began to repent very much indeed, because she knew the value of money. Still, it was probable that the blind man was overestimating the value of his work. Gentlemen, she knew, were absurdly particular about their things. She giggled as a nervous housemaid giggles when she tries to explain the breakage of a pipe.

"I'm very sorry, but you remember I was—I was angry with you before Mr. Torpenhow went away?"

"You were very angry, child; and on my word I think you had some right to be."

"Then I—but aren't you sure Mr. Torpenhow didn't tell you?"

"Tell me what? Good gracious, what are you making such a fuss about when you might just as well be giving me another kiss?"

He was beginning to learn, not for the first time in his experience, that kissing is a cumulative poison. The more you get of it, the more you want. Bessie gave the kiss promptly, whispering, as she did so, "I was so angry I rubbed out that picture with the turpentine. You aren't angry, are you?"

"What? Say that again." The man's hand had closed on her wrist.

"I rubbed it out with turps and the knife," faltered Bessie. "I thought you'd only have to do it over again. You did do it over again, didn't you? Oh, let go of my wrist; you're hurting me."

"Isn't there anything left of the thing?"

"N'nothing that looks like anything. I'm sorry—I didn't know you'd take on about it; I only meant to do it in fun. You aren't going to hit me?"

"Hit you! No! Let's think."

He did not relax his hold upon her wrist but stood staring at the carpet. Then he shook his head as a young steer shakes it when the lash of the stock-whip across his nose warns him back to the path to the shambles that he would escape. For weeks he had forced himself not to think of the Melancolia, because she was a part of his dead life. With Bessie's return and certain new prospects that had developed themselves, the Melancolia—lovelier in his imagination than she had ever been on canvas—reappeared. By her aid he might have procured more money wherewith to amuse Bess and to forget Maisie, as well as another taste of an almost forgotten success. Now, thanks to a vicious little housemaid's folly, there was nothing to look for—not even the hope that he might some day take an abiding interest in the housemaid. Worst of all, he had been made to appear ridiculous in Maisie's eyes. A woman will forgive the man who has ruined her life's work so long as he gives her love: a man may forgive those who ruin the love of his life, but he will never forgive the destruction of his work.

"Tck—tck—tck," said Dick between his teeth, and then laughed softly. "It's an omen, Bessie, and—a good many things considered, it serves me right for doing what I have done. By Jove! that accounts for Maisie's running away. She must have thought me perfectly mad—small blame to her! The whole picture ruined, isn't it so? What made you do it?"

"Because I was that angry. I'm not angry now—I'm awful sorry."

"I wonder.—It doesn't matter, anyhow. I'm to blame for making the mistake."

"What mistake?"

"Something you wouldn't understand, dear. Great heavens! to think that a little piece of dirt like you could throw me out of my stride!" Dick was talking to himself as Bessie tried to shake off his grip on her wrist.

"I ain't a piece of dirt, and you shouldn't call me so! I did it 'cause I hated you, and I'm only sorry now 'cause you're—'cause you're——"

"Exactly—because I'm blind. There's nothing like tact in little things."

Bessie began to sob. She did not like being shackled against her will; she was afraid of the blind face and the look upon it, and was sorry too that her great revenge had only made Dick laugh.

"Don't cry," he said, and took her into his arms. "You only did what you thought right."

"I—I ain't a little piece of dirt, and if you say that I'll never come to you again."

"You don't know what you've done to me. I'm not angry—indeed, I'm not. Be quiet for a minute."

Bessie remained in his arms shrinking. Dick's first thought was connected with Maisie, and it hurt him as white-hot iron hurts an open sore.

Not for nothing is a man permitted to ally himself to the wrong woman. The first pang—the first sense of things lost is but the prelude to the play, for the very just Providence who delights in causing pain has decreed that the agony shall return, and that in the midst of keenest pleasure. They know this pain equally who have forsaken or been forsaken by the love of their life, and in their new wives' arms are compelled to realize it. It is better to remain alone and suffer only the misery of being alone, so long as it is possible to find distraction in daily work. When that resource goes the man is to be pitied and left alone.

These things and some others Dick considered while he was holding Bessie to his heart.

"Though you mayn't know it," he said, raising his head, "the Lord is a just and a terrible God, Bess; with a very strong sense of humour. It serves me right—how it serves me right! Torp could understand it if he were here; he must have suffered something at your hands, child, but only for a minute or so. I saved him. Set that to my credit, some one."

"Let me go," said Bess, her face darkening. "Let me go."

"All in good time. Did you ever attend Sunday school?"

"Never. Let me go, I tell you; you're making fun of me."

"Indeed, I'm not. I'm making fun of myself. . . . Thus. 'He saved others, himself he cannot save.' It isn't exactly a school-board text." He released her wrist, but since he was between her and the door, she could not escape. "What an enormous amount of mischief one little woman can do!"

"I'm sorry; I'm awfully sorry about the picture."

"I'm not. I'm grateful to you for spoiling it. . . . What were we talking about before you mentioned the thing?"

"About getting away—and money. Me and you going away."

"Of course. We will get away—that is to say, I will."

"And me?"

"You shall have fifty whole pounds for spoiling a picture."

"Then you won't——?"

"I'm afraid not, dear. Think of fifty pounds for pretty things all to yourself."

"You said you couldn't do anything without me."

"That was true a little while ago. I'm better now, thank you. Get me my hat."

"S'pose I don't?"

"Beeton will, and you'll lose fifty pounds. That's all. Get it."

Bessie cursed under her breath. She had pitied the man sincerely, had kissed him with almost equal sincerity, for he was not unhandsome; it pleased her to be in a way and for a time his protector, and above all there were four thousand pounds to be handled by some one. Now through a slip of the tongue and a little feminine desire to give a little, not too much, pain she had lost the money, the blessed idleness and the pretty things, the companionship, and the chance of looking outwardly as respectable as a real lady.

"Now fill me a pipe. Tobacco doesn't taste, but it doesn't matter, and I'll think things out. What's the day of the week, Bess?"

"Tuesday."

"Then Thursday's mail-day. What a fool—what a blind fool I have been! Twenty-two pounds covers my passage home again. Allow ten for additional expenses. We must put up at Madame Binat's for old sake's sake. Thirty-two pounds altogether. Add a hundred for the cost of the last trip—Gad, won't Torp stare to see me!—a hundred and thirty-two leaves seventy-eight for *baksheesh*—I shall need it—and to play with. What are you crying for, Bess? It wasn't your fault, child; it was mine altogether. Oh, you funny little opossum, mop your eyes and take me out! I want the pass-book and the check-book. Stop a minute. Four thousand pounds at four per cent—that's safe interest—means a hundred and sixty pounds a year; one hundred and twenty pounds a year—also safe—is two eighty, and two hundred and eighty pounds added to three hundred a year means gilded luxury for a single woman. Bess, we'll go to the bank."

Richer by two hundred and ten pounds stored in his money-belt, Dick caused Bessie, now thoroughly bewildered, to hurry from the bank to the P. and O. offices, where he explained things tersely.

"Port Said, single first; cabin as close to the baggage-hatch as possible. What ship's going?"

"The *Colgong,*" said the clerk.

"She's a wet little hooker. Is it Tilbury and a tender, or Galleons and the docks?"

"Galleons. Twelve-forty, Thursday."

"Thanks. Change, please. I can't see very well—will you count it into my hand?"

"If they all took their passages like that instead of talking about their trunks, life would be worth something," said the clerk to his neighbour, who was trying to explain to a harassed mother of many that condensed milk is just as good for babes at sea as daily dairy. Being nineteen and unmarried, he spoke with conviction.

"We are now," quoth Dick, as they returned to the studio, patting the place where his money-belt covered ticket and money, "beyond the reach of man, or devil, or woman—which is much more important. I've three little affairs to carry through before Thursday, but I needn't ask you to help, Bess. Come here on Thursday morning at nine. We'll breakfast, and you shall take me down to Galleons Station."

"What are you going to do?"

"Going away, of course. What should I stay for?"

"But you can't look after yourself?"

"I can do anything. I didn't realize it before, but I can. I've done a great deal already. Resolution shall be treated to one kiss if Bessie doesn't object." Strangely enough, Bessie objected and Dick laughed. "I suppose you're right. Well, come at nine the day after to-morrow and you'll get your money."

"Shall I sure?"

"I don't bilk, and you won't know whether I do or not unless you come. Oh, but it's long and long to wait! Good-bye, Bessie,—send Beeton here as you go out."

The housekeeper came.

"What are all the fittings of my rooms worth?" said Dick, imperiously.

"'Tisn't for me to say, sir. Some things is very pretty and some is wore out dreadful."

"I'm insured for two hundred and seventy."

"Insurance policies is no criterion, though I don't say——"

"Oh, damn your longwindedness! You've made your pickings out of me and the other tenants. Why, you talked of retiring and buying a public-house the other day. Give a straight answer to a straight question."

"Fifty," said Mr. Beeton, without a moment's hesitation.

"Double it; or I'll break up half my sticks and burn the rest."

He felt his way to a bookstand that supported a pile of sketch-books, and wrenched out one of the mahogany pillars.

"That's sinful, sir," said the housekeeper, alarmed.

"It's my own. One hundred or——"

"One hundred it is. It'll cost me three and six to get that there pilaster mended."

"I thought so. What an out and out swindler you must have been to spring that price at once!"

"I hope I've done nothing to dissatisfy any of the tenants, least of all you, sir."

"Never mind that. Get me the money to-morrow, and see that all my clothes are packed in the little brown bullock-trunk. I'm going."

"But the quarter's notice?"

"I'll pay forfeit. Look after the packing and leave me alone."

Mr. Beeton discussed this new departure with his wife, who decided that Bessie was at the bottom of it all. Her husband took a more charitable view.

"It's very sudden—but then he was always sudden in his ways. Listen to him now!"

There was a sound of chanting from Dick's room.

"We'll never come back any more, boys,
We'll never come back no more;
We'll go to the deuce on any excuse,
And never come back no more!
Oh say we're afloat or ashore, boys,
Oh say we're afloat or ashore;
But we'll never come back any more, boys,
We'll never come back no more!

"Mr. Beeton! Mr. Beeton! Where the deuce is my pistol?"

"Quick, he's going to shoot himself—'avin' gone mad!" said Mrs. Beeton.

Mr. Beeton addressed Dick soothingly, but it was some time before the latter, threshing up and down his bedroom, could realize the intention of the promises to "find everything to-morrow, sir."

"Oh, you copper-nosed old fool—you impotent Academician!" he shouted at last. "Do you suppose I want to shoot myself? Take the pistol in your silly shaking hand then. If *you* touch it, it will go off, because it's loaded. It's among my campaign-kit somewhere—in the parcel at the bottom of the trunk."

Long ago Dick had carefully possessed himself of a forty-pound weight field-equipment constructed by the knowledge of his own experience. It was this put-away treasure that he was trying to find and rehandle. Mr. Beeton whipped the revolver out of its place on the top of the package, and Dick drove his hand among the *khaki* coat and breeches, the blue cloth leg-bands, and the heavy flannel shirts doubled over a pair of swan-neck spurs. Under these and the water-bottle lay a sketch-book and a pigskin case of stationery.

"These we don't want; you can have them, Mr. Beeton. Everything else I'll keep. Pack 'em on the top right-hand side of my trunk. When you've done that come into the studio with your wife. I want you both. Wait a minute; get me a pen and a sheet of notepaper."

It is not an easy thing to write when you cannot see, and Dick had particular reasons for wishing that his work should be clear. So he began, following his right hand with his left: "'The badness of this writing is because I am blind and cannot see my pen.' H'mph!—even a lawyer can't mistake that. It must be signed, I suppose, but it needn't be witnessed. Now an inch lower—why did I never learn to use a type-writer?—'This is the last will and testament of me, Richard Heldar. I am in sound bodily and mental health, and there is no previous will to revoke.'—That's all right. Damn the pen! Whereabouts on the paper was I?—'I leave everything that I possess in the world, including four thousand pounds, and two thousand seven hundred and twenty-eight pounds held for me'—oh, I can't get this straight." He tore off half the sheet and began again with the caution about the handwriting. Then: "I leave all the money I possess in the world to"—here followed Maisie's name, and the names of the two banks that held his money.

"It mayn't be quite regular, but no one has a shadow of a right to dispute it, and I've given Maisie's address. Come in, Mr. Beeton. This is my signature; you've seen it often enough to know it; I want you and your wife to witness it. Thanks. To-morrow you must take me to the landlord and I'll pay forfeit for leaving without notice, and I'll lodge this paper with him in case anything happens when I'm away. Now we're going to light up the studio stove. Stay with me, and give me my papers as I want 'em."

No one knows until he has tried how fine a blaze a year's accumulation of bills, letters, and dockets can make. Dick stuffed into the stove every document in the studio—saving only three unopened letters: destroyed sketch-books, rough note-books, new and half-finished canvases alike.

"What a lot of rubbish a tenant gets about him if he stays long enough in one place, to be sure," said Mr. Beeton, at last.

"He does. Is there anything more left?" Dick felt round the walls.

"Not a thing, and the stove's nigh red-hot."

"Excellent, and you've lost about a thousand pounds' worth of sketches. Ho! ho! Quite a thousand pounds' worth, if I can remember what I used to be."

"Yes, sir," politely. Mr. Beeton was quite sure that Dick had gone mad, otherwise he would have never parted with his excellent furniture for a song. The canvas things took up storage room and were much better out of the way.

There remained only to leave the little will in safe hands: that could not be accomplished till to-mororw. Dick groped about the floor picking up the last pieces of paper, assured himself again and again that there remained no written word or sign of his past life in drawer or desk, and sat down before the stove till the fire died out and the contracting iron cracked in the silence of the night.

CHAPTER XV

With a heart of furious fancies,
Whereof I am commander;
With a burning spear and a horse of air,
To the wilderness I wander.
With a knight of ghosts and shadows
I summoned am to tourney—
Ten leagues beyond the wide world's end,
Methinks it is no journey.

—TOM A' BEDLAM'S SONG

"GOOD-BYE, Bess; I promised you fifty. Here's a hundred—all that I got for my furniture from Beeton. That will keep you in pretty frocks for some time. You've been a good little girl, all things considered, but you've given me and Torpenhow a fair amount of trouble."

"Give Mr. Torpenhow my love if you see him, won't you?"

"Of course I will, dear. Now take me up the gangplank and into the cabin. Once aboard the lugger and the maid is—and I am free, I mean."

"Who'll look after you on the ship?"

"The head-steward, if there's any use in money. The doctor when we come to Port Said, if I know anything of P. and O. doctors. After that, the Lord will provide, as He used to do."

Bess found Dick his cabin in the world turmoil of a ship full of leavetakers and weeping relatives. Then he kissed her, and laid himself down in his bunk until the decks should be clear. He who had taken so long to move about his own darkened rooms well understood the geography of a ship, and the necessity of seeing to his own comforts was as wine to him. Before the screw began to thrash the ship along the Docks he had been introduced to the head-steward, had royally tipped him, secured a good place at table, opened out his baggage, and settled himself down with joy in the cabin. It was scarcely necessary to feel his way as he moved about, for he knew everything so well. Then God was very kind: a deep sleep of weariness came upon him just as he would have thought of

Maisie, and he slept till the steamer had cleared the mouth of the Thames and was lifting to the pulse of the Channel.

The rattle of the engines, the reek of oil and paint, and a very familiar sound in the next cabin roused him to his new inheritance.

"Oh, it's good to be alive again!" He yawned, stretched himself vigorously, and went on deck to be told that they were almost abreast of the lights of Brighton. This is no more open water than Trafalgar Square is a common; the free levels begin at Ushant; but none the less Dick could feel the healing of the sea at work upon him already. A boisterous little cross-swell swung the steamer disrespectfully by the nose; and one wave breaking far aft spattered the quarterdeck and the pile of new deck-chairs. He heard the foam fall with the clash of broken glass, was stung in the face by a cupful, and sniffing luxuriously, felt his way to the smoking-room by the wheel. There a strong breeze found him, blew his cap off and left him bareheaded in the doorway, and the smoking-room steward, understanding that he was a voyager of experience, said that the weather would be stiff in the chops off the Channel and more than half a gale in the Bay. These things fell as they were foretold, and Dick enjoyed himself to the utmost. It is allowable and even necessary at sea to lay firm hold upon tables, stanchions, and ropes in moving from place to place. On land the man who feels with his hands is patently blind. At sea even a blind man who is not sea-sick can jest with the doctor over the weakness of his fellows. Dick told the doctor many tales—and these are coin of more value than silver if properly handled—smoked with him till unholy hours of the night, and so won his short-lived regard that he promised Dick a few hours of his time when they came to Port Said.

And the sea roared or was still as the winds blew, and the engines sang their song day and night, and the sun grew stronger day by day, and Tom the Lascar barber shaved Dick of a morning under the opened hatch-grating where the cool winds blew, and the awnings were spread and the passengers made merry, and at last they came to Port Said.

"Take me," said Dick, to the doctor, "to Madame Binat's—if you know where that is."

"Whew!" said the doctor, "I do. There's not much to choose between 'em; but I suppose you're aware that that's one of the worst houses in the place. They'll rob you to begin with, and knife you later."

"Not they. Take me there, and I can look after myself."

So he was brought to Madame Binat's and filled his nostrils with the well-remembered smell of the East, that runs without a change from the Canal head to Hong-Kong, and his mouth with the villainous Lingua Franca of the Levant. The heat smote him between the shoulder-blades with the buffet of an old friend, his feet slipped on the sand, and his coat-sleeve was warm as new-baked bread when he lifted it to his nose.

Madame Binat smiled with the smile that knows no astonishment when Dick entered the drinking-shop which was one source of her gains. But for a little accident of complete darkness he could hardly realize that he had ever quitted the old life that hummed in his ears. Somebody opened a bottle of peculiarly strong Schiedam. The smell reminded Dick of Monsieur Binat, who, by the way, had spoken of art and degradation. Binat was dead; Madame said as much when the doctor departed, scandalized, so far as a ship's doctor can be, at the warmth of Dick's reception. Dick was delighted at it. "They remember me here after a year. They have forgotten me across the water by this time. Madame, I want a long talk with you when you're at liberty. It is good to be back again."

In the evening she set an iron-topped café-table out on the sands, and Dick and she sat by it, while the house behind them filled with riot, merriment, oaths, and threats. The stars came out and the lights of the shipping in the harbour twinkled by the head of the Canal.

"Yes. The war is good for trade, my friend; but what dost thou do here? We have not forgotten thee."

"I was over there in England and I went blind."

"But there was the glory first. We heard of it here, even here—I and Binat; and thou hast used the head of Yellow

'Tina—she is still alive—so often and so well that 'Tina laughed when the papers arrived by the mail-boats. It was always something that we here could recognize in the paintings. And then there was always the glory and the money for thee."

"I am not poor—I shall pay you well."

"Not to me. Thou hast paid for everything." Under her breath, "Mon Dieu, to be blind and so young! What horror!"

Dick could not see her face with the pity on it, or his own with the discoloured hair at the temples. He did not feel the need of pity; he was too anxious to get to the front once more, and explained his desire.

"And where? The Canal is full of the English ships. Sometimes they fire as they used to do when the war was here—ten years ago. Beyond Cairo there is fighting, but how canst thou go there without a correspondent's passport? And in the desert there is always fighting, but that is impossible also," said she.

"I must go to Suakin." He knew, thanks to Alf's readings, that Torpenhow was at work with the column that was protecting the construction of the Suakin-Berber line. P. and O. steamers do not touch at that port, and, besides, Madame Binat knew everybody whose help or advice was worth anything. They were not respectable folk, but they could cause things to be accomplished, which is much more important when there is work toward.

"But at Suakin they are always fighting. That desert breeds men always—and always more men. And they are so bold! Why at Suakin?"

"My friend is there."

"Thy friend! Chtt! Thy friend is death, then."

Madame Binat dropped a fat arm on the table-top, filled Dick's glass anew, and looked at him closely under the stars. There was no need that he should bow his head in assent and say—

"No. He is a man, but—if it should arrive . . . blamest thou?"

"I blame?" she laughed shrilly. "Who am I that I should

blame any one—except those who try to cheat me over their consommations. But it is very terrible."

"I must go to Suakin. Think for me. A great deal has changed within the year, and the men I knew are not here. The Egyptian lighthouse steamer goes down the Canal to Suakin—and the post-boats—But even then——"

"Do not think any longer. *I* know, and it is for me to think. Thou shalt go—thou shalt go and see thy friend. Be wise. Sit here until the house is a little quiet—I must attend to my guests—and afterwards go to bed. Thou shalt go, in truth, thou shalt go."

"To-morrow?"

"As soon as may be." She was talking as though he were a child.

He sat at the table listening to the voices in the harbour and the streets, and wondering how soon the end would come, till Madame Binat carried him off to bed and ordered him to sleep. The house shouted and sang and danced and revelled, Madame Binat moving through it with one eye on the liquor payments and the girls and the other on Dick's interests. To this latter end she smiled upon scowling and furtive Turkish officers of fellaheen regiments, was gracious to Cypriote commissariat underlings, and more than kind to camel agents of no nationality whatever.

In the early morning, being then appropriately dressed in a flaming red silk ball-dress, with a front of tarnished gold embroidery and a necklace of plate-glass diamonds, she made chocolate and carried it in to Dick.

"It is only I, and I am of discreet age, eh? Drink and eat the roll too. Thus in France mothers bring their sons, when those behave wisely, the morning chocolate." She sat down on the side of the bed whispering:—

"It is all arranged. Thou wilt go by the lighthouse boat. That is a bribe of ten pounds English. The captain is never paid by the Government. The boat comes to Suakin in four days. There will go with thee George, a Greek muleteer. Another bribe of ten pounds. I will pay; they must not know of thy money. George will go with thee as far as he goes with his mules. Then he comes back to me, for his well-beloved is here, and if I do not receive a telegram from Suakin saying that thou art well, the girl answers for George."

"Thank you." He reached out sleepily for the cup. "You are much too kind, Madame."

"If there were anything that I might do I would say, stay here and be wise; but I do not think that would be best for thee." She looked at her liquor-stained dress with a sad smile. "Nay, thou shalt go, in truth, thou shalt go. It is best so. My boy, it is best so."

She stooped and kissed Dick between the eyes. "That is for good-morning," she said, going away. "When thou art dressed we will speak to George and make everything ready. But first we must open the little trunk. Give me the keys."

"The amount of kissing lately has been simply scandalous. I shall expect Torp to kiss me next. He is more likely to swear at me for getting in his way, though. Well, it won't last long.—Ohé, Madame, help me to my toilette of the guillotine! There will be no chance of dressing properly out yonder."

He was rummaging among his new campaign-kit, and rowelling his hands with the spurs. There are two ways of wearing well-oiled ankle-jacks, spotless blue leg-bands, *khaki* coat and breeches, and a perfectly pipeclayed helmet. The right way is the way of the untired man, master of himself, setting out upon an expedition, well pleased.

"Everything must be very correct," Dick explained. "It will become dirty afterwards, but now it is good to feel well dressed. Is everything as it should be?"

He patted the revolver neatly hidden under the fulness of the blouse on the right hip and fingered his collar.

"I can do no more," Madame said, between laughing and crying. "Look at thyself—but I forgot."

"I am very content." He stroked the creaseless spirals of his leggings. "Now let us go and see the captain and George and the lighthouse boat. Be quick, Madame."

"But thou canst not be seen by the harbour walking with me in the daylight. Figure to yourself if some English ladies——"

"There are no English ladies; and if there are, I have forgotten them. Take me there."

In spite of his burning impatience it was nearly evening ere the lighthouse boat began to move. Madame had said a great deal both to George and the captain touching the arrangements that were to be made for Dick's benefit. Very few men who had the honour of her acquaintance cared to disregard Madame's advice. That sort of contempt might end in being knifed by a stranger in a gambling hell upon surprisingly short provocation.

For six days—two of them were wasted in the crowded Canal—the little steamer worked her way to Suakin, where she was to pick up the superintendent of lighthouses; and Dick made it his business to propitiate George, who was distracted with fears for the safety of his light-of-love and half inclined to make Dick responsible for his own discomfort. When they arrived George took him under his wing, and together they entered the red-hot seaport, encumbered with the material and wastage of the Suakin-Berber line, from locomotives in disconsolate fragments to mounds of chairs and pot-sleepers.

"If you keep with me," said George, "nobody will ask for passports or what you do. They are all very busy."

"Yes; but I should like to hear some of the Englishmen talk. They might remember me. I was known here a long time ago—when I was some one indeed."

"A long time ago is a very long time ago here. The graveyards are full. Now listen. This new railway runs out so far as Tanai-el-Hassan—that is seven miles. Then there is a camp. They say that beyond Tanai-el-Hassan the English troops go forward, and everything that they require will be brought to them by this line."

"Ah! Base camp. I see. That's a better business than fighting the Fuzzies in the open."

"For this reason even the mules go up in the iron-train."

"Iron what?"

"It is all covered with iron, because it is still being shot at."

"An armoured train. Better and better! Go on, faithful George."

"And I go up with my mules to-night. Only those who particularly require to go to the camp go out with the train. They begin to shoot not far from the city."

"The dears—they always used to!" Dick snuffed the smell of parched dust, heated iron, and flaking paint with delight. Certainly the old life was welcoming him back most generously.

"When I have got my mules together I go up to-night, but you must first send a telegram to Port Said declaring that I have done you no harm."

"Madame has you well in hand. Would you stick a knife into me if you had the chance?"

"I have no chance," said the Greek. "*She* is there with that woman."

"I see. It's a bad thing to be divided between love of woman and the chance of loot. I sympathize with you, George."

They went to the telegraph-office unquestioned, for all the world was desperately busy and had scarcely time to turn its head, and Suakin was the last place under sky that would be chosen for holiday-ground. On their return the voice of an English subaltern asked Dick what he was doing. The blue goggles were over his eyes and he walked with his hand on George's elbow as he replied—

"Egyptian Government—mules. My orders are to give them over to the A. C. G. at Tanai-el-Hassan. Any occasion to show my papers?"

"Oh, certainly not. I beg your pardon. I'd no right to ask, but not seeing your face before I——"

"I go out in the train to-night, I suppose," said Dick, boldly. "There will be no difficulty in loading up the mules, will there?"

"You can see the horse-platforms from here. You must have them loaded up early." The young man went away wondering what sort of broken-down waif this might be who talked like a gentleman and consorted with Greek muleteers. Dick felt unhappy. To outface an English officer is no small thing, but the bluff loses relish when one plays it from the utter dark, and stumbles up and down rough ways, thinking and eternally thinking of what might have been if things had fallen out otherwise, and all had been as it was not.

George shared his meal with Dick and went off to the mule-lines. His charge sat alone in a shed with his face in his hands. Before his tight-shut eyes danced the face of Maisie, laughing, with parted lips. There was a great bustle and clamour about him. He grew afraid and almost called for George.

"I say, have you got your mules ready?" It was the voice of the subaltern over his shoulder.

"My man's looking after them. The—the fact is I've a touch of ophthalmia and I can't see very well."

"By Jove! that's bad. You ought to lie up in hospital for a while. I've had a turn of it myself. It's as bad as being blind."

"So I find it. When does this armoured train go?"

"At six o'clock. It takes an hour to cover the seven miles."

"Are the Fuzzies on the rampage—eh?"

"About three nights a week. Fact is I'm in acting command of the night-train. It generally runs back empty to Tanai for the night."

"Big camp at Tanai, I suppose?"

"Pretty big. It has to feed our desert-column somehow."

"Is that far off?"

"Between thirty and forty miles—in an infernal thirsty country."

"Is the country quiet between Tanai and our men?"

"More or less. I shouldn't care to cross it alone, or with a subaltern's command for the matter of that, but the scouts get through in some extraordinary fashion."

"They always did."

"Have you been here before, then?"

"I was through most of the trouble when it first broke out."

"In the service and cashiered," was the subaltern's first thought, so he refrained from putting any questions.

"There's your man coming up with the mules. It seems rather queer——"

"That I should be mule-leading?" said Dick.

"I didn't mean to say so, but it is. Forgive me—it's beastly impertinence I know, but you speak like a man who has been at a public school. There's no mistaking the tone."

"I am a public school man."

"I thought so. I say, I don't want to hurt your feelings, but you're a little down on your luck, aren't you? I saw you sitting with your head in your hands, and that's why I spoke."

"Thanks. I am about as thoroughly and completely broke as a man need be."

"Suppose—I mean I'm a public school man myself. Couldn't I perhaps—take it as a loan y'know and——"

"You're much too good, but on my honour I've as much money as I want. . . . I tell you what you could do for me, though, and put me under an everlasting obligation. Let me come into the bogie truck of the train. There is a fore-truck, isn't there?"

"Yes. How d'you know?"

"I've been in an armoured train before. Only let me see—hear some of the fun I mean, and I'll be grateful. I go at my own risk as a non-combatant."

The young man thought for a minute. "All right," he said. "We're supposed to be an empty train, and there's no one to blow me up at the other end."

George and a horde of yelling amateur assistants had loaded up the mules, and the narrow-gauge armoured train, plated with three-eighths inch boiler-plate till it looked like one long coffin, stood ready to start.

Two bogie trucks running before the locomotive were completely covered in with plating, except that the leading one was pierced in front for the nozzle of a machine-gun, and the second at either side for lateral fire. The trucks together made one long iron-vaulted chamber in which a score of artillerymen were rioting.

"Whitechapel—last train! Ah, I see yer kissin' in the first class there!" somebody shouted, just as Dick was clambering into the forward truck.

"Lordy! 'Ere's a real live passenger for the Kew, Tanai, Acton, and Ealin' train. *Echo,* sir. Speshul edition! *Star,* sir."—"Shall I get you a foot-warmer?" said another.

"Thanks. I'll pay my footing," said Dick, and relations of the most amicable were established ere silence came with the arrival of the subaltern, and the train jolted out over the rough track.

"This is an immense improvement on shooting the unimpressionable Fuzzy in the open," said Dick, from his place in the corner.

"Oh, but he's still unimpressed. There he goes!" said the subaltern, as a bullet struck the outside of the truck. "We always have at least one demonstration against the night-train. Generally they attack the rear-truck, where my junior commands. He gets all the fun of the fair."

"Not to-night though! Listen!" said Dick. A flight of heavy-handed bullets was succeeded by yelling and shouts. The children of the desert valued their nightly amusement, and the train was an excellent mark.

"Is it worth while giving them half a hopper full?" the subaltern asked of the engine, which was driven by a Lieutenant Sappers.

"I should just think so! This is my section of the line. They'll be playing old Harry with my permanent way if we don't stop 'em."

"Right O!"

"Hrrmph!" said the machine-gun through all its five noses as the subaltern drew the lever home. The empty cartridges clashed on the floor and the smoke blew back through the truck. There was indiscriminate firing at the rear of the train, and return fire from the darkness without and unlimited howling. Dick stretched himself on the floor, wild with delight at the sounds and the smells.

"God is very good—I never thought I'd hear this again. Give 'em hell, men. Oh, give 'em hell!" he cried.

The train stopped for some obstruction on the line ahead and a party went out to reconnoitre, but came back cursing, for spades. The children of the desert had piled sand and gravel on the rails, and twenty minutes were lost in clearing it away. Then the slow progress recommenced, to be varied with more shots, more shoutings, the steady clack and kick of the machine-guns, and a final difficulty with a half-lifted rail ere the train came under the protection of the roaring camp at Tanai-el-Hassan.

"Now, you see why it takes an hour and a half to fetch her through," said the subaltern, unshipping the cartridge-hopper above his pet gun.

"It was a lark, though. I only wish it had lasted twice as long. How superb it must have looked from outside!" said Dick, sighing regretfully.

"It palls after the first few nights. By the way, when you've settled about your mules, come and see what we can find to eat in my tent. I'm Bennil of the Gunners—in the artillery lines—and mind you don't fall over my tent-ropes in the dark."

But it was all dark to Dick. He could only smell the camels, the hay-bales, the cooking, the smoky fires, and the tanned canvas of the tents as he stood, where he had dropped from the train, shouting for George. There was a sound of light-hearted kicking on the iron skin of the rear trucks, with squealing and grunting. George was unloading the mules.

The engine was blowing off steam nearly in Dick's ear; a cold wind of the desert danced between his legs; he was hungry, and felt tired and dirty—so dirty that he tried to brush his coat with his hands. That was a hopeless job; he thrust his hands into his pockets and began to count over the many times that he had waited in strange or remote places for trains or camels, mules or horses, to carry him to his business. In those days he could see—few men more clearly—and the spectacle of an armed camp at dinner under the stars was an ever fresh pleasure to the eye. There was colour, light, and motion, without which no man has much pleasure in living. This night there remained for him only one more journey through the darkness that never lifts to tell a man how far he has travelled. Then he would grip Torpenhow's hand again—Torpenhow, who was alive and strong, and lived in the midst of the action that had once made the reputation of a man called Dick Heldar: not in the least to be confused with the blind, bewildered vagabond who seemed to answer to the same name. Yes, he would find Torpenhow, and come as near to the old life as might be. Afterwards he would forget everything: Bessie, who had wrecked the Melancolia and so nearly wrecked his life; Beeton, who lived in a strange unreal city full of tin-tacks and gas-plugs and matters that no men needed; that irrational being who had offered him love and loyalty for nothing, but had not signed her name; and most of all Maisie, who, from her own point of view, was undeniably right in all she did, but oh, at this distance, so tantalizingly fair.

George's hand on his arm pulled him back to the situation.

"And what now?" said George.

"Oh yes, of course. What now? Take me to the camel-men. Take me to where the scouts sit when they come in from the desert. They sit by their camels, and the camels eat grain out of a black blanket held up at the corners, and the men eat by their side just like camels. Take me there!"

The camp was rough and rutty, and Dick stumbled many times over the stumps of scrub. The scouts were sitting by their beasts, as Dick knew they would. The light of the dung-fires flickered on their bearded faces, and the camels bubbled and mumbled beside them at rest. It was no part of Dick's policy to go into the desert with a convoy of supplies. That would lead to impertinent questions, and since a blind non-combatant is not needed at the front, he would probably be forced to return to Suakin. He must go up alone, and go immediately.

"Now for one last bluff—the biggest of all," he said. "Peace be with you, brethren!" The watchful George steered him to the circle of the nearest fire. The heads of the camel-sheiks bowed gravely, and the camels, scenting a European, looked sideways curiously like brooding hens, half ready to get to their feet.

"A beast and a driver to go to the fighting line to-night," said Dick.

"A Mulaid?" said a voice, scornfully naming the best baggage-breed that he knew.

"A Bisharin," returned Dick, with perfect gravity. "A

Bisharin without saddle-galls. Therefore no charge of thine, shock-head."

Two or three minutes passed. Then—

"We be knee-haltered for the night. There is no going out from the camp."

"Not for money?"

"H'm! Ah! English money?"

Another depressing interval of silence.

"How much?"

"Twenty-five pounds English paid into the hand of the driver at my journey's end, and as much more into the hand of the camel-sheik here, to be paid when the driver returns."

This was royal payment, and the sheik, who knew that he would get his commission on the deposit, stirred in Dick's behalf.

"For scarcely one night's journey—fifty pounds. Land and wells and good trees and wives to make a man content for the rest of his days. Who speaks?" said Dick.

"I," said a voice. "I will go—but there is no going from the camp."

"Fool! I know that a camel can break his knee-halter, and the sentries do not fire if one goes in chase. Twenty-five pounds and another twenty-five pounds. But the beast must be a good Bisharin; I will take no baggage-camel."

Then the bargaining began, and at the end of half an hour the first deposit was paid over to the sheik, who talked in low tones to the driver. Dick heard the latter say: "A little way out only. Any baggage-beast will serve. Am I a fool to waste my cattle for a blind man?"

"And though I cannot see"—Dick lifted his voice a little—"yet I carry that which has six eyes, and the driver will sit before me. If we do not reach the English troops in the dawn he will be dead."

"But where, in God's name, are the troops?"

"Unless thou knowest let another man ride. *Dost* thou know? Remember it will be life or death to thee."

"I know," said the driver, sullenly. "Stand back from my beast. I am going to slip him."

"Not so swiftly. George, hold the camel's head a moment. I want to feel his cheek." The hands wandered over the hide till they found the branded half-circle that is the mark of the Bisharin, the light-built riding-camel. "That is well. Cut this one loose. Remember no blessing of God comes on those who try to cheat the blind."

The men chuckled by the fires at the camel-driver's discomfiture. He had intended to substitute a slow, saddle-galled baggage-colt.

"Stand back!" one shouted, lashing the Bisharin under the belly with a quirt. Dick obeyed as soon as he felt the nose-ring tighten in his hand,—and a cry went up, "Illaha! Aho! He is loose."

With a roar and a grunt the Bisharin rose to his feet and plunged forward towards the desert, his driver following with shouts and lamentation. George caught Dick's arm and hurried him stumbling and tripping past a disgusted sentry who was used to stampeding camels.

"What's the row now?" he cried.

"Every stitch of my kit on that blasted dromedary," Dick answered, after the manner of a common soldier.

"Go on, and take care your throat's not cut outside—you and your dromedary's."

The outcries ceased when the camel had disappeared behind a hillock, and his driver had called him back and made him kneel down.

"Mount first," said Dick. Then climbing into the second seat and gently screwing the pistol muzzle into the small of his companion's back, "Go on in God's name, and swiftly. Good-bye, George. Remember me to Madame, and have a good time with your girl. Get forward, child of the Pit!"

A few minutes later he was shut up in a great silence, hardly broken by the creaking of the saddle and the soft pad of the tireless feet. Dick adjusted himself comfortably to the rock and pitch of the pace, girthed his belt tighter, and felt the darkness slide past. For an hour he was conscious only of the sense of rapid progress.

"A good camel," he said at last.

"He has never been underfed. He is my own and clean bred," the driver replied.

"Go on."

His head dropped on his chest and he tried to think, but the tenor of his thoughts was broken because he was very sleepy. In the half doze it seemed that he was learning a punishment hymn at Mrs. Jennett's. He had committed some crime as bad as Sabbath-breaking, and she had locked him up in his bedroom. But he could never repeat more than the first two lines of the hymn—

When Israel of the Lord beloved
Out of the land of bondage came.

He said them over and over thousands of times. The driver turned in the saddle to see if there were any chance of capturing the revolver and ending the ride. Dick roused, struck him over the head with the butt, and stormed himself wide awake. Somebody hidden in a clump of camel-thorn shouted as the camel toiled up rising ground. A shot was fired, and the silence shut down again, bringing the desire to sleep. Dick could think no longer. He was too tired and stiff and cramped to do more than nod uneasily from time to time, waking with a start and punching the driver with the pistol.

"Is there a moon?" he asked drowsily.

"She is near her setting."

"I wish that I could see her. Halt the camel. At least let me hear the desert talk."

The man obeyed. Out of the utter stillness came one breath of wind. It rattled the dead leaves of a shrub some distance away and ceased. A handful of dry earth detached itself from the edge of a rain trench and crumbled softly to the bottom.

"Go on. The night is very cold."

Those who have watched till the morning know how the last hour before the light lengthens itself into many eternities. It seemed to Dick that he had never since the beginning of original darkness done anything at all save jolt through the air. Once in a thousand years he would finger the nail-heads on the saddle-front and count them all carefully. Centuries later he would shift his revolver from his right hand to his left and allow the eased arm to drop down at his side. From the safe distance of London he was watching himself thus employed,—watching critically. Yet whenever he put out his hand to the canvas that he might paint the tawny yellow desert under the glare of the sinking moon, the black shadow of the camel and the two bowed figures atop, that hand held a revolver and the arm was numbed from wrist to collar-bone. Moreover, he was in the dark, and could see no canvas of any kind whatever.

The driver grunted, and Dick was conscious of a change in the air.

"I smell the dawn," he whispered.

"It is here, and yonder are the troops. Have I done well?"

The camel stretched out its neck and roared as there came down wind the pungent reek of camels in square.

"Go on. We must get there swiftly. Go on."

"They are moving in their camp. There is so much dust that I cannot see what they do."

"Am I in better case? Go forward."

They could hear the hum of voices ahead, the howling and the bubbling of the beasts and the hoarse cries of the soldiers girthing up for the day. Two or three shots were fired.

"Is that at us? Surely they can see that I am English," Dick spoke angrily.

"Nay, it is from the desert," the driver answered, cowering in his saddle. "Go forward, my child! Well it is that the dawn did not uncover us an hour ago."

The camel headed straight for the column and the shots behind multiplied. The children of the desert had arranged that most uncomfortable of surprises, a dawn attack for the English troops, and were getting their distance by snap-shots at the only moving object without the square.

"What luck! What stupendous and imperial luck!" said Dick. "It's 'just before the battle, mother.' Oh, God has been most good to me! Only"—the agony of the thought made him screw up his eyes for an instant—"Maisie . . ."

"Allahu! We are in," said the man, as he drove into the rearguard and the camel knelt.

"Who the deuce are you? Despatches or what? What's the strength of the enemy behind that ridge? How did you get through?" asked a dozen voices. For all answer Dick took a long breath, unbuckled his belt, and shouted from the saddle at the top of a wearied and dusty voice, "Torpenhow! Ohé, Torp! Coo-ee, Tor-pen-how."

A bearded man raking in the ashes of a fire for a light to his pipe moved very swiftly towards that cry, as the rearguard, facing about, began to fire at the puffs of smoke from the hillocks around. Gradually the scattered white cloudlets drew out into long lines of banked white that hung heavily in the stillness of the dawn before they turned over wave-like and glided into the valleys. The soldiers in the square were coughing and swearing as their own smoke obstructed their view, and they edged forward to get beyond it. A wounded camel leaped to its feet and roared aloud, the cry ending in a bubbling grunt. Some one had cut its throat to prevent confusion. Then came the thick sob of a man receiving his death-wound from a bullet; then a yell of agony and redoubled firing.

There was no time to ask questions.

"Get down, man! Get down behind the camel!"

"No. Put me, I pray, in the forefront of the battle." Dick turned his face to Torpenhow and raised his hand to set his helmet straight, but, miscalculating the distance, knocked it off. Torpenhow saw that his hair was gray on the temples, and that his face was the face of an old man.

"Come down, you damned fool! Dickie, come off!"

And Dick came obediently, but as a tree falls, pitching sideways from the Bisharin's saddle at Torpenhow's feet. His luck had held to the last, even to the crowning mercy of a kindly bullet through his head.

Torpenhow knelt under the lee of the camel, with Dick's body in his arms.

From JUST SO STORIES *1902*

HOW THE WHALE GOT HIS THROAT 1897

IN THE SEA, once upon a time, O my Best Beloved, there was a Whale, and he ate fishes. He ate the starfish and the garfish, and the crab and the dab, and the plaice and the dace, and the skate and his mate, and the mackereel and the pickereel, and the really truly twirly-whirly eel. All the fishes he could find in all the sea he ate with his mouth—so! Till at last there was only one small fish left in all the sea, and he was a small 'Stute Fish, and he swam a little behind the Whale's right ear, so as to be out of harm's way. Then the Whale stood up on his tail and said, "I'm hungry." And the small 'Stute Fish said in a small 'stute voice, "Noble and generous Cetacean, have you ever tasted Man?"

"No," said the Whale. "What is it like?"

"Nice," said the small 'Stute Fish. "Nice but nubbly."

"Then fetch me some," said the Whale, and he made the sea froth up with his tail.

"One at a time is enough," said the 'Stute Fish. "If you swim to latitude Fifty North, longitude Forty West (that is magic), you will find, sitting *on* a raft, *in* the middle of the sea, with nothing on but a pair of blue canvas breeches, a pair of suspenders (you must *not* forget the suspenders, Best Beloved), and a jack-knife, one shipwrecked Mariner, who, it is only fair to tell you, is a man of infinite-resource-and-sagacity."

So the Whale swam and swam to latitude Fifty North,

THIS is the picture of the Whale swallowing the Mariner with his infinite-resource-and-sagacity, and the raft and the jack-knife *and* his suspenders, which you must *not* forget. The buttony-things are the Mariner's suspenders, and you can see the knife close by them. He is sitting on the raft, but it has tilted up sideways, so you don't see much of it. The whity thing by the Mariner's left hand is a piece of wood that he was trying to row the raft with when the Whale came along. The piece of wood is called the jaws-of-a-gaff. The Mariner left it outside when he went in. The Whale's name was Smiler, and the Mariner was called Mr. Henry Albert Bivvens, A.B. The little 'Stute Fish is hiding under the Whale's tummy, or else I would have drawn him. The reason that the sea looks so ooshy-skooshy is because the Whale is sucking it all into his mouth so as to suck in Mr. Henry Albert Bivvens and the raft and the jack-knife and the suspenders. You must never forget the suspenders.

longitude Forty West, as fast as he could swim, and *on* a raft, *in* the middle of the sea, *with* nothing to wear except a pair of blue canvas breeches, a pair of suspenders (you must particularly remember the suspenders, Best Beloved), *and* a jack-knife, he found one single, solitary shipwrecked Mariner, trailing his toes in the water. (He had his mummy's leave to paddle, or else he would never have done it, because he was a man of infinite-resource-and-sagacity.)

Then the Whale opened his mouth back and back and back till it nearly touched his tail, and he swallowed the shipwrecked Mariner, and the raft he was sitting on, and his blue canvas breeches, and the suspenders (which you *must* not forget), *and* the jack-knife—He swallowed them all down into his warm, dark, inside cupboards, and then he smacked his lips—so, and turned round three times on his tail.

But as soon as the Mariner, who was a man of infinite-resource-and-sagacity, found himself truly inside the Whale's warm, dark, inside cupboards, he stumped and he jumped and he thumped and he bumped, and he pranced and he danced, and he banged and he clanged, and he hit and he bit, and he leaped and he creeped, and he prowled and he howled, and he hopped and he dropped, and he cried and he sighed, and he crawled and he bawled, and he stepped and he lepped, and he danced hornpipes where he shouldn't, and the Whale felt most unhappy indeed. (*Have* you forgotten the suspenders?)

So he said to the 'Stute Fish, "This man is very nubbly, and besides he is making me hiccough. What shall I do?"

"Tell him to come out," said the 'Stute Fish.

So the Whale called down his own throat to the shipwrecked Mariner, "Come out and behave yourself. I've got the hiccoughs."

"Nay, nay!" said the Mariner. "Not so, but far otherwise. Take me to my natal-shore and the white-cliffs-of-Albion, and I'll think about it." And he began to dance more than ever.

"You had better take him home," said the 'Stute Fish to the Whale. "I ought to have warned you that he is a man of infinite-resource-and-sagacity."

HERE is the Whale looking for the little 'Stute Fish, who is hiding under the Door-sills of the Equator. The little 'Stute Fish's name was Pingle. He is hiding among the roots of the big seaweed that grows in front of the Doors of the Equator. I have drawn the Doors of the Equator. They are shut. They are always kept shut, because a door ought always to be kept shut. The ropy-thing right across is the Equator itself; and the things that look like rocks are the two giants Moar and Koar, that keep the Equator in order. They drew the shadow-pictures on the doors of the Equator, and they carved all those twisty fishes under the Doors. The beaky-fish are called beaked Dolphins, and the other fish with the queer heads are called Hammer-headed Sharks. The Whale never found the little 'Stute Fish till he got over his temper, and then they became good friends again.

So the Whale swam and swam and swam, with both flippers and his tail, as hard as he could for the hiccoughs; and at last he saw the Mariner's natal-shore and the white-cliffs-of-Albion, and he rushed half-way up the beach and opened his mouth wide and wide and wide, and said, "Change here for Winchester, Ashuelot, Nashua, Keene, and stations on the *Fitch*burg Road"; and just as he said "Fitch" the Mariner walked out of his mouth. But while the Whale had been swimming, the Mariner, who was indeed a person of infinite-resource-and-sagacity, had taken his jack-knife and cut up the raft into a little square grating all running criss-cross, and he had tied it firm with his suspenders (*now* you know why you were not to forget the suspenders!), and he dragged that grating good and tight into the Whale's throat, and there it stuck! Then he recited the following Sloka, which, as you have not heard it, I will now proceed to relate—

By means of a grating
I have stopped your ating.

For the Mariner he was also an Hi-ber-ni-an. And he stepped out on the shingle, and went home to his mother, who had given him leave to trail his toes in the water; and he married and lived happily ever afterward. So did the Whale. But from that day on, the grating in his throat, which he could neither cough up nor swallow down, prevented him eating anything except very, very small fish; and this is the reason why whales nowadays never eat men or boys or little girls.

The small 'Stute Fish went and hid himself in the mud under the Door-sills of the Equator. He was afraid that the Whale might be angry with him.

The sailor took the jack-knife home. He was wearing the blue canvas breeches when he walked out on the shingle. The suspenders were left behind, you see, to tie that grating with; and that is the end of *that* tale.

1902

When the cabin port-holes are dark and green
  Because of the seas outside;
When the ship goes *wop* (with a wiggle between)
And the steward falls into the soup-tureen,
  And the trunks begin to slide;
When Nursey lies on the floor in a heap,
And Mummy tells you to let her sleep,
And you aren't waked or washed or dressed,
Why, then you will know (if you haven't guessed)
You're "Fifty North and Forty West!"

1902

China-going P. and O.'s
Pass Pau Amma's playground close,
And his Pusat Tasek lies
Near the track of most B.I.'s
N.Y.K. and N.D.L.
Know Pau Amma's home as well
As the Fisher of the Sea knows
"Bens," M.M.'s and Rubattinos.
But (and this is rather queer)
A.T.L.'s can *not* come here;
O. and O. and D.O.A.
Must go round another way.
Orient, Anchor, Bibby, Hall,
Never go that way at all.
U.C.S. would have a fit
If it found itself on it.
And if "Beavers" took their cargoes
To Penang instead of Lagos,
Or a fat Shaw-Savill bore
Passengers to Singapore,
Or a White Star were to try a
Little trip to Sourabaya,
Or a B.S.A. went on

Past Natal to Cheribon,
Then great Mr. Lloyds would come
With a wire and drag them home!

. . . .

You'll know what my riddle means
When you've eaten mangosteens.
The Crab That Played with the Sea.

HOW THE RHINOCEROS GOT HIS SKIN

1898

NCE upon a time, on an uninhabited island on the shores of the Red Sea, there lived a Parsee from whose hat the rays of the sun were reflected in more-than-oriental splendour. And the Parsee lived by the Red Sea with nothing but his hat and his knife and a cooking stove of the kind that you must particularly never touch. And one day he took flour and water and currants and plums and sugar and things and made himself one cake which was two feet across and three feet thick. It was indeed a Superior Comestible (*that's* magic), and he put it on the stove because *he* was allowed to cook on that stove, and he baked it and he baked it till it was all done brown and smelt most sentimental. But just as he was going to eat it there came down to the beach from the Altogether Uninhabited Interior one Rhinoceros with a horn on his nose, two piggy eyes, and few manners. In those days the Rhinoceros's skin fitted him quite tight. There were no wrinkles in it anywhere. He looked exactly like a Noah's Ark Rhinoceros, but of course much bigger. All the same, he had no manners then, and he has no manners now, and he never will have any

THIS is the picture of the Parsee beginning to eat his cake on the Uninhabited Island in the Red Sea on a very hot day; and of the Rhinoceros coming down from the Altogether Uninhabited Interior, which, as you can truthfully see, is all rocky. The Rhinoceros's skin is quite smooth, and the three buttons that button it up are underneath, so you can't see them. The squiggly things on the Parsee's hat are the rays of the sun reflected in more-than-oriental splendour, because if I had drawn real rays they would have filled up all the picture. The cake has currants in it; and the wheel-thing lying on the sand in front belonged to one of Pharaoh's chariots when he tried to cross the Red Sea. The Parsee found it, and kept it to play with. The Parsee's name was Pestonjee Bomonjee, and the Rhinoceros was called Strorks, because he breathed through his mouth instead of his nose. I wouldn't ask anything about the cooking-stove if *I* were you.

manners. He said, "How!" and the Parsee left that cake and climbed to the top of a palm tree with nothing on but his hat, from which the rays of the sun were always reflected in more-than-oriental splendour. And the Rhinoceros upset the oil-stove with his nose, and the cake rolled on the sand, and he spiked that cake on the horn of his nose, and he ate it, and he went away, waving his tail, to the desolate and Exclusively Uninhabited Interior which abuts on the islands of Mazanderan, Socotra, and the Promontories of the Larger Equinox. Then the Parsee came down from his palm-tree and put the stove on its legs and recited the following *Sloka,* which, as you have not heard, I will now proceed to relate:

Them that takes cakes
Which the Parsee-man bakes
Makes dreadful mistakes.

And there was a great deal more in that than you would think.

Because, five weeks later, there was a heat-wave in the Red Sea, and everybody took off all the clothes they had. The Parsee took off his hat; but the Rhinoceros took off his skin and carried it over his shoulder as he came down to the beach to bathe. In those days it buttoned underneath with three buttons and looked like a waterproof. He said nothing whatever about the Parsee's cake, because he had eaten it all; and he never had any manners, then, since, or henceforward. He waddled straight into the water and blew bubbles through his nose, leaving his skin on the beach.

Presently the Parsee came by and found the skin, and he smiled one smile that ran all round his face two times. Then he danced three times round the skin and rubbed his hands. Then he went to his camp and filled his hat with cake-crumbs, for the Parsee never ate anything but cake, and never swept out his camp. He took that skin, and he shook that skin, and he scrubbed that skin, and he rubbed that skin just as full of old, dry, stale, tickly cake-crumbs and some burned currants as ever it could *possibly* hold. Then he climbed to the top of his palm-tree and waited for the Rhinoceros to come out of the water and put it on.

And the Rhinoceros did. He buttoned it up with the three buttons, and it tickled like cake-crumbs in bed. Then he wanted to scratch, but that made it worse; and then he lay down on the sands and rolled and rolled and rolled, and every time he rolled the cake-crumbs tickled him worse and worse and worse. Then he ran to the palm-tree and rubbed and rubbed and rubbed himself against it. He rubbed so much and so hard that he rubbed his skin into a great fold over his shoulders, and another fold underneath, where the buttons used to be (but he rubbed the buttons off), and he rubbed some more folds over his legs. And it spoiled his temper, but it didn't make the least difference to the cake-crumbs. They were inside his skin and they tickled. So he went home, very angry indeed and horribly scratchy; and from that day to this every rhinoceros has great folds in his skin and a very bad temper, all on account of the cake-crumbs inside.

But the Parsee came down from his palm-tree, wearing his hat, from which the rays of the sun were reflected in more-than-oriental splendour, packed up his cooking-stove, and went away in the direction of Orotavo, Amygdala, the Upland Meadows of Anantarivo and the Marshes of Sonaput.

This is the Parsee Pestonjee Bomonjee sitting in his palm-tree and watching the Rhinoceros Strorks bathing near the beach of the Altogether Uninhabited Island after Strorks had taken off his skin. The Parsee has put the cake-crumbs into the skin, and he is smiling to think how they will tickle Strorks when Strorks puts it on again. The skin is just under the rocks below the palm-tree in a cool place; that is why you can't see it. The Parsee is wearing a new more-than-oriental-splendour hat of the sort that Parsees wear; and he has a knife in his hand to cut his name on palm-trees. The black thing on the islands out at sea are bits of ships that got wrecked going down the Red Sea; but all the passengers were saved and went home.

The black thing in the water close to the shore is not a wreck at all. It is Strorks the Rhinoceros bathing without his skin. He was just as black underneath his skin as he was outside. I wouldn't ask anything about the cooking-stove if *I* were you.

THE CAT THAT WALKED BY HIMSELF

1902

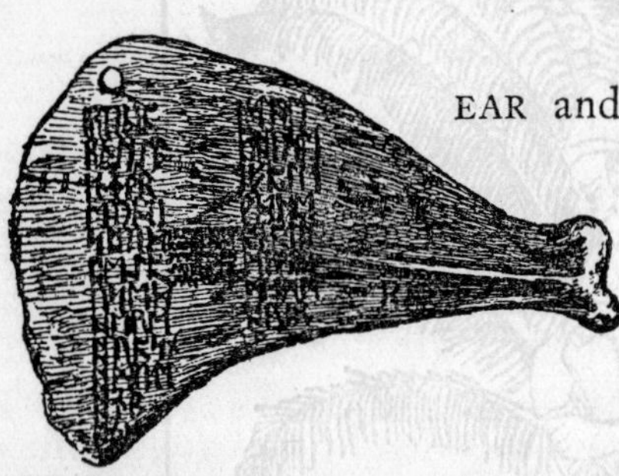

HEAR and attend and listen; for this befell and behappened and became and was, O my Best Beloved, when the Tame animals were wild. The Dog was wild, and the Horse was wild, and the Cow was wild, and the Sheep was wild, and the Pig was wild—as wild as wild could be—and they walked in the Wet Wild Woods by their wild lones. But the wildest of all the wild animals was the Cat. He walked by himself, and all places were alike to him.

Of course the Man was wild too. He was dreadfully wild. He didn't even begin to be tame till he met the Woman, and she told him that she did not like living in his wild ways. She picked out a nice dry Cave, instead of a heap of wet leaves, to lie down in; and she strewed clean sand on the floor; and she lit a nice fire of wood at the back of the Cave; and she hung a dried wild-horse skin, tail-down, across the opening of the Cave; and she said, "Wipe your feet, dear, when you come in, and now we'll keep house."

That night, Best Beloved, they ate wild sheep roasted on the hot stones, and flavoured with wild garlic and wild pepper; and wild duck stuffed with wild rice and wild fenugreek and wild coriander; and marrow-bones of wild oxen; and wild cherries, and wild grenadillas. Then the Man went to sleep in front of the fire ever so happy; but the Woman sat up, combing her hair. She took the bone of the shoulder of mutton—the big fat blade-bone—and she looked at the wonderful marks on it, and she threw more wood on the fire, and she made a Magic. She made the First Singing Magic in the world.

Out in the Wet Wild Woods all the wild animals gathered together where they could see the light of the fire a long way off, and they wondered what it meant.

The Wild Horse stamped with his wild foot and said, "O my Friends and O my Enemies, why have the Man and the Woman made that great light in that great Cave, and what harm will it do us?"

Wild Dog lifted up his wild nose and smelled the smell of roast mutton, and said, "I will go up and look, and say; for I think it is good. Cat, come with me."

"Nenni!" said the Cat. "I am the Cat who walks by himself, and all places are alike to me. I will not come."

"Then we can never be friends again," said Wild Dog, and he trotted off to the Cave. But when he had gone a little way the Cat said to himself, "All places are alike to me. Why should I not go too and see and look and come away at my own liking." So he slipped after Wild Dog softly, very softly, and hid himself where he could hear everything.

When Wild Dog reached the mouth of the Cave he lifted up the dried horse-skin with his nose and sniffed the beautiful smell of the roast mutton, and the Woman, looking at the blade-bone, heard him, and laughed, and said, "Here comes the first. Wild Thing out of the Wild Woods, what do you want?"

Wild Dog said, "O my Enemy and Wife of my Enemy, what is this that smells so good in the Wild Woods?"

Then the Woman picked up a roasted mutton-bone and threw it to Wild Dog, and said, "Wild Thing out of the Wild Woods, taste and try." Wild Dog gnawed the bone and it was more delicious than anything he had ever tasted, and he said, "O my Enemy and Wife of my Enemy, give me another."

The Woman said, "Wild Thing out of the Wild Woods, help my Man to hunt through the day and guard this Cave at night, and I will give you as many roast bones as you need."

"Ah!" said the Cat, listening. "This is a very wise Woman, but she is not so wise as I am."

THIS is the picture of the Cave where the Man and the Woman lived first of all. It was really a very nice Cave, and much warmer than it looks. The Man had a canoe. It is on the edge of the river, being soaked in the water to make it swell up. The tattery-looking thing across the river is the Man's salmon-net to catch salmon with. There are nice clean stones leading up from the river to the mouth of the Cave, so that the Man and the Woman could go down for water without getting sand between their toes. The things like black-beetles far down the beach are really trunks of dead trees that floated down the river from the Wet Wild Woods on the other bank. The Man and the Woman used to drag them out and dry them and cut them up for firewood. I haven't drawn the horse-hide curtain at the mouth of the Cave, because the Woman has just taken it down to be cleaned. All those little smudges on the sand between the Cave and the river are the marks of the Woman's feet and the Man's feet.

The Man and the Woman are both inside the Cave eating their dinner. They went to another cosier Cave when the Baby came, because the Baby used to crawl down to the river and fall in, and the Dog had to pull him out.

Wild Dog crawled into the Cave and laid his head on the Woman's lap, and said, "O my Friend and Wife of my Friend, I will help your Man to hunt through the day, and at night I will guard your Cave."

"Ah!" said the Cat, listening. "That is a very foolish Dog." And he went back through the Wet Wild Woods waving his wild tail, and walking by his wild lone. But he never told anybody.

When the Man waked up he said, "What is Wild Dog doing here?" And the Woman said, "His name is not Wild Dog any more, but the First Friend, because he will be our friend for always and always and always. Take him with you when you go hunting."

Next night the Woman cut great green armfuls of fresh grass from the water-meadows, and dried it before the fire, so that it smelt like new-mown hay, and she sat at the mouth of the Cave and plaited a halter out of horse-hide, and she looked at the shoulder of mutton-bone—at the big broad blade-bone —and she made a Magic. She made the Second Singing Magic in the world.

Out in the Wild Woods all the wild animals wondered what had happened to Wild Dog, and at last Wild Horse stamped with his foot and said, "I will go and see and say why Wild Dog has not returned. Cat, come with me."

"Nenni!" said the Cat. "I am the Cat who walks by himself, and all places are alike to me. I will not come." But all the same he followed Wild Horse softly, very softly, and hid himself where he could hear everything.

When the Woman heard Wild Horse tripping and stumbling on his long mane, she laughed and said, "Here comes the second. Wild Thing out of the Wild Woods what do you want?"

Wild Horse said, "O my Enemy and Wife of my Enemy, where is Wild Dog?"

The Woman laughed, and picked up the blade-bone and looked at it, and said, "Wild Thing out of the Wild Woods, you did not come here for Wild Dog, but for the sake of this good grass."

And Wild Horse, tripping and stumbling on his long mane, said, "That is true; give it me to eat."

The Woman said, "Wild Thing out of the Wild Woods, bend your wild head and wear what I give you, and you shall eat the wonderful grass three times a day."

"Ah," said the Cat, listening, "this is a clever Woman, but she is not so clever as I am."

Wild Horse bent his wild head, and the Woman slipped the plaited hide halter over it, and Wild Horse breathed on the Woman's feet and said, "O my Mistress, and Wife of my Master, I will be your servant for the sake of the wonderful grass."

"Ah," said the Cat, listening, "that is a very foolish Horse." And he went back through the Wet Wild Woods, waving his wild tail and walking by his wild lone. But he never told anybody.

When the Man and the Dog came back from hunting, the Man said, "What is Wild Horse doing here?" And the Woman said, "His name is not Wild Horse any more, but the First Servant, because he will carry us from place to place for always and always and always. Ride on his back when you go hunting."

Next day, holding her wild head high that her wild horns should not catch in the wild trees, Wild Cow came up to the Cave, and the Cat followed, and hid himself just the same as before; and everything happened just the same as before; and the Cat said the same things as before, and when Wild Cow had promised to give her milk to the Woman every day in exchange for the wonderful grass, the Cat went back through the Wet Wild Woods waving his wild tail and walking by his wild lone, just the same as before. But he never told anybody. And when the Man and the Horse and the Dog came home from hunting and asked the same questions same as before, the Woman said, "Her name is not Wild Cow any more, but the Giver of Good Food. She will give us the warm white milk for always and always and always, and I will take care of her while you and the First Friend and the First Servant go hunting."

THIS is the picture of the Cat that Walked by Himself walking by his wild lone through the Wet Wild Woods and waving his wild tail. There is nothing else in the picture except some toadstools. They had to grow there because the woods were so wet. The lumpy thing on the low branch is n't a bird. It is moss that grew there because the Wild Woods were so wet.

Underneath the truly picture is a picture of the cosey Cave that the Man and the Woman went to after the Baby came. It was their summer Cave, and they planted wheat in front of it. The Man is riding on the Horse to find the Cow and bring her back to the Cave to be milked. He is holding up his hand to call the Dog, who has swum across to the other side of the river, looking for rabbits.

Next day the Cat waited to see if any other Wild thing would go up to the Cave, but no one moved in the Wet Wild Woods, so the Cat walked there by himself; and he saw the Woman milking the Cow, and he saw the light of the fire in the Cave, and he smelt the smell of the warm white milk.

Cat said, "O my Enemy and Wife of my Enemy, where did Wild Cow go?"

The Woman laughed and said, "Wild Thing out of the Wild Woods, go back to the Woods again, for I have braided up my hair, and I have put away the magic blade-bone, and we have no more need of either friends or servants in our Cave."

Cat said, "I am not a friend, and I am not a servant. I am the Cat who walks by himself, and I wish to come into your cave."

Woman said, "Then why did you not come with First Friend on the first night?"

Cat grew very angry and said, "Has Wild Dog told tales of me?"

Then the Woman laughed and said, "You are the Cat who walks by himself, and all places are alike to you. You are neither a friend nor a servant. You have said it yourself. Go away and walk by yourself in all places alike."

Then Cat pretended to be sorry and said, "Must I never come into the Cave? Must I never sit by the warm fire? Must I never drink the warm white milk? You are very wise and very beautiful. You should not be cruel even to a Cat."

Woman said, "I knew I was wise, but I did not know I was beautiful. So I will make a bargain with you. If ever I say one word in your praise you may come into the Cave."

"And if you say two words in my praise?" said the Cat.

"I never shall," said the Woman, "but if I say two words in your praise, you may sit by the fire in the Cave."

"And if you say three words?" said the Cat.

"I never shall," said the Woman, "but if I say three words in your praise, you may drink the warm white milk three times a day for always and always and always."

Then the Cat arched his back and said, "Now let the Curtain at the mouth of the Cave, and the Fire at the back of the Cave, and the Milk-pots that stand beside the Fire, remember what my Enemy and the Wife of my Enemy has said." And he went away through the Wet Wild Woods waving his wild tail and walking by his wild lone.

That night when the Man and the Horse and the Dog came home from hunting, the Woman did not tell them of the bargain that she had made with the Cat, because she was afraid that they might not like it.

Cat went far and far away and hid himself in the Wet Wild Woods by his wild lone for a long time till the Woman forgot all about him. Only the Bat—the little upside-down Bat—that hung inside the Cave, knew where Cat hid; and every evening Bat would fly to Cat with news of what was happening.

One evening Bat said, "There is a Baby in the Cave. He is new and pink and fat and small, and the Woman is very fond of him."

"Ah," said the Cat, listening, "but what is the Baby fond of?"

"He is fond of things that are soft and tickle," said the Bat. "He is fond of warm things to hold in his arms when he goes to sleep. He is fond of being played with. He is fond of all those things."

"Ah," said the Cat, listening, "then my time has come."

Next night Cat walked through the Wet Wild Woods and hid very near the Cave till morning-time, and Man and Dog and Horse went hunting. The Woman was busy cooking that morning, and the Baby cried and interrupted. So she carried him outside the Cave and gave him a handful of pebbles to play with. But still the Baby cried.

Then the Cat put out his paddy paw and patted the Baby on the cheek, and it cooed; and the Cat rubbed against its fat knees and tickled it under its fat chin with his tail. And the Baby laughed; and the Woman heard him and smiled.

Then the Bat—the little upside-down Bat—that hung in the mouth of the Cave said, "O my Hostess and Wife of my Host and Mother of my Host's Son, a Wild Thing from the

Wild Woods is most beautifully playing with your Baby."

"A blessing on that Wild Thing whoever he may be," said the Woman, straightening her back, "for I was a busy woman this morning and he has done me a service."

That very minute and second, Best Beloved, the dried horse-skin Curtain that was stretched tail-down at the mouth of the Cave fell down—*woosh!*—because it remembered the bargain she had made with the Cat, and when the Woman went to pick it up—lo and behold!—the Cat was sitting quite comfy inside the Cave.

"O my Enemy and Wife of my Enemy and Mother of my Enemy," said the Cat, "it is I: for you have spoken a word in my praise, and now I can sit within the Cave for always and always and always. But still I am the Cat who walks by himself, and all places are alike to me."

The Woman was very angry, and shut her lips tight and took up her spinning-wheel and began to spin.

But the Baby cried because the Cat had gone away, and the Woman could not hush it, for it struggled and kicked and grew black in the face.

"O my Enemy and Wife of my Enemy and Mother of my Enemy," said the Cat, "take a strand of the wire that you are spinning and tie it to your spinning-whorl and drag it along the floor, and I will show you a magic that shall make your Baby laugh as loudly as he is now crying."

"I will do so," said the Woman, "because I am at my wits' end; but I will not thank you for it."

She tied the thread to the little clay spindle-whorl and drew it across the floor, and the Cat ran after it and patted it with his paws and rolled head over heels, and tossed it backward over his shoulder and chased it between his hind legs and pretended to lose it, and pounced down upon it again, till the Baby laughed as loudly as it had been crying, and scrambled after the Cat and frolicked all over the Cave till it grew tired and settled down to sleep with the Cat in its arms.

"Now," said the Cat, "I will sing the Baby a song that shall keep him asleep for an hour." And he began to purr, loud and low, low and loud, till the Baby fell fast asleep. The Woman smiled as she looked down upon the two of them and said, "That was wonderfully done. No question but you are very clever, O Cat."

That very minute and second, Best Beloved, the smoke of the fire at the back of the Cave came down in clouds from the roof—*puff!*—because it remembered the bargain she had made with the Cat, and when it had cleared away—lo and behold! —the Cat was sitting quite comfy close to the fire.

"O my Enemy and Wife of my Enemy and Mother of my Enemy," said the Cat, "it is I, for you have spoken a second word in my praise, and now I can sit by the warm fire at the back of the Cave for always and always and always. But still I am the Cat who walks by himself, and all places are alike to me."

Then the Woman was very very angry, and let down her hair and put more wood on the fire and brought out the broad blade-bone of the shoulder of mutton and began to make a Magic that should prevent her from saying a third word in praise of the Cat. It was not a Singing Magic, Best Beloved, it was a Still Magic; and by and by the Cave grew so still that a little wee-wee mouse crept out of a corner and ran across the floor.

"O my Enemy and Wife of my Enemy and Mother of my Enemy," said the Cat, "is that little mouse part of your magic?"

"Ouh! Chee! No indeed!" said the Woman, and she dropped the blade-bone and jumped upon the footstool in front of the fire and braided up her hair very quick for fear that the mouse should run up it.

"Ah," said the Cat, watching, "then the mouse will do me no harm if I eat it?"

"No," said the Woman, braiding up her hair, "eat it quickly and I will ever be grateful to you."

Cat made one jump and caught the little mouse, and the Woman said, "A hundred thanks. Even the First Friend is not quick enough to catch little mice as you have done. You must be very wise."

That very moment and second, O Best Beloved, the Milk-pot that stood by the fire cracked in two pieces—*ffft*—because it remembered the bargain she had made with the Cat, and when the Woman jumped down from the footstool—lo and behold!—the Cat was lapping up the warm white milk that lay in one of the broken pieces.

"O my Enemy and Wife of my Enemy and Mother of my Enemy," said the Cat, "it is I: for you have spoken three words in my praise, and now I can drink the warm white milk three times a day for always and always and always. But *still* I am the Cat who walks by himself, and all places are alike to me."

Then the Woman laughed and set the Cat a bowl of the warm white milk and said, "O Cat, you are as clever as a man, but remember that your bargain was not made with the Man or the Dog, and I do not know what they will do when they come home."

"What is that to me?" said the Cat. "If I have my place in the Cave by the fire and my warm white milk three times a day I do not care what the Man or the Dog can do."

That evening when the Man and the Dog came into the Cave, the Woman told them all the story of the bargain while the Cat sat by the fire and smiled. Then the Man said, "Yes, but he has not made a bargain with *me* or with all proper Men after me." Then he took off his two leather boots and he took up his little stone axe (that makes three) and he fetched a piece of wood and a hatchet (that is five alogether), and he set them out in a row and he said, "Now we will make *our* bargain. If you do not catch mice when you are in the Cave for always and always and always, I will throw these five things at you whenever I see you, and so shall all proper Men do after me."

"Ah," said the Woman, listening, "this is a very clever Cat, but he is not so clever as my Man."

The Cat counted the five things (and they looked very knobby) and he said, "I will catch mice when I am in the Cave for always and always and always; but *still* I am the Cat who walks by himself, and all places are alike to me."

"Not when I am near," said the Man. "If you had not said that last I would have put all these things away for always and always and always; but I am now going to throw my two boots and my little stone axe (that makes three) at you whenever I meet you. And so shall all proper Men do after me!"

Then the Dog said, "Wait a minute. He has not made a bargain with *me* or with all proper Dogs after me." And he showed his teeth and said, "If you are not kind to the Baby while I am in the Cave for always and always and always, I will hunt you till I catch you, and when I catch you I will bite you. And so shall all proper Dogs do after me."

"Oh," said the Woman, listening, "this is a very clever Cat, but he is not so clever as the Dog."

Cat counted the Dog's teeth (and they looked very pointed) and he said, "I will be kind to the Baby while I am in the Cave, as long as he does not pull my tail too hard, for always and always and always. But *still* I am the Cat that walks by himself, and all places are alike to me."

"Not when I am near," said the Dog. "If you had not said that last I would have shut my mouth for always and always and always; but *now* I am going to hunt you up a tree whenever I meet you. And so shall all proper Dogs do after me."

Then the Man threw his two boots and his little stone axe (that makes three) at the Cat, and the Cat ran out of the Cave and the Dog chased him up a tree; and from that day to this, Best Beloved, three proper Men out of five will always throw things at a Cat whenever they meet him, and all proper Dogs will chase him up a tree. But the Cat keeps his side of the bargain too. He will kill mice and he will be kind to Babies when he is in the house, just as long as they do not pull his tail too hard. But when he has done that, and between times, and when the moon gets up and night comes, he is the Cat that walks by himself, and all places are alike to him. Then he goes out to the Wet Wild Woods or up the Wet Wild Trees or on the Wet Wild Roofs, waving his wild tail and walking by his wild lone.

1902

I keep six honest serving-men;
(They taught me all I knew)
Their names are What and Where and When
And How and Where and Who.
I send them over land and sea,
I send them east and west;
But after they have worked for me,
I *give them all a rest.*

I *let them rest from nine till five,*
For I am busy then,
As well as breakfast, lunch, and tea,
For they are hungry men:
But different folk have different views,
I know a person small—
She keeps ten million serving-men,
Who get no rest at all!

She sends 'em abroad on her own affairs,
From the second she opens her eyes—
One million Hows, two million Wheres,
And seven million Whys!

KASPAR'S SONG IN "VARDA"

(*From the Swedish of Stagnelius.*)

Eyes aloft, over dangerous places,
The children follow where Psyche flies,
And, in the sweat of their upturned faces,
Slash with a net at the empty skies.

So it goes they fall amid brambles,
And sting their toes on the nettle-tops,
Till after a thousand scratches and scrambles
They wipe their brows, and the hunting stops.

Then to quiet them comes their father
And stills the riot of pain and grief,
Saying, "Little ones, go and gather
Out of my garden a cabbage leaf.

"You will find on its whorls and clots of
Dull grey eggs that, properly fed,
Turn, by way of the worm, to lots of
Radiant Psyches raised from the dead."

. . . . . .

"Heaven is beautiful, Earth is ugly,"
The three-dimensioned preacher saith,
So we must not look where the snail and the slug lie
For Psyche's birth. . . . And that is our death.

"WIRELESS"

1902

IT's a funny thing, this Marconi business, isn't it?' said Mr. Shaynor, coughing heavily. "Nothing seems to make any difference, by what they tell me—storms, hills, or anything; but if that's true we shall know before morning."

"Of course it's true," I answered, stepping behind the counter. "Where's old Mr. Cashell?"

"He's had to go to bed on account of his influenza. He said you'd very likely drop in."

"Where's his nephew?"

"Inside, getting the things ready. He told me that the last time they experimented they put the pole on the roof of one of the big hotels here, and the batteries electrified all the water-supply, and"—he giggled—"the ladies got shocks when they took their baths."

"I never heard of that."

"The hotel wouldn't exactly advertise it, would it? Just now, by what Mr. Cashell tells me, they're trying to signal from here to Poole, and they're using stronger batteries than ever. But, you see, he being the guvnor's nephew and all that (and it will be in the papers too), it doesn't matter how they electrify things in this house. Are you going to watch?"

"Very much. I've never seen this game. Aren't you going to bed?"

"We don't close till ten on Saturdays. There's a good deal of influenza in town, too, and there'll be a dozen prescriptions coming in before morning. I generally sleep in the chair here. It's warmer than jumping out of bed every time. Bitter cold, isn't it?"

"Freezing hard. I'm sorry your cough's worse."

"Thank you. I don't mind cold so much. It's this wind that fair cuts me to pieces." He coughed again hard and hackingly, as an old lady came in for ammoniated quinine. "We've just run out of it in bottles, madam," said Mr. Shaynor, returning to the professional tone, "but if you will wait two minutes, I'll make it up for you, madam."

I had used the shop for some time, and my acquaintance with the proprietor had ripened into friendship. It was Mr. Cashell who revealed to me the purpose and power of Apothecaries' Hall what time a fellow-chemist had made an error in a prescription of mine, had lied to cover his sloth, and when error and lie were brought home to him had written vain letters.

"A disgrace to our profession," said the thin, mild-eyed

man, hotly, after studying the evidence. "You couldn't do a better service to the profession than report him to Apothecaries' Hall."

I did so, not knowing what djinns I should evoke; and the result was such an apology as one might make who had spent a night on the rack. I conceived great respect for Apothecaries' Hall, and esteem for Mr. Cashell, a zealous craftsman who magnified his calling. Until Mr. Shaynor came down from the North his assistants had by no means agreed with Mr. Cashell. "They forget," said he, "that, first and foremost, the compounder is a medicine-man. On him depends the physician's reputation. He holds it literally in the hollow of his hand, Sir."

Mr. Shaynor's manners had not, perhaps, the polish of the grocery and Italian warehouse next door, but he knew and loved his dispensary work in every detail. For relaxation he seemed to go no farther afield than the romance of drugs—their discovery, preparation, packing, and export—but it led him to the ends of the earth, and on this subject, and the Pharmaceutical Formulary, and Nicholas Culpepper, most confident of physicians, we met.

Little by little I grew to know something of his beginnings and his hopes—of his mother, who had been a school-teacher in one of the northern counties, and of his red-headed father, a small job-master at Kirby Moors, who died when he was a child; of the examinations he had passed and of their exceeding and increasing difficulty; of his dreams of a shop in London; of his hate for the price-cutting Co-operative stores; and most interesting, of his mental attitude towards customers.

"There's a way you get into," he told me, "of serving them carefully, and I hope, politely, without stopping your own thinking. I've been reading Christy's *New Commercial Plants* all this autumn, and that needs keeping your mind on it, I can tell you. So long as it isn't a prescription, of course, I can carry as much as half a page of Christie in my head, and at the same time I could sell out all that window twice over, and not a penny wrong at the end. As to prescriptions, I think I could make up the general run of 'em in my sleep, almost."

For reasons of my own, I was deeply interested in Marconi experiments at their outset in England; and it was of a piece with Mr. Cashell's unvarying thoughtfulness that, when his nephew the electrician appropriated the house for a long-range installation, he should, as I have said, invite me to see the result.

The old lady went away with her medicine, and Mr. Shaynor and I stamped on the tiled floor behind the counter to keep ourselves warm. The shop, by the light of the many electrics, looked like a Paris-diamond mine, for Mr. Cashell believed in all the ritual of his craft. Three superb glass jars—red, green, and blue—of the sort that led Rosamund to parting with her shoes—blazed in the broad plate-glass windows, and there was a confused smell of orris, Kodak films, vulcanite, tooth-powder, sachets, and almond-cream in the air. Mr. Shaynor fed the dispensary stove, and we sucked cayenne-pepper jujubes and menthol lozenges. The brutal east wind had cleared the streets, and the few passers-by were muffled to their puckered eyes. In the Italian warehouse next door some gay feathered birds and game, hung upon hooks, sagged to the wind across the left edge of our window-frame.

"They ought to take these poultry in—all knocked about like that," said Mr. Shaynor. "Doesn't it make you feel fair perishing? See that old hare! The wind's nearly blowing the fur off him."

I saw the belly-fur of the dead beast blown apart in ridges and streaks as the wind caught it, showing bluish skin underneath. "Bitter cold," said Mr. Shaynor, shuddering. "Fancy going out on a night like this! Oh, here's young Mr. Cashell."

The door of the inner office behind the dispensary opened, and an energetic, spade-bearded man stepped forth, rubbing his hands.

"I want a bit of tin-foil, Shaynor," he said. "Good-evening. My uncle told me you might be coming." This to me, as I began the first of a hundred questions.

"I've everything in order," he replied. "We're only waiting until Poole calls us up. Excuse me a minute. You can come in whenever you like—but I'd better be with the instruments. Give me that tin-foil. Thanks."

While we were talking, a girl—evidently no customer—had come into the shop, and the face and bearing of Mr. Shaynor changed. She leaned confidently across the counter.

"But I can't," I heard him whisper uneasily—the flush on his cheek was dull red, and his eyes shone like a drugged moth's. "I can't. I tell you I'm alone in the place."

"No, you aren't. Who's *that?* Let him look after it for half an hour. A brisk walk will do you good. Ah, come now, John."

"But he isn't——"

"I don't care. I want you to; we'll only go round by St. Agnes. If you don't——"

He crossed to where I stood in the shadow of the dispensary counter, and began some sort of broken apology about a lady-friend.

"Yes," she interrupted. "You take the shop for half an hour—to oblige *me,* won't you?"

She had a singularly rich and promising voice that well matched her outline.

"All right," I said. "I'll do it—but you'd better wrap yourself up, Mr. Shaynor."

"Oh, a brisk walk ought to help me. We're only going round by the church." I heard him cough grievously as they went out together.

I refilled the stove, and, after reckless expenditure of Mr. Cashell's coal, drove some warmth into the shop. I explored many of the glass-knobbed drawers that lined the walls, tasted some disconcerting drugs, and, by the aid of a few cardamoms, ground ginger, chloric-ether, and dilute alcohol, manufactured a new and wildish drink, of which I bore a glassful to young Mr. Cashell, busy in the back office. He laughed shortly when I told him that Mr. Shaynor had stepped out—but a frail coil of wire held all his attention, and he had no word for me bewildered among the batteries and rods. The noise of the sea on the beach began to make itself heard as the traffic in the street ceased. Then briefly, but very lucidly, he gave me the names and uses of the mechanism that crowded the tables and the floor.

"When do you expect to get the message from Poole?" I demanded, sipping my liquor out of a graduated glass.

"About midnight, if everything is in order. We've got our installation-pole fixed to the roof of the house. I shouldn't advise you to turn on a tap or anything to-night. We've connected up with the plumbing, and all the water will be electrified." He repeated to me the history of the agitated ladies at the hotel at the time of the first installation.

"But what *is* it?" I asked. "Electricity is out of my beat altogether."

"Ah, if you knew *that* you'd know something nobody knows. It's just It—what we call Electricity, but the magic—the manifestations—the Hertzian waves—are all revealed by *this*. The coherer, we call it."

He picked up a glass tube not much thicker than a thermometer, in which, almost touching, were two tiny silver plugs, and between them an infinitesimal pinch of metallic dust. "That's all," he said, proudly, as though himself responsible for the wonder. "That is the thing that will reveal to us the Powers—whatever the Powers may be—at work—through space—a long distance away."

Just then Mr. Shaynor returned alone and stood coughing his heart out on the mat.

"Serves you right for being such a fool," said young Mr. Cashell, as annoyed as myself at the interruption. "Never mind—we've all the night before us to see wonders."

Shaynor clutched the counter, his handkerchief to his lips. When he brought it away I saw two bright red stains.

"I—I've got a bit of a rasped throat from smoking cigarettes," he panted. "I think I'll try a cubeb."

"Better take some of this. I've been compounding while you've been away." I handed him the brew.

"'Twon't make me drunk, will it? I'm almost a teetotaller. My word! That's grateful and comforting."

He sat down the empty glass to cough afresh.

"Brr! But it was cold out there! I shouldn't care to be lying in my grave a night like this. Don't *you* ever have a sore throat from smoking?" He pocketed the handkerchief after a furtive peep.

"Oh, yes, sometimes," I replied, wondering, while I spoke, into what agonies of terror I should fall if ever I saw those bright-red danger-signals under my nose. Young Mr. Cashell among the batteries coughed slightly to show that he was quite ready to continue his scientific explanations, but I was thinking still of the girl with the rich voice and the significantly cut mouth, at whose command I had taken charge of the shop. It flashed across me that she distantly resembled the seductive shape on a gold-framed toilet-water advertisement whose charms were unholily heightened by the glare from the red bottle in the window. Turning to make sure, I saw Mr. Shaynor's eyes bent in the same direction, and by instinct recognized that the flamboyant thing was to him a shrine. "What do you take for your—cough?" I asked.

"Well, I'm the wrong side of the counter to believe much in patent medicines. But there are asthma cigarettes and there are pastilles. To tell you the truth, if you don't object to the smell, which is very like incense, I believe, though I'm not a Roman Catholic, Blaudett's Cathedral Pastilles relieve me as much as anything."

"Let's try." I had never raided a chemist's shop before, so I was thorough. We unearthed the pastilles—brown, gummy cones of benzoin—and set them alight under the toilet-water advertisement, where they fumed in thin blue spirals.

"Of course," said Mr. Shaynor, to my question, "what one uses in the shop for one's self comes out of one's pocket. Why, stock-taking in our business is nearly the same as with jewellers —and I can't say more than that. But one gets them"—he pointed to the pastille-box—"at trade prices." Evidently the censing of the gay, seven-tinted wench with the teeth was an established ritual which cost something.

"And when do we shut up shop?"

"We stay like this all night. The gov—old Mr. Cashell—doesn't believe in locks and shutters as compared with electric light. Besides it brings trade. I'll just sit here in the chair by the stove and write a letter, if you don't mind. Electricity isn't my prescription."

The energetic young Mr. Cashell snorted within, and Shaynor settled himself up in his chair over which he had thrown a staring red, black, and yellow Austrian jute blanket, rather like a table-cover. I cast about, amid patent medicine pamphlets, for something to read, but finding little, returned to the manufacture of the new drink. The Italian warehouse took down its game and went to bed. Across the street blank shutters flung back the gaslight in cold smears; the dried pavement seemed to rough up in goose-flesh under the scouring of the savage wind, and we could hear long ere he passed, the policeman flapping his arms to keep himself warm. Within, the flavours of cardamoms and chloric-ether disputed those of the pastilles and a score of drugs and perfume and soap scents. Our electric lights, set low down in the windows before the tunbellied Rosamund jars, flung inward three monstrous daubs of red, blue, and green, that broke into kaleidoscopic lights on the facetted knobs of the drug-drawers, the cut-glass scent flagons, and the bulbs of the sparklet bottles. They flushed the white-tiled floor in gorgeous patches; splashed along the nickel-silver counter-rails, and turned the polished mahogany counter-panels to the likeness of intricate grained marbles—slabs of porphyry and malachite. Mr. Shaynor unlocked a drawer, and ere he began to write, took out a meagre bundle of letters. From my place by the stove, I could see the scalloped edges of the paper with a flaring monogram in the corner and could even smell the reek of chypre. At each page he turned toward the toilet-water lady of the advertisement and devoured her with over-luminous eyes. He had drawn the Austrian blanket over his shoulders, and among those warring lights he looked more than ever the incarnation of a drugged moth—a tiger-moth as I thought.

He put his letter into an envelope, stamped it with stiff mechanical movements, and dropped it in the drawer. Then I became aware of the silence of a great city asleep—the silence that underlaid the even voice of the breakers along the sea-front—a thick, tingling quiet of warm life stilled down for its appointed time, and unconsciously I moved about the glittering shop as one moves in a sick-room. Young Mr. Cashell was adjusting some wire that crackled from time to time with the tense, knuckle-stretching sound of the electric spark. Upstairs, where a door shut and opened swiftly, I could hear his uncle coughing abed.

"Here," I said, when the drink was properly warmed, "take some of this, Mr. Shaynor."

He jerked in his chair with a start and a wrench, and held out his hand for the glass. The mixture, of a rich port-wine colour, frothed at the top.

"It looks," he said, suddenly, "it looks—those bubbles—like a string of pearls winking at you—rather like the pearls round that young lady's neck." He turned again to the advertisement where the female in the dove-coloured corset had seen fit to put on all her pearls before she cleaned her teeth.

"Not bad, is it?" I said.

"Eh?"

He rolled his eyes heavily full on me, and, as I stared, I beheld all meaning and consciousness die out of the swiftly dilating pupils. His figure lost its stark rigidity, softened into the chair, and, chin on chest, hands dropped before him, he rested open-eyed, absolutely still.

"I'm afraid I've rather cooked Shaynor's goose," I said, bearing the fresh drink to young Mr. Cashell. "Perhaps it was the chloric ether."

"Oh, he's all right." The spade-bearded man glanced at him pityingly. "Consumptives go off in those sort of doses very often. It's exhaustion . . . I don't wonder. I dare say the liquor will do him good. It's grand stuff," he finished his share appreciatively. "Well, as I was saying—before he interrupted—about this little coherer. The pinch of dust, you see, is nickel-filings. The Hertzian waves, you see, come out of space from the station that despatches 'em, and all these little particles are attracted together—cohere, we call it—for just so long as the current passes through them. Now, it's important to remember that the current is an induced current. There are a good many kinds of induction——"

"Yes, but what *is* induction?"

"That's rather hard to explain untechnically. But the long and the short of it is that when a current of electricity passes through a wire there's a lot of magnetism present round that wire; and if you put another wire parallel to, and within what we call its magnetic field—why then, the second wire will also become charged with electricity."

"On its own account?"

"On its own account."

"Then let's see if I've got it correctly. Miles off, at Poole, or wherever it is——"

"It will be anywhere in ten years."

"You've got a charged wire——"

"Charged with Hertzian waves which vibrate, say, two hundred and thirty million times a second." Mr. Cashell snaked his forefinger rapidly through the air.

"All right—a charged wire at Poole, giving out these waves into space. Then this wire of yours sticking out into space—on the roof of the house—in some mysterious way gets charged with those waves from Poole——"

"Or anywhere—it only happens to be Poole to-night."

"And those waves set the coherer at work, just like an ordinary telegraph-office ticker?"

"No! That's where so many people make the mistake. The Hertzian waves wouldn't be strong enough to work a great heavy Morse instrument like ours. They can only just make that dust cohere, and while it coheres (a little while for a dot and a longer while for a dash) the current from this battery—the home battery"—he laid his hand on the thing—"can get through to the Morse printing-machine to record the dot or dash. Let me make it clearer. Do you know anything about steam?"

"Very little. But go on."

"Well, the coherer is like a steam-valve. Any child can open a valve and start a steamer's engines, because a turn of the hand lets in the main steam, doesn't it? Now, this home battery here ready to print is the main steam. The coherer is the valve, always ready to be turned on. The Hertzian wave is the child's hand that turns it."

"I see. That's marvellous."

"Marvellous, isn't it? And, remember, we're only at the beginning. There's nothing we sha'n't be able to do in ten years. I want to live—my God, how I want to live, and see it develop!" He looked through the door at Shaynor breathing lightly in his chair. "Poor beast! And he wants to keep company with Fanny Brand."

"Fanny *who?*" I said, for the name struck an obscurely familiar chord in my brain—something connected with a stained handkerchief, and the word "arterial."

"Fanny Brand—the girl you kept shop for." He laughed. "That's all I know about her, and for the life of me I can't see what Shaynor sees in her, or she in him."

"*Can't* you see what he sees in her?" I insisted.

"Oh, yes, if *that's* what you mean. She's a great, big, fat lump of a girl, and so on. I suppose that's why he's so crazy after her. She isn't his sort. Well, it doesn't matter. My uncle says he's bound to die before the year's out. Your drink's given him a good sleep, at any rate." Young Mr. Cashell could not catch Mr. Shaynor's face, which was half turned to the advertisement.

I stoked the stove anew, for the room was growing cold, and lighted another pastille. Mr. Shaynor in his chair, never moving, looked through and over me with eyes as wide and lustreless as those of a dead hare.

"Poole's late," said young Mr. Cashell, when I stepped back. "I'll just send them a call."

He pressed a key in the semi-darkness, and with a rending crackle there leaped between two brass knobs a spark, streams of sparks, and sparks again.

"Grand, isn't it? *That's* the Power—our unknown Power—kicking and fighting to be let loose," said young Mr. Cashell. "There she goes—kick—kick—kick into space. I never get over the strangeness of it when I work a sending-machine—waves going into space, you know. T. R. is our call. Poole ought to answer with L. L. L."

We waited two, three, five minutes. In that silence, of which the boom of the tide was an orderly part, I caught the clear *"kiss—kiss—kiss"* of the halliards on the roof, as they were blown against the installation-pole.

"Poole is not ready. I'll stay here and call you when he is."

I returned to the shop, and set down my glass on a marble slab with a careless clink. As I did so, Shaynor rose to his feet, his eyes fixed once more on the advertisement, where the young woman bathed in the light from the red jar simpered pinkly over her pearls. His lips moved without cessation. I stepped nearer to listen. "And threw—and threw—and threw," he repeated, his face all sharp with some inexplicable agony.

I moved forward astonished. But it was then he found words—delivered roundly and clearly. These:—

And threw warm gules on Madeleine's young breast.

The trouble passed off his countenance, and he returned lightly to his place, rubbing his hands.

It had never occurred to me, though we had many times discussed reading and prize-competitions as a diversion, that Mr. Shaynor ever read Keats, or could quote him at all appositely. There was, after all, a certain stained-glass effect of light on the high bosom of the highly-polished picture which might, by stretch of fancy, suggest, as a vile chromo recalls some incomparable canvas, the line he had spoken. Night, my drink, and solitude were evidently turning Mr. Shaynor into a poet. He sat down again and wrote swiftly on his villainous note-paper, his lips quivering.

I shut the door into the inner office and moved up behind him. He made no sign that he saw or heard. I looked over his shoulder, and read, amid half-formed words, sentences, and wild scratches:—

——Very cold it was. Very cold
The hare—the hare—the hare—
The birds——

He raised his head sharply, and frowned toward the blank shutters of the poulterer's shop where they jutted out against our window. Then one clear line came:—

The hare, in spite of fur, was very cold.

The head, moving machine-like, turned right to the advertisement where the Blaudett's Cathedral pastille reeked abominably. He grunted, and went on:—

Incense in a censer—
Before her darling picture framed in gold—
Maiden's picture—angel's portrait—

"Hsh!" said Mr. Cashell guardedly from the inner office, as though in the presence of spirits. "There's something coming through from somewhere; but it isn't Poole." I heard the crackle of sparks as he depressed the keys of the transmitter. In my own brain, too, something crackled, or it might have been the hair on my head. Then I heard my own voice, in a harsh whisper: "Mr. Cashell, there is something coming through here, too. Leave me alone till I tell you."

"But I thought you'd come to see this wonderful thing—Sir," indignantly at the end.

"Leave me alone till I tell you. Be quiet."

I watched—I waited. Under the blue-veined hand—the dry hand of the consumptive—came away clear, without erasure:

And my weak spirit fails
To think how the dead must freeze—

he shivered as he wrote—

Beneath the churchyard mould.

Then he stopped, laid the pen down, and leaned back.

For an instant, that was half an eternity, the shop spun before me in a rainbow-tinted whirl, in and through which my own soul most dispassionately considered my own soul as that fought with an over-mastering fear. Then I smelt the strong smell of cigarettes from Mr. Shaynor's clothing, and heard, as though it had been the rending of trumpets, the rattle of his breathing. I was still in my place of observation, much as one would watch a rifle-shot at the butts, half-bent, hands on my knees, and head within a few inches of the black, red, and yellow blanket of his shoulder. I was whispering encouragement, evidently to my other self, sounding sentences, such as men pronounce in dreams.

"If he has read Keats, it proves nothing. If he hasn't—like causes *must* beget like effects. There is no escape from this law. *You* ought to be grateful that you know 'St. Agnes Eve' without the book; because, given the circumstances, such as Fanny Brand, who is the key of the enigma, and approximately represents the latitude and longitude of Fanny Brawne; allowing also for the bright red colour of the arterial blood upon the handkerchief, which was just what you were puzzling over in the shop just now; and counting the effect of the professional environment, here almost perfectly duplicated—the result is logical and inevitable. As inevitable as induction."

Still, the other half of my soul refused to be comforted. It was cowering in some minute and inadequate corner—at an immense distance.

Hereafter, I found myself one person again, my hands still gripping my knees, and my eyes glued on the page before Mr. Shaynor. As dreamers accept and explain the upheaval of landscapes and the resurrection of the dead, with excerpts from the evening hymn or the multiplication-table, so I had accepted the facts, whatever they might be, that I should witness, and had devised a theory, sane and plausible to my mind, that explained them all. Nay, I was even in advance of my facts, walking hurriedly before them, assured that they would fit my theory. And all that I now recall of that epoch-making theory are the lofty words: "If he has read Keats it's the chloric-ether. If he hasn't, it's the identical bacillus, or Hertzian wave of tuberculosis, *plus* Fanny Brand and the professional status which, in conjunction with the main-stream of subconscious thought common to all mankind, has thrown up temporarily an induced Keats."

Mr. Shaynor returned to his work, erasing and rewriting as before with swiftness. Two or three blank pages he tossed aside. Then he wrote, muttering:

The little smoke of a candle that goes out.

"No," he muttered. "Little smoke—little smoke—little smoke. What else?" He thrust his chin forward toward the advertisement, whereunder the last of the Blaudett's Cathedral pastilles fumed in its holder. "Ah!" Then with relief:—

The little smoke that dies in moonlight cold.

Evidently he was snared by the rhymes of his first verse, for he wrote and rewrote "gold—cold—mould" many times. Again he sought inspiration from the advertisement, and set down, without erasure, the line I had overheard:

And threw warm gules on Madeleine's young breast.

As I remembered the original it is "fair"—a trite word—instead of "young," and I found myself nodding approval, though I admitted that the attempt to reproduce "its little smoke in pallid moonlight died" was a failure.

Followed without a break ten or fifteen lines of bald prose—the naked soul's confession of its physical yearning for its beloved—unclean as we count uncleanliness; unwholesome, but human exceedingly; the raw material, so it seemed to me in that hour and in that place, whence Keats wove the twenty-sixth, seventh, and eighth stanzas of his poem. Shame I had none in overseeing this revelation; and my fear had gone with the smoke of the pastille.

"That's it," I murmured. "That's how it's blocked out. Go on! Ink it in, man. Ink it in!"

Mr. Shaynor returned to broken verse wherein "loveliness" was made to rhyme with a desire to look upon "her empty dress." He picked up a fold of the gay, soft blanket, spread it over one hand, caressed it with infinite tenderness, thought, muttered, traced some snatches which I could not decipher, shut his eyes drowsily, shook his head, and dropped the stuff. Here I found myself at fault, for I could not then see (as I do now) in what manner a red, black, and yellow Austrian blanket coloured his dreams.

In a few minutes he laid aside his pen, and, chin on hand, considered the shop with thoughtful and intelligent eyes. He threw down the blanket, rose, passed along a line of drug-drawers, and read the names on the labels aloud. Returning, he took from his desk Christy's *New Commercial Plants* and the old Culpepper that I had given him, opened and laid them side by side with a clerky air, all trace of passion gone from his face, read first in one and then in the other, and paused with pen behind his ear.

"What wonder of Heaven's coming now?" I thought.

"Manna—manna—manna," he said at last, under wrinkled brows. "That's what I wanted. Good! Now then! Now then! Good! Good! Oh, by God, that's good!" His voice rose and he spoke rightly and fully without a falter:—

> *Candied apple, quince and plum and gourd,*
> *And jellies smoother than the creamy curd,*
> *And lucent syrups tinct with cinnamon,*
> *Manna and dates in Argosy transferred*
> *From Fez; and spiced dainties, every one*
> *From silken Samarcand to cedared Lebanon.*

He repeated it once more, using "blander" for "smoother" in the second line; then wrote it down without erasure, but this time (my set eyes missed no stroke of any word) he substituted "soother" for his atrocious second thought, so that it came away under his hand as it is written in the book—as it is written in the book.

A wind went shouting down the street, and on the heels of the wind followed a spurt and rattle of rain.

After a smiling pause—and good right had he to smile—he began anew, always tossing the last sheet over his shoulder:—

"The sharp rain falling on the window-pane,
Rattling sleet—the wind-blown sleet."

Then prose: "It is very cold of mornings when the wind brings rain and sleet with it. I heard the sleet on the window-pane outside, and thought of you, my darling. I am always thinking of you. I wish we could both run away like two lovers into the storm and get that little cottage by the sea which we are always thinking about, my own dear darling. We could sit and watch the sea beneath our windows. It would be a fairy-land all of our own—a fairy sea—a fairy sea. . . ."

He stopped, raised his head, and listened. The steady drone of the Channel along the sea-front that had borne us company so long leaped up a note to the sudden fuller surge that signals the change from ebb to flood. It beat in like the change of step throughout an army—this renewed pulse of the sea—and filled our ears till they, accepting it, marked it no longer.

"A fairyland for you and me
Across the foam—beyond . . .
A magic foam, a perilous sea."

He grunted again with effort and bit his underlip. My throat dried, but I dared not gulp to moisten it lest I should break the spell that was drawing him nearer and nearer to the high-water mark but two of the sons of Adam have reached. Remember that in all the millions permitted there are no more than five—five little lines—of which one can say: "These are the pure Magic. These are the clear Vision. The rest is only poetry." And Mr. Shaynor was playing hot and cold with two of them.

I vowed no unconscious thought of mine should influence the blindfold soul, and pinned myself desperately to the other three, repeating and re-repeating:

A savage spot as holy and enchanted
As e'er beneath a waning moon was haunted
By woman wailing for her demon lover

But though I believed my brain thus occupied, my every sense hung upon the writing under the dry, bony hand, all brown-fingered with chemicals and cigarette-smoke.

Our windows fronting on the dangerous foam,

(he wrote, after long, irresolute snatches), and then—

"Our open casements facing desolate seas
Forlorn—forlorn—"

Here again his face grew peaked and anxious with that sense of loss I had first seen when the Power snatched him. But this time the agony was tenfold keener. As I watched it mounted like mercury in the tube. It lighted his face from within till I thought the visibly scourged soul must leap forth naked between his jaws, unable to endure. A drop of sweat trickled from my forehead down my nose and splashed on the back of my hand.

"Our windows facing on the desolate seas
And pearly foam of magic fairyland—"

"Not yet—not yet," he muttered, "wait a minute. *Please* wait a minute. I shall get it then—

"Our magic windows fronting on the sea,
The dangerous foam of desolate seas . . .
for aye.

Ouh, my God!"

From head to heel he shook—shook from the marrow of his bones outwards—then leaped to his feet with raised arms, and slid the chair screeching across the tiled floor where it struck the drawers behind and fell with a jar. Mechanically, I stooped to recover it.

As I rose, Mr. Shaynor was stretching and yawning at leisure.

"I've had a bit of a doze," he said. "How did I come to knock the chair over? You look rather——"

"The chair startled me," I answered. "It was so sudden in this quiet."

Young Mr. Cashell behind his shut door was offendedly silent.

"I suppose I must have been dreaming," said Mr. Shaynor.

"I suppose you must," I said. "Talking of dreams—I—I noticed you writing—before——"

He flushed consciously.

"I meant to ask you if you've ever read anything written by a man called Keats."

"Oh! I haven't much time to read poetry, and I can't say that I remember the name exactly. Is he a popular writer?"

"Middling. I thought you might know him because he's the only poet who was ever a druggist. And he's rather what's called the lover's poet."

"Indeed. I must dip into him. What did he write about?"

"A lot of things. Here's a sample that may interest you."

Then and there, carefully, I repeated the verse he had twice spoken and once written not ten minutes ago.

"Ah. Anybody could see he was a druggist from that line about the tinctures and syrups. It's a fine tribute to our profession."

"I don't know," said young Mr. Cashell, with icy politeness, opening the door one half-inch, "if you still happen to be interested in our trifling experiments. But, should such be the case——"

I drew him aside, whispering, "Shaynor seemed going off into some sort of fit when I spoke to you just now. I thought, even at the risk of being rude, it wouldn't do to take you off your instruments just as the call was coming through. Don't you see?"

"Granted—granted as soon as asked," he said unbending. "I *did* think it a shade odd at the time. So that was why he knocked the chair down?"

"I hope I haven't missed anything," I said.

"I'm afraid I can't say that, but you're just in time for the end of a rather curious performance. You can come in, too, Mr. Shaynor. Listen, while I read it off."

The Morse instrument was ticking furiously. Mr. Cashell interpreted: "'*K.K.V. Can make nothing of your signals.*'" A pause: "'*M.M.V. M.M.V. Signals unintelligible. Purpose anchor Sandown Bay. Examine instruments to-morrow.*' Do you know what that means? It's a couple of men-o'-war working Marconi signals off the Isle of Wight. They are trying to talk to each other. Neither can read the other's messages, but all their messages are being taken in by our receiver here. They've been going on for ever so long. I wish you could have heard it."

"How wonderful!" I said. "Do you mean we're overhearing Portsmouth ships trying to talk to each other—that we're eavesdropping across half South England?"

"Just that. Their transmitters are all right, but their receivers are out of order, so they only get a dot here and a dash there. Nothing clear."

"Why is that?"

"God knows—and Science will know to-morrow. Perhaps the induction is faulty; perhaps the receivers aren't tuned to receive just the number of vibrations per second that the transmitter sends. Only a word here and there. Just enough to tantalize."

Again the Morse sprang to life.

"That's one of 'em complaining now. Listen: '*Disheartening—most disheartening.*' It's quite pathetic. Have you ever seen a spiritualistic seance? It reminds me of that sometimes—odds and ends of messages coming out of nowhere—a word here and there—no good at all."

"But mediums are all impostors," said Mr. Shaynor, in the doorway, lighting an asthma-cigarette. "They only do it for the money they can make. I've seen 'em."

"Here's Poole, at last—clear as a bell. L.L.L. *Now* we sha'n't be long." Mr. Cashell rattled the keys merrily. "Anything you'd like to tell 'em?"

"No, I don't think so," I said. "I'll go home and get to bed. I'm feeling a little tired."

PUCK'S SONG
1906

SEE you the ferny ride that steals
Into the oak-woods far?
O that was whence they hewed the keels
That rolled to Trafalgar.

And mark you where the ivy clings
To Bayham's mouldering walls?
O there we cast the stout railings
That stand around St. Paul's.

See you the dimpled track that runs
All hollow through the wheat?
O that was where they hauled the guns
That smote King Philip's fleet.

(Out of the Weald, the secret Weald,
Men sent in ancient years,
The horse-shoes red at Flodden Field,
The arrows at Poitiers!)

See you our little mill that clacks,
So busy by the brook?
She has ground her corn and paid her tax
Ever since Domesday Book.

See you our stilly woods of oak,
And the dread ditch beside?
O that was where the Saxons broke
On the day that Harold died.

See you the windy levels spread
About the gates of Rye?
O that was where the Northmen fled,
When Alfred's ships came by.

See you our pastures wide and lone,
Where the red oxen browse?
O there was a City thronged and known,
Ere London boasted a house.

And see you, after rain, the trace
Of mound and ditch and wall?
O that was a Legion's camping-place,
When Cæsar sailed from Gaul.

And see you marks that show and fade,
Like shadows on the Downs?
O they are the lines the Flint Men made,
To guard their wondrous towns.

Trackway and Camp and City lost,
Salt Marsh where now is corn—
Old Wars, old Peace, old Arts that cease,
And so was England born!

She is not any common Earth,
Water or wood or air,
But Merlin's Isle of Gramarye,
Where you and I will fare!

WELAND'S SWORD
1906

THE children were at the Theatre, acting to Three Cows as much as they could remember of *Midsummer Night's Dream.* Their father had made them a small play out of the big Shakespeare one, and they had rehearsed it with him and with their mother till they could say it by heart. They began where Nick Bottom the weaver comes out of the bushes with a donkey's head on his shoulder, and finds Titania, Queen of the Fairies, asleep. Then they skipped to the part where Bottom asks three little fairies to scratch his head and bring him honey, and they ended where he falls asleep in Titania's arms. Dan was Puck and Nick Bottom, as well as all three Fairies. He wore a pointy-eared cloth cap for Puck, and a paper donkey's head out of a Christmas cracker—but it tore if you were not careful—for Bottom. Una was Titania, with a wreath of columbines and a foxglove wand.

The Theatre lay in a meadow called the Long Slip. A little mill-stream, carrying water to a mill two or three fields away, bent round one corner of it, and in the middle of the bend lay a large old fairy Ring of darkened grass, which was their stage. The mill-stream banks, overgrown with willow, hazel, and guelder rose made convenient places to wait in till your turn came; and a grown-up who had seen it said that Shakespeare himself could not have imagined a more suitable setting for his play. They were not, of course, allowed to act on Midsummer Night itself, but they went down after tea on Midsummer Eve, when the shadows were growing, and they took their supper—hard-boiled eggs, Bath Oliver biscuits, and salt in an envelope—with them. Three Cows had been milked and were grazing steadily with a tearing noise that one could hear all down the meadow; and the noise of the mill at work sounded like bare feet running on hard ground. A cuckoo sat on a gatepost singing his broken June tune, "cuckoo-cuk," while a busy kingfisher crossed from the mill-stream to the brook which ran on the other side of the meadow. Everything else was a sort of thick, sleepy stillness smelling of meadow-sweet and dry grass.

Their play went beautifully. Dan remembered all his parts—Puck, Bottom, and the three Fairies—and Una never forgot a word of Titania—not even the difficult piece where she tells the Fairies how to feed Bottom with "apricocks, ripe figs, and dewberries," and all the lines end in "ies." They were both so pleased that they acted it three times over from beginning to end before they sat down in the unthistly centre of the Ring to eat eggs and Bath Olivers. This was when they heard a whistle among the alders on the bank, and they jumped.

The bushes parted. In the very spot where Dan had stood as Puck they saw a small, brown, broad-shouldered, pointy-eared person with a snub nose, slanting blue eyes, and a grin that ran right across his freckled face. He shaded his forehead as though he were watching Quince, Snout, Bottom, and the others rehearsing *Pyramis and Thisbe,* and, in a voice as deep as Three Cows asking to be milked, he began:

"What hempen homespuns have we swaggering here,
So near the cradle of our fairy Queen?"

He stopped, hollowed one hand round his ear, and, with a wicked twinkle in his eye, went on:

"What a play toward? I'll be auditor,
An actor too, perhaps, if I see cause."

The children looked and gasped. The small thing—he was no taller than Dan's shoulder—stepped quietly into the Ring.

"I'm rather out of practice," said he; "but that's the way my part ought to be played."

Still the children stared at him—from his dark blue cap, like a big columbine flower, to his bare, hairy feet. At last he laughed.

"Please don't look like that. It isn't *my* fault. What else could you expect?" he said.

"We didn't expect any one," Dan answered, slowly. "This is our field."

"Is it?" said their visitor, sitting down. "Then what on Human Earth made you act *Midsummer Night's Dream* three times over, *on* Midsummer Eve, *in* the middle of a Ring, and under—right *under* one of my oldest hills in Old England? Pook's Hill—Puck's Hill—Puck's Hill—Pook's Hill! It's as plain as the nose on my face."

He pointed to the bare, fern-covered slope of Pook's Hill that runs up from the far side of the mill-stream to a dark wood. Beyond that wood the ground rises and rises for five hundred feet, till at last you climb out on the bare top of Beacon Hill, to look over the Pevensey Levels and the Channel and half the naked South Downs.

"By Oak, Ash, and Thorn!" he cried, still laughing. "If this had happened a few hundred years ago you'd have had all the People of the Hills out like bees in June!"

"We didn't know it was wrong," said Dan.

"Wrong!" The little fellow shook with laughter. "Indeed, it isn't wrong. You've done something that Kings and Knights and Scholars in old days would have given their crowns and spurs and books to find out. If Merlin himself had helped you, you couldn't have managed better! You've broken the Hills—you've broken the Hills! It hasn't happened in a thousand years."

"We—we didn't mean to," said Una.

"Of course you didn't! That's just why you did it. Unluckily the Hills are empty now, and all the People of the Hills are gone. I'm the only one left. I'm Puck, the oldest Old Thing in England, very much at your service if—if you care to have anything to do with me. If you don't, of course you've only to say so, and I'll go."

He looked at the children and the children looked at him for quite half a minute. His eyes did not twinkle any more. They were very kind, and there was the beginning of a good smile on his lips.

Una put out her hand. "Don't go," she said. "We like you."

"Have a Bath Oliver," said Dan, and he passed over the squashy envelope with the eggs.

"By Oak, Ash, and Thorn!" cried Puck, taking off his blue cap, "I like you too. Sprinkle a little salt on the biscuit, Dan, and I'll eat it with you. That'll show you the sort of person I am. Some of us"—he went on, with his mouth full—"couldn't abide Salt, or Horse-shoes over a door, or Mountain-ash berries, or Running Water, or Cold Iron, or the sound of Church Bells. But I'm Puck!"

He brushed the crumbs carefully from his doublet and shook hands.

"We always said, Dan and I," Una stammered, "that if it ever happened we'd know ex-actly what to do; but—but now it seems all different somehow."

"She means meeting a fairy," said Dan. "*I* never believed in 'em—not after I was six, anyhow."

"I did," said Una. "At least, I sort of half believed till we learned 'Farewell Rewards.' Do you know 'Farewell Rewards and Fairies'?"

"Do you mean this?" said Puck. He threw his big head back and began at the second line:—

> *"Good housewives now may say,*
> *For now foul sluts in dairies*
> *Do fare as well as they;*
> *For though they sweep their hearths no less*

("Join in, Una!")

> *"Than maids were wont to do,*
> *Yet who of late for cleanliness*
> *Finds sixpence in her shoe?"*

The echoes flapped all along the flat meadow.

"Of course I know it," he said.

"And then there's the verse about the Rings," said Dan. "When I was little it always made me feel unhappy in my inside."

"'Witness those rings and roundelays,' do you mean?" boomed Puck, with a voice like a great church organ.

"Of theirs which yet remain,
Were footed in Queen Mary's days
On many a grassy plain.
But since of late Elizabeth,
And later James came in,
Are never seen on any heath
As when the time hath been.

"It's some time since I heard that sung, but there's no good beating about the bush: it's true. The People of the Hills have all left. I saw them come into Old England and I saw them go. Giants, trolls, kelpies, brownies, goblins, imps; wood, tree, mound, and water spirits; heath-people, hill-watchers, treasure-guards, good people, little people, pishogues, leprechauns, night-riders, pixies, nixies, gnomes and the rest—gone, all gone! I came into England with Oak, Ash, and Thorn, and when Oak, Ash, and Thorn are gone I shall go too."

Dan looked round the meadow—at Una's oak by the lower gate, at the line of ash trees that overhang Otter Pool where the mill-stream spills over when the mill does not need it, and at the gnarled old white-thorn where Three Cows scratched their necks.

"It's all right," he said; and added, "I'm planting a lot of acorns this autumn too."

"Then aren't you most awfully old?" said Una.

"Not old—fairly long-lived, as folk say hereabouts. Let me see—my friends used to set my dish of cream for me o' nights when Stonehenge was new. Yes, before the Flint Men made the Dewpond under Chanctonbury Ring."

Una clasped her hands, cried "Oh!" and nodded her head.

"She's thought a plan," Dan explained. "She always does like that when she thinks a plan."

"I was thinking—suppose we saved some of our porridge and put it in the attic for you. They'd notice if we left it in the nursery."

"Schoolroom," said Dan, quickly, and Una flushed, because they had made a solemn treaty that summer not to call the schoolroom the nursery any more.

"Bless your heart o' gold!" said Puck. "You'll make a fine considering wench some market-day. I really don't want you to put out a bowl for me; but if ever I need a bite, be sure I'll tell you."

He stretched himself at length on the dry grass, and the children stretched out beside him, their bare legs waving happily in the air. They felt they could not be afraid of him any more than of their particular friend old Hobden, the hedger. He did not bother them with grown-up questions, or laugh at the donkey's head, but lay and smiled to himself in the most sensible way.

"Have you a knife on you?" he said at last.

Dan handed over his big one-bladed outdoor knife, and Puck began to carve out a piece of turf from the centre of the Ring.

"What's that for—Magic?" said Una, as he pressed up the square of chocolate loam that cut like so much cheese.

"One of my little Magics," he answered, and cut another. "You see, I can't let you into the Hills because the People of the Hills have gone; but if you care to take seizin from me, I may be able to show you something out of the common here on Human Earth. You certainly deserve it."

"What's taking seizin?" said Dan, cautiously.

"It's an old custom the people had when they bought and sold land. They used to cut out a clod and hand it over to the buyer, and you weren't lawfully seized of your land—it didn't really belong to you—till the other fellow had actually given you a piece of it—like this." He held out the turves.

"But it's our own meadow," said Dan, drawing back. "Are you going to magic it away?"

Puck laughed. "I know it's your meadow, but there's a great deal more in it than you or your father ever guessed. Try!"

He turned his eyes on Una.

"I'll do it," she said. Dan followed her example at once.

"Now are you two lawfully seized and possessed of all Old

England," began Puck, in a sing-song voice. "By Right of Oak, Ash, and Thorn are you free to come and go and look and know where I shall show or best you please. You shall see What you shall see and you shall hear What you shall hear, though It shall have happened three thousand year; and you shall know neither Doubt nor Fear. Fast! Hold fast all I give you."

The children shut their eyes, but nothing happened.

"Well?" said Una, disappointedly opening them. "I thought there would be dragons."

"Though It shall have happened three thousand year," said Puck, and counted on his fingers. "No; I'm afraid there were no dragons three thousand years ago."

"But there hasn't happened anything at all," said Dan.

"Wait awhile," said Puck. "You don't grow an oak in a year—and Old England's older than twenty oaks. Let's sit down again and think. *I* can do that for a century at a time."

"Ah, but you are a fairy," said Dan.

"Have you ever heard me use that word yet?" said Puck, quickly.

"No. You talk about 'the People of the Hills,' but you never say 'fairies,'" said Una. "I was wondering at that. Don't you like it?"

"How would you like to be called 'mortal' or 'human being' all the time?" said Puck; "or 'son of Adam' or 'daughter of Eve'?"

"I shouldn't like it at all," said Dan. "That's how the Djinns and Afrits talk in the *Arabian Nights.*"

"And that's how *I* feel about saying—that word that I don't say. Besides, what you call *them* are made-up things the People of the Hills have never heard of—little buzzflies with butterfly wings and gauze petticoats, and shiny stars in their hair, and a wand like a schoolteacher's cane for punishing bad boys and rewarding good ones. *I* know 'em!"

"We don't mean that sort," said Dan. "We hate 'em too."

"Exactly," said Puck. "Can you wonder that the People of the Hills don't care to be confused with that painty-winged, wand-waving, sugar-and-shake-your-head set of impostors?

Butterfly wings, indeed! I've seen Sir Huon and a troop of his people setting off from Tintagel Castle for Hy-Brasil in the teeth of a sou'-westerly gale, with the spray flying all over the castle, and the Horses of the Hill wild with fright. Out they'd go in a lull, screaming like gulls, and back they'd be driven five good miles inland before they could come head to wind again. Butterfly-wings! It was Magic—Magic as black as Merlin could make it, and the whole sea was green fire and white foam with singing mermaids in it. And the Horses of the Hill picked their way from one wave to another by the lightning flashes! *That* was how it was in the old days!"

"Splendid," said Dan, but Una shuddered.

"I'm glad they're gone, then; but what made the People of the Hills go away?" Una asked.

"Different things. I'll tell you one of them some day—the thing that made the biggest flit of any," said Puck. "But they didn't all flit at once. They dropped off, one by one, through the centuries. Most of them were foreigners who couldn't stand our climate. *They* flitted early."

"How early?" said Dan.

"A couple of thousand years or more. The fact is they began as Gods. The Phœnicians brought some over when they came to buy tin; and the Gauls, and the Jutes, and the Danes, and the Frisians, and the Angles brought more when they landed. They were always landing in those days, or being driven back to their ships, and they always brought their Gods with them. England is a bad country for Gods. Now *I* began as I mean to go on. A bowl of porridge, a dish of milk, and a little quiet fun with the country folk in the lanes was enough for me then, as it is now. I belong here, you see, and I have been mixed up with people all my days. But most of the others insisted on being Gods, and having temples, and altars, and priests, and sacrifices of their own."

"People burned in wicker baskets?" said Dan. "Like Miss Blake tells us about?"

"All sorts of sacrifices," said Puck. "If it wasn't men, it was horses, or cattle, or pigs, or metheglin—that's a sticky, sweet sort of beer. *I* never liked it. They were a stiff-necked, extravagant set of idols, the Old Things. But what was the result? Men don't like being sacrificed at the best of times; they don't even like sacrificing their farm-horses. After a while men simply left the Old Things alone, and the roofs of their temples fell in, and the Old Things had to scuttle out and pick up a living as they could. Some of them took to hanging about trees, and hiding in graves and groaning o' nights. If they groaned loud enough and long enough they might frighten a poor countryman into sacrificing a hen, or leaving a pound of butter for them. I remember one Goddess called Belisama. She became a common wet water-spirit somewhere in Lancashire. And there were hundreds of other friends of mine. First they were Gods. Then they were People of the Hills, and then they flitted to other places because they couldn't get on with the English for one reason or another. There was only one Old Thing, I remember, who honestly worked for his living after he came down in the world. He was called Weland, and he was a smith to some Gods. I've forgotten their names, but he used to make them swords and spears. I think he claimed kin with Thor of the Scandinavians."

"*Heroes of Asgard* Thor?" said Una. She had been reading the book.

"Perhaps," answered Puck. "None the less, when bad times came, he didn't beg or steal. He worked; and I was lucky enough to be able to do him a good turn."

"Tell us about it," said Dan. "I think I like hearing of Old Things."

They rearranged themselves comfortably, each chewing a grass stem. Puck propped himself on one strong arm and went on:

"Let's think! I met Weland first on a November afternoon in a sleet storm, on Pevensey Level——"

"Pevensey? Over the hill, you mean?" Dan pointed south.

"Yes; but it was all marsh in those days, right up to Horsebridge and Hydeneye. I was on Beacon Hill—they called it Brunanburgh then—when I saw the pale flame that burning thatch makes, and I went down to look. Some pirates—I think they must have been Peofn's men—were burning a village on the Levels, and Weland's image—a big, black wooden thing with amber beads round its neck—lay in the bows of a black thirty-two-oar galley that they had just beached. Bitter cold it was! There were icicles hanging from her deck, and the oars were glazed over with ice, and there was ice on Weland's lips. When he saw me he began a long chant in his own tongue, telling me how he was going to rule England, and how I should smell the smoke of his altars from Lincolnshire to the Isle of Wight. *I* didn't care! I'd seen too many Gods charging into Old England to be upset about it. I let him sing himself out while his men were burning the village, and then I said (I don't know what put it into my head), 'Smith of the Gods,' I said, 'the time comes when I shall meet you plying your trade for hire by the wayside.' "

"What did Weland say?" said Una. "Was he angry?"

"He called me names and rolled his eyes, and I went away to wake up the people inland. But the pirates conquered the country, and for centuries Weland was a most important God. He had temples everywhere—from Lincolnshire to the Isle of Wight, as he said—and his sacrifices were simply scandalous. To do him justice, he preferred horses to men; but men *or* horses, I knew that presently he'd have to come down in the world—like the other Old Things. I gave him lots of time—I gave him about a thousand years—and at the end of 'em I went into one of his temples near Andover to see how he prospered. There was his altar, and there was his image, and there were his priests, and there were the congregation, and everybody seemed quite happy, except Weland and the priests. In the old days the congregation were unhappy until the priests had chosen their sacrifices; and so would *you* have been. When the service began a priest rushed out, dragged a man up to the altar, pretended to hit him on the head with a little gilt axe, and the man fell down and pretended to die. Then everybody shouted: 'A sacrifice to Weland! A sacrifice to Weland!' "

"And the man wasn't really dead?" said Una.

"Not a bit. All as much pretence as a dolls' tea-party. Then they brought out a splendid white horse, and the priest cut some hair from its mane and tail and burned it on the altar, shouting, 'A sacrifice!' That counted the same as if a man and a horse had been killed. I saw poor Weland's face through the smoke, and I couldn't help laughing. He looked so disgusted and so hungry, and all he had to satisfy himself was a horrid smell of burning hair. Just a dolls' tea-party!

"I judged it better not to say anything then ('twouldn't have been fair), and the next time I came to Andover, a few hundred years later, Weland and his temple were gone, and there was a Christian bishop in a Church there. None of the People of the Hills could tell me anything about him, and I supposed that he had left England." Puck turned; lay on the other elbow, and thought for a long time.

"Let's see," he said at last. "It must have been some few years later—a year or two before the Conquest, I think—that I came back to Pook's Hill here, and one evening I heard old Hobden talking about Weland's Ford."

"If you mean old Hobden the hedger, he's only seventy-two. He told me so himself," said Dan. "He's a intimate friend of ours."

"You're quite right," Puck replied. "I meant old Hobden's ninth great-grandfather. He was a free man and burned charcoal hereabouts. I've known the family, father and son, so long that I get confused sometimes. Hob of the Dene was my Hobden's name, and he lived at the Forge cottage. Of course, I pricked up my ears when I heard Weland mentioned, and I scuttled through the woods to the Ford just beyond Bog Wood yonder." He jerked his head westward, where the valley narrows between wooded hills and steep hopfields.

"Why, that's Willingford Bridge," said Una. "We go there for walks often. There's a kingfisher there."

"It was Weland's Ford then, dear. A road led down to it from the Beacon on the top of the hill—a shocking bad road it was—and all the hillside was thick, thick oak-forest, with deer in it. There was no trace of Weland, but presently I saw a fat old farmer riding down from the Beacon under the greenwood tree. His horse had cast a shoe in the clay, and when he came to the Ford he dismounted, took a penny out of his purse, laid it on a stone, tied the old horse to an oak, and called out: 'Smith, Smith, here is work for you!' Then he sat down and went to sleep. You can imagine how *I* felt when I saw a white-bearded, bent old blacksmith in a leather apron creep out from behind the oak and begin to shoe the horse. It was Weland himself. I was so astonished that I jumped out and said: 'What on Human Earth are you doing here, Weland?' "

"Poor Weland!" sighed Una.

"He pushed the long hair back from his forehead (he didn't recognize me at first). Then he said: '*You* ought to know. You foretold it, Old Thing. I'm shoeing horses for hire. I'm not even Weland now,' he said. 'They call me Wayland-Smith.' "

"Poor chap!" said Dan. "What did you say?"

"What could I say? He looked up, with the horse's foot on his lap, and he said, smiling, 'I remember the time when I wouldn't have accepted this old bag of bones as a sacrifice, and now I'm glad enough to shoe him for a penny.'

" 'Isn't there any way for you to get back to Valhalla, or wherever you come from?' I said.

" 'I'm afraid not,' he said, rasping away at the hoof. He had a wonderful touch with horses. The old beast was whinnying on his shoulder. 'You may remember that I was not a gentle God in my Day and my Time and my Power. I shall never be released till some human being truly wishes me well.'

" 'Surely,' said I, 'the farmer can't do less than that. You're shoeing the horse all round for him.'

" 'Yes,' said he, 'and my nails will hold a shoe from one full moon to the next. But farmers and Weald Clay,' said he, 'are both uncommon cold and sour.'

"Would you believe it, that when that farmer woke and found his horse shod he rode away without one word of thanks? I was so angry that I wheeled his horse right round and walked him back three miles to the Beacon just to teach the old sinner politeness."

"Were you invisible?" said Una. Puck nodded, gravely.

"The Beacon was always laid in those days ready to light, in case the French landed at Pevensey; and I walked the horse about and about it that lee-long summer night. The farmer thought he was bewitched—well, he *was*, of course—and began to pray and shout. *I* didn't care! I was as good a Christian as he any fair-day in the County, and about four o'clock in the morning a young novice came along from the monastery that used to stand on the top of Beacon hill."

"What's a novice?" said Dan.

"It really means a man who is beginning to be a monk, but in those days people sent their sons to a monastery just the same as a school. This young fellow had been to a monastery in France for a few months every year, and he was finishing his studies in the monastery close to his home here. Hugh was his name, and he had got up to go fishing hereabouts. His people owned all this valley. Hugh heard the farmer shouting, and asked him what in the world he meant. The old man spun him a wonderful tale about fairies and goblins and witches; and I *know* he hadn't seen a thing except rabbits and red deer all that night. (The People of the Hills are like otters—they don't show except when they choose.) But the novice wasn't a fool. He looked down at the horse's feet, and saw the new shoes fastened as only Weland knew how to fasten 'em. (Weland had a way of turning down the nails that folks called the Smith's Clinch.)

" 'H'm!' said the novice. 'Where did you get your horse shod?'

"The farmer wouldn't tell him at first, because the priests never liked their people to have any dealings with the Old Things. At last he confessed that the Smith had done it. 'What did you pay him?' said the novice. 'Penny,' said the farmer, very sulkily. 'That's less than a Christian would have charged,' said the novice. 'I hope you threw a "Thank you" into the bargain.' 'No,' said the farmer; 'Wayland-Smith's a heathen.' 'Heathen or no heathen,' said the novice, 'you took his help, and where you get help there you must give thanks.' 'What?' said the farmer—he was in a furious temper because I was walking the old horse in circles all this time—'What, you young jackanapes?' said he. 'Then by your reasoning I ought to say "Thank you" to Satan if he helped me?' 'Don't roll about up there splitting reasons with me,' said the novice.

'Come back to the Ford and thank the Smith, or you'll be sorry.'

"Back the farmer had to go! I led the horse, though no one saw me, and the novice walked beside us, his gown swishing through the shiny dew and his fishing-rod across his shoulders spearwise. When we reached the Ford again—it was five o'clock and misty still under the oaks—the farmer simply wouldn't say 'Thank you.' He said he'd tell the Abbot that the novice wanted him to worship heathen gods. Then Hugh the novice lost his temper. He just cried, 'Out!' put his arm under the farmer's fat leg, and heaved him from his saddle on to the turf, and before he could rise he caught him by the back of the neck and shook him like a rat till the farmer growled, 'Thank you, Wayland-Smith.'"

"Did Weland see all this?" said Dan.

"Oh, yes, and he shouted his old war-cry when the farmer thudded on to the ground. He was delighted. Then the novice turned to the oak and said, 'Ho! Smith of the Gods, I am ashamed of this rude farmer; but for all you have done in kindness and charity to him and to others of our people, I thank you and wish you well.' Then he picked up his fishing-rod—it looked more like a tall spear than ever—and tramped off down your valley."

"And what did poor Weland do?" said Una.

"He laughed and cried with joy, because he had been released at last, and could go away. But he was an honest Old Thing. He had worked for his living and he paid his debts before he left. 'I shall give that novice a gift,' said Weland. 'A gift that shall do him good the wide world over, and Old England after him. Blow up my fire, Old Thing, while I get the iron for my last task.' Then he made a sword—a dark grey, wavy-lined sword—and I blew the fire while he hammered. By Oak, Ash, and Thorn, I tell you, Weland was a Smith of the Gods! He cooled that sword in running water twice, and the third time he cooled it in the evening dew, and he laid it out in the moonlight and said Runes (that's charms) over it, and he carved Runes of Prophecy on the blade. 'Old Thing,' he said to me, wiping his forehead, 'this is the best blade that Weland ever made. Even the user will never know how good it is. Come to the monastery.'

"We went to the dormitory where the monks slept. We saw the novice fast asleep in his cot, and Weland put the sword into his hand, and I remember the young fellow gripped it in his sleep. Then Weland strode as far as he dared into the Chapel and threw down all his shoeing-tools—his hammer, and pincers, and rasps—to show that he had done with them for ever. It sounded like suits of armour falling, and the sleepy monks ran in, for they thought the monastery had been attacked by the French. The novice came first of all, waving his new sword and shouting Saxon battle-cries. When they saw the shoeing-tools they were very bewildered, till the novice asked leave to speak, and told what he had done to the farmer, and what he had said to Wayland-Smith, and how, though the dormitory light was burning, he had found the wonderful rune-carved sword in his cot.

"The Abbot shook his head at first, and then he laughed and said to the novice: 'Son Hugh, it needed no sign from a heathen God to show me that you will never be a monk. Take your sword, and keep your sword, and go with your sword, and be as gentle as you are strong and courteous. We will hang up the Smith's tools before the Altar,' he said, 'because, whatever the Smith of the Gods may have been in the old days, we know that he worked honestly for his living and made gifts to Mother Church.' Then they went to bed again, all except the novice, and he sat up in the garth playing with his sword. Then Weland said to me by the stables: 'Farewell, Old Thing; you had the right of it. You saw me come to England, and you see me go. Farewell!'

"With that he strode down the hill to the corner of the Great Woods—Woods Corner, you call it now—to the very place where he had first landed—and I heard him moving through the thickets towards Horsebridge for a little, and then he was gone. That was how it happened. I saw it."

Both children drew a long breath.

"But what happened to Hugh the novice?" said Una.

"And the sword?" said Dan.

Puck looked down the meadow that lay all quiet and cool in the shadow of Pook's Hill. A corncrake jarred in a hayfield near by, and the small trouts of the brook began to jump. A big white moth flew unsteadily from the alders and flapped round the children's heads, and the least little haze of water-mist rose from the brook.

"Do you really want to know?" Puck said.

"We do," cried the children. "Awfully!"

"Very good. I promised you that you shall see What you shall see, and you shall hear What you shall hear, though It shall have happened three thousand year; but just now it seems to me that, unless you go back to the house, people will be looking for you. I'll walk with you as far as the gate."

"Will you be here when we come again?" they asked.

"Surely, sure-ly," said Puck. "I've been here some time already. One minute first, please."

He gave them each three leaves—one of Oak, one of Ash, and one of Thorn.

"Bite these," said he. "Otherwise you might be talking at home of what you've seen and heard, and—if I know human beings—they'd send for the doctor. Bite!"

They bit hard, and found themselves walking side by side to the lower gate. Their father was leaning over it.

"And how did your play go?" he asked.

"Oh, splendidly," said Dan. "Only afterwards, I think, we went to sleep. It was very hot and quiet. Don't you remember, Una?"

Una shook her head and said nothing.

"I see," said her father.

"Late—late in the evening Kilmeny came home,
For Kilmeny had been she could not tell where,
And Kilmeny had seen what she could not declare.

But why are you chewing leaves at your time of life, daughter? For fun?"

"No. It was for something, but I can't azactly remember," said Una.

And neither of them could till—

YOUNG MEN AT THE MANOR
1906

THEY were fishing, a few days later, in the bed of the brook that for centuries had cut deep into the soft valley soil. The trees closing overhead made long tunnels through which the sunshine worked in blobs and patches. Down in the tunnels were bars of sand and gravel, old roots and trunks covered with moss or painted red by the irony water; foxgloves growing lean and pale towards the light; clumps of fern and thirsty shy flowers who could not live away from moisture and shade. In the pools you could see the wave thrown up by the trouts as they charged hither and yon, and the pools were joined to each other—except in flood time, when all was one brown rush—by sheets of thin broken water that poured themselves chuckling round the darkness of the next bend.

This was one of the children's most secret hunting-grounds, and their particular friend, old Hobden the hedger, had shown them how to use it. Except for the click of a rod hitting a low willow, or a switch and tussle among the young ash-leaves as a line hung up for the minute, nobody in the hot pasture could have guessed what game was going on among the trouts below the banks.

"We's got half-a-dozen," said Dan, after a warm, wet hour. "I vote we go up to Stone Bay and try Long Pool."

Una nodded—most of her talk was by nods—and they crept from the gloom of the tunnels towards the tiny weir that turns the brook into the mill-stream. Here the banks are low and bare, and the glare of the afternoon sun on the Long Pool below the weir makes your eyes ache.

When they were in the open they nearly fell down with astonishment. A huge grey horse, whose tail-hairs crinkled the glassy water, was drinking in the pool, and the ripples about his muzzle flashed like melted gold. On his back sat an old, white-haired man dressed in a loose glimmery gown of chain-mail. He was bareheaded, and a nut-shaped iron helmet hung at his saddle-bow. His reins were of red leather five or six inches deep, scalloped at the edges, and his high padded saddle with its red girths was held fore and aft by a red leather breastband and crupper.

"Look!" said Una, as though Dan were not staring his very eyes out. "It's like the picture in your room—'Sir Isumbras at the Ford.' "

The rider turned towards them, and his thin, long face was just as sweet and gentle as that of the knight who carries the children in that picture.

"They should be here now, Sir Richard," said Puck's deep voice among the willow-herb.

"They are here," the knight said, and he smiled at Dan with the string of trouts in his hand. "There seems no great change in boys since mine fished this water."

"If your horse has drunk, we shall be more at ease in the Ring," said Puck; and he nodded to the children as though he had never magicked away their memories the week before.

The great horse turned and hoisted himself into the pasture with a kick and a scramble that tore the clods down rattling.

"Your pardon!" said Sir Richard to Dan. "When these lands were mine, I never loved that mounted men should cross the brook except by the paved ford. But my Swallow here was thirsty, and I wished to meet you."

"We're very glad you've come, sir," said Dan. "It doesn't matter in the least about the banks."

He trotted across the pasture on the sword-side of the mighty horse, and it was a mighty iron-handled sword that swung from Sir Richard's belt. Una walked behind with Puck. She remembered everything now.

"I'm sorry about the Leaves," he said, "but it would never have done if you had gone home and told, would it?"

"I s'pose not," Una answered. "But you said that all the fair—People of the Hills had left England."

"So they have; but I told you that you should come and

go and look and know, didn't I? The knight isn't a fairy. He's Sir Richard Dalyngridge, a very old friend of mine. He came over with William the Conqueror, and he wants to see you particularly."

"What for?" said Una.

"On account of your great wisdom and learning," Puck replied, without a twinkle.

"Us?" said Una. "Why, I don't know my Nine Times—not to say it dodging; and Dan makes the most *awful* mess of fractions. He can't mean *us!*"

"Una!" Dan called back. "Sir Richard says he is going to tell what happened to Weland's sword. He's got it. Isn't it splendid?"

"Nay—nay," said Sir Richard, dismounting as they reached the Ring, in the bend of the mill-stream bank. "It is you that must tell me, for I hear the youngest child in our England to-day is as wise as our wisest clerk." He slipped the bit out of Swallow's mouth, dropped the ruby-red reins over his head, and the wise horse moved off to graze.

Sir Richard (they noticed he limped a little) unslung his great sword.

"That's it," Dan whispered to Una.

"This is the sword that Brother Hugh had from Wayland-Smith," Sir Richard said. "Once he gave it to me, but I would not take it; but at the last it became mine after such a fight as never christened man fought. See!" He half drew it from its sheath and turned it before them. On either side just below the handle, where the Runic letters shivered as though they were alive, were two deep gouges in the dull, deadly steel. "Now, what Thing made those?" said he. "I know not, but you, perhaps, can say."

"Tell them all the tale, Sir Richard," said Puck. "It concerns their land somewhat."

"Yes, from the very beginning," Una pleaded, for the knight's good face and the smile on it more than ever reminded her of "Sir Isumbras at the Ford."

They settled down to listen, Sir Richard bare-headed to the sunshine, dandling the sword in both hands, while the grey horse cropped outside the Ring, and the helmet on the saddle-bow clinged softly each time he jerked his head.

"From the beginning, then," Sir Richard said, "since it concerns your land, I will tell the tale. When our Duke came out of Normandy to take his England, great knights (have ye heard?) came and strove hard to serve the Duke, because he promised them lands here, and small knights followed the great ones. My folk in Normandy were poor; but a great knight, Engerrard of the Eagle—Engenulf De Aquila—who was kin to my father, followed the Earl of Mortain, who followed William the Duke, and I followed De Aquila. Yes, with thirty men-at-arms out of my father's house and a new sword, I set out to conquer England three days after I was made knight. I did not then know that England would conquer me. We went up to Santlache with the rest—a very great host of us."

"Does that mean the Battle of Hastings—Ten Sixty-Six?" Una whispered, and Puck nodded, so as not to interrupt.

"At Santlache, over the hill yonder"—he pointed south-eastward towards Fairlight—"we found Harold's men. We fought. At the day's end they ran. My men went with De Aquila's to chase and plunder, and in that chase Engerrard of the Eagle was slain, and his son Gilbert took his banner and his men forward. This I did not know till after, for Swallow here was cut in the flank, so I stayed to wash the wound at a brook by a thorn. There a single Saxon cried out to me in French, and we fought together. I should have known his voice, but we fought together. For a long time neither had any advantage, till by pure ill-fortune his foot slipped and his sword flew from his hand. Now I had but newly been made knight, and wished, above all, to be courteous and fame-worthy, so I forebore to strike and bade him get his sword again. 'A plague on my sword,' said he. 'It has lost me my first fight. You have spared my life. Take my sword.' He held it out to me, but as I stretched my hand the sword groaned like a stricken man, and I leaped back crying, 'Sorcery!'

[The children looked at the sword as though it might speak again.]

"Suddenly a clump of Saxons ran out upon me and, seeing a Norman alone, would have killed me, but my Saxon cried out that I was his prisoner, and beat them off. Thus, see you, he saved my life. He put me on my horse and led me through the woods ten long miles to this valley."

"To here, d'you mean?" said Una.

"To this very valley. We came in by the Lower Ford under the King's Hill yonder"—he pointed eastward where the valley widens.

"And was that Saxon Hugh the novice?" Dan asked.

"Yes, and more than that. He had been for three years at the monastery at Bec by Rouen, where"—Sir Richard chuckled—"the Abbot Herluin would not suffer me to remain."

"Why wouldn't he?" said Dan.

"Because I rode my horse into the refectory, when the scholars were at meat, to show the Saxon boys we Normans were not afraid of an abbot. It was that very Saxon Hugh tempted me to do it, and we had not met since that day. I thought I knew his voice even inside my helmet, and, for all that our Lords fought, we each rejoiced we had not slain the other. He walked by my side, and he told me how a Heathen God, as he believed, had given him his sword, but he said he had never heard it sing before. I remember I warned him to beware of sorcery and quick enchantments." Sir Richard smiled to himself. "I was very young—very young!

"When we came to his house here we had almost forgotten that we had been at blows. It was near midnight, and the Great Hall was full of men and women waiting news. There I first saw his sister, the Lady Ælueva, of whom he had spoken to us in France. She cried out fiercely at me, and would have had me hanged in that hour, but her brother said that I had spared his life—he said not how he saved mine from his Saxons—and that our Duke had won the day; and even while they wrangled over my poor body, of a sudden he fell down in a swoon from his wounds.

" 'This is *thy* fault,' said the Lady Ælueva to me, and she kneeled above him and called for wine and cloths.

" 'If I had known,' I answered, 'he should have ridden and I walked. But he set me on my horse; he made no complaint; he walked beside me and spoke merrily throughout. I pray I have done him no harm.'

" 'Thou hast need to pray,' she said, catching up her under-lip. 'If he dies, thou shalt hang!'

"They bore off Hugh to his chamber; but three tall men of the house bound me and set me under the beam of the Great Hall with a rope round my neck. The end of the rope they flung over the beam, and they sat them down by the fire to wait word whether Hugh lived or died. They cracked nuts with their knife-hilts the while."

"And how did you feel?" said Dan.

"Very weary; but I did heartily pray for my schoolmate Hugh his health. About noon I heard horses in the valley, and the three men loosed my ropes and fled out, and De Aquila's men rode up. Gilbert de Aquila came with them, for it was his boast that, like his father, he forgot no man that served him. He was little, like his father, but terrible, with a nose like an eagle's nose and yellow eyes like an eagle. He rode tall war-horses—roans, which he bred himself—and he could never abide to be helped into the saddle. He saw the rope hanging from the beam and laughed, and his men laughed, for I was too stiff to rise.

" 'This is poor entertainment for a Norman knight,' he said, 'but, such as it is, let us be grateful. Show me, boy, to whom thou owest most, and we will pay them out of hand.' "

"What did he mean? To kill 'em?" said Dan.

"Assuredly. But I looked at the Lady Ælueva where she stood among her maids, and her brother beside her. De Aquila's men had driven them all into the Great Hall."

"Was she pretty?" said Una.

"In all my life I had never seen woman fit to strew rushes before my Lady Ælueva," the knight replied, quite simply and quietly. "As I looked at her I thought I might save her and her house by a jest.

" 'Seeing that I came somewhat hastily and without warning,' said I to De Aquila, 'I have no fault to find with the courtesy that these Saxons have shown me.' But my voice shook. It is—it was not good to jest with that little man.

"All were silent awhile, till De Aquila laughed. 'Look, men—a miracle!' said he. 'The fight is scarce sped, my father is not yet buried, and here we find our youngest knight already set down in his Manor, while his Saxons—ye can see it in their fat faces—have paid him homage and service! By the Saints,' he said, rubbing his nose, 'I never thought England would be so easy won! Surely I can do no less than give the lad what he has taken. This Manor shall be thine, boy,' he said, 'till I come again, or till thou art slain. Now, mount, men, and ride. We follow our Duke into Kent to make him King of England.'

"He drew me with him to the door while they brought his horse—a lean roan, taller than my Swallow here, but not so well girthed.

" 'Hark to me,' he said, fretting with his great war-gloves. 'I have given thee this Manor, which is a Saxon hornets' nest, and I think thou wilt be slain in a month—as my father was slain. Yet if thou canst keep the roof on the hall, the thatch on the barn, and the plough in the furrow till I come back, thou shalt hold the Manor from me; for the Duke has promised our Earl Mortain all the lands by Pevensey, and Mortain will give me of them what he would have given my father. God knows if thou or I shall live till England is won; but remember, boy, that here and now fighting is foolishness and'—he reached for the reins—'craft and cunning is all.'

" 'Alas, I have no cunning,' said I.

" 'Not yet,' said he, hopping abroad, foot in stirrup, and poking his horse in the belly with his toe. 'Not yet, but I think thou hast a good teacher. Farewell! Hold the Manor and live. Lose the Manor and hang,' he said, and spurred out, his shield-straps squeaking behind him.

"So, children, here was I, little more than a boy, and Santlache fight not two days old, left alone with my thirty men-at-arms, in a land I knew not, among a people whose tongue

I could not speak, to hold down the land which I had taken from them."

"And that was here at home?" said Una.

"Yes, here. See! From the Upper Ford, Weland's Ford, to the Lower Ford, by the Belle Allée, west and east it ran half a league. From the Beacon of Brunanburgh behind us here, south and north it ran a full league—and all the woods were full of broken men from Santlache, Saxon thieves, Norman plunderers, robbers, and deerstealers. A hornets' nest indeed!

"When De Aquila had gone, Hugh would have thanked me for saving their lives; but Lady Ælueva said that I had done it only for the sake of receiving the Manor.

" 'How could I know that De Aquila would give it me?' I said. 'If I had told him I had spent my night in your halter he would have burned the place twice over by now.'

" 'If any man had put *my* neck in a rope,' she said, 'I would have seen his house burned thrice over before *I* would have made terms.'

" 'But it was a woman,' I said; and I laughed and she wept and said that I mocked her in her captivity.

" 'Lady,' said I, 'there is no captive in this valley except one, and he is not a Saxon.'

"At this she cried that I was a Norman thief, who came with false, sweet words, having intended from the first to turn her out in the fields to beg her bread. Into the fields! She had never seen the face of war!

"I was angry, and answered, 'This much at least I can disprove, for I swear'—and on my sword-hilt I swore it in that place—'I swear I will never set foot in the Great Hall till the Lady Ælueva herself shall summons me there.'

"She went away, saying nothing, and I walked out, and Hugh limped after me, whistling dolorously (that is a custom of the English), and we came upon the three Saxons that had bound me. They were now bound by my men-at-arms, and behind them stood some fifty stark and sullen churls of the House and the Manor, waiting to see what should fall. We heard De Aquila's trumpets blow thin through the woods Kentward.

" 'Shall we hang these?' said my men.

" 'Then my churls will fight,' said Hugh, beneath his breath; but I bade him ask the three what mercy they hoped for.

" 'None,' said they all. 'She bade us hang thee if our master died. And we would have hanged thee. There is no more to it.'

"As I stood doubting a woman ran down from the oak wood above the King's Hill yonder, and cried out that some Normans were driving off the swine there.

" 'Norman or Saxon,' said I, 'we must beat them back, or they will rob us every day. Out at them with any arms ye have!' So I loosed those three carles and we ran together, my men-at-arms and the Saxons with bills and bows which they had hidden in the thatch of their huts, and Hugh led them. Half-way up the King's Hill we found a false fellow from Picardy—a sutler that sold wine in the Duke's camp—with a dead knight's shield on his arm, a stolen horse under him, and some ten or twelve wastrels at his tail, all cutting and slashing at the pigs. We beat them off, and saved our pork. One hundred and seventy pigs we saved in that great battle." Sir Richard laughed.

"That, then, was our first work together, and I bade Hugh tell his folk that so would I deal with any man, knight or churl, Norman or Saxon, who stole as much as one egg from our valley. Said he to me, riding home: 'Thou hast gone far to conquer England this evening.' I answered: 'England must be thine and mine, then. Help me, Hugh, to deal aright with this people. Make them to know that if they slay me De Aquila will surely send to slay them, and he will put a worse man in my place.' 'That may well be true,' said he, and gave me his hand. 'Better the devil we know than the devil we know not, till we can pack you Normans home.' And so, too, said his Saxons; and they laughed as we drove the pigs downhill. But I think some of them, even then, began not to hate me."

"I like Brother Hugh," said Una, softly.

"Beyond question he was the most perfect, courteous, valiant, tender, and wise knight that ever drew breath," said

Richard, caressing the sword. "He hung up his sword—this sword—on the wall of the Great Hall, because he said it was fairly mine, and never he took it down till De Aquila returned, as I shall presently show. For three months his men and mine guarded the valley, till all robbers and nightwalkers learned there was nothing to get from us save hard tack and a hanging. Side by side we fought against all who came—thrice a week sometimes we fought—against thieves and landless knights looking for good manors. Then we were in some peace, and I made shift by Hugh's help to govern the valley—for all this valley of yours was my Manor—as a knight should. I kept the roof on the hall and the thatch on the barn, but . . . The English are a bold people. His Saxons would laugh and jest with Hugh, and Hugh with them, and—this was marvellous to me—if even the meanest of them said that such and such a thing was the Custom of the Manor, then straightway would Hugh and such old men of the Manor as might be near forsake everything else to debate the matter—I have seen them stop the mill with the corn half ground—and if the custom or usage were proven to be as it was said, why, that was the end of it, even though it were flat against Hugh, his wish and command. Wonderful!"

"Aye," said Puck, breaking in for the first time. "The Custom of Old England was here before your Norman knights came, and it outlasted them, though they fought against it cruel."

"Not I," said Richard. "I let the Saxons go their stubborn way, but when my own men-at-arms, Normans not six months in England, stood up and told me what was the custom of the country, *then* I was angry. Ah, good days! Ah, wonderful people! And I loved them all."

The knight lifted his arms as though he would hug the whole dear valley, and Swallow, hearing the chink of his chain-mail, looked up and whinnied softly.

"At last," he went on, "after a year of striving and contriving and some little driving, De Aquila came to the valley, alone and without warning. I saw him first at the Lower Ford, with a swine-herd's brat on his saddle-bow.

" 'There is no need for thee to give any account of thy stewardship,' said he. 'I have it all from the child here.' And he told me how the young thing had stopped his tall horse at the Ford, by waving of a branch, and crying that the way was barred. 'And if one bold, bare babe be enough to guard the Ford in these days, thou hast done well,' said he, and puffed and wiped his head.

He pinched the child's cheek, and looked at our cattle in the flat by the brook.

" 'Both fat,' said he, rubbing his nose. 'This is craft and cunning such as I love. What did I tell thee when I rode away, boy?'

" 'Hold the Manor or hang,' said I. I had never forgotten it.

" 'True. And thou hast held.' He clambered from his saddle and with sword's point cut out a turf from the bank and gave it me where I kneeled."

Dan looked at Una, and Una looked at Dan.

"That's seizin," said Puck, in a whisper.

" 'Now thou art lawfully seized of the Manor, Sir Richard,' said he—'twas the first time he ever called me that—'thou and thy heirs for ever. This must serve till the King's clerks write out thy title on a parchment. England is all ours—if we can hold it.'

" 'What service shall I pay?' I asked, and I remember I was proud beyond words.

" 'Knight's fee, boy, knight's fee!' said he, hopping round his horse on one foot. (Have I said he was little, and could not endure to be helped to his saddle?) 'Six mounted men or twelve archers thou shalt send me whenever I call for them, and—where got you that corn?' said he, for it was near harvest, and our corn stood well. 'I have never seen such bright straw. Send me three bags of the same seed yearly, and furthermore, in memory of our last meeting—with the rope round thy neck—entertain me and my men for two days of each year in the Great Hall of thy Manor.'

" 'Alas!' said I, 'then my Manor is already forfeit. I am

under vow not to enter the Great Hall.' And I told him what I had sworn to the Lady Ælueva."

"And hadn't you ever been into the house since?" said Una.

"Never," Sir Richard answered smiling. "I had made me a little hut of wood up the hill, and there I did justice and slept. . . . De Aquila wheeled aside, and his shield shook on his back. 'No matter, boy,' said he. 'I will remit the homage for a year.' "

"He meant Sir Richard needn't give him dinner there the first year," Puck explained.

"De Aquila stayed with me in the hut and Hugh, who could read and write and cast accounts, showed him the roll of the Manor, in which were written all the names of our fields and men, and he asked a thousand questions touching the land, the timber, the grazing, the mill, and the fish-ponds, and the worth of every man in the valley. But never he named the Lady Ælueva's name, nor went he near the Great Hall. By night he drank with us in the hut. Yes, he sat on the straw like an eagle ruffled in her feathers, his yellow eyes rolling above the cup, and he pounced in his talk like an eagle, swooping from one thing to another, but always binding fast. Yes; he would lie still awhile, and then rustle in the straw, and speak sometimes as though he were King William himself, and anon he would speak in parables and tales, and if at once we saw not his meaning he would yerk us in the ribs with his scabbarded sword.

" 'Look you, boys,' said he, 'I am born out of my due time. Five hundred years ago I would have made all England such an England as neither Dane, Saxon, nor Norman should have conquered. Five hundred years hence I should have been such a councillor to Kings as the world hath never dreamed of. 'Tis all here,' said he, tapping his big head, 'but it hath no play in this black age. Now Hugh here is a better man than thou art, Richard.' He had made his voice harsh and croaking, like a raven's.

" 'Truth,' said I. 'But for Hugh, his help and patience and long-suffering, I could never have kept the Manor.'

" 'Nor thy life either,' said De Aquila. 'Hugh has saved

thee not once, but a hundred times. Be still, Hugh!' he said. 'Dost thou know, Richard, why Hugh slept, and why he still sleeps, among thy Norman men-at-arms?'

" 'To be near me,' said I, for I thought this was truth.

" 'Fool!' said De Aquila. 'It is because his Saxons have begged him to rise against thee, and to sweep every Norman out of the valley. No matter how I know. It is truth. Therefore Hugh hath made himself an hostage for thy life, well knowing that if any harm befell thee from his Saxons thy Normans would slay him without remedy. And this his Saxons know. It is true, Hugh?'

" 'In some sort,' said Hugh, shamefacedly; 'at least, it was true half a year ago. My Saxons would not harm Richard now. I think they know him; but I judged it best to make sure.'

"Look, children, what that man had done—and I had never guessed it! Night after night had he lain down among my men-at-arms, knowing that if one Saxon had lifted knife against me his life would have answered for mine.

" 'Yes,' said De Aquila. 'And he is a swordless man.' He pointed to Hugh's belt, for Hugh had put away his sword—did I tell you?—the day after it flew from his hand at Santlache. He carried only the short knife and the long-bow. 'Swordless and landless art thou, Hugh; and they call thee kin to Earl Godwin.' (Hugh was indeed of Godwin's blood.) 'The Manor that was thine was given to this boy and to his children for ever. Sit up and beg, for he can turn thee out like a dog, Hugh!'

"Hugh said nothing, but I heard his teeth grind, and I bade De Aquila, my own overlord, hold his peace, or I would stuff his words down his throat. Then De Aquila laughed till the tears ran down his face.

" 'I warned the King,' said he, 'what would come of giving England to us Norman thieves. Here art thou, Richard, less than two days confirmed in thy Manor, and already thou hast risen against thy overlord. What shall do to him, *Sir* Hugh?'

" 'I am a swordless man,' said Hugh. 'Do not jest with me,' and he laid his head on his knees and groaned.

" 'The greater fool thou,' said De Aquila, and all his voice changed; 'for I have given thee the Manor of Dallington up the hill this half-hour since,' and he yerked at Hugh with his scabbard across the straw.

" 'To me?' said Hugh. 'I am a Saxon, and, except that I love Richard here, I have not sworn fealty to any Norman.'

" 'In God's good time, which because of my sins I shall not live to see, there will be neither Saxon nor Norman in England,' said De Aquila. 'If I know men, thou art more faithful unsworn than a score of Normans I could name. Take Dallington, and join Sir Richard to fight me to-morrow, if it please thee!'

" 'Nay,' said Hugh. 'I am no child. Where I take a gift, there I render service'; and he put his hands between De Aquila's, and swore to be faithful, and, as I remember, I kissed him, and De Aquila kissed us both.

"We sat afterwards outside the hut while the sun rose, and De Aquila marked our churls going to their work in the fields, and talked of holy things, and how we should govern our Manors in time to come, and of hunting and of horse-breeding, and of the King's wisdom and unwisdom; for he spoke to us as though we were in all sorts now his brothers. Anon a churl stole up to me—he was one of the three I had not hanged a year ago—and he bellowed—which is the Saxon for whispering—that the Lady Ælueva would speak to me at the Great House. She walked abroad daily in the Manor, and it was her custom to send me word whither she went, that I might set an archer or two behind and in front to guard her. Very often I myself lay up in the woods and watched on her also.

"I went swiftly, and as I passed the great door it opened from within, and there stood my Lady Ælueva, and she said to me: 'Sir Richard, will it please you enter your Great Hall?' Then she wept, but we were alone."

The knight was silent for a long time, his face turned across the valley, smiling.

"Oh, well done!" said Una, and clapped her hands very softly. "She was sorry, and she said so."

"Aye, she was sorry, and she said so," said Sir Richard, coming back with a little start. "Very soon—but *he* said it was two full hours later—De Aquila rode to the door, with his shield new scoured (Hugh had cleansed it), and demanded entertainment, and called me a false knight, that would starve his overlord to death. Then Hugh cried out that no man should work in the valley that day, and our Saxons blew horns, and set about feasting and drinking, and running of races, and dancing and singing; and De Aquila climbed upon a horse-block and spoke to them in what he swore was good Saxon, but no man understood it. At night we feasted in the Great Hall, and when the harpers and the singers were gone we four sat late at the high table. As I remember, it was a warm night with a full moon, and De Aquila bade Hugh take down his sword from the wall again, for the honour of the Manor of Dallington, and Hugh took it gladly enough. Dust lay on the hilt, for I saw him blow it off.

"She and I sat talking a little apart, and at first we thought the harpers had come back, for the Great Hall was filled with a rushing noise of music. De Aquila leaped up; but there was only the moonlight fretty on the floor.

" 'Hearken!' said Hugh. 'It is my sword,' and as he belted it on the music ceased.

" 'Over Gods, forbid that I should ever belt blade like that,' said De Aquila. 'What does it foretell?'

" 'The Gods that made it may know. Last time it spoke was at Hastings, when I lost all my lands. Belike it sings now that I have new lands and am a man again,' said Hugh.

"He loosed the blade a little and drove it back happily into the sheath, and the sword answered him low and crooningly, as—as a woman would speak to a man, her head on his shoulder.

"Now that was the second time in all my life I heard this Sword sing." . . .

"Look!" said Una. "There's mother coming down the Long Slip. What will she say to Sir Richard? She can't help seeing him."

"And Puck can't magic us this time," said Dan.

"Are you sure?" said Puck; and he leaned forward and whispered to Sir Richard, who, smiling, bowed his head.

"But what befell the sword and my brother Hugh I will tell on another time," said he, rising. "Ohé, Swallow!"

The great horse cantered up from the far end of the meadow, close to mother.

They heard mother say: "Children, Gleason's old horse has broken into the meadow again. Where did he get through?"

"Just below Stone Bay," said Dan. "He tore down simple flobs of the bank! We noticed it just now. And we've caught no end of fish. We've been at it all the afternoon."

And they honestly believed that they had. They never noticed the Oak, Ash, and Thorn leaves that Puck had slyly thrown into their laps.

A CHARM
1910

TAKE of English earth as much
As either hand may rightly clutch.
In the taking of it breathe
Prayer for all who lie beneath.
Not the great nor well-bespoke,
But the mere uncounted folk
Of whose life and death is none
Report or lamentation.
  Lay that earth upon thy heart,
  And thy sickness shall depart!

It shall sweeten and make whole
Fevered breath and festered soul.
It shall mightily restrain
Over-busied hand and brain.
It shall ease thy mortal strife
'Gainst the immortal woe of life,
Till thyself, restored, shall prove
By what grace the Heavens do move.

Take of English flowers these—
Spring's full-facèd primroses,
Summer's wild wide-hearted rose,
Autumn's wall-flower of the close,
And, thy darkness to illume,
Winter's bee-thronged ivy-bloom.
Seek and serve them where they bide
From Candlemas to Christmas-tide,
  For these simples, used aright,
  Can restore a failing sight.

These shall cleanse and purify
Webbed and inward-turning eye;
These shall show thee treasure hid,
Thy familiar fields amid;
And reveal (which is thy need)
Every man a King indeed!

COLD IRON
1909

WHEN Dan and Una had arranged to go out before breakfast, they did not remember it was Midsummer Morning. They only wanted to see the otter which, old Hobden said, had been fishing their brook for weeks; and early morning was the time to surprise him. As they tip-toed out of the house into the wonderful stillness, the church clock struck five. Dan took a few steps across the dew-blobbed lawn, and looked at his black footprints.

"I think we ought to be kind to our poor boots," he said. "They'll get horrid wet."

It was their first Summer in boots, and they hated them, so they took them off and slung them round their necks, and paddled joyfully over the dripping turf where the shadows lay the wrong way, like evening in the East.

The sun was well up and warm, but, by the brook, the last of the night mist still fumed off the water. They picked up the chain of otter's footprints on the mud, and followed it from the bank, between the weeds and the drenched mowing, while the birds shouted with surprise. Then the track left the brook and became a smear, as though a log had been dragged along.

They traced it into Three Cows meadow, over the mill-sluice to the Forge, round Hobden's garden, and then up the slope till it ran out on the short turf and fern of Pook's Hill, and they heard the cock-pheasants crowing in the woods behind them.

"No use!" said Dan, questing like a puzzled hound. "The dew's drying off, and old Hobden says otters'll travel for miles."

"I'm sure we've travelled miles." Una fanned herself with her hat. "How still it is! It's going to be a regular roaster." She looked down the valley, where no chimney yet smoked.

"Hobden's up!" Dan pointed to the open door of the Forge cottage. "What d'you suppose he has for breakfast?"

"One of *them*. He says they eat good all times of the year." Una jerked her head at some stately pheasants going down to the brook for a drink.

A few steps farther on a fox broke almost under their bare feet, yapped, and trotted off.

"Ah, Mus' Reynolds—Mus' Reynolds,"—Dan was quoting from old Hobden—"If I knowed all you knowed, I'd know something."[1]

"I say," Una lowered her voice, "you know that funny feeling of things having happened before. I felt it when you said 'Mus' Reynolds.'"

"So did I," Dan began. "What is it?"

They faced each other stammering with excitement.

"Wait a shake! I'll remember in a minute. Wasn't it something about a fox—last year. Oh, I nearly had it then!" Dan cried.

"Be quiet!" said Una, prancing excitedly. "There was something happened before we met the fox last year. Hills! Broken Hills—the play at the theatre—see what you see——"

"I remember now," Dan shouted. "It's as plain as the nose on your face—Pook's Hill—Puck's Hill—Puck!"

"I remember, too," said Una. "And it's Midsummer Day again!"

The young fern on a knoll rustled, and Puck walked out, chewing a green-topped rush.

"Good Midsummer Morning to you! Here's a happy meet-

[1]See "The Winged Hats" in *Puck of Pook's Hill.*

ing," said he. They shook hands all round, and asked questions.

"You've wintered well," he said after a while, and looked them up and down. "Nothing much wrong with you, seemingly."

"They've put us into boots," said Una. "Look at my feet—they're all pale white, and my toes are squdged together awfully."

"Yes—boots make a difference," Puck wriggled his brown, square, hairy foot, and cropped a dandelion flower between the big toe and the next.

"I could do that—last year," Dan said dismally, as he tried and failed. "And boots simply ruin one's climbing."

"There must be some advantage to them, I suppose," said Puck, "or folk wouldn't wear them. Shall we come this way?"

They sauntered along side by side till they reached the gate at the far end of the hillside. Here they halted just like cattle, and let the sun warm their backs while they listened to the flies in the wood.

"Little Lindens is awake," said Una, as she hung with her chin on the top rail. "See the chimney smoke?"

"To-day's Thursday, isn't it?" Puck turned to look at the old pink farmhouse across the little valley. "Mrs. Vincey's baking day. Bread should rise well this weather." He yawned, and that set them both yawning.

The bracken about rustled and ticked and shook in every direction. They felt that little crowds were stealing past.

"Doesn't that sound like—er—the People of the Hills?" said Una.

"It's the birds and wild things drawing up to the woods before people get about," said Puck, as though he were Ridley the keeper.

"Oh, we know that. I only said it sounded like."

"As I remember 'em, the People of the Hills used to make more noise. They'd settle down for the day rather like small birds settling down for the night. But that was in the days when they carried the high hand. Oh, me! The deeds that I've had act and part in, you'd scarcely believe!"

"I like that!" said Dan. "After all you told us last year, too!"

"Only, the minute you went away, you made us forget everything," said Una.

Puck laughed and shook his head. "I shall this year, too. I've given you seizin of Old England, and I've taken away your Doubt and Fear, but your memory and remembrance between whiles I'll keep where old Billy Trott kept his night-lines—and that's where he could draw 'em up and hide 'em at need. Does that suit?" He twinkled mischievously.

"It's got to suit," said Una, and laughed. "We can't magic back at you." She folded her arms and leaned against the gate. "Suppose, now, you wanted to magic me into something—an otter? Could you?"

"Not with those boots round your neck."

"I'll take them off." She threw them on the turf. Dan's followed immediately. "Now!" she said.

"Less than ever now you've trusted me. Where there's true faith, there's no call for magic." Puck's slow smile broadened all over his face.

"But what have boots to do with it?" said Una, perching on the gate.

"There's cold iron in them," said Puck, and settled beside her. "Nails in the soles, I mean. It makes a difference."

"How?"

"Can't you feel it does? You wouldn't like to go back to bare feet again, same as last year, would you? Not really?"

"No—o. I suppose I shouldn't—not for always. I'm growing up, you know," said Una.

"But you told us last year, in the Long Slip—when we met you—that you didn't mind Cold Iron," said Dan.

"*I* don't; but folk in housen, as the People of the Hills call them, must be ruled by Cold Iron. Folk in housen are born on the near side of Cold Iron—there's iron in every man's house, isn't there? They handle Cold Iron every day of their lives, and their fortune's made or spoilt by Cold Iron in some shape or other. That's how it goes with Flesh and Blood, and one can't prevent it."

"I don't quite see. How do you mean?" said Dan.

"It would take me some time to tell you."

"Oh, it's ever so long to breakfast," said Dan. "We looked in the larder before we came out." He unpocketed one big hunk of bread and Una another, which they shared with Puck.

"That's Little Lindens' baking," he said, as his white teeth sunk in it. "I know Mrs. Vincey's hand." He ate with a slow sideways thrust and grind, just like old Hobden, and, like Hobden, hardly dropped a crumb. The sun flashed on Little Lindens' windows, and the cloudless sky grew stiller and hotter in the valley.

"Ah—Cold Iron," he said at last to the impatient children. "Folk in housen, as the People of the Hills say, grow so careless about Cold Iron. They'll nail the Horseshoe over the front door, and forget to put it over the back. Then, some time or other, the People of the Hills slip in, find the cradle-babe in the corner, and——"

"Oh, I know. Steal it and leave a changeling," Una cried.

"No," said Puck, firmly. "All that talk of changelings is people's excuse for their own neglect. Never believe 'em. I'd whip 'em at the cart-tail through three parishes if I had my way."

"But they don't do it now," said Una.

"Whip, or neglect children? Umm! Some folks and some fields never alter. But the People of the Hills didn't work any changeling tricks. They'd tip-toe in and whisper, and weave round the cradle-babe in the chimney-corner—a fag-end of a charm here, or half a spell there—like kettles singing; but when the babe's mind came to bud out afterwards, it would act differently from other people in its station. That's no advantage to man or maid. So I wouldn't allow it with my folks' babies here. I told Sir Huon so once."

"Who was Sir Huon?" Dan asked, and Puck turned on him in quiet astonishment.

"Sir Huon of Bordeaux—he succeeded King Oberon. He had been a bold knight once, but he was lost on the road to

Babylon, a long while back. Have you ever heard, 'How many miles to Babylon?' "

"Of course," said Dan.

"Well, Sir Huon was young when that song was new. But about tricks on mortal babies. I said to Sir Huon in the fern here, on just such a morning as this: 'If you crave to act and influence on folk in housen, which I know is your desire, why don't you take some human cradle-babe by fair dealing, and bring him up among yourselves on the far side of Cold Iron—as Oberon did in time past? Then you could make him a splendid fortune, and send him out into the world?'

" 'Time past is past time,' says Sir Huon. 'I doubt if we could do it. For one thing, the babe would have to be taken without wronging man, woman or child. For another, he'd have to be born on the far side of Cold Iron—in some house where no Cold Iron ever stood,—and for yet the third, he'd have to be kept from Cold Iron all his days till we let him find his fortune. No, it's not easy,' he said, and he rode off, thinking. You see, Sir Huon had been a man once.

"I happened to attend Lewes Market next Woden's Day even, and watched the slaves being sold there—same as pigs are sold at Robertsbridge Market nowadays. Only the pigs have rings on their noses, and the slaves had rings round their necks."

"What sort of rings?" said Dan.

"A ring of Cold Iron, four fingers wide, and a thumb thick, just like a quoit, but with a snap to it for to snap around the slave's neck. They used to do a big trade in slave-rings at the Forge here, and ship them to all parts of Old England, packed in oak sawdust. But, as I was saying, there was a farmer out of the Weald who had bought a woman with a babe in her arms, and he didn't want any encumbrances to her driving his beasts home for him."

"Beast himself!" said Una, and kicked her bare heel on the gate.

"So he blamed the auctioneer. 'It's none o' my baby,' the wench puts in. 'I took it off a woman in our gang who died on Terrible Down yesterday.' 'I'll take it off to the Church then,' says the farmer. 'Mother Church'll make a monk of it, and we'll step along home.'

"It was dusk then. He slipped down to St. Pancras' Church, and laid the babe at the cold chapel door. I breathed on the back of his stooping neck—and—I've *heard* he never could be warm at any fire afterwards. I should have been surprised if he could! Then I whipped up the babe, and came flying home here like a bat to his belfry.

"On the dewy break of morning of Thor's own day—just such a day as this—I laid the babe outside the Hill here, and the People flocked up and wondered at the sight.

" 'You've brought him, then?' Sir Huon said, staring like any mortal man.

" 'Yes, and he's brought his mouth with him too,' I said. The babe was crying loud for his breakfast.

" 'What is he?" says Sir Huon, when the women-folk had drawn him under to feed him.

" 'Full Moon and Morning Star may know,' I says. '*I* don't. By what I could make out of him in the moonlight, he's without brand or blemish. I'll answer for it that he's born on the far side of Cold Iron, for he was born under a shaw on Terrible Down; and I've wronged neither man, woman nor child in taking him, for he is the son of a dead slave woman.'

" 'All to the good, Robin,' Sir Huon said. 'He'll be the less anxious to leave us. Oh, we'll give him a splendid fortune, and he shall act and influence on folk in housen as we have always craved.' His Lady came up then, and drew him under to watch the babe's wonderful doings."

"Who was his Lady?" said Dan.

"The Lady Esclairmonde. She had been a woman once, till she followed Sir Huon across the fern, as we say. Babies are no special treat to me—I've watched too many of them—so I stayed on the Hill. Presently I heard hammering down at the Forge there," Puck pointed toward Hobden's cottage. "It was too early for any workmen, but it passed through my mind that the breaking day was Thor's own day. A slow North-East wind blew up and set the oaks sawing and fretting in a way I remembered: so I slipped over to see what I could see."

"And what did you see?"

"A smith forging something or other out of Cold Iron. When it was finished, he weighed it in his hand (his back was toward me), and tossed it from him a longish quoit-throw down the valley. I saw Cold Iron flash in the sun, but I couldn't quite make out where it fell. *That* didn't trouble me. I knew it would be found sooner or later by some one."

"How did you know?" Dan went on.

"Because I knew the Smith that made it," said Puck quietly.

"Wayland Smith?"[1] Una suggested.

"No. I should have passed the time o' day with Wayland Smith, of course. This other was different. So"—Puck made a queer crescent in the air with his finger—"I counted the blades of grass under my nose till the wind dropped and he had gone—he and his Hammer."

"Was it Thor then?" Una murmured under her breath.

"Who else? It was Thor's own day." Puck repeated the sign. "I didn't tell Sir Huon or his Lady what I'd seen. Borrow trouble for yourself if that's your nature, but don't lend it to your neighbours. Moreover, I might have been mistaken about the Smith's work. He might have been making things for mere amusement, though it wasn't like him, or he might have thrown away an old piece of made iron. One can never be sure. So I held my tongue and enjoyed the babe. He was a wonderful child—and the People of the Hills were so set on him, they wouldn't have believed me. He took to me wonderfully. As soon as he could walk he'd putter forth with me all about my Hill here. Fern makes soft falling! He knew when day broke on earth above, for he'd thump, thump, thump, like an old buck-rabbit in a bury and I'd hear him say 'Opy!' till some one who knew the Charm let him out, and then it would be 'Robin! Robin!' all round Robin Hood's barn, as we say, till he'd found me."

"The dear!" said Una. "I'd like to have seen him!"

"Yes, he was a boy. And when it came to learning his words

[1]See "Weland's Sword" in *Puck of Pook's Hill.*

—spells and such like—he'd sit on the Hill in the long shadows, worrying out bits of charms to try on passers-by. And when the bird flew to him, or the tree bowed to him for pure love's sake (like everything else on my Hill), he'd shout, 'Robin! Look—see! Look, see, Robin!' and sputter out some spell or other that they had taught him, *all* wrong end first, till I hadn't the heart to tell him it was his own dear self and not the words that worked the wonder. When he got more abreast of his Words, and could cast spells for sure, as we say, he took more and more notice of things and people in the world. People of course, always drew him, for he was mortal all through.

"Seeing that he was free to move among folk in housen, under or over Cold Iron, I used to take him along with me night-walking, where he could watch folk, and I could keep him from touching Cold Iron. That wasn't so difficult as it sounds, because there are plenty of things besides Cold Iron in housen to catch a boy's fancy. He *was* a handful, though! I shan't forget when I took him to Little Lindens—his first night under a roof. The smell of the rushlights and the bacon on the beams—they were stuffing a feather-bed too, and it was a drizzling warm night—got into his head. Before I could stop him—we were hiding in the bakehouse—he'd whipped up a storm of wildfire, with flashlights and voices, which sent the folk shrieking into the garden, and a girl overset a hive there, and,—of course *he* didn't know till then such things could touch him—he got badly stung, and came home with his face looking like kidney-potatoes!

"You can imagine how angry Sir Huon and Lady Esclairmonde were with poor Robin! They said the Boy was never to be trusted with me night-walking any more—and he took about as much notice of their order as he did of the bee-stings. Night after night, as soon as it was dark, I'd pick up his whistle in the wet fern, and off we'd flit together among folk in housen till break of day—he asking questions, and I answering according to my knowledge. Then we fell into mischief again!" Puck laughed till the gate rattled.

"We came across a man up at Brightling who was beating his wife with a bat in the garden. I was just going to toss the man over his own woodlump when the Boy jumped the hedge, and ran at him. Of course the woman took her husband's part, and while the man beat him, the woman scratted his face. It wasn't till I danced among the cabbages like Brightling Beacon all ablaze that they gave up and ran indoors. The Boy's fine green-and-gold clothes were torn all to pieces, and he had been welted in twenty places with the man's bat, and scratted by the woman's nails *to* pieces. He looked like a Robertsbridge hopper on a Monday morning.

" 'Robin,' said he, while I was trying to clean him down with a bunch of hay, 'I don't quite understand folk in housen. I went to help that old woman, and she hit me, Robin!'

" 'What else did you expect?' I said. 'That was the one time when you might have worked some of your charms, instead of running into three times your weight.'

" 'I didn't think,' he says. 'But I caught the man one on the head that was as good as any charm. Did you see it work, Robin?'

" 'Mind your nose!' I said. 'Bleed it on a dockleaf—not your sleeve, for pity's sake.' I knew what the Lady Esclairmonde would say.

"*He* didn't care. He was as happy as a gipsy with a stolen pony, and the front part of his gold coat, all blood and grass stains, looked like ancient sacrifices.

"Of course the People of the Hills laid the blame on me. The Boy could do nothing wrong, in their eyes.

" 'You are bringing him up to act and influence on folk in housen, when you're ready to let him go,' I said. 'Now he's begun to do it, why do you cry shame on me? That's no shame. It's his nature drawing him to his kind.'

" 'But we don't want him to begin *that* way,' the Lady Esclairmonde said. 'We intend a splendid fortune for him—not your flitter-by-night, hedge-jumping, gipsy-work.'

" 'I don't blame you, Robin,' says Sir Huon, 'but I *do* think you might look after the Boy more closely.'

" 'I've kept him away from Cold Iron these sixteen years,' I said. 'You know as well as I do, the first time he touches

Cold Iron, he'll find his own fortune, in spite of everything you intend for him. You owe me something for that.'

"Sir Huon, having been a man, was going to allow me the right of it; but the Lady Esclairmonde, being the Mother of all Mothers, overpersuaded him.

" 'We're very grateful,' Sir Huon said, 'but we think that just for the present, you are about too much with him on the Hill.'

" 'Though you have said it,' I said, 'I will give you a second chance.' I did not like being called to account for my doings on my own Hill. I wouldn't have stood it even that far except I loved the Boy.

" 'No! No!' says the Lady Esclairmonde. 'He's never any trouble when he's left to me and himself. It's your fault.'

" 'You have said it,' I answered. 'Hear me! From now on till the Boy has found his fortune, whatever that may be, I vow to you all on my Hill, by Oak, and Ash, and Thorn, *and* by the Hammer of Asa Thor' "—again Puck made that curious double-cut in the air—" 'that you may leave me out of all your counts and reckonings.' Then I went out,"—he snapped his fingers—"like the puff of a candle, and though they called and cried, they made nothing by it. I didn't promise not to keep an eye on the Boy, though. I watched him close—close—close!

"When he found what his people had forced me to do, he gave them a piece of his mind, but they all kissed and cried round him, and being only a boy, he came over to their way of thinking (I don't blame him), and called himself unkind, and ungrateful; and it all ended in fresh shows and plays, and magics to distract him from folk in housen. Dear heart alive! How he used to call and call on me, and I couldn't answer, or even let him know that I was near!"

"Not even once?" said Una. "If he was very lonely?"

"No, he couldn't," said Dan, who had been thinking. "Didn't you swear by the Hammer of Thor that you wouldn't, Puck?"

"By that Hammer!" was the deep rumbled reply. Then

he came back to his soft speaking voice. "And the Boy *was* lonely, when he couldn't see me any more. He began to try to learn all learning (he had good teachers), but I saw him lift his eyes from the big black books toward folk in housen all the time. He studied song-making (good teachers he had too!), but he sung those songs with his back toward the Hill, and his face toward folk. *I* know! I have sat and grieved over him grieving within a rabbit's jump of him. Then he studied the High, Low and Middle Magic. He had promised the Lady Esclairmonde he would never go near folk in housen, so he had to make shows and shadows for his mind to chew on."

"What sort of shows?" said Dan.

"Just boy's magic, as we say. I'll show you some, some time. It pleased him for the while, and it didn't hurt any one in particular except a few men coming home late from the taverns. But I knew what it was a sign of, and I followed him like a weasel follows a rabbit. As good a boy as ever lived! I've seen him with Sir Huon and the Lady Esclairmonde stepping just as they stepped to avoid the track of Cold Iron in a furrow, or walking wide of some old ash-tot because a man had left his swop-hook or spade there; and all his heart aching to go straightforward among folk in housen all the time. Oh, a good boy! They always intended a fine fortune for him—but they could never find it in their heart to let him begin. I've heard that many warned them, but they wouldn't be warned. So it happened *as* it happened.

"One hot night I saw the Boy roving about here wrapped in his flaming discontents. There was flash on flash against the clouds, and rush on rush of shadows down the valley till the shaws were full of his hounds giving tongue, and the woodways were packed with his knights in armour riding down into the water-mists—all his own magic, of course. Behind them you could see great castles lifting slow and splendid on arches of moonshine, with maidens waving their hands at the windows, which all turned into roaring rivers; and then would come the darkness of his own young heart wiping out the whole slateful. But boy's magic doesn't trouble me—or Merlin's either for that matter. I followed the boy by the flashes and the whirling wildfire of his discontent, and oh, but I grieved for him! Oh, but I grieved for him! He pounded back and forth like a bullock in a strange pasture—sometimes alone—sometimes waist-deep among his shadow-hounds—sometimes leading his shadow-knights on a hawk-winged horse to rescue his shadow-girls. I never guessed he had such magic at his command; but it's often that way with boys.

"Just when the owl comes home for the second time, I saw Sir Huon and the Lady ride down my Hill where there's not much magic allowed except mine. They were very pleased at the Boy's magic—our valley flared with it—and I heard them settling his splendid fortune when they should find it in their hearts to let him go to act and influence among folk in housen. Sir Huon was for making him a great King somewhere or other, and the Lady was for making him a marvellous wise man whom all should praise for his skill and kindness. She was very kind-hearted.

"Of a sudden we saw the flashes of his discontent turned back on the clouds, and his shadow-hounds stopped baying.

" 'There's Magic fighting Magic over yonder,' the Lady Esclairmonde cried, reining up. 'Who is against him?'

"I could have told her, but I did not count it any of my business to speak of Asa Thor's comings and goings."

"How did you know?" said Una.

"A slow North-East wind blew up, sawing and fretting through the oaks in a way I remembered. The wildfire roared up, one last time in one sheet, and snuffed out like a rush-light, and a bucketful of stinging hail fell. We heard the Boy walking in the Long Slip—where I first met you last year.

" 'Here, oh, come here!' said the Lady Esclairmonde, and stretched out her arms in the dark.

"He was coming slowly, but he stumbled in the footpath, being, of course, mortal man.

" 'Why, what's this?' he said to himself. We three heard him.

" 'Hold, lad, hold! 'Ware Cold Iron!' said Sir Huon, and they two swept down like night-jars, crying as they rode.

"I ran at their stirrups, but it was too late. We felt that the Boy had touched Cold Iron somewhere in the dark, for the Horses of the Hill shied off, and whipped round, snorting.

"Then I judged it was time for me to show myself in my own shape; so I did.

" 'Whatever it is,' I said, 'he has taken hold of it. Now we must find out whatever it *is* that he has taken hold of: for that will be his fortune.'

" 'Come here, Robin,' the Boy shouted, as soon as he heard my voice. 'I don't know what I've hold of.'

" 'It is in your hands,' I called back. 'Tell us if it is hard and cold, with jewels atop. For that will be a King's Sceptre.'

" 'Not by a furrow-long,' he said, and stooped and tugged in the dark. We heard him.

" 'Has it a handle and two cutting edges?' I called. 'For that'll be a Knight's Sword.'

" 'No, it hasn't,' he says. 'It's neither ploughshare, whittle, hook, nor crook, nor aught I've yet seen men handle.' By this time he was scratting in the dirt to prize it up.

" 'Whatever it is, you know who put it there, Robin,' said Sir Huon to me, 'or you would not ask those questions. You should have told me as soon as you knew.'

" 'What could you or I have done against the Smith that made it and laid it for him to find?' I said, and I whispered Sir Huon what I had seen at the Forge on Thor's Day, when the babe was first brought to the Hill.

" 'Oh, good-bye, our dreams!' said Sir Huon. 'It's neither sceptre, sword nor plough! Maybe yet it's a bookful of learning, bound with iron clasps. There's a chance for a splendid fortune in that sometimes.'

"But we knew we were only speaking to comfort ourselves, and the Lady Esclairmonde, having been a woman, said so.

" 'Thur aie! Thor help us!' the Boy called. 'It is round, without end, Cold Iron, four fingers wide and a thumb thick, and there is writing on the breadth of it.'

" 'Read the writing if you have the learning,' I called. The darkness had lifted by then, and the owl was out over the fern again.

"He called back, reading the runes on the iron:—

> *"Few can see*
> *Further forth*
> *Than when the Child*
> *Meets the Cold Iron."*

and there he stood, in clear starlight, with a new, heavy, shining slave-ring round his proud neck.

" 'Is this how it goes?' he asked, while the Lady Esclairmonde cried.

" 'That is how it goes,' I said. He hadn't snapped the catch home yet, though.

" 'What fortune does it mean for him?' said Sir Huon, while the Boy fingered the ring. 'You who walk under Cold Iron, you must tell us and teach us.'

" 'Tell I can, but teach I cannot,' I said. 'The virtue of the Ring is only that he must go among folk in housen henceforward, doing what they want done, or what he knows they need, all Old England over. Never will he be his own master, nor yet ever any man's. He will get half he gives, and give twice what he gets, till his life's last breath; and if he lays aside his load before he draws that last breath, all his work will go for naught.'

" 'Oh, cruel, wicked Thor!' cried the Lady Esclairmonde. 'Ah, look, see, all of you! The catch is still open! He hasn't locked it. He can still take it off. He can still come back. Come back!' She went as near as she dared, but she could not lay hands on Cold Iron. The Boy could have taken it off, yes. We waited to see if he would, but he put up his hand, and the snap locked home.

" 'What else could I have done?' said he.

" 'Surely, then, you will do,' I said. 'Morning's coming, and if you three have any farewells to make, make them now, for after sunrise, Cold Iron must be your master.'

"So they three sat down, cheek by wet cheek, telling over

their farewells till morning light. As good a boy as ever lived, he was."

"And what happened to him?" asked Dan.

"When morning came, Cold Iron was master of him and his fortune, and he went to work among folk in housen. Presently he came across a maid like-minded with himself, and they were wedded, and had bushels of children, as the saying is. Perhaps you'll meet some of his breed, this year."

"Thank you," said Una. "But what did the poor Lady Esclairmonde do?"

"What *can* you do when Asa Thor lays the Cold Iron in a lad's path? She and Sir Huon were comforted to think they had given the Boy good store of learning to act and influence on folk in housen. For he *was* a good boy! Isn't it getting on for breakfast time? I'll walk with you a piece."

When they were well in the centre of the bone-dry fern, Dan nudged Una, who stopped and put on a boot as quickly as she could.

"Now," she said, "you can't get any Oak, Ash, and Thorn leaves from here, and"—she balanced wildly on one leg—"I'm standing on Cold Iron. What'll you do if we don't go away?"

"E-eh? Of all mortal impudence!" said Puck, as Dan, also in one boot, grabbed his sister's hand to steady himself. He walked round them, shaking with delight. "You think I can only work with a handful of dead leaves? This comes of taking away your Doubt and Fear! I'll show you!"

. . . .

A minute later they charged into old Hobden at his simple breakfast of cold roast pheasant, shouting that there was a wasps' nest in the fern which they had nearly stepped on, and asking him to come and smoke it out.

"It's too early for wops-nestes, an' I don't go diggin' in the Hill, not for shillin's," said the old man placidly. "You've a thorn in your foot, Miss Una. Sit down, and put on your t'other boot. You're too old to be caperin' barefoot on a empty stomach. Stay it with this chicken o' mine."

IF—
1910

IF YOU can keep your head when all about you
Are losing theirs and blaming it on you,
If you can trust yourself when all men doubt you,
But make allowance for their doubting too;
If you can wait and not be tired by waiting,
Or being lied about, don't deal in lies,
Or being hated don't give way to hating,
And yet don't look too good, nor talk too wise:

If you can dream—and not make dreams your master;
If you can think—and not make thoughts your aim;
If you can meet with Triumph and Disaster
And treat those two impostors just the same;
If you can bear to hear the truth you've spoken
Twisted by knaves to make a trap for fools,
Or watch the things you gave your life to, broken,
And stoop and build 'em up with worn-out tools:

If you can make one heap of all your winnings
And risk it on one turn of pitch-and-toss,
And lose, and start again at your beginnings
And never breathe a word about your loss;
If you can force your heart and nerve and sinew
To serve your turn long after they are gone,
And so hold on when there is nothing in you
Except the Will which says to them: "Hold on!"

If you can talk with crowds and keep your virtue,
  Or walk with Kings—nor lose the common touch,
If neither foes nor loving friends can hurt you,
  If all men count with you, but none too much;
If you can fill the unforgiving minute
  With sixty seconds' worth of distance run,
Yours is the Earth and everything that's in it,
  And—which is more—you'll be a Man, my son!

THE MOTHER HIVE

1908

IF THE stock had not been old and overcrowded, the Wax-moth would never have entered; but where bees are too thick on the comb there must be sickness or parasites. The heat of the hive had risen with the June honey-flow, and though the fanners worked, until their wings ached, to keep people cool, everybody suffered.

A young bee crawled up the greasy trampled alighting-board. "Excuse me," she began, "but it's my first honey-flight. Could you kindly tell me if this is my——"

"——own hive?" the Guard snapped. "Yes! Buzz in, and be foul-brooded to you! Next!"

"Shame!" cried half a dozen old workers with worn wings and nerves, and there was a scuffle and a hum.

The little grey Wax-moth, pressed close in a crack in the alighting-board, had waited this chance all day. She scuttled in like a ghost, and, knowing the senior bees would turn her out at once, dodged into a brood-frame, where youngsters who had not yet seen the winds blow or the flowers nod discussed life. Here she was safe, for young bees will tolerate any sort of stranger. Behind her came the bee who had been slanged by the Guard.

"What is the world like, Melissa?" said a companion.

"Cruel! I brought in a full load of first-class stuff, and the Guard told me to go and be foul-brooded!" She sat down in the cool draught across the combs.

"If you'd only heard," said the Wax-moth silkily, "the insolence of the Guard's tone when she cursed our sister. It aroused the Entire Community." She laid an egg. She had stolen in for that purpose.

"There *was* a bit of a fuss on the Gate," Melissa chuckled. "You were there, Miss——?" She did not know how to address the slim stranger.

"Don't call me 'Miss.' I'm a sister to all in affliction—just a working-sister. My heart bled for you beneath your burden." The Wax-moth caressed Melissa with her soft feelers and laid another egg.

"You mustn't lay here," cried Melissa. "You aren't a Queen."

"My dear child, I give you my most solemn word of honour those aren't eggs. Those are my principles, and I am ready to die for them." She raised her voice a little above the rustle and tramp round her. "If you'd like to kill me, pray do."

"Don't be unkind, Melissa," said a young bee, impressed by the chaste folds of the Wax-moth's wing, which hid her ceaseless egg-dropping.

"*I* haven't done anything," Melissa answered. "She's doing it all."

"Ah, don't let your conscience reproach you later, but when you've killed me, write me, at least, as one that loved her fellow-workers."

Laying at every sob, the Wax-moth backed into a crowd of young bees, and left Melissa bewildered and annoyed. So she lifted up her little voice in the darkness and cried, "Stores!" till a gang of cell-fillers hailed her, and she left her load with them.

"I'm afraid I foul-brooded you just now," said a voice over her shoulder. "I'd been on the Gate for three hours, and one would foul-brood the Queen herself after that. No offence meant."

"None taken," Melissa answered cheerily. "I shall be on Guard myself, some day. What's next to do?"

"There's a rumour of Death's Head Moths about. Send a gang of youngsters to the Gate, and tell them to narrow it in with a couple of stout scrap-wax pillars. It'll make the Hive hot, but we can't have Death's Headers in the middle of our honey-flow."

"My Only Wings! I should think not!" Melissa had all a

sound bee's hereditary hatred against the big, squeaking, feathery Thief of the Hives. "Tumble out!" she called across the youngsters' quarters. "All you who aren't feeding babies, show a leg. Scrap-wax pillars for the Ga-ate!" She chanted the order at length.

"That's nonsense," a downy, day-old bee answered. "In the first place, I never heard of a Death's Header coming into a hive. People don't *do* such things. In the second, building pillars to keep 'em out is purely a Cypriote trick, unworthy of British bees. In the third, if you trust a Death's Head, he will trust you. Pillar-building shows lack of confidence. Our dear sister in grey says so."

"Yes. Pillars are un-English and provocative, and a waste of wax that is needed for higher and more practical ends," said the Wax-moth from an empty store-cell.

"The safety of the Hive is the highest thing I've ever heard of. You mustn't teach us to refuse work," Melissa began.

"You misunderstand me, as usual, love. Work's the essence of life; but to expend precious unreturning vitality and real labour against imaginary danger, *that* is heartbreakingly absurd! If I can only teach a—a little toleration—a little ordinary kindness here toward that absurd old bogey you call the Death's Header, I shan't have lived in vain."

"She *hasn't* lived in vain, the darling!" cried twenty bees together. "You should see her saintly life, Melissa! She just devotes herself to spreading her principles, and—and—she looks lovely!"

An old, baldish bee came up the comb.

"Pillar-workers for the Gate! Get out and chew scraps. Buzz off!" she said. The Wax-moth slipped aside.

The young bees trooped down the frame, whispering.

"What's the matter with 'em?" said the oldster. "Why do they call each other 'ducky' and 'darling'? 'Must be the weather." She sniffed suspiciously. "Horrid stuffy smell here. Like stale quilts. Not Wax-moth, I hope, Melissa?"

"Not to my knowledge," said Melissa, who, of course, only knew the Wax-moth as a lady with principles, and had never thought to report her presence. She had always imagined Wax-moths to be like blood-red dragon-flies.

"You had better fan out this corner for a little," said the old bee and passed on. Melissa dropped her head at once, took firm hold with her fore-feet, and fanned obediently at the regulation stroke—three hundred beats to the second. Fanning tries a bee's temper, because she must always keep in the same place where she never seems to be doing any good, and, all the while, she is wearing out her only wings. When a bee cannot fly, a bee must not live; and a bee knows it. The Wax-moth crept forth, and caressed Melissa again.

"I see," she murmured, "that at heart you are one of Us."

"I work with the Hive," Melissa answered briefly.

"It's the same thing. We and the Hive are one."

"Then why are your feelers different from ours? Don't cuddle so."

"Don't be provincial, *carissima*. You can't have all the world alike—yet."

"But why do you lay eggs?" Melissa insisted. "You lay 'em like a Queen—only you drop them in patches all over the place. I've watched you."

"Ah, Brighteyes, so you've pierced my little subterfuge? Yes, they are eggs. By and by they'll spread our principles. Aren't you glad?"

"You gave me your most solemn word of honour that they were not eggs."

"That was my little subterfuge, dearest—for the sake of the Cause. Now I must reach the young." The Wax-moth tripped towards the fourth brood-frame where the young bees were busy feeding the babies.

It takes some time for a sound bee to realize a malignant and continuous lie. "She's very sweet and feathery," was all that Melissa thought, "but her talk sounds like ivy honey tastes. I'd better get to my field-work again."

She found the Gate in a sulky uproar. The youngsters told off to the pillars had refused to chew scrap-wax because it made their jaws ache, and were clamouring for virgin stuff.

"Anything to finish the job!" said the badgered Guards.

"Hang up, some of you, and make wax for these slack-jawed sisters."

Before a bee can make wax she must fill herself with honey. Then she climbs to safe foothold and hangs, while other gorged bees hang on to her in a cluster. There they wait in silence till the wax comes. The scales are either taken out of the maker's pockets by the workers, or tinkle down on the workers while they wait. The workers chew them (they are useless unchewed) into the all-supporting, all-embracing Wax of the Hive.

But now, no sooner was the wax-cluster in position than the workers below broke out again.

"Come down!" they cried. "Come down and work! Come on, you Levantine parasites! Don't think to enjoy yourselves up there while we're sweating down here!"

The cluster shivered, as from hooked fore-foot to hooked hind-foot it telegraphed uneasiness. At last a worker sprang up, grabbed the lowest wax-maker, and swung, kicking above her companions.

"I can make wax too!" she bawled. "Give me a full gorge and I'll make tons of it."

"Make it, then," said the bee she had grappled. The spoken word snapped the current through the cluster. It shook and glistened like a cat's fur in the dark. "Unhook!" it murmured. "No wax for any one to-day."

"You lazy thieves! Hang up at once and produce our wax," said the bees below.

"Impossible! The sweat's gone. To make your wax we must have stillness, warmth, and food. Unhook! Unhook!"

They broke up as they murmured, and disappeared among the other bees, from whom, of course, they were undistinguishable.

"Seems as if we'd have to chew scrap-wax for these pillars, after all," said a worker.

"Not by a whole comb," cried the young bee who had broken the cluster. "Listen here! I've studied the question more than twenty minutes. It's as simple as falling off a daisy. You've heard of Cheshire, Root and Langstroth?"

They had not, but they shouted "Good old Langstroth!" just the same.

"Those three know all that there is to be known about making hives. One or t'other of 'em must have made ours, and if they've made it, they're bound to look after it. Ours is a 'Guaranteed Patent Hive.' You can see it on the label behind."

"Good old guarantee! Hurrah for the label behind!" roared the bees.

"Well, such being the case, *I* say that when we find they've betrayed us, we can exact from them a terrible vengeance."

"Good old vengeance! Good old Root! 'Nuff said! Chuck it!" The crowd cheered and broke away as Melissa dived through.

"D'you know where Langstroth, Root and Cheshire live if you happen to want 'em?" she asked of the proud and panting orator.

"Gum me if I know they ever lived at all! But aren't they beautiful names to buzz about? Did you see how it worked up the sisterhood?"

"Yes; but it didn't defend the Gate," she replied.

"Ah, perhaps that's true, but think how delicate *my* position is, sister. I've a magnificent appetite, and I don't like working. It's bad for the mind. My instinct tells me that I can act as a restraining influence on others. They would have been worse, but for me."

But Melissa had already risen clear, and was heading for a breadth of virgin white clover, which to an overtired bee is as soothing as plain knitting to a woman.

"I think I'll take this load to the nurseries," she said, when she had finished. "It was always quiet there in my day," and she topped off with two little pats of pollen for the babies.

She was met on the fourth brood-comb by a rush of excited sisters all buzzing together.

"One at a time! Let me put down my load. Now, what is it, Sacharissa?" she said.

"Grey Sister—that fluffy one, I mean—she came and said we ought to be out in the sunshine gathering honey, because life was short. She said any old bee could attend to our babies, and some day old bees would. That isn't true, Melissa, is it? No old bees can take us away from our babies, can they?"

"Of course not. You feed the babies while your heads are soft. When your heads harden, you go on to field-work. Any one knows that."

"We told her so! We *told* her so; but she only waved her feelers, and said we could all lay eggs like Queens if we chose. And I'm afraid lots of the weaker sisters believe her, and are trying to do it. *So* unsettling!"

Sacharissa sped to a sealed worker-cell whose lid pulsated, as the bee within began to cut its way out.

"Come along, precious!" she murmured, and thinned the frail top from the other side. A pale, damp creased thing hoisted itself feebly on to the comb. Sacharissa's note changed at once. "No time to waste! Go up the frame and preen yourself!" she said. "Report for nursing-duty in my ward tomorrow evening at six. Stop a minute. What's the matter with your third right leg?"

The young bee held it out in silence—unmistakably a drone leg incapable of packing pollen.

"Thank you. You needn't report till the day after tomorrow." Sacharissa turned to her companion. "That's the fifth oddity hatched in my ward since noon. I don't like it."

"There's always a certain number of 'em," said Melissa. "You can't stop a few working sisters from laying, now and then, when they overfeed themselves. They only raise dwarf drones."

"But we're hatching out drones with workers' stomachs; workers with drones' stomachs; and albinoes and mixed-leggers who can't pack pollen—like that poor little beast yonder. I don't mind dwarf drones any more than you do (they all die in July), but this steady hatch of oddities frightens me, Melissa!"

"How narrow of you! They are all so delightfully clever and unusual and interesting," piped the Wax-moth from a crack above them. "Come here, you dear, downy duck, and tell us all about your feelings."

"I wish she'd go!" Sacharissa lowered her voice. "She meets these—er—oddities as they dry out, and cuddles 'em in corners."

"I suppose the truth is that we're over-stocked and too well fed to swarm," said Melissa.

"That *is* the truth," said the Queen's voice behind them. They had not heard the heavy royal footfall which sets empty cells vibrating. Sacharissa offered her food at once. She ate and dragged her weary body forward. "Can you suggest a remedy?" she said.

"New principles!" cried the Wax-moth from her crevice. "We'll apply them quietly—later."

"Suppose we sent out a swarm?" Melissa suggested. "It's a little late, but it might ease us off."

"It would save us, but—I know the Hive! You shall see for yourself." The old Queen cried the Swarming Cry, which to a bee of good blood should be what the trumpet was to Job's war-horse. In spite of her immense age (three years), it rang between the cañon-like frames as a pibroch rings in a mountain pass; the fanners changed their note, and repeated it up in every gallery; and the broad-winged drones, burly and eager, ended it on one nerve-thrilling outbreak of bugles: *"La Reine le veult! Swarm! Swar-rm! Swar-r-rm!"*

But the roar which should follow the Call was wanting. They heard a broken grumble like the murmur of a falling tide.

"Swarm? What for? Catch me leaving a good bar-frame Hive, with fixed foundations, for a rotten old oak out in the open where it may rain any minute! *We're* all right! It's a 'Patent Guaranteed Hive.' Why do they want to turn us out? Swarming be gummed! Swarming was invented to cheat a worker out of her proper comforts. Come on off to bed!"

The noise died out as the bees settled in empty cells for the night.

"You hear?" said the Queen. "I know the Hive!"

"Quite between ourselves, *I* taught them that," cried the

Wax-moth. "Wait till my principles develop, and you'll see the light from a new quarter."

"You speak truth for once," the Queen said suddenly, for she recognized the Wax-moth. "That Light will break into the top of the Hive. A Hot Smoke will follow it, and your children will not be able to hide in any crevice."

"Is it possible?" Melissa whispered. "I—we have sometimes heard a legend like it."

"It is no legend," the old Queen answered. "I had it from my mother, and she had it from hers. After the Wax-moth has grown strong, a Shadow will fall across the gate; a Voice will speak from behind a Veil; there will be Light, and Hot Smoke, and earthquakes, and those who live will see everything that they have done, all together in one place, burned up in one great fire." The old Queen was trying to tell what she had been told of the Bee Master's dealings with an infected hive in the apiary, two or three seasons ago; and, of course, from her point of view the affair was as important as the Day of Judgment.

"And then?" asked horrified Sacharissa.

"Then, I have heard that a little light will burn in a great darkness, and perhaps the world will begin again. Myself, I think not."

"Tut! Tut!" the Wax-moth cried. "You good, fat people always prophesy ruin if things don't go exactly your way. But I grant you there will be changes."

There were. When her eggs hatched, the wax was riddled with little tunnels, coated with the dirty clothes of the caterpillars. Flannelly lines ran through the honey-stores, the pollen-larders, the foundations, and, worst of all, through the babies in their cradles, till the Sweeper Guards spent half their time tossing out useless little corpses. The lines ended in a maze of sticky webbing on the face of the comb. The caterpillars could not stop spinning as they walked, and as they walked everywhere, they smarmed and garmed everything. Even where it did not hamper the bees' feet, the stale, sour smell of the stuff put them off their work; though some of the bees who had taken to egg-laying said it encouraged them to be mothers and maintain a vital interest in life.

When the caterpillars became moths, they made friends with the ever-increasing Oddities—albinoes, mixed-leggers, single-eyed composites, faceless drones, half-queens and laying sisters; and the ever-dwindling band of the old stock worked themselves bald and fray-winged to feed their queer charges. Most of the Oddities would not, and many, on account of their malformations, could not, go through a day's field-work; but the Wax-moths, who were always busy on the brood-comb, found pleasant home occupations for them. One albino, for instance, divided the number of pounds of honey in stock by the number of bees in the Hive, and proved that if every bee only gathered honey for seven and three quarter minutes a day, she would have the rest of the time to herself, and could accompany the drones on their mating flights. The drones were not at all pleased.

Another, an eyeless drone with no feelers, said that all brood-cells should be perfect circles, so as not to interfere with the grub or the workers. He proved that the old six-sided cell was solely due to the workers building against each other on opposite sides of the wall, and that if there were no interference, there would be no angles. Some bees tried the new plan for a while, and found it cost eight times more wax than the old six-sided specification; and, as they never allowed a cluster to hang up and make wax in peace, real wax was scarce. However, they eked out their task with varnish stolen from new coffins at funerals, and it made them rather sick. Then they took to cadging round sugar-factories and breweries, because it was easiest to get their material from those places, and the mixture of glucose and beer naturally fermented in store and blew the store-cells out of shape, besides smelling abominably. Some of the sound bees warned them that ill-gotten gains never prosper, but the Oddities at once surrounded them and balled them to death. That was a punishment they were almost as fond of as they were of eating, and they expected the sound bees to feed them. Curiously enough the age-old instinct of loyalty and devotion towards the Hive made the sound bees do this, though their reason told them they ought to slip away and unite with some other healthy stock in the apiary.

"What about seven and three-quarter minutes' work now?" said Melissa one day as she came in. "I've been at it for five hours, and I've only half a load."

"Oh, the Hive subsists on the Hival Honey which the Hive produces," said a blind Oddity squatting in a store-cell.

"But honey is gathered from flowers outside—two miles away sometimes," cried Melissa.

"Pardon me," said the blind thing, sucking hard. "But this is the Hive, is it not?"

"It was. Worse luck, it is."

"And the Hival Honey is here, is it not?" It opened a fresh store-cell to prove it.

"Ye-es, but it won't be long at this rate," said Melissa.

"The rates have nothing to do with it. This Hive produces the Hival Honey. You people never seem to grasp the economic simplicity that underlies all life."

"Oh, me!" said poor Melissa, "haven't you ever been beyond the Gate?"

"Certainly not. A fool's eyes are in the ends of the earth. Mine are in my head." It gorged till it bloated.

Melissa took refuge in her poorly paid field-work and told Sacharissa the story.

"Hut!" said that wise bee, fretting with an old maid of a thistle. "Tell us something new. The Hive's full of such as him—it, I mean."

"What's the end to be? All the honey going out and none coming in. Things *can't* last this way!" said Melissa.

"Who cares?" said Sacharissa. "I know now how drones feel the day before they're killed. A short life and a merry one for me."

"If it only were merry! But think of those awful, solemn, lop-sided Oddities waiting for us at home—crawling and clambering and preaching—and dirtying things in the dark."

"I don't mind that so much as their silly songs, after we've fed 'em, all about 'work among the merry, merry blossoms,' " said Sacharissa from the deeps of a stale Canterbury bell.

"I do. How's our Queen?" said Melissa.

"Cheerfully hopeless, as usual. But she lays an egg now and then."

"Does she so?" Melissa backed out of the next bell with a jerk. "Suppose now, we sound workers tried to raise a Princess in some clean corner?"

"You'd be put to it to find one. The Hive's all Wax-moth and muckings. But—well?"

"A Princess might help us in the time of the Voice behind the Veil that the Queen talks of. And anything is better than working for Oddities that chirrup about work that they can't do, and waste what we bring home."

"Who cares?" said Sacharissa. "I'm with you, for the fun of it. The Oddities would ball us to death, if they knew. Come home, and we'll begin."

. . . .

There is no room to tell how the experienced Melissa found a far-off frame so messed and mishandled by abandoned cell-building experiments that, for very shame, the bees never went there. How in that ruin she blocked out a Royal Cell of sound wax, but disguised by rubbish till it looked like a kopje among deserted kopjes. How she prevailed upon the hopeless Queen to make one last effort and lay a worthy egg. How the Queen obeyed and died. How her spent carcass was flung out on the rubbish heap, and how a multitude of laying sisters went about dropping drone-eggs where they listed, and said there was no more need of Queens. How, covered by this confusion, Sacharissa educated certain young bees to educate certain new-born bees in the almost lost art of making Royal Jelly. How the nectar for it was won out of hours in the teeth of chill winds. How the hidden egg hatched true—no drone, but Blood Royal. How it was capped, and how desperately they worked to feed and double-feed the now swarming Oddities, lest any break in the food-supplies should set them to instituting inquiries, which, with songs about work, was their favourite amusement. How in an auspicious hour, on a moonless night, the Princess came forth—a Princess indeed, and how Melissa smuggled her into a dark empty honey-magazine, to bide her time; and how the drones, knowing she was there, went about singing the deep disreputable love-songs of the old days—to the scandal of the laying sisters, who do not think well of drones. These things are written in the Book of Queens, which is laid up in the hollow of the Great Ash Ygdrasil.

After a few days the weather changed again and became glorious. Even the Oddities would now join the crowd that hung out on the alighting-board, and would sing of work among the merry, merry blossoms till an untrained ear might have received it for the hum of a working hive. Yet, in truth, their store-honey had been eaten long ago. They lived from day to day on the efforts of the few sound bees, while the Wax-moth fretted and consumed again their already ruined wax. But the sound bees never mentioned these matters. They knew, if they did, the Oddities would hold a meeting and ball them to death.

"Now you see what we have done," said the Wax-moths. "We have created New Material, a New Convention, a New Type, as we said we would."

"And new possibilities for us," said the laying sisters gratefully. "You have given us a new life's work, vital and paramount."

"More than that," chanted the Oddities in the sunshine; "you have created a new heaven and a new earth. Heaven, cloudless and accessible" (it was a perfect August evening) "and Earth teeming with the merry, merry blossoms, waiting only our honest toil to turn them all to good. The—er—Aster, and the Crocus, and the—er—Ladies' Smock in her season, the Chrysanthemum after her kind, and the Guelder Rose bringing forth abundantly withal."

"Oh, Holy Hymettus!" said Melissa, awestruck. "I knew they didn't know how honey was made, but they've forgotten the Order of the Flowers! What will become of them?"

A Shadow fell across the alighting-board as the Bee Master and his son came by. The Oddities crawled in and a Voice behind a Veil said: "I've neglected the old Hive too long. Give me the smoker."

Melissa heard and darted through the gate. "Come, oh come!" she cried. "It is the destruction the Old Queen foretold. Princess, come!"

"Really, you are too archaic for words," said an Oddity in an alley-way. "A cloud, I admit, may have crossed the sun; but why hysterics? Above all, why Princesses so late in the day? Are you aware it's the Hival Tea-time? Let's sing grace."

Melissa clawed past him with all six legs. Sacharissa had run to what was left of the fertile brood-comb. "Down and out!" she called across the brown breadth of it. "Nurses, guards, fanners, sweepers—out! Never mind the babies. They're better dead. Out, before the Light and the Hot Smoke!"

The Princess's first clear fearless call (Melissa had found her) rose and drummed through all the frames. *"La Reine le veult! Swarm! Swar-rm! Swar-r-rm!"*

The Hive shook beneath the shattering thunder of a stuck-down quilt being torn back.

"Don't be alarmed, dears," said the Wax-moths. "That's our work. Look up, and you'll see the dawn of the New Day."

Light broke in the top of the hive as the Queen had prophesied—naked light on the boiling, bewildered bees.

Sacharissa rounded up her rearguard, which dropped headlong off the frame, and joined the Princess's detachment thrusting toward the Gate. Now panic was in full blast, and each sound bee found herself embraced by at least three Oddities. The first instinct of a frightened bee is to break into the stores and gorge herself with honey; but there were no stores left, so the Oddities fought the sound bees.

"You must feed us, or we shall die!" they cried, holding and clutching and slipping, while the silent scared earwigs and little spiders twisted between their legs. "Think of the Hive, traitors! The Holy Hive!"

"You should have thought before!" cried the sound bees. "Stay and see the dawn of your New Day."

They reached the Gate at last over the soft bodies of many to whom they had ministered.

"On! Out! Up!" roared Melissa in the Princess's ear. "For the Hive's sake! To the Old Oak!"

The Princess left the alighting-board, circled once, flung herself at the lowest branch of the Old Oak, and her little loyal swarm—you could have covered it with a pint mug—followed, hooked, and hung.

"Hold close!" Melissa gasped. "The old legends have come true! Look!"

The Hive was half hidden by smoke, and Figures moved through the smoke. They heard a frame crack stickily, saw it heaved high and twirled round between enormous hands—a blotched, bulged, and perished horror of grey wax, corrupt brood, and small drone-cells, all covered with crawling Oddities, strange to the sun.

"Why, this isn't a hive! This is a museum of curiosities," said the Voice behind the Veil. It was only the Bee Master talking to his son.

"Can you blame 'em, father?" said a second voice. "It's rotten with Wax-moth. See here!"

Another frame came up. A finger poked through it, and it broke away in rustling flakes of ashy rottenness.

"Number Four Frame! That was your mother's pet comb once," whispered Melissa to the Princess. "Many's the good egg I've watched her lay there."

"Aren't you confusing *post hoc* with *propter hoc?*" said the Bee Master. "Wax-moth only succeed when weak bees let them in." A third frame crackled and rose into the light. "All this is full of laying workers' brood. That never happens till the stock's weakened. Phew!"

He beat it on his knee like a tambourine, and it also crumbled to pieces.

The little swarm shivered as they watched the dwarf drone-grubs squirm feebly on the grass. Many sound bees had nursed on that frame, well knowing their work was useless; but the actual sight of even useless work destroyed disheartens a good worker.

"No, they have some recuperative power left," said the second voice. "Here's a Queen cell!"

"But it's tucked away among—— What on earth *has* come to the little wretches? They seem to have lost the instinct of cell-building." The father held up the frame where the bees had experimented in circular cell-work. It looked like the pitted head of a decaying toadstool.

"Not altogether," the son corrected. "There's one line, at least, of perfectly good cells."

"My work," said Sacharissa to herself. "I'm glad Man does me justice before——"

That frame, too, was smashed out and thrown atop of the others and the foul earwiggy quilts.

As frame after frame followed it, the swarm beheld the upheaval, exposure, and destruction of all that had been well or ill done in every cranny of their Hive for generations past. There was black comb so old that they had forgotten where it hung; orange, buff, and ochre-varnished store-comb, built as bees were used to build before the days of artificial foundations; and there was a little, white, frail new work. There were sheets on sheets of level, even brood-comb that had held in its time unnumbered thousands of unnamed workers; patches of obsolete drone-comb, broad and high-shouldered, showing to what marks the male grub was expected to grow; and two-inch deep honey-magazines, empty, but still magnificent, the whole gummed and glued into twisted scrap-work, awry on the wires; half-cells, beginnings abandoned, or grandiose, weak-walled, composite cells pieced out with rubbish and capped with dirt.

Good or bad, every inch of it was so riddled by the tunnels of the Wax-moth that it broke in clouds of dust as it was flung on the heap.

"Oh, see!" cried Sacharissa. "The Great Burning that Our Queen foretold. Who can bear to look?"

A flame crawled up the pile of rubbish, and they smelt singeing wax.

The Figures stooped, lifted the Hive and shook it upside down over the pyre. A cascade of Oddities, chips of broken comb, scale, fluff, and grubs slid out, crackled, sizzled, popped a little, and then the flames roared up and consumed all that fuel.

"We must disinfect," said a Voice. "Get me a sulphur-candle, please."

The shell of the Hive was returned to its place, a light was set in its sticky emptiness, tier by tier the Figures built it up, closed the entrance, and went away. The swarm watched the light leaking through the cracks all the long night. At dawn one Wax-moth came by, fluttering impudently.

"There has been a miscalculation about the New Day, my dears," she began; "one can't expect people to be perfect all at once. That was our mistake."

"No, the mistake was entirely ours," said the Princess.

"Pardon me," said the Wax-moth. "When you think of the enormous upheaval—call it good or bad—which our influence brought about, you will admit that we, and we alone——"

"You?" said the Princess. "Our stock was not strong. So *you* came—as any other disease might have come. Hang close, all my people."

When the sun rose, Veiled Figures came down, and saw their swarm at the bough's end waiting patiently within sight of the old Hive—a handful, but prepared to go on.

THE BEES AND THE FLIES
1909

A FARMER of the Augustan age
Perused in Virgil's golden page,
The story of the secret won
From Proteus by Cyrene's son—
How the dank sea-god showed the swain
Means to restore his hives again:
More briefly, how a slaughtered bull
Breeds honey by the bellyful.

The egregious rustic put to death
A bull by stopping of its breath:
Disposed the carcass in a shed
With fragrant herbs and branches spread.
And, having thus performed the charm,
Sat down to wait the promised swarm.

Nor waited long. The God of Day
Impartial, quickening with his ray
Evil and good alike, beheld
The carcass—and the carcass swelled!
Big with new birth the belly heaves
Beneath its screen of scented leaves;
Past any doubt, the bull conceives!

The farmer bids men bring more hives
To house the profit that arrives;
Prepares on pan, and key and kettle,
Sweet music that shall make 'em settle;
But when to crown the work he goes,
Gods! What a stink salutes his nose!

Where are the honest toilers? Where
The gravid mistress of their care?
A busy scene, indeed, he sees,
But not a sign or sound of bees.
Worms of the riper grave unhid
By any kindly coffin lid,
Obscene and shameless to the light,
Seethe in insatiate appetite,
Through putrid offal; while above
The hissing blow-fly seeks his love,
Whose offspring, supping where they supt,
Consume corruption twice corrupt.

WITH THE NIGHT MAIL

1905

A STORY OF 2000 A.D.

AT NINE O'CLOCK of a gusty winter night I stood on the lower stages of one of the G. P. O. outward mail towers. My purpose was a run to Quebec in "Postal Packet 162 or such other as may be appointed"; and the Postmaster-General himself countersigned the order. This talisman opened all doors, even those in the despatching-caisson at the foot of the tower, where they were delivering the sorted Continental mail. The bags lay packed close as herrings in the long grey underbodies which our G. P. O. still calls "coaches." Five such coaches were filled as I watched, and were shot up the guides to be locked on to their waiting packets three hundred feet nearer the stars.

From the despatching-caisson I was conducted by a courteous and wonderfully learned official—Mr. L. L. Geary, Second Despatcher of the Western Route—to the Captains' Room (this wakes an echo of old romance), where the mail captains come on for their turn of duty. He introduces me to the captain of "162"—Captain Purnall, and his relief, Captain Hodgson. The one is small and dark; the other large and red; but each has the brooding sheathed glance characteristic of eagles and aeronauts. You can see it in the pictures of our racing professionals, from L. V. Rautsch to little Ada Warrleigh—that fathomless abstraction of eyes habitually turned through naked space.

On the notice-board in the Captains' Room, the pulsing arrows of some twenty indicators register, degree by geographical degree, the progress of as many homeward-bound packets. The word "Cape" rises across the face of a dial; a gong strikes: the South African mid-weekly mail is in at the

Highgate Receiving Towers. That is all. It reminds one comically of the traitorous little bell which in pigeon-fanciers' lofts notifies the return of a homer.

"Time for us to be on the move," says Captain Purnall, and we are shot up by the passenger-lift to the top of the despatch-towers. "Our coach will lock on when it is filled and the clerks are aboard." . . .

"No. 162" waits for us in Slip E of the topmost stage. The great curve of her back shines frostily under the lights, and some minute alteration of trim makes her rock a little in her holding down slips.

Captain Purnall frowns and dives inside. Hissing softly, "162" comes to rest as level as a rule. From her North Atlantic Winter nose-cap (worn bright as diamond with boring through uncounted leagues of hail, snow, and ice) to the inset of her three built-out propeller-shafts is some two hundred and forty feet. Her extreme diameter, carried well forward, is thirty-seven. Contrast this with the nine hundred by ninety-five of any crack liner, and you will realize the power that must drive a hull through all weathers at more than the emergency speed of the *Cyclonic!*

The eye detects no joint in her skin plating save the sweeping hair-crack of the bow-rudder—Magniac's rudder that assured us the dominion of the unstable air and left its inventor penniless and half-blind. It is calculated to Castelli's "gull-wing" curve. Raise a few feet of that all but invisible plate three-eighths of an inch and she will yaw five miles to port or starboard ere she is under control again. Give her full helm and she returns on her track like a whip-lash. Cant the whole forward—a touch on the wheel will suffice—and she sweeps at your good direction up or down. Open the complete circle and she presents to the air a mushroom-head that will bring her up all standing within a half mile.

"Yes," says Captain Hodgson, answering my thought, "Castelli thought he'd discovered the secret of controlling aeroplanes when he'd only found out how to steer dirigible balloons. Magniac invented his rudder to help war-boats ram each other; and war went out of fashion and Magniac he went out of his mind because he said he couldn't serve his country any more. I wonder if any of us ever know what we're really doing."

"If you want to see the coach locked you'd better go aboard. It's due now," says Mr. Geary. I enter through the door amidships. There is nothing here for display. The inner skin of the gas-tanks comes down to within a foot or two of my head and turns over just short of the turn of the bilges. Liners and yachts disguise their tanks with decoration, but the G. P. O. serves them raw under a lick of grey official paint. The inner skin shuts off fifty feet of the bow and as much of the stern, but the bow-bulkhead is recessed for the lift-shunting apparatus as the stern is pierced for the shaft-tunnels. The engine-room lies almost amidships. Forward of it, extending to the turn of the bow tanks, is an aperture—a bottomless hatch at present—into which our coach will be locked. Onc looks down over the coamings three hundred feet to the despatching-caisson whence voices boom upward. The light below is obscured to a sound of thunder, as our coach rises on its guides. It enlarges rapidly from a postage-stamp to a playing-card; to a punt and last a pontoon. The two clerks, its crew, do not even look up as it comes into place. The Quebec letters fly under their fingers and leap into the docketed racks, while both captains and Mr. Geary satisfy themselves that the coach is locked home. A clerk passes the way-bill over the hatch-coaming. Captain Purnall thumb-marks and passes it to Mr. Geary. Receipt has been given and taken. "Pleasant run," says Mr. Geary, and disappears through the door which a foot-high pneumatic compressor locks after him.

"A-ah!" sighs the compressor released. Our holding-down clips part with a tang. We are clear.

Captain Hodgson opens the great colloid underbody port-hole through which I watch over-lighted London slide east-ward as the gale gets hold of us. The first of the low winter clouds cuts off the well-known view and darkens Middlesex. On the south edge of it I can see a postal packet's light plough-ing through the white fleece. For an instant she gleams like a star ere she drops toward the Highgate Receiving Towers. "The Bombay Mail," says Captain Hodgson, and looks at his watch. "She's forty minutes late."

"What's our level?" I ask.

"Four thousand. Aren't you coming up on the bridge?"

The bridge (let us ever praise the G. P. O. as a repository of ancientest tradition!) is represented by a view of Captain Hodgson's legs where he stands on the Control Platform that runs thwart-ships overhead. The bow colloid is unshuttered and Captain Purnall, one hand on the wheel, is feeling for a fair slant. The dial shows 4300 feet.

"It's steep to-night," he mutters, as tier on tier of cloud drops under. "We generally pick up an easterly draught below three thousand at this time o' the year. I hate slathering through fluff."

"So does Van Cutsem. Look at him huntin' for a slant!" says Captain Hodgson. A fog-light breaks cloud a hundred fathoms below. The Antwerp Night Mail makes her signal and rises between two racing clouds far to port, her flanks blood-red in the glare of Sheerness Double Light. The gale will have us over the North Sea in half-an-hour, but Captain Purnall lets her go composedly—nosing to every point of the compass as she rises.

"Five thousand—six, six thousand eight hundred"—the dip-dial reads ere we find the easterly drift, heralded by a flurry of snow at the thousand fathom level. Captain Purnall rings up the engines and keys down the governor on the switch before him. There is no sense in urging machinery when Æolus himself gives you good knots for nothing. We are away in earnest now—our nose notched home on our chosen star. At this level the lower clouds are laid out, all neatly combed by the dry fingers of the East. Below that again is the strong westerly blow through which we rose. Overhead, a film of southerly drifting mist draws a theatrical gauze across the firmament. The moonlight turns the lower strata to silver without a stain except where our shadow underruns us. Bristol and Cardiff Double Lights (those statelily inclined beams over Severnmouth) are dead ahead of us; for we keep the Southern

Winter Route. Coventry Central, the pivot of the English system, stabs upward once in ten seconds its spear of diamond light to the north; and a point or two off our starboard bow The Leek, the great cloud-breaker of Saint David's Head, swings its unmistakable green beam twenty-five degrees each way. There must be half a mile of fluff over it in this weather, but it does not affect The Leek.

"Our planet's overlighted if anything," says Captain Purnall at the wheel, as Cardiff-Bristol slides under. "I remember the old days of common white verticals that 'ud show two or three hundred feet up in a mist, if you knew where to look for 'em. In really fluffy weather they might as well have been under your hat. One could get lost coming home then, an' have some fun. Now, it's like driving down Piccadilly."

He points to the pillars of light where the cloud-breakers bore through the cloud-floor. We see nothing of England's outlines: only a white pavement pierced in all directions by these manholes of variously coloured fire—Holy Island's white and red—St. Bee's interrupted white, and so on as far as the eye can reach. Blessed be Sargent, Ahrens, and the Dubois brothers, who invented the cloud-breakers of the world whereby we travel in security!

"Are you going to lift for The Shamrock?" asks Captain Hodgson. Cork Light (green, fixed) enlarges as we rush to it. Captain Purnall nods. There is heavy traffic hereabouts—the cloud-bank beneath us is streaked with running fissures of flame where the Atlantic boats are hurrying Londonward just clear of the fluff. Mail-packets are supposed, under the Conference rules, to have the five-thousand-foot lanes to themselves, but the foreigner in a hurry is apt to take liberties with English air. "No. 162" lifts to a long-drawn wail of the breeze in the fore-flange of the rudder and we make Valencia (white, green, white) at a safe 7000 feet, dipping our beam to an incoming Washington packet.

There is no cloud on the Atlantic, and faint streaks of cream round Dingle Bay show where the driven seas hammer the coast. A big S. A. T. A. liner (*Société Anonyme des Transports Aëriens*) is diving and lifting half a mile below us in search of some break in the solid west wind. Lower still lies a disabled Dane: she is telling the liner all about it in International. Our General Communication dial has caught her talk and begins to eavesdrop. Captain Hodgson makes a motion to shut it off but checks himself. "Perhaps you'd like to listen," he says.

"*Argol* of St. Thomas," the Dane whimpers. "Report owners three starboard shaft collar-bearings fused. Can make Flores as we are, but impossible further. Shall we buy spares at Fayal?"

The liner acknowledges and recommends inverting the bearings. The *Argol* answers that she has already done so without effect, and begins to relieve her mind about cheap German enamels for collar-bearings. The Frenchman assents cordially, cries "*Courage, mon ami,*" and switches off.

Their lights sink under the curve of the ocean.

"That's one of Lundt & Bleamers' boats," says Captain Hodgson. "Serves 'em right for putting German compos in their thrust-blocks. *She* won't be in Fayal to-night! By the way, wouldn't you like to look round the engine-room?"

I have been waiting eagerly for this invitation and I follow Captain Hodgson from the control-platform, stooping low to avoid the bulge of the tanks. We know that Fleury's gas can lift anything, as the world-famous trials of '89 showed, but its almost indefinite powers of expansion necessitate vast tank room. Even in this thin air the lift-shunts are busy taking out one-third of its normal lift, and still "162" must be checked by an occasional downdraw of the rudder or our flight would become a climb to the stars. Captain Purnall prefers an over-lifted to an underlifted ship; but no two captains trim ship alike. "When *I* take the bridge," says Captain Hodgson, "you'll see me shunt forty per cent. of the lift out of the gas and run her on the upper rudder. With a swoop upward instead of a swoop downward, *as* you say. Either way will do. It's only habit. Watch our dip-dial! Tim fetches her down once every thirty knots as regularly as breathing."

So is it shown on the dip-dial. For five or six minutes the arrow creeps from 6700 to 7300. There is the faint "szgee" of the rudder, and back slides the arrow to 6000 on a falling slant of ten or fifteen knots.

"In heavy weather you jockey her with the screws as well," says Captain Hodgson, and, unclipping the jointed bar which divides the engine-room from the bare deck, he leads me on to the floor.

Here we find Fleury's Paradox of the Bulk-headed Vacuum —which we accept now without thought—literally in full blast. The three engines are H. T. & T. assisted-vacuo Fleury turbines running from 3000 to the Limit—that is to say, up to the point when the blades make the air "bell"—cut out a vacuum for themselves precisely as over-driven marine propellers used to do. "162's" Limit is low on account of the small size of her nine screws, which, though handier than the old colloid Thelussons, "bell" sooner. The midships engine, generally used as a reinforce, is not running; so the port and starboard turbine vacuum-chambers draw direct into the return-mains.

The turbines whistle reflectively. From the low-arched expansion-tanks on either side the valves descend pillarwise to the turbine-chests, and thence the obedient gas whirls through the spirals of blades with a force that would whip the teeth out of a power-saw. Behind, is its own pressure held in leash or spurred on by the lift-shunts; before it, the vacuum where Fleury's Ray dances in violet-green bands and whirled turbillons of flame. The jointed U-tubes of the vacuum-chamber are pressure-tempered colloid (no glass would endure the strain for an instant) and a junior engineer with tinted spectacles watches the Ray intently. It is the very heart of the machine—a mystery to this day. Even Fleury who begat it and, unlike Magniac, died a multi-millionaire, could not explain how the restless little imp shuddering in the U-tube can, in the fractional fraction of a second, strike the furious blast of gas into a chill greyish-green liquid that drains (you can hear it trickle) from the far end of the vacuum through the eduction-pipes and the mains back to the bilges. Here it returns to its gaseous, one had almost written sagacious, state and climbs to work afresh. Bilge-tank, upper tank, dorsal-tank, expansion-chamber, vacuum, main-return (as a liquid), and bilge-tank once more is the ordained cycle. Fleury's Ray sees to that; and the engineer with the tinted spectacles sees to Fleury's Ray. If a speck of oil, if even the natural grease of the human finger touch the hooded terminals, Fleury's Ray will wink and disappear and must be laboriously built up again. This means half a day's work for all hands and an expense of one hundred and seventy-odd pounds to the G. P. O. for radium-salts and such trifles.

"Now look at our thrust-collars. You won't find much German compo there. Full-jewelled, you see," says Captain Hodgson as the engineer shunts open the top of a cap. Our shaft-bearings are C. M. C. (Commercial Minerals Company) stones, ground with as much care as the lens of a telescope. They cost £37 apiece. So far we have not arrived at their term of life. These bearings came from "No. 97," which took them over from the old *Dominion of Light* which had them out of the wreck of the *Perseus* aeroplane in the years when men still flew wooden kites over oil engines!

They are a shining reproof to all low-grade German "ruby" enamels, so-called "boort" facings, and the dangerous and unsatisfactory alumina compounds which please dividend-hunting owners and turn skippers crazy.

The rudder-gear and the gas lift-shunt, seated side by side under the engine-room dials, are the only machines in visible motion. The former sighs from time to time as the oil plunger rises and falls half an inch. The latter, cased and guarded like the U-tube aft, exhibits another Fleury Ray, but inverted and more green than violet. Its function is to shunt the lift out of the gas, and this it will do without watching. That is all! A tiny pump-rod wheezing and whining to itself beside a sputtering green lamp. A hundred and fifty feet aft down the flat-topped tunnel of the tanks a violet light, restless and irresolute. Between the two, three white-painted turbine-trunks, like eel-baskets laid on their side, accentuate the empty perspectives. You can hear the trickle of the liquefied gas flowing from the vacuum into the bilge-tanks and the soft *gluck-glock* of gas-locks closing as Captain Purnall brings "162" down by the head. The hum of the turbines and the boom of the air on our skin is no more than a cotton-wool wrapping to the universal stillness. And we are running an eighteen-second mile.

I peer from the fore end of the engine-room over the hatch-coamings into the coach. The mail-clerks are sorting the Winnipeg, Calgary, and Medicine Hat bags; but there is a pack of cards ready on the table.

Suddenly a bell thrills; the engineers run to the turbine-valves and stand by; but the spectacled slave of the Ray in the U-tube never lifts his head. He must watch where he is. We are hard-braked and going astern; there is language from the Control Platform.

"Tim's sparking badly about something," says the unruffled Captain Hodgson. "Let's look."

Captain Purnall is not the suave man we left half an hour since, but the embodied authority of the G. P. O. Ahead of us floats an ancient, aluminum-patched, twin-screw tramp of the dingiest, with no more right to the 5000-foot lane than has a horse-cart to a modern road. She carries an obsolete "barbette" conning-tower—a six-foot affair with railed platform forward—and our warning beam plays on the top of it as a policeman's lantern flashes on the area sneak. Like a sneak-thief, too, emerges a shock-headed navigator in his shirt-sleeves. Captain Purnall wrenches open the colloid to talk with him man to man. There are times when Science does not satisfy.

"What under the stars are you doing here, you sky-scraping chimney-sweep?" he shouts as we two drift side by side. "Do you know this is a Mail-lane? You call yourself a sailor, sir? You ain't fit to peddle toy balloons to an Esquimaux. Your name and number! Report and get down, and be——!"

"I've been blown up once," the shock-headed man cries, hoarsely, as a dog barking. "I don't care two flips of a contact for anything *you* can do, Postey."

"Don't you, sir? But I'll make you care. I'll have you towed stern first to Disko and broke up. You can't recover insurance if you're broke for obstruction. Do you understand *that?*"

Then the stranger bellows: "Look at my propellers! There's been a wulli-wa down below that has knocked us into umbrella-frames! We've been blown up about forty thousand feet! We're all one conjuror's watch inside! My mate's arm's broke; my engineer's head's cut open; my Ray went out when the engines smashed; and . . . and . . . for pity's sake give me my height, Captain! We doubt we're dropping."

"Six thousand eight hundred. Can you hold it?" Captain Purnall overlooks all insults, and leans half out of the colloid, staring and snuffing. The stranger leaks pungently.

"We ought to blow into St. John's with luck. We're trying to plug the fore-tank now, but she's simply whistling it away," her captain wails.

"She's sinking like a log," says Captain Purnall in an undertone. "Call up the Banks Mark Boat, George." Our dip-dial shows that we, keeping abreast the tramp, have dropped five hundred feet the last few minutes.

Captain Purnall presses a switch and our signal beam begins to swing through the night, twizzling spokes of light across infinity.

"That'll fetch something," he says, while Captain Hodgson watches the General Communicator. He has called up the North Banks Mark Boat, a few hundred miles west, and is reporting the case.

"I'll stand by you," Captain Purnall roars to the lone figure on the conning-tower.

"Is it as bad as that?" comes the answer. "She isn't insured. She's mine."

"Might have guessed as much," mutters Hodgson. "Owner's risk is the worst risk of all!"

"Can't I fetch St. John's—not even with this breeze?" the voice quavers.

"Stand by to abandon ship. Haven't you *any* lift in you, fore or aft?"

"Nothing but the midship tanks, and they're none too tight. You see, my Ray gave out and——" he coughs in the reek of the escaping gas.

"You poor devil!" This does not reach our friend. "What does the Mark Boat say, George?"

"Wants to know if there's any danger to traffic. Says she's in a bit of weather herself, and can't quit station. I've turned in a General Call, so even if they don't see our beam some one's bound to help—or else we must. Shall I clear our slings? Hold on! Here we are! A Planet liner, too! She'll be up in a tick!"

"Tell her to have her slings ready," cries his brother captain. "There won't be much time to spare . . . Tie up your mate," he roars to the tramp.

"My mate's all right. It's my engineer. He's gone crazy."

"Shunt the lift out of him with a spanner. Hurry!"

"But I can make St. John's if you'll stand by."

"You'll make the deep, wet Atlantic in twenty minutes. You're less than fifty-eight hundred now. Get your papers."

A Planet liner, east bound, heaves up in a superb spiral and takes the air of us humming. Her underbody colloid is open and her transporter-slings hang down like tentacles. We shut off our beam as she adjusts herself—steering to a hair—over the tramp's conning-tower. The mate comes up, his arm strapped to his side, and stumbles into the cradle. A man with a ghastly scarlet head follows, shouting that he must go back and build up his Ray. The mate assures him that he will find a nice new Ray all ready in the liner's engine-room. The bandaged head goes up wagging excitedly. A youth and a woman follow. The liner cheers hollowly above us, and we see the passengers' faces at the saloon colloid.

"That's a pretty girl. What's the fool waiting for now?" says Captain Purnall.

The skipper comes up, still appealing to us to stand by and see him fetch St. John's. He dives below and returns—at which we little human beings in the void cheer louder than ever—with the ship's kitten. Up fly the liner's hissing slings; her underbody crashes home and she hurtles away again. The dial shows less than 3000 feet.

The Mark Boat signals we must attend to the derelict, now

whistling her death-song, as she falls beneath us in long sick zigzags.

"Keep our beam on her and send out a General Warning," says Captain Purnall, following her down.

There is no need. Not a liner in air but knows the meaning of that vertical beam and gives us and our quarry a wide berth.

"But she'll drown in the water, won't she?" I ask.

"Not always," is his answer. "I've known a derelict up-end and sift her engines out of herself and flicker round the Lower Lanes for three weeks on her forward tanks only. We'll run no risks. Pith her, George, and look sharp. There's weather ahead."

Captain Hodgson opens the underbody colloid, swings the heavy pithing-iron out of its rack which in liners is generally cased as a smoking-room settee, and at two hundred feet releases the catch. We hear the whir of the crescent-shaped arms opening as they descend. The derelict's forehead is punched in, starred across, and rent diagonally. She falls stern first, our beam upon her; slides like a lost soul down that pitiless ladder of light, and the Atlantic takes her.

"A filthy business," says Hodgson. "I wonder what it must have been like in the old days?"

The thought had crossed my mind, too. What if that wavering carcass had been filled with the men of the old days, each one of them taught (*that* is the horror of it!) that after death he would very possibly go for ever to unspeakable torment?

And scarcely a generation ago, we (one knows now that we are only our fathers re-enlarged upon the earth), *we,* I say, ripped and rammed and pithed to admiration.

Here Tim, from the Control Platform, shouts that we are to get into our inflators and to bring him his at once.

We hurry into the heavy rubber suits—the engineers are already dressed—and inflate at the air-pump taps. G. P. O. inflators are thrice as thick as a racing man's "flickers," and chafe abominably under the armpits. George takes the wheel until Tim has blown himself up to the extreme of rotundity. If you kicked him off the c. p. to the deck he would bounce back. But it is "162" that will do the kicking.

"The Mark Boat's mad—stark ravin' crazy," he snorts, returning to command. "She says there's a bad blow-out ahead and wants me to pull over to Greenland. I'll see her pithed first! We wasted half an hour fussing over that dead duck down under, and now I'm expected to go rubbin' my back all round the Pole. What does she think a Postal packet's made of? Gummed silk? Tell her we're coming on straight, George."

George buckles him into the Frame and switches on the Direct Control. Now under Tim's left toe lies the port-engine Accelerator; under his left heel the Reverse, and so with the other foot. The lift-shunt stops stand out on the rim of the steering-wheel where the fingers of his left hand can play on them. At his right hand is the midships engine lever ready to be thrown into gear at a moment's notice. He leans forward in his belt, eyes glued to the colloid, and one ear cocked toward the General Communicator. Henceforth he is the strength and direction of "162," through whatever may befall.

The Banks Mark Boat is reeling out pages of A. B. C. Directions to the traffic at large. We are to secure all "loose objects"; hood up our Fleury Rays; and "on no account to attempt to clear snow from our conning-towers till the weather abates." Under-powered craft, we are told, can ascend to the limit of their lift, mail-packets to look out for them accordingly; the lower lanes westward are pitting very badly, "with frequent blow-outs, vortices, laterals, etc."

Still the clear dark holds up unblemished. The only warning is the electric skin-tension (I feel as though I were a lace-maker's pillow) and an irritability which the gibbering of the General Communicator increases almost to hysteria.

We have made eight thousand feet since we pithed the tramp and our turbines are giving us an honest two hundred and ten knots.

Very far to the west an elongated blur of red, low down, shows us the North Banks Mark Boat. There are specks of fire round her rising and falling—bewildered planets about an unstable sun—helpless shipping hanging on to her light for company's sake. No wonder she could not quit station.

She warns us to look out for the back-wash of the bad vortex in which (her beam shows it) she is even now reeling.

The pits of gloom about us begin to fill with very faintly luminous films—wreathing and uneasy shapes. One forms itself into a globe of pale flame that waits shivering with eagerness till we sweep by. It leaps monstrously across the blackness, alights on the precise tip of our nose, pirouettes there an instant, and swings off. Our roaring bow sinks as though that light were lead—sinks and recovers to lurch and stumble again beneath the next blow-out. Tim's fingers on the lift-shunt strike chords of numbers—1:4:7:—2:4:6:—7:5:3, and so on; for he is running by his tanks only, lifting or lowering her against the uneasy air. All three engines are at work, for the sooner we have skated over this thin ice the better. Higher we dare not go. The whole upper vault is charged with pale krypton vapours, which our skin friction may excite to unholy manifestations. Between the upper and lower levels—5000 and 7000, hints the Mark Boat—we may perhaps bolt through if . . . Our bow clothes itself in blue flame and falls like a sword. No human skill can keep pace with the changing tensions. A vortex has us by the beak and we dive down a two-thousand foot slant at an angle (the dip-dial and my bouncing body record it) of thirty-five. Our turbines scream shrilly; the propellers cannot bite on the thin air; Tim shunts the lift out of five tanks at once and by sheer weight drives her bullet-wise through the maelstrom till she cushions with a jar on an up-gust, three thousand feet below.

"*Now* we've done it," says George in my ear. "Our skin-friction, that last slide, has played Old Harry with the tensions! Look out for laterals, Tim; she'll want some holding."

"I've got her," is the answer. "Come *up,* old woman."

She comes up nobly, but the laterals buffet her left and right like the pinions of angry angels. She is jolted off her course four ways at once, and cuffed into place again, only to be swung aside and dropped into a new chaos. We are never without a corposant grinning on our bows or rolling head over heels from nose to midships, and to the crackle of electricity around and within us is added once or twice the rattle of hail—hail that will never fall on any sea. Slow we must or we may break our back, pitch-poling.

"Air's a perfectly elastic fluid," roars George above the tumult. "About as elastic as a head sea off the Fastnet, ain't it?"

He is less than just to the good element. If one intrudes on the Heavens when they are balancing their volt-accounts; if one disturbs the High Gods' market-rates by hurling steel hulls at ninety knots across tremblingly adjusted electric tensions, one must not complain of any rudeness in the reception. Tim met it with an unmoved countenance, one corner of his under lip caught up on a tooth, his eyes fleeting into the blackness twenty miles ahead, and the fierce sparks flying from his knuckles at every turn of the hand. Now and again he shook his head to clear the sweat trickling from his eyebrows, and it was then that George, watching his chance, would slide down the life-rail and swab his face quickly with a big red handkerchief. I never imagined that a human being could so continuously labour and so collectedly think as did Tim through that Hell's half-hour when the flurry was at its worst. We were dragged hither and yon by warm or frozen suctions, belched up on the tops of wulli-was, spun down by vortices and clubbed aside by laterals under a dizzying rush of stars in the company of a drunken moon. I heard the rushing click of the midship-engine-lever sliding in and out, the low growl of the lift-shunts, and, louder than the yelling winds without, the scream of the bow-rudder gouging into any lull that promised hold for an instant. At last we began to claw up on a cant, bow-rudder and port-propeller together; only the nicest balancing of tanks saved us from spinning like the rifle-bullet of the old days.

"We've got to hitch to windward of that Mark Boat somehow," George cried.

"There's no windward," I protested feebly, where I swung shackled to a stanchion. "How can there be?"

He laughed—as we pitched into a thousand foot blow-out—that red man laughed beneath his inflated hood!

"Look!" he said. "We must clear those refugees with a high lift."

The Mark Boat was below and a little to the sou'west of us, fluctuating in the centre of her distraught galaxy. The air was thick with moving lights at every level. I take it most of them were trying to lie head to wind, but, not being hydras, they failed. An under-tanked Moghrabi boat had risen to the limit of her lift, and, finding no improvement, had dropped a couple of thousand. There she met a superb wulli-wa, and was blown up spinning like a dead leaf. Instead of shutting off she went astern and, naturally, rebounded as from a wall almost into the Mark Boat, whose language (our G. C. took it in) was humanly simple.

"If they'd only ride it out quietly it 'ud be better," said George in a calm, while we climbed like a bat above them all. "But some skippers *will* navigate without enough lift. What does that Tad-boat think she is doing, Tim?"

"Playin' kiss in the ring," was Tim's unmoved reply. A Trans-Asiatic Direct liner had found a smooth and butted into it full power. But there was a vortex at the tail of that smooth, so the T. A. D. was flipped out like a pea from off a finger-nail, braking madly as she fled down and all but over-ending.

"Now I hope she's satisfied," said Tim. "I'm glad I'm not a Mark Boat . . . Do I want help?" The General Communicator dial had caught his ear. "George, you may tell that gentleman with my love—love, remember, George—that I do not want help. Who *is* the officious sardine-tin?"

"A Rimouski drogher on the look-out for a tow."

"Very kind of the Rimouski drogher. This postal packet isn't being towed at present."

"Those droghers will go anywhere on a chance of salvage," George explained. "We call 'em kittiwakes."

A long-beaked, bright steel ninety-footer floated at ease for one instant within hail of us, her slings coiled ready for rescues, and a single hand in her open tower. He was smoking. Surrendered to the insurrection of the airs through which we tore our way, he lay in absolute peace. I saw the smoke of his pipe ascend untroubled ere his boat dropped, it seemed, like a stone in a well.

We had just cleared the Mark Boat and her disorderly neighbours when the storm ended as suddenly as it had begun. A shooting-star to northward filled the sky with the green blink of a meteorite dissipating itself in our atmosphere.

Said George: "That may iron out all the tensions." Even as he spoke, the conflicting winds came to rest; the levels filled; the laterals died out in long, easy swells; the air-ways were smoothed before us. In less than three minutes the covey round the Mark Boat had shipped their power-lights and whirred away upon their businesses.

"What's happened?" I gasped. The nerve-storm within and the volt-tingle without had passed: my inflators weighed like lead.

"God, He knows!" said Captain George soberly. "That old shooting-star's skin-friction has discharged the different levels. I've seen it happen before. Phew! What a relief!"

We dropped from ten to six thousand and got rid of our clammy suits. Tim shut off and stepped out of the Frame. The Mark Boat was coming up behind us. He opened the colloid in that heavenly stillness and mopped his face.

"Hello, Williams!" he cried. "A degree or two out o' station, ain't you?"

"May be," was the answer from the Mark Boat. "I've had some company this evening."

"So I noticed. Wasn't that quite a little draught?"

"I warned you. Why didn't you pull out north? The east-bound packets have."

"Me? Not till I'm running a Polar consumptives' sanatorium boat. I was squinting through a colloid before you were out of your cradle, my son."

"I'd be the last man to deny it," the captain of the Mark Boat replies softly. "The way you handled her just now—I'm a pretty fair judge of traffic in a volt-hurry—it was a thousand revolutions beyond anything even *I*'ve ever seen."

Tim's back supples visibly to this oiling. Captain George on the c. p. winks and points to the portrait of a singularly attractive maiden pinned up on Tim's telescope bracket above the steering-wheel.

I see. Wholly and entirely do I see!

There is some talk overhead of "coming round to tea on Friday," a brief report of the derelict's fate, and Tim volunteers as he descends: "For an A. B. C. man young Williams is less of a high-tension fool than some. . . . Were you thinking of taking her on, George? Then I'll just have a look round that port-thrust—seems to me it's a trifle warm—and we'll jog along."

The Mark Boat hums off joyously and hangs herself up in her appointed eyrie. Here she will stay a shutterless observatory; a life-boat station; a salvage tug; a court of ultimate appeal-cum-meteorological bureau for three hundred miles in all directions, till Wednesday next when her relief slides across the stars to take her buffeted place. Her black hull, double conning-tower, and ever-ready slings represent all that remains to the planet of that odd old word authority. She is responsible only to the Aerial Board of Control—the A. B. C. of which Tim speaks so flippantly. But that semi-elected, semi-nominated body of a few score of persons of both sexes, controls this planet. "Transportation is Civilization," our motto runs. Theoretically, we do what we please so long as we do not interfere with the traffic *and all it implies*. Practically, the A. B. C. confirms or annuls all international arrangements and, to judge from its last report, finds our tolerant, humorous, lazy little planet only too ready to shift the whole burden of public administration on its shoulders.

I discuss this with Tim sipping maté on the c. p. while George fans her along over the white blur of the Banks in beautiful upward curves of fifty miles each. The dip-dial translates them on the tape in flowing freehand.

Tim gathers up a skein of it and surveys the last few feet, which record "162's" path through the volt-flurry.

"I haven't had a fever-chart like this to show up in five years," he says ruefully.

A postal packet's dip-dial records every yard of every run. The tapes then go to the A. B. C., which collates and makes composite photographs of them for the instruction of captains. Tim studies his irrevocable past, shaking his head.

"Hello! Here's a fifteen-hundred-foot drop at fifty-five degrees! We must have been standing on our heads then, George."

"You don't say so," George answers. "I fancied I noticed it at the time."

George may not have Captain Purnall's catlike swiftness, but he is all an artist to the tips of the broad fingers that play on the shunt-stops. The delicious flight-curves come away on the tape with never a waver. The Mark Boat's vertical spindle of light lies down to eastward, setting in the face of the following stars. Westward, where no planet should rise, the triple verticals of Trinity Bay (we keep still to the Southern route) make a low-lifting haze. We seem the only thing at rest under all the heavens; floating at ease till the earth's revolution shall turn up our landing-towers.

And minute by minute our silent clock gives us a sixteen-second mile.

"Some fine night," says Tim, "we'll be even with that clock's Master."

"He's coming now," says George, over his shoulder. "I'm chasing the night west."

The stars ahead dim no more than if a film of mist had been drawn under unobserved, but the deep air-boom on our skin changes to a joyful shout.

"The dawn-gust," says Tim. "It'll go on to meet the Sun. Look! Look! There's the dark being crammed back over our bows! Come to the after-colloid. I'll show you something."

The engine-room is hot and stuffy; the clerks in the coach are asleep, and the Slave of the Ray is ready to follow them. Tim slides open the aft colloid and reveals the curve of the world—the ocean's deepest purple—edged with fuming and intolerable gold. Then the Sun rises and through the colloid strikes out our lamps. Tim scowls in his face.

"Squirrels in a cage," he mutters. "That's all we are.

Squirrels in a cage! He's going twice as fast as us. Just you wait a few years, my shining friend, and we'll take steps that will amaze you. *We*'ll Joshua you!"

Yes, that is our dream: to turn all earth into the Vale of Ajalon at our pleasure. So far, we can drag out the dawn to twice its normal length in these latitudes. But some day—even on the Equator—we shall hold the Sun level in his full stride.

Now we look down on a sea thronged with heavy traffic. A big submersible breaks water suddenly. Another and another follows with a swash and a suck and a savage bubbling of relieved pressures. The deep-sea freighters are rising to lung up after the long night, and the leisurely ocean is all patterned with peacock's eyes of foam.

"We'll lung up, too," says Tim, and when we return to the c. p. George shuts off, the colloids are opened, and the fresh air sweeps her out. There is no hurry. The old contracts (they will be revised at the end of the year) allow twelve hours for a run which any packet can put behind her in ten. So we breakfast in the arms of an easterly slant which pushes us along at a languid twenty.

To enjoy life, and tobacco, begin both on a sunny morning half a mile or so above the dappled Atlantic cloud-belts and after a volt-flurry which has cleared and tempered your nerves. While we discussed the thickening traffic with the superiority that comes of having a high level reserved to ourselves, we heard (and I for the first time) the morning hymn on a Hospital boat.

She was cloaked by a skein of ravelled fluff beneath us and we caught the chant before she rose into the sunlight. *"Oh, ye Winds of God,"* sang the unseen voices: *"bless ye the Lord! Praise Him and magnify Him for ever!"*

We slid off our caps and joined in. When our shadow fell across her great open platforms they looked up and stretched out their hands neighbourly while they sang. We could see the doctors and the nurses and the white-button-like faces of the cot-patients. She passed slowly beneath us, heading northward, her hull, wet with the dews of the night, all ablaze in the sunshine. So took she the shadow of a cloud and vanished, her song continuing. *"Oh, ye holy and humble men of heart, bless ye the Lord! Praise Him and magnify Him for ever."*

"She's a public lunger or she wouldn't have been singing the *Benedicite;* and she's a Greenlander or she wouldn't have snow-blinds over her colloids," said George at last. "She'll be bound for Frederikshavn or one of the Glacier sanatoriums for a month. If she was an accident ward she'd be hung up at the eight-thousand-foot level. Yes—consumptives."

"Funny how the new things are the old things. I've read in books," Tim answered, "that savages used to haul their sick and wounded up to the tops of hills because microbes were fewer there. We hoist 'em into sterilized air for a while. Same idea. How much do the doctors say we've added to the average life of a man?"

"Thirty years," says George with a twinkle in his eye. "Are we going to spend 'em all up here, Tim?"

"Flap ahead, then. Flap ahead. Who's hindering?" the senior captain laughed, as we went in.

We held a good lift to clear the coastwise and Continental shipping; and we had need of it. Though our route is in no sense a populated one, there is a steady trickle of traffic this way along. We met Hudson Bay furriers out of the Great Preserve, hurrying to make their departure from Bonavista with sable and black fox for the insatiable markets. We over-crossed Keewatin liners, small and cramped; but their captains, who see no land between Trepassy and Blanco, know what gold they bring back from West Africa. Trans-Asiatic Directs we met, soberly ringing the world round the Fiftieth Meridian at an honest seventy knots; and white-painted Ackroyd & Hunt fruiters out of the south fled beneath us, their ventilated hulls whistling like Chinese kites. Their market is in the North among the northern sanatoria where you can smell their grape-fruit and bananas across the cold snows. Argentine beef boats we sighted too, of enormous capacity and unlovely outline. They, too, feed the northern health stations in ice-bound ports where submersibles dare not rise.

Yellow-bellied ore-flats and Ungava petrol-tanks punted

down leisurely out of the north, like strings of unfrightened wild duck. It does not pay to "fly" minerals and oil a mile farther than is necessary; but the risks of transhipping to submersibles in the ice-pack off Nain or Hebron are so great that these heavy freighters fly down to Halifax direct, and scent the air as they go. They are the biggest tramps aloft except the Athabasca grain-tubs. But these last, now that the wheat is moved, are busy, over the world's shoulder, timber-lifting in Siberia.

We held to the St. Lawrence (it is astonishing how the old water-ways still pull us children of the air), and followed his broad line of black between its drifting ice-blocks, all down the Park that the wisdom of our fathers—but every one knows the Quebec run.

We dropped to the Heights Receiving Towers twenty minutes ahead of time, and there hung at ease till the Yokohama Intermediate Packet could pull out and give us our proper slip. It was curious to watch the action of the holding-down clips all along the frosty river front as the boats cleared or came to rest. A big Hamburger was leaving Pont Levis and her crew, unshipping the platform railings, began to sing "Elsinore"—the oldest of our chanteys. You know it of course:

Mother Rugen's tea-house on the Baltic—
Forty couple waltzing on the floor!
And you can watch my Ray,
For I must go away
And dance with Ella Sweyn at Elsinore!

Then, while they sweated home the covering-plates

Nor-Nor-Nor-Nor-
West from Sourabaya to the Baltic—
Ninety knot an hour to the Skaw!
Mother Rugen's tea-house on the Baltic
And a dance with Ella Sweyn at Elsinore!

The clips parted with a gesture of indignant dismissal, as though Quebec, glittering under her snows, were casting out these light and unworthy lovers. Our signal came from the Heights. Tim turned and floated up, but surely then it was with passionate appeal that the great tower arms flung open—or did I think so because on the upper staging a little hooded figure also opened her arms wide toward her father?

. . . .

In ten seconds the coach with its clerks clashed down to the receiving-caisson; the hostlers displaced the engineers at the idle turbines, and Tim, prouder of this than all, introduced me to the maiden of the photograph on the shelf. "And by the way," said he to her, stepping forth in sunshine under the hat of civil life, "I saw young Williams in the Mark Boat. I've asked him to tea on Friday."

THE FOUR ANGELS

1909

As ADAM lay a-dreaming beneath the Apple Tree,
The Angel of the Earth came down, and offered Earth in fee.
But Adam did not need it,
Nor the plough he would not speed it,
Singing:—"Earth and Water, Air and Fire,
What more can mortal man desire?"
(The Apple Tree's in bud.)

As Adam lay a-dreaming beneath the Apple Tree,
The Angel of the Waters offered all the Seas in fee.
But Adam would not take 'em,
Nor the ships he wouldn't make 'em,
Singing:—"Water, Earth and Air and Fire,
What more can mortal man desire?"
(The Apple Tree's in leaf.)

As Adam lay a-dreaming beneath the Apple Tree,
The Angel of the Air he offered all the Air in fee.
But Adam did not crave it,
Nor the flight he wouldn't brave it,
Singing:—"Air and Water, Earth and Fire,
What more can mortal man desire?"
(The Apple Tree's in bloom.)

As Adam lay a-dreaming beneath the Apple Tree,
The Angel of the Fire rose up and not a word said he.
But he wished a fire and made it,
And in Adam's heart he laid it,
Singing:—"Fire, Fire, burning Fire,
Stand up and reach your heart's desire!"
(The Apple Blossom's set.)

As Adam was a-working outside of Eden-Wall,
He used the Earth, he used the Seas, he used the Air and all;
And out of black disaster
He arose to be the master
Of Earth and Water, Air and Fire,
But never reached his heart's desire!
(The Apple Tree's cut down!)

AS EASY AS A.B.C.
1912

The A.B.C., that semi-elected, semi-nominated body of a few score persons, controls the Planet. Transportation is Civilization, our motto runs. Theoretically we do what we please, so long as we do not interfere with the traffic and all it implies. *Practically, the A.B.C. confirms or annuls all international arrangements, and, to judge from its last report, finds our tolerant, humorous, lazy little Planet only too ready to shift the whole burden of public administration on its shoulders.*

—"WITH THE NIGHT MAIL."

ISN'T it almost time that our Planet took some interest in the proceedings of the Aërial Board of Control? One knows that easy communications nowadays, and lack of privacy in the past, have killed all curiosity among mankind, but as the Board's Official Reporter I am bound to tell my tale.

At 9.30 A.M., August 26, A.D. 2065, the Board, sitting in London, was informed by De Forest that the District of Northern Illinois had riotously cut itself out of all systems and would remain disconnected till the Board should take over and administer it direct.

Every Northern Illinois freight and passenger tower was, he reported, out of action; all District main, local, and guiding lights had been extinguished; all General Communications were dumb, and through traffic had been diverted. No reason had been given, but he gathered unofficially from the Mayor of Chicago that the District complained of "crowd-making and invasion of privacy."

As a matter of fact, it is of no importance whether Northern Illinois stay in or out of planetary circuit; as a matter of policy, any complaint of invasion of privacy needs immediate investigation, lest worse follow.

By 9.45 A.M. De Forest, Dragomiroff (Russia), Takahira (Japan), and Pirolo (Italy) were empowered to visit Illinois and "to take such steps as might be necessary for the resumption of traffic and *all that that implies.*" By 10 A.M. the Hall was empty, and the four Members and I were abroad what Pirolo insisted on calling "my leetle godchild"—that is to say, the new *Victor Pirolo*. Our Planet prefers to know Victor Pirolo as a gentle, grey-haired enthusiast who spends his time near Foggia, inventing or creating new breeds of Spanish-Italian olive-trees; but there is another side to his nature—the manufacture of quaint inventions, of which the *Victor Pirolo* is, perhaps, not the least surprising. She and a few score sister-craft of the same type embody his latest ideas. But she is not comfortable. An A.B.C. boat does not take the air with the level-keeled lift of a liner, but shoots up rocket-fashion like the "aeroplane" of our ancestors, and makes her height at top-speed from the first. That is why I found myself sitting suddenly on the large lap of Eustace Arnott, who commands the A.B.C. Fleet. One knows vaguely that there is such a thing as a Fleet somewhere on the Planet, and that, theoretically, it exists for the purposes of what used to be known as "war." Only a week before, while visiting a glacier sanatorium behind Gothaven, I had seen some squadrons making false auroras far to the north while they manœuvred round the Pole; but, naturally, it had never occurred to me that the things could be used in earnest.

Said Arnott to De Forest as I staggered to a seat on the chart-room divan. "We're tremendously grateful to 'em in Illinois. We've never had a chance of exercising all the Fleet together. I've turned in a General Call, and I expect we'll have at least two hundred keels aloft this evening."

"Well aloft?" De Forest asked.

"Of course, sir. Out of sight till they're called for."

Arnott laughed as he lolled over the transparent chart-table where the map of the summer-blue Atlantic slid along, degree by degree, in exact answer to our progress. Our dial already showed 320 m. p. h. and we were two thousand feet above the uppermost traffic lines.

"Now, where is this Illinois District of yours?" said Dragomiroff. "One travels so much, one sees so little. Oh, I remember! It is in North America."

De Forest, whose business it is to know the out districts, told us that it lay at the foot of Lake Michigan, on a road to nowhere in particular, was about half an hour's run from end to end, and, except in one corner, as flat as the sea. Like most flat countries nowadays, it was heavily guarded against invasion of privacy by forced timber—fifty-foot spruce and tamarack, grown in five years. The population was close on two millions, largely migratory between Florida and California, with a backbone of small farms (they call a thousand acres a farm in Illinois) whose owners come into Chicago for amusements and society during the winter. They were, he said, noticeably kind, quiet folk, but a little exacting, as all flat countries must be, in their notions of privacy. There had, for instance, been no printed news-sheet in Illinois for twenty-seven years. Chicago argued that engines for printed news sooner or later developed into engines for invasion of privacy, which in turn might bring the old terror of Crowds and blackmail back to the Planet. So news-sheets were not.

"And that's Illinois," De Forest concluded. "You see, in the Old Days, she was in the forefront of what they used to call 'progress,' and Chicago——"

"Chicago?" said Takahira. "That's the little place where there is Salati's Statue of the Nigger in Flames? A fine bit of old work."

"When did you see it?" asked De Forest quickly. "They only unveil it once a year."

"I know. At Thanksgiving. It was then," said Takahira, with a shudder. "And they sang MacDonough's Song, too."

"Whew!" De Forest whistled. "I did not know that! I wish you'd told me before. MacDonough's Song may have had its uses when it was composed, but it was an infernal legacy for any man to leave behind."

"It's protective instinct, my dear fellows," said Pirolo,

rolling a cigarette. "The Planet, she has had her dose of popular government. She suffers from inherited agoraphobia. She has no—ah—use for Crowds."

Dragomiroff leaned forward to give him a light. "Certainly," said the white-bearded Russian, "the Planet has taken all precautions against Crowds for the past hundred years. What is our total population to-day? Six hundred million, we hope; five hundred, we think; but—but if next year's census shows more than four hundred and fifty, I myself will eat all the extra little babies. We have cut the birth-rate out—right out! For a long time we have said to Almighty God, 'Thank You, Sir, but we do not much like Your game of life, so we will not play.'"

"Anyhow," said Arnott defiantly, "men live a century apiece on the average now."

"Oh, that is quite well! I am rich—you are rich—we are all rich and happy because we are so few and we live so long. Only *I* think Almighty God He will remember what the Planet was like in the time of Crowds and the Plague. Perhaps He will send us nerves. Eh, Pirolo?"

The Italian blinked into space. "Perhaps," he said, "He has sent them already. Anyhow, you cannot argue with the Planet. She does not forget the Old Days, and—what can you do?"

"For sure we can't remake the world." De Forest glanced at the map flowing smoothly across the table from west to east. "We ought to be over our ground by nine to-night. There won't be much sleep afterwards."

On which hint we dispersed, and I slept till Takahira waked me for dinner. Our ancestors thought nine hours' sleep ample for their little lives. We, living thirty years longer, feel ourselves defrauded with less than eleven out of the twenty-four.

By ten o'clock we were over Lake Michigan. The west shore was lightless, except for a dull ground-glare at Chicago, and a single traffic-directing light—its leading beam pointing north—at Waukegan on our starboard bow. None of the Lake villages gave any sign of life; and inland, westward, so far as we could see, blackness lay unbroken on the level earth.

We swooped down and skimmed low across the dark, throwing calls county by county. Now and again we picked up the faint glimmer of a house-light, or heard the rasp and rend of a cultivator being played across the fields, but Northern Illinois as a whole was one inky, apparently uninhabited, waste of high, forced woods. Only our illuminated map, with its little pointer switching from county to county as we wheeled and twisted, gave us any idea of our position. Our calls, urgent, pleading, coaxing or commanding, through the General Communicator brought no answer. Illinois strictly maintained her own privacy in the timber which she grew for that purpose.

"Oh, this is absurd!" said De Forest. "We're like an owl trying to work a wheat-field. Is this Bureau Creek? Let's land, Arnott, and get hold of some one."

We brushed over a belt of forced woodland—fifteen-year-old maple sixty feet high—grounded on a private meadow-dock, none too big, where we moored to our own grapnels, and hurried out through the warm dark night towards a light in a verandah. As we neared the garden gate I could have sworn we had stepped knee-deep in quicksand, for we could scarcely drag our feet against the prickling currents that clogged them. After five paces we stopped, wiping our foreheads, as hopelessly stuck on dry smooth turf as so many cows in a bog.

"Pest!" cried Pirolo angrily. "We are ground-circuited. And it is my own system of ground-circuits too! I know the pull."

"Good evening," said a girl's voice from the verandah. "Oh, I'm sorry! We've locked up. Wait a minute."

We heard the click of a switch, and almost fell forward as the currents round our knees were withdrawn.

The girl laughed, and laid aside her knitting. An old-fashioned Controller stood at her elbow, which she reversed from time to time, and we could hear the snort and clank of the obedient cultivator half a mile away, behind the guardian woods.

"Come in and sit down," she said. "I'm only playing a

plough. Dad's gone to Chicago to—Ah! Then it was *your* call I heard just now!"

She had caught sight of Arnott's Board uniform, leaped to the switch, and turned it full on.

We were checked, gasping, waist-deep in current this time, three yards from the verandah.

"We only want to know what's the matter with Illinois?" said De Forest placidly.

"Then hadn't you better go to Chicago and find out?" she answered. "There's nothing wrong here. We own ourselves."

"How can we go anywhere if you won't loose us?" De Forest went on, while Arnott scowled. Admirals of Fleets are still quite human when their dignity is touched.

"Stop a minute—you don't know how funny you look!" She put her hands on her hips and laughed mercilessly.

"Don't worry about that," said Arnott, and whistled. A voice answered from the *Victor Pirolo* in the meadow.

"Only a single-fuse ground-circuit!" Arnott called. "Sort it out gently, please."

We heard the ping of a breaking lamp; a fuse blew out somewhere in the verandah roof, frightening a nestful of birds. The ground-circuit was open. We stooped and rubbed our tingling ankles.

"How rude—how very rude of you!" the maiden cried.

" 'Sorry, but we haven't time to look funny," said Arnott. "We've got to go to Chicago; and if I were you, young lady, I'd go into the cellars for the next two hours, and take mother with me."

Off he strode, with us at his heels, muttering indignantly, till the humour of the thing struck and doubled him up with laughter at the foot of the gangway ladder.

"The Board hasn't shown what you might call a fat spark on this occasion," said De Forest, wiping his eyes. "I hope I didn't look as big a fool as you did, Arnott! Hullo! What on earth is that? Dad coming home from Chicago?"

There was a rattle and a rush, and a five-plough cultivator, blades in air like so many teeth, trundled itself at us round the edge of the timber, fuming and sparking furiously.

"Jump!" said Arnott, as we bundled ourselves through the none-too-wide door. "Never mind about shutting it. Up!"

The *Victor Pirolo* lifted like a bubble, and the vicious machine shot just underneath us, clawing high as it passed.

"There's a nice little spit-kitten for you!" said Arnott, dusting his knees. "We ask her a civil question. First she circuits us and then she plays a cultivator at us!"

"And then we fly," said Dragamiroff. "If I were forty years more young, I would go back and kiss her. Ho! Ho!"

"I," said Pirolo, "would smack her! My pet ship has been chased by a dirty plough; a—how do you say?—agricultural implement."

"Oh, that is Illinois all over," said De Forest. "They don't content themselves with talking about privacy. They arrange to have it. And now, where's your alleged fleet, Arnott? We must assert ourselves against this wench."

Arnott pointed to the black heavens.

"Waiting on—up there," said he. "Shall I give them the whole installation, sir?"

"Oh, I don't think the young lady is quite worth that," said De Forest. "Get over Chicago, and perhaps we'll see something."

In a few minutes we were hanging at two thousand feet over an oblong block of incandescence in the centre of the little town.

"That looks like the old City Hall. Yes, there's Salati's Statue in front of it," said Takahira. "But what on earth are they doing to the place? I thought they used it for a market nowadays! Drop a little, please."

We could hear the sputter and crackle of road-surfacing machines—the cheap Western type which fuse stone and rubbish into lava-like ribbed glass for their rough country roads. Three or four surfacers worked on each side of a square of ruins. The brick and stone wreckage crumbled, slid forward, and presently spread out into white-hot pools of sticky slag, which the levelling-rods smoothed more or less flat. Already a third of the big block had been so treated, and was cooling to dull red before our astonished eyes.

"It is the Old Market," said De Forest. "Well, there's nothing to prevent Illinois from making a road through a market. It doesn't interfere with traffic, that I can see."

"Hsh!" said Arnott, gripping me by the shoulder. "Listen! They're singing. Why on the earth are they singing?"

We dropped again till we could see the black fringe of people at the edge of that glowing square.

At first they only roared against the roar of the surfacers and levellers. Then the words came up clearly—the words of the Forbidden Song that all men knew, and none let pass their lips—poor Pat MacDonough's Song, made in the days of the Crowds and the Plague—every silly word of it loaded to sparking-point with the Planet's inherited memories of horror, panic, fear and cruelty. And Chicago—innocent, contented little Chicago—was singing it aloud to the infernal tune that carried riot, pestilence and lunacy round our Planet a few generations ago!

"Once there was The People—Terror gave it birth;
Once there was The People, and it made a hell of earth!"

(Then the stamp and pause):

"Earth arose and crushed it. Listen, oh, ye slain!
Once there was The People—it shall never be again!"

The levellers thrust in savagely against the ruins as the song renewed itself again, again and again, louder than the crash of the melting walls.

De Forest frowned.

"I don't like that," he said. "They've broken back to the Old Days! They'll be killing somebody soon. I think we'd better divert 'em, Arnott."

"Ay, ay, sir." Arnott's hand went to his cap, and we heard the hull of the *Victor Pirolo* ring to the command: "Lamps! Both watches stand by! Lamps! Lamps! Lamps!"

"Keep still!" Takahira whispered to me. "Blinkers, please, quartermaster."

"It's all right—all right!" said Pirolo from behind, and to

my horror slipped over my head some sort of rubber helmet that locked with a snap. I could feel thick colloid bosses before my eyes, but I stood in absolute darkness.

"To save the sight," he explained, and pushed me on to the chart-room divan. "You will see in a minute."

As he spoke I became aware of a thin thread of almost intolerable light, let down from heaven at an immense distance—one vertical hairsbreadth of frozen lightning.

"Those are our flanking ships," said Arnott at my elbow. "That one is over Galena. Look south—that other one's over Keithburg. Vincennes is behind us, and north yonder is Winthrop Woods. The Fleet's in position, sir"—this to De Forest. "As soon as you give the word."

"Ah no! No!" cried Dragomiroff at my side. I could feel the old man tremble. "I do not know all that you can do, but be kind! I ask you to be a little kind to them below! This is horrible—horrible!"

"When a Woman kills a Chicken,
Dynasties and Empires sicken,"

Takahira quoted. "It is too late to be gentle now."

"Then take off my helmet! Take off my helmet!" Dragomiroff began hysterically.

Pirolo must have put his arm round him.

"Hush," he said, "I am here. It is all right, Ivan, my dear fellow."

"I'll just send our little girl in Bureau County a warning," said Arnott. "She don't deserve it, but we'll allow her a minute or two to take mamma to the cellar."

In the utter hush that followed the growling spark after Arnott had linked up his Service Communicator with the invisible Fleet, we heard MacDonough's Song from the city beneath us grow fainter as we rose to position. Then I clapped my hand before my mask lenses, for it was as though the floor of Heaven had been riddled and all the inconceivable blaze of suns in the making was poured through the manholes.

"You needn't count," said Arnott. I had had no thought of

such a thing. "There are two hundred and fifty keels up there, five miles apart. Full power, please, for another twelve seconds."

The firmament, as far as eye could reach, stood on pillars of white fire. One fell on the glowing square at Chicago, and turned it black.

"Oh! Oh! Oh! Can men be allowed to do such things?" Dragomiroff cried, and fell across our knees.

"Glass of water, please," said Takahira to a helmeted shape that leaped forward. "He is a little faint."

The lights switched off, and the darkness stunned like an avalanche. We could hear Dragomiroff's teeth on the glass edge.

Pirolo was comforting him.

"All right, all ra-ight," he repeated. "Come and lie down. Come below and take off your mask. I give you my word, old friend, it is all right. They are my siege-lights. Little Victor Pirolo's leetle lights. You know *me!* I do not hurt people."

"Pardon!" Dragomiroff moaned. "I have never seen Death. I have never seen the Board take action. Shall we go down and burn them alive, or is that already done?"

"Oh, hush," said Pirolo, and I think he rocked him in his arms.

"Do we repeat, sir?" Arnott asked De Forest.

"Give 'em a minute's break," De Forest replied. "They may need it."

We waited a minute, and then MacDonough's Song, broken but defiant, rose from undefeated Chicago.

"They seem fond of that tune," said De Forest. "I should let 'em have it, Arnott."

"Very good, sir," said Arnott, and felt his way to the Communicator keys.

No lights broke forth, but the hollow of the skies made herself the mouth for one note that touched the raw fibre of the brain. Men hear such sounds in delirium, advancing like tides from horizons beyond the ruled foreshores of space.

"That's our pitch-pipe," said Arnott. "We may be a bit ragged. I've never conducted two hundred and fifty performers before." He pulled out the couplers, and struck a full chord on the Service Communicators.

The beams of light leaped down again, and danced, solemnly and awfully, a stilt-dance, sweeping thirty or forty miles left and right at each stiff-legged kick, while the darkness delivered itself—there is no scale to measure against that utterance—of the tune to which they kept time. Certain notes—one learnt to expect them with terror—cut through one's marrow, but, after three minutes, thought and emotion passed in indescribable agony.

We saw, we heard, but I think we were in some sort swooning. The two hundred and fifty beams shifted, re-formed, straddled and split, narrowed, widened, rippled in ribbons, broke into a thousand white-hot parallel lines, melted and revolved in interwoven rings like old-fashioned engine-turning, flung up to the zenith, made as if to descend and renew the torment, halted at the last instant, twizzled insanely round the horizon, and vanished, to bring back for the hundredth time darkness more shattering than their instantly renewed light over all Illinois. Then the tune and lights ceased together, and we heard one single devastating wail that shook all the horizon as a rubbed wet finger shakes the rim of a bowl.

"Ah, that is my new siren," said Pirolo. "You can break an iceberg in half, if you find the proper pitch. They will whistle by squadrons now. It is the wind through pierced shutters in the bows."

I had collapsed beside Dragomiroff, broken and snivelling feebly, because I had been delivered before my time to all the terrors of Judgment Day, and the Archangels of the Resurrection were hailing me naked across the Universe to the sound of the music of the spheres.

Then I saw De Forest smacking Arnott's helmet with his open hand. The wailing died down in a long shriek as a black shadow swooped past us, and returned to her place above the lower clouds.

"I hate to interrupt a specialist when he's enjoying himself," said De Forest. "But, as a matter of fact, all Illinois has been asking us to stop for these last fifteen seconds."

"What a pity." Arnott slipped off his mask. "I wanted you to hear us really hum. Our lower C can lift street-paving."

"It is Hell—Hell!" cried Dragomiroff, and sobbed aloud.

Arnott looked away as he answered:

"It's a few thousand volts ahead of the old shoot-'em-and-sink-'em game, but I should scarcely call it *that*. What shall I tell the Fleet, sir?"

"Tell 'em we're very pleased and impressed. I don't think they need wait on any longer. There isn't a spark left down there." De Forest pointed. "They'll be deaf and blind."

"Oh, I think not, sir. The demonstration lasted less than ten minutes."

"Marvellous!" Takahira sighed. "I should have said it was half a night. Now, shall we go down and pick up the pieces?"

"But first a small drink," said Pirolo. "The Board must not arrive weeping at its own works."

"I am an old fool—an old fool!" Dragomiroff began piteously. "I did not know what would happen. It is all new to me. We reason with them in Little Russia."

Chicago North landing-tower was unlighted, and Arnott worked his ship into the clips by her own lights. As soon as these broke out we heard groanings of horror and appeal from many people below.

"All right," shouted Arnott into the darkness. "We aren't beginning again!" We descended by the stairs, to find ourselves knee-deep in a grovelling crowd, some crying that they were blind, others beseeching us not to make any more noises, but the greater part writhing face downward, their hands or their caps before their eyes.

It was Pirolo who came to our rescue. He climbed the side of a surfacing-machine, and there, gesticulating as though they could see, made oration to those afflicted people of Illinois.

"You stchewpids!" he began. "There is nothing to fuss for. Of course, your eyes will smart and be red to-morrow. You will look as if you and your wives had drunk too much, but in a little while you will see again as well as before. I tell you this, and I—*I* am Pirolo. Victor Pirolo!"

The crowd with one accord shuddered, for many legends

attach to Victor Pirolo of Foggia, deep in the secrets of God.

"Pirolo?" An unsteady voice lifted itself. "Then tell us was there anything except light in those lights of yours just now?"

The question was repeated from every corner of the darkness.

Pirolo laughed.

"No!" he thundered. (Why have small men such large voices?) "I give you my word and the Board's word that there was nothing except light—just light! You stchewpids! Your birth-rate is too low already as it is. Some day I must invent something to send it up, but send it down—never!"

"Is that true?—We thought—somebody said——"

One could feel the tension relax all round.

"You *too* big fools," Pirolo cried. "You could have sent us a call and we would have told you."

"Send you a call!" a deep voice shouted. "I wish you had been at our end of the wire."

"I'm glad I wasn't," said De Forest. "It was bad enough from behind the lamps. Never mind! It's over now. Is there any one here I can talk business with? I'm De Forest—for the Board."

"You might begin with me, for one—I'm Mayor," the bass voice replied.

A big man rose unsteadily from the street, and staggered towards us where we sat on the broad turf-edging, in front of the garden fences.

"I ought to be the first on my feet. Am I?" said he.

"Yes," said De Forest, and steadied him as he dropped down beside us.

"Hello, Andy. Is that you?" a voice called.

"Excuse me," said the Mayor; "that sounds like my Chief of Police, Bluthner!"

"Bluthner it is; and here's Mulligan and Keefe—on their feet."

"Bring 'em up please, Blut. We're supposed to be the Four in charge of this hamlet. What we says, goes. And, De Forest, what do you say?"

"Nothing—yet," De Forest answered, as we made room for

the panting, reeling men. "*You*'ve cut out of system. Well?"

"Tell the steward to send down drinks, please," Arnott whispered to an orderly at his side.

"Good!" said the Mayor, smacking his dry lips. "Now I suppose we can take it, De Forest, that henceforward the Board will administer us direct?"

"Not if the Board can avoid it," De Forest laughed. "The A.B.C. is responsible for the planetary traffic only."

"*And all that that implies.*" The big Four who ran Chicago chanted their Magna Charta like children at school.

"Well, get on," said De Forest wearily. "What is your silly trouble anyway?"

"Too much dam' Democracy," said the Mayor, laying his hand on De Forest's knee.

"So? I thought Illinois had had her dose of that."

"She has. That's why. Blut, what did you do with our prisoners last night?"

"Locked 'em in the water-tower to prevent the women killing 'em," the Chief of Police replied. "I'm too blind to move just yet, but——"

"Arnott, send some of your people, please, and fetch 'em along," said De Forest.

"They're triple-circuited," the Mayor called. "You'll have to blow out three fuses." He turned to De Forest, his large outline just visible in the paling darkness. "I hate to throw any more work on the Board. I'm an administrator myself, but we've had a little fuss with our Serviles. What? In a big city there's bound to be a few men and women who can't live without listening to themselves, and who prefer drinking out of pipes they don't own both ends of. They inhabit flats and hotels all the year round. They say it saves 'em trouble. Anyway, it gives 'em more time to make trouble for their neighbours. We call 'em Serviles locally. And they are apt to be tuberculous."

"Just so!" said the man called Mulligan. "Transportation is Civilization. Democracy is Disease. I've proved it by the blood-test, every time."

"Mulligan's our Health Officer, and a one-idea man," said

the Mayor, laughing. "But it's true that most Serviles haven't much control. They *will* talk; and when people take to talking as a business, anything may arrive—mayn't it, De Forest?"

"Anything—except the facts of the case," said De Forest, laughing.

"I'll give you those in a minute," said the Mayor. "Our Serviles got to talking—first in their houses and then on the streets, telling men and women how to manage their own affairs. (You can't teach a Servile not to finger his neighbour's soul.) That's invasion of privacy, of course, but in Chicago we'll suffer anything sooner than make Crowds. Nobody took much notice, and so I let 'em alone. My fault! I was warned there would be trouble, but there hasn't been a Crowd or murder in Illinois for nineteen years."

"Twenty-two," said his Chief of Police.

"Likely. Anyway, we'd forgot such things. So, from talking in the houses and on the streets, our Serviles go to calling a meeting at the Old Market yonder." He nodded across the square where the wrecked buildings heaved up grey in the dawn-glimmer behind the square-cased statue of The Negro in Flames. "There's nothing to prevent any one calling meetings except that it's against human nature to stand in a Crowd, besides being bad for the health. I ought to have known by the way our men and women attended that first meeting that trouble was brewing. There were as many as a thousand in the market-place, touching each other. Touching! Then the Serviles turned in all tongue-switches and talked, and we——"

"What did they talk about?" said Takahira.

"First, how badly things were managed in the city. That pleased us Four—we were on the platform—because we hoped to catch one or two good men for City work. You know how rare executive capacity is. Even if we didn't it's—it's refreshing to find any one interested enough in our job to damn our eyes. You don't know what it means to work, year in, year out, without a spark of difference with a living soul."

"Oh, don't we!" said De Forest. "There are times on the Board when we'd give our positions if any one would kick us out and take hold of things themselves."

"But they won't," said the Mayor ruefully. "I assure you, sir, we Four have done things in Chicago, in the hope of rousing people, that would have discredited Nero. But what do they say? 'Very good, Andy. Have it your own way. Anything's better than a Crowd. I'll go back to my land.' You *can't* do anything with folk who can go where they please, and don't want anything on God's earth except their own way. There isn't a kick or a kicker left on the Planet."

"Then I suppose that little shed yonder fell down by itself?" said De Forest. We could see the bare and still smoking ruins, and hear the slag-pools crackle as they hardened and set.

"Oh, that's only amusement. 'Tell you later. As I was saying, our Serviles held the meeting, and pretty soon we had to ground-circuit the platform to save 'em from being killed. And that didn't make our people any more pacific."

"How d'you mean?" I ventured to ask.

"If you've ever been ground-circuited," said the Mayor, "you'll know it don't improve any man's temper to be held up straining against nothing. No, sir! Eight or nine hundred folk kept pawing and buzzing like flies in treacle for two hours, while a pack of perfectly safe Serviles invades their mental and spiritual privacy, may be amusing to watch, but they are not pleasant to handle afterwards."

Pirolo chuckled.

"Our folk own themselves. They were of opinion things were going too far and too fiery. I warned the Serviles; but they're born house-dwellers. Unless a fact hits 'em on the head they cannot see it. Would you believe me, they went on to talk of what they called 'popular government'? They did! They wanted us to go back to the old Voodoo-business of voting with papers and wooden boxes, and word-drunk people and printed formulas, and news-sheets! They said they practised it among themselves about what they'd have to eat in their flats and hotels. Yes, sir! They stood up behind Bluthner's doubled ground-circuits, and they said that, in this present year of grace, *to* self-owning men and women, *on* that very spot! Then they finished"—he lowered his voice cautiously—"by talking about 'The People.' And then Bluthner he had to sit up all night in charge of the circuits because he couldn't trust his men to keep 'em shut."

"It was trying 'em too high," the Chief of Police broke in. "But we couldn't hold the Crowd ground-circuited for ever. I gathered in all the Serviles on charge of Crowd-making, and put 'em in the water-tower, and then I let things cut loose. I had to! The District lit like a sparked gas-tank!"

"The news was out over seven degrees of country," the Mayor continued; "and when once it's a question of invasion of privacy, good-bye to right and reason in Illinois! They began turning out traffic-lights and locking up landing-towers on Thursday night. Friday, they stopped all traffic and asked for the Board to take over. Then they wanted to clean Chicago off the side of the Lake and rebuild elsewhere—just for a souvenir of 'The People' that the Serviles talked about. I suggested that they should slag the Old Market where the meeting was held, while I turned in a call to you all on the Board. That kept 'em quiet till you came along. And—and now *you* can take hold of the situation."

" 'Any chance of their quieting down?" De Forest asked.

"You can try," said the Mayor.

De Forest raised his voice in the face of the reviving Crowd that had edged in towards us. Day was come.

"Don't you think this business can be arranged?" he began. But there was a roar of angry voices:

"We've finished with Crowds! We aren't going back to the Old Days! Take us over! Take the Serviles away! Administer direct or we'll kill 'em! Down with The People!"

An attempt was made to begin MacDonough's Song. It got no further than the first line, for the *Victor Pirolo* sent down a warning drone on one stopped horn. A wrecked side-wall of the Old Market tottered and fell inwards on the slag-pools. None spoke or moved till the last of the dust had settled down again, turning the steel case of Salati's Statue ashy grey.

"You see you'll just *have* to take us over," the Mayor whispered.

De Forest shrugged his shoulders.

"You talk as if executive capacity could be snatched out of the air like so much horse-power. Can't you manage yourselves on any terms?" he said.

"We can, if you say so. It will only cost those few lives to begin with."

The Mayor pointed across the square, where Arnott's men guided a stumbling group of ten or twelve men and women to the lake front and halted them under the Statue.

"Now I think," said Takahira under his breath, "there will be trouble."

The mass in front of us growled like beasts.

At that moment the sun rose clear, and revealed the blinking assembly to itself. As soon as it realized that it was a crowd we saw the shiver of horror and mutual repulsion shoot across it precisely as the steely flaws shot across the lake outside. Nothing was said, and, being half blind, of course it moved slowly. Yet in less than fifteen minutes most of that vast multitude—three thousand at the lowest count—melted away like frost on south eaves. The remnant stretched themselves on the grass, where a crowd feels and looks less like a crowd.

"These mean business," the Mayor whispered to Takahira. "There are a goodish few women there who've borne children. I don't like it."

The morning draught off the lake stirred the trees round us with promise of a hot day; the sun reflected itself dazzlingly on the canister-shaped covering of Salati's Statue; cocks crew in the gardens, and we could hear gate-latches clicking in the distance as people stumblingly resought their homes.

"I'm afraid there won't be any morning deliveries," said De Forest. "We rather upset things in the country last night."

"That makes no odds," the Mayor returned. "We're all provisioned for six months. *We* take no chances."

Nor, when you come to think of it, does any one else. It must be three-quarters of a generation since any house or city faced a food shortage. Yet is there house or city on the Planet to-day that has not half a year's provisions laid in? We are like the shipwrecked seamen in the old books, who, having once nearly starved to death, ever afterwards hide away bits of food and biscuit. Truly we trust no Crowds, nor system based on Crowds!

De Forest waited till the last footstep had died away. Meantime the prisoners at the base of the Statue shuffled, posed, and fidgeted, with the shamelessness of quite little children. None of them were more than six feet high, and many of them were as grey-haired as the ravaged, harassed heads of old pictures. They huddled together in actual touch, while the crowd, spaced at large intervals, looked at them with congested eyes.

Suddenly a man among them began to talk. The Mayor had not in the least exaggerated. It appeared that our Planet lay sunk in slavery beneath the heel of the Aërial Board of Control. The orator urged us to arise in our might, burst our prison doors and break our fetters (all his metaphors, by the way, were of the most mediæval). Next he demanded that every matter of daily life, including most of the physical functions, should be submitted for decision at any time of the week, month, or year to, I gathered, anybody who happened to be passing by or residing within a certain radius, and that everybody should forthwith abandon his concerns to settle the matter, first by crowd-making, next by talking to the crowds made, and lastly by describing crosses on pieces of paper, which rubbish should later be counted with certain mystic ceremonies and oaths. Out of this amazing play, he assured us, would automatically arise a higher, nobler, and kinder world, based—he demonstrated this with the awful lucidity of the insane—based on the sanctity of the Crowd and the villainy of the single person. In conclusion, he called loudly upon God to testify to his personal merits and integrity. When the flow ceased, I turned bewildered to Takahira, who was nodding solemnly.

"Quite correct," said he. "It is all in the old books. He has left nothing out, not even the war-talk."

"But I don't see how this stuff can upset a child, much less a district," I replied.

"Ah, you are too young," said Dragomiroff. "For another

thing, you are not a mamma. Please look at the mammas."

Ten or fifteen women who remained had separated themselves from the silent men, and were drawing in towards the prisoners. It reminded one of the stealthy encircling, before the rush in at the quarry, of wolves round musk-oxen in the North. The prisoners saw, and drew together more closely. The Mayor covered his face with his hands for an instant. De Forest, bareheaded, stepped forward between the prisoners and the slowly, stiffly moving line.

"That's all very interesting," he said to the dry-lipped orator. "But the point seems that you've been making crowds and invading privacy."

A woman stepped forward, and would have spoken, but there was a quick assenting murmur from the men, who realized that De Forest was trying to pull the situation down to ground-line.

"Yes! Yes!" they cried. "We cut out because they made crowds and invaded privacy! Stick to that! Keep on that switch! Lift the Serviles out of this! The Board's in charge! Hsh!"

"Yes, the Board's in charge," said De Forest. "I'll take formal evidence of crowd-making if you like, but the Members of the Board can testify to it. Will that do?"

The women had closed in another pace, with hands that clenched and unclenched at their sides.

"Good! Good enough!" the men cried. "We're content. Only take them away quickly."

"Come along up!" said De Forest to the captives. "Breakfast is quite ready."

It appeared, however, that they did not wish to go. They intended to remain in Chicago and make crowds. They pointed out that De Forest's proposal was gross invasion of privacy.

"My dear fellow," said Pirolo to the most voluble of the leaders, "you hurry, or your crowd that can't be wrong will kill you!"

"But that would be murder," answered the believer in crowds; and there was a roar of laughter from all sides that seemed to show the crisis had broken.

A woman stepped forward from the line of women, laughing, I protest, as merrily as any of the company. One hand, of course, shaded her eyes, the other was at her throat.

"Oh, they needn't be afraid of being killed!" she called.

"Not in the least," said De Forest. "But don't you think that, now the Board's in charge, you might go home while we get these people away?"

"I shall be home long before that. It—it has been rather a trying day."

She stood up to her full height, dwarfing even De Forest's six-foot-eight, and smiled, with eyes closed against the fierce light.

"Yes, rather," said De Forest. "I'm afraid you feel the glare a little. We'll have the ship down."

He motioned to the *Pirolo* to drop between us and the sun, and at the same time to loop-circuit the prisoners, who were a trifle unsteady. We saw them stiffen to the current where they stood. The woman's voice went on, sweet and deep and unshaken:

"I don't suppose you men realize how much this—this sort of thing means to a woman. I've borne three. We women don't want our children given to Crowds. It must be an inherited instinct. Crowds make trouble. They bring back the Old Days. Hate, fear, blackmail, publicity, 'The People'—*That! That! That!*" She pointed to the Statue, and the crowd growled once more.

"Yes, if they are allowed to go on," said De Forest. "But this little affair——"

"It means so much to us women that this—this little affair should never happen again. Of course, never's a big word, but one feels so strongly that it is important to stop crowds at the very beginning. Those creatures"—she pointed with her left hand at the prisoners swaying like seaweed in a tideway as the circuit pulled them—"those people have friends and wives and children in the city and elsewhere. One doesn't want anything done to *them,* you know. It's terrible to force a human being out of fifty or sixty years of good life. I'm only forty myself. *I* know. But, at the same time, one feels that an example should be made, because no price is too heavy to pay if—if these people and *all that they imply* can be put an end to. Do you quite understand, or would you be kind enough to tell your men to take the casing off the Statue? It's worth looking at."

"I understand perfectly. But I don't think anybody here wants to see the Statue on an empty stomach. Excuse me one moment." De Forest called up to the ship, "A flying loop ready on the port side, if you please." Then to the woman he said with some crispness, "You might leave us a little discretion in the matter."

"Oh, of course. Thank you for being so patient. I know my arguments are silly, but——" She half turned away and went on in a changed voice, "Perhaps this will help you to decide."

She threw out her right arm with a knife in it. Before the blade could be returned to her throat or her bosom it was twitched from her grip, sparked as it flew out of the shadow of the ship above, and fell flashing in the sunshine at the foot of the Statue fifty yards away. The outflung arm was arrested, rigid as a bar for an instant, till the releasing circuit permitted her to bring it slowly to her side. The other women shrank back silent among the men.

Pirolo rubbed his hands, and Takahira nodded.

"That was clever of you, De Forest," said he.

"What a glorious pose!" Dragomiroff murmured, for the frightened woman was on the edge of tears.

"Why did you stop me? I would have done it!" she cried.

"I have no doubt you would," said De Forest. "But we can't waste a life like yours on these people. I hope the arrest didn't sprain your wrist; it's so hard to regulate a flying loop. But I think you are quite right about those persons' women and children. We'll take them all away with us if you promise not to do anything stupid to yourself."

"I promise—I promise." She controlled herself with an effort. "But it is so important to us women. We know what it means; and I thought if you saw I was in earnest——"

"I saw you were, and you've gained your point. I shall take all your Serviles away with me at once. The Mayor will make lists of their friends and families in the city and the district, and he'll ship them after us this afternoon."

"Sure," said the Mayor, rising to his feet. "Keefe, if you can see, hadn't you better finish levelling off the Old Market? It don't look sightly the way it is now, and we shan't use it for crowds any more."

"I think you had better wipe out that Statue as well, Mr. Mayor," said De Forest. "I don't question its merits as a work of art, but I believe it's a shade morbid."

"Certainly, sir. Oh, Keefe! Slag the Nigger before you go on to fuse the Market. I'll get to the Communicators and tell the District that the Board is in charge. Are you making any special appointments, sir?"

"None. We haven't men to waste on these backwoods. Carry on as before, but under the Board. Arnott, run your Serviles aboard, please. Ground ship and pass them through the bilge-doors. We'll wait till we've finished with this work of art."

The prisoners trailed past him, talking fluently, but unable to gesticulate in the drag of the current. Then the surfacers rolled up, two on each side of the Statue. With one accord the spectators looked elsewhere, but there was no need. Keefe turned on full power, and the thing simply melted within its case. All I saw was a surge of white-hot metal pouring over the plinth, a glimpse of Salati's inscription, "To the Eternal Memory of the Justice of the People," ere the stone base itself cracked and powdered into finest lime. The crowd cheered.

"Thank you," said De Forest; "but we want our breakfasts, and I expect you do too. Good-bye, Mr. Mayor! Delighted to see you at any time, but I hope I shan't have to, officially, for the next thirty years. Good-bye, madam. Yes. We're all given to nerves nowadays. I suffer from them myself. Good-bye, gentlemen all! You're under the tyrannous heel of the Board from this moment, but if ever you feel like breaking your fetters you've only to let us know. This is no treat to us. Good luck!"

We embarked amid shouts, and did not check our lift till

they had dwindled into whispers. Then De Forest flung himself on the chart-room divan and mopped his forehead.

"I don't mind men," he panted, "but women are the devil!"

"Still the devil," said Pirolo cheerfully. "That one would have suicided."

"I know it. That was why I signalled for the flying loop to be clapped on her. I owe you an apology for that, Arnott. I hadn't time to catch your eye, and you were busy with our caitiffs. By the way, who actually answered my signal? It was a smart piece of work."

"Ilroy," said Arnott; "but he overloaded the wave. It may be pretty gallery-work to knock a knife out of a lady's hand, but didn't you notice how she rubbed 'em? He scorched her fingers. Slovenly, I call it."

"Far be it from me to interfere with Fleet discipline, but don't be too hard on the boy. If that woman had killed herself they would have killed every Servile and everything related to a Servile throughout the district by nightfall."

"That was what she was playing for," Takahira said. "And with our Fleet gone we could have done nothing to hold them."

"I may be ass enough to walk into a ground-circuit," said Arnott, "but I don't dismiss my Fleet till I'm reasonably sure that trouble is over. They're in position still, and I intend to keep 'em there till the Serviles are shipped out of the district. That last little crowd meant murder, my friends."

"Nerves! All nerves!" said Pirolo. "You cannot argue with agoraphobia."

"And it is not as if they had seen much dead—or *is* it?" said Takahira.

"In all my ninety years I have never seen Death." Dragomiroff spoke as one who would excuse himself. "Perhaps that was why—last night——"

Then it came out as we sat over breakfast, that, with the exception of Arnott and Pirolo, none of us had ever seen a corpse, or knew in what manner the spirit passes.

"We're a nice lot to flap about governing the Planet," De Forest laughed. "I confess, now it's all over, that my main fear was I mightn't be able to pull it off without losing a life."

"I thought of that too," said Arnott; "but there's no death reported, and I've inquired everywhere. What are we supposed to do with our passengers? I've fed 'em."

"We're between two switches," De Forest drawled. "If we drop them in any place that isn't under the Board the natives will make their presence an excuse for cutting out, same as Illinois did, and forcing the Board to take over. If we drop them in any place under the Board's control they'll be killed as soon as our backs are turned."

"If you say so," said Pirolo thoughtfully, "I can guarantee that they will become extinct in process of time, quite happily. What is their birth-rate now?"

"Go down and ask 'em," said De Forest.

"I think they might become nervous and tear me to bits," the philosopher of Foggia replied.

"Not really? Well?"

"Open the bilge-doors," said Takahira with a downward jerk of the thumb.

"Scarcely—after all the trouble we've taken to save 'em," said De Forest.

"Try London," Arnott suggested. "You could turn Satan himself loose there, and they'd only ask him to dinner."

"Good man! You've given me an idea. Vincent! Oh, Vincent!" He threw the General Communicator open so that we could all hear, and in a few minutes the chart-room filled with the rich, fruity voice of Leopold Vincent, who has purveyed all London her choicest amusements for the last thirty years. We answered with expectant grins, as though we were actually in the stalls of, say, the Combination on a first night.

"We've picked up something in your line," De Forest began.

"That's good, dear man. If it's old enough. There's nothing to beat the old things for business purposes. Have you seen *London, Chatham, and Dover* at Earl's Court? No? I thought I missed you there. Immense! I've had the real steam locomotive engines built from the old designs and the iron rails cast specially by hand. Cloth cushions in the carriages, too! Immense! And paper railway tickets. And Polly Milton."

"Polly Milton back again!" said Arnott rapturously. "Book me two stalls for to-morrow night. What's she singing now, bless her?"

"The old songs. Nothing comes up to the old touch. Listen to this, dear men." Vincent carolled with flourishes:

Oh, cruel lamps of London,
If tears your light could drown,
Your victims' eyes would weep them,
Oh, lights of London Town!

"Then they weep."

"You see?" Pirolo waved his hands at us. "The old world always weeped when it saw crowds together. It did not know why, but it weeped. We know why, but we do not weep, except when we pay to be made to by fat, wicked old Vincent."

"Old, yourself!" Vincent laughed. "I'm a public benefactor. I keep the world soft and united."

"And I'm De Forest of the Board," said De Forest acidly, "trying to get a little business done. As I was saying, I've picked up a few people in Chicago."

"I cut out. Chicago is——"

"Do listen! They're perfectly unique."

"Do they build houses of baked mudblocks while you wait—eh? That's an old contact."

"They're an untouched primitive community, with all the old ideas."

"Sewing-machines and maypole-dances? Cooking on coal-gas stoves, lighting pipes with matches, and driving horses? Gerolstein tried that last year. An absolute blow-out!"

De Forest plugged him wrathfully, and poured out the story of our doings for the last twenty-four hours on the top-note.

"And they do it *all* in public," he concluded. "You can't stop 'em. The more public, the better they are pleased. They'll talk for hours—like you! Now you can come in again!"

"Do you really mean they know how to vote?" said Vincent. "Can they act it?"

"Act? It's their life to 'em! And you never saw such faces! Scarred like volcanoes. Envy, hatred, and malice in plain sight. Wonderfully flexible voices. They weep, too."

"Aloud? In public?"

"I guarantee. Not a spark of shame or reticence in the entire installation. It's the chance of your career."

"D'you say you've brought their voting props along—those papers and ballot-box things?"

"No, confound you! I'm not a luggage-lifter. Apply direct to the Mayor of Chicago. He'll forward you everything. Well?"

"Wait a minute. Did Chicago want to kill 'em? That 'ud look well on the Communicators."

"Yes! They were only rescued with difficulty from a howling mob—if you know what that is."

"But I don't," answered the Great Vincent simply.

"Well then, they'll tell you themselves. They can make speeches hours long."

"How many are there?"

"By the time we ship 'em all over they'll be perhaps a hundred, counting children. An old world in miniature. Can't you see it?"

"M-yes; but I've got to pay for it if it's a blow-out, dear man."

"They can sing the old war songs in the streets. They can get word-drunk, and make crowds, and invade privacy in the genuine old-fashioned way; and they'll do the voting trick as often as you ask 'em a question."

"Too good!" said Vincent.

"You unbelieving Jew! I've got a dozen head aboard here. I'll put you through direct. Sample 'em yourself."

He lifted the switch and we listened. Our passengers on the lower deck at once, but not less than five at a time, explained themselves to Vincent. They had been taken from the bosom of their families, stripped of their possessions, given food without finger-bowls, and cast into captivity in a noisome dungeon.

"But look here," said Arnott aghast; "they're saying what

isn't true. My lower deck isn't noisome, and I saw to the finger-bowls myself."

"My people talk like that sometimes in Little Russia," said Dragomiroff. "We reason with them. We never kill. No!"

"But it's not true," Arnott insisted. "What can you do with people who don't tell facts? They're mad!"

"Hsh!" said Pirolo, his hand to his ear. "It is such a little time since all the Planet told lies."

We heard Vincent silkily sympathetic. Would they, he asked, repeat their assertions in public—before a vast public? Only let Vincent give them a chance, and the Planet, they vowed, should ring with their wrongs. Their aim in life—two women and a man explained it together—was to reform the world. Oddly enough, this also had been Vincent's life-dream. He offered them an arena in which to explain, and by their living example to raise the Planet to loftier levels. He was eloquent on the moral uplift of a simple, old-world life presented in its entirety to a deboshed civilization.

Could they—would they—for three months certain, devote themselves under his auspices, as missionaries, to the elevation of mankind at a place called Earl's Court, which he said, with some truth, was one of the intellectual centres of the Planet? They thanked him, and demanded (we could hear his chuckle of delight) time to discuss and to vote on the matter. The vote, solemnly managed by counting heads—one head, one vote—was favourable. His offer, therefore, was accepted, and they moved a vote of thanks to him in two speeches—one by what they called the "proposer" and the other by the "seconder."

Vincent threw over to us, his voice shaking with gratitude:

"I've got 'em! Did you hear those speeches? That's Nature, dear men. Art can't teach *that*. And they voted as easily as lying. I've never had a troupe of natural liars before. Bless you, dear men! Remember, you're on my free lists for ever, anywhere—all of you. Oh, Gerolstein will be sick—sick!"

"Then you think they'll do?" said De Forest.

"Do? The Little Village'll go crazy! I'll knock up a series

of old-world plays for 'em. Their voices will make you laugh and cry. My God, dear men, where *do* you suppose they picked up all their misery from, on this sweet earth? I'll have a pageant of the world's beginnings, and Mosenthal shall do the music. I'll——"

"Go and knock up a village for 'em by to-night. We'll meet you at No. 15 West Landing Tower," said De Forest. "Remember the rest will be coming along to-morrow."

"Let 'em all come!" said Vincent. "You don't know how hard it is nowadays even for me, to find something that really gets under the public's damned iridium-plated hide. But I've got it at last. Good-bye!"

"Well," said De Forest when we had finished laughing, "if any one understood corruption in London I might have played off Vincent against Gerolstein, and sold my captives at enormous prices. As it is, I shall have to be their legal adviser to-night when the contracts are signed. And they won't exactly press any commission on me, either."

"Meantime," said Takahira, "we cannot, of course, confine members of Leopold Vincent's last-engaged company. Chairs for the ladies, please, Arnott."

"Then I go to bed," said De Forest. "I can't face any more women!" And he vanished.

When our passengers were released and given another meal (finger-bowls came first this time) they told us what they thought of us and the Board; and, like Vincent, we all marvelled how they had contrived to extract and secrete so much bitter poison and unrest out of the good life God gives us. They raged, they stormed, they palpitated, flushed and exhausted their poor, torn nerves, panted themselves into silence, and renewed the senseless, shameless attacks.

"But can't you understand," said Pirolo pathetically to a shrieking woman, "that if we'd left you in Chicago you'd have been killed?"

"No, we shouldn't. You were bound to save us from being murdered."

"Then we should have had to kill a lot of other people."

"That doesn't matter. We were preaching the Truth. You

can't stop us. We shall go on preaching in London; and *then* you'll see!"

"You can see now," said Pirolo, and opened a lower shutter.

We were closing on the Little Village, with her three million people spread out at ease inside her ring of girdling Main-Traffic lights—those eight fixed beams at Chatham, Tonbridge, Redhill, Dorking, Woking, St. Albans, Chipping Ongar, and Southend.

Leopold Vincent's new company looked, with small pale faces, at the silence, the size, and the separated houses.

Then some began to weep aloud, shamelessly—always without shame.

A PREFACE

1923

TO ALL to whom this little book may come—
Health for yourselves and those you hold most dear!
Content abroad, and happiness at home,
And—one grand Secret in your private ear:—
Nations have passed away and left no traces,
And History gives the naked cause of it—
One single, simple reason in all cases;
They fell because their peoples were not fit.

Now, though your Body be mis-shapen, blind,
Lame, feverish, lacking substance, power or skill,
Certain it is that men can school the Mind
To school the sickliest Body to her will—
As many have done, whose glory blazes still
Like mighty flames in meanest lanterns lit:
Wherefore, we pray the crippled, weak and ill—
Be fit—be fit! In mind at first be fit!

And, though your Spirit seem uncouth or small,
Stubborn as clay or shifting as the sand,
Strengthen the Body, and the Body shall
Strengthen the Spirit till she take command;
As a bold rider brings his horse in hand
At the tall fence, with voice and heel and bit,
And leaps while all the field are at a stand.
Be fit—be fit! In body next be fit!

Nothing on earth—no Arts, no Gifts, nor Graces—
No Fame, no Wealth—outweighs the want of it.
This is the Law which every law embraces—
Be fit—be fit! In mind and body be fit!

The even heart that seldom slurs its beat—
The cool head weighing what that heart desires—
The measuring eye that guides the hands and feet—
The Soul unbroken when the Body tires—
These are the things our weary world requires
Far more than superfluities of wit;
Wherefore we pray you, sons of generous sires,
Be fit—be fit! For Honour's sake be fit.

There is one lesson at all Times and Places—
One changeless Truth on all things changing writ,
For boys and girls, men, women, nations, races—
Be fit—be fit! And once again, be fit!

AN ENGLISH SCHOOL

A.D. 1878–1882

1893

OF ALL things in the world there is nothing, always excepting a good mother, so worthy of honour as a good school. Our School was created for the sons of officers in the Army and Navy, and filled with boys who meant to follow their father's calling.

It stood within two miles of Amyas Leigh's house at Northam, overlooking the Burroughs and the Pebble-ridge, and the mouth of the Torridge whence the *Rose* sailed in search of Don Guzmán. From the front dormitory windows, across the long rollers of the Atlantic, you could see Lundy

Island and the Shutter Rock, where the *Santa Catherina* galleon cheated Amyas out of his vengeance by going ashore. If you have ever read Kingsley's "Westward Ho!" you will remember how all these things happened.

Inland lay the rich Devonshire lanes and the fat orchards, and to the west the gorse and the turf ran along the tops of the cliffs in combe after combe till you come to Clovelly and the Hobby and Gallantry Bower, and the homes of the Devonshire people that were old when the Armada was new.

The Burroughs, lying between the school and the sea, was a waste of bent rush and grass running out into hundreds of acres of fascinating sand-hills called the Bunkers, where a few old people played golf. In the early days of the School there was a small Club-house for golfers close to the Pebble-ridge, but, one wild winter night, the sea got up and drove the Pebble-ridge clean through the Club basement, and the walls fell out, and we rejoiced, for even then golfers wore red coats and did not like us to use the links. We played as a matter of course and thought nothing of it.

Now there is a new Club-house, and cars take the old, red, excited men to and from their game and all the great bunkers are known and written about; but we were there first, long before golf became a fashion or a disease, and we turned out one of the earliest champion amateur golfers of all England.

It was a good place for a school, and that School considered itself the finest in the world, excepting perhaps Haileybury, because it was modelled on Haileybury lines and our caps were Haileybury colours; and there was a legend that, in the old days when the School was new, half the boys had been Haileyburians.

Our Head-master had been Head of the Modern Side at Haileybury, and, talking it over with boys from other public schools afterwards, I think that one secret of his great hold over us was that he was not a clergyman, as so many head-masters are. As soon as a boy begins to think in the misty way that boys do, he is suspicious of a man who punishes him one day and preaches at him the next. But the Head was different, and in our different ways we loved him.

Through all of five years I never saw him lose his temper, nor among two hundred boys did any one at any time say or hint that he had his favourites. If you went to him with any trouble you were heard out to the end, and answered without being talked at or about or around, but always *to*. So we trusted him absolutely, and when it came to the choice of the various ways of entering the Army, what he said was so.

He knew boys naturally better than their fathers knew them, and considerably better than they knew themselves. When the time came to read for the Final Army Examinations, he knew the temper and powers of each boy, the amount of training each would stand and the stimulus or restraint that each needed, and handled them accordingly till they had come through the big race that led into the English Army. Looking back on it all, one can see the perfect judgment, knowledge of boys, patience, and above all, power, that the Head must have had.

Some of the masters, particularly on the classical side, vowed that Army examinations were making education no more than mark-hunting; but there are a great many kinds of education, and I think the Head knew it, for he taught us hosts of things that we never found out we knew till afterwards. And surely it must be better to turn out men who do real work than men who write about what they think about what other people have done or ought to do.

A scholar may, as the Latin masters said, get more pleasure out of his life than an Army officer, but only little children believe that a man's life is given him to decorate with pretty little things, as though it were a girl's room or a picture-screen. Besides, scholars are apt, all their lives, to judge from one point of view only, and by the time that an Army officer has knocked about the world for a few years he comes to look at men and things "by and large," as the sailors say. No books in the world will teach that knack.

So we trusted the Head at school, and afterwards trusted him more.

There was a boy in the Canadian Mounted Police, I think, who stumbled into a fortune—he was the only one of us who ever did—and as he had never drawn more than seven shillings a day he very properly wrote to the Head from out of his North Western wilds and explained his situation proposing that the Head should take charge of and look after all his wealth till he could attend to it; and was a little impatient when the Head pointed out that executors and trustees and that sort of bird wouldn't hand over cash in that casual way. The Head was worth trusting—he saved a boy's life from diphtheria once at much greater risk than being shot at, and nobody knew anything about it till years afterwards.

But I come back to the School that he made and put his mark upon. The boys said that those with whom Cheltenham could do nothing, whom Sherbourne found too tough, and whom even Marlborough had politely asked to leave, had been sent to the School at the beginning of things and turned into men. They were, perhaps, a shade rough sometimes. One very curious detail, which I have never seen or heard of in any school before or since, was that the Army Class, which meant the Prefects, and was generally made up of boys from seventeen and a half to nineteen or thereabouts, was allowed to smoke pipes (cigarettes were then reckoned the direct invention of the Evil One) in the country outside the College. One result of this was that, though these great men talked a good deal about the grain of their pipes, the beauty of their pouches, and the flavour of their tobacco, they did not smoke to any ferocious extent. The other, which concerned me more directly, was that it went much harder with a junior whom they caught smoking than if he had been caught by a master, because the action was flagrant invasion of their privilege, and, therefore, rank insolence—to be punished as such. Years later, the Head admitted that he thought something of this kind would happen when he gave the permission. If any Headmaster is anxious to put down smoking nowadays, he might do worse than give this scheme a trial.

The School motto was, "Fear God, Honour the King"; and so the men she made went out to Boerland and Zululand and India and Burma and Cyprus and Hongkong, and lived or died as gentlemen and officers.

Even the most notorious bully, for whom an awful ending was prophesied, went to Canada and was mixed up in Riel's rebellion, and came out of it with a fascinating reputation of having led a forlorn hope and behaved like a hero.

All these matters were noted by the older boys, and when their fathers, the grey-whiskered colonels and generals, came down to see them, or the directors, who were K. C. B.'s and had been officers in their time, made a tour of inspection, it was reported that the School tone was "healthy."

Sometimes an old boy who had blossomed into a Subaltern of the Queen would come down for a last few words with the Head-master, before sailing with the regiment for foreign parts; and the lower-school boys were distracted with envy, and the prefects of the Sixth Form pretended not to be proud when he walked with one of their number and talked about "my men, you know," till life became unendurable.

There was an unwritten law by which an old boy, when he came back to pay his respects to the School, was entitled to a night in his old dormitory. The boys expected it and sat up half the night listening to the tales of a subaltern that the boy brought with him—stories about riots in Ireland and camps at Aldershot, and all his first steps in the wonderful world.

Sometimes news came in that a boy had died with his men fighting, and the school said, "Killed in action, of course," as though that were an honour reserved for it alone, and wondered when its own chance would come.

It was a curiously quiet School in many ways. When a boy was fourteen or fifteen he was generally taken in hand for the Army Preliminary Examination, and when that was past he was put down to "grind" for the entrance into Sandhurst or Woolwich; for it was our pride that we passed direct from the School to the Army, without troubling the "crammers." We spoke of "the Shop," which means Woolwich, as though we owned it. Sandhurst was our private reserve; and the old boys came back from foreign parts and told us that India was only Westward Ho! spread thin.

On account of this incessant getting ready for examinations there was hardly time for us (but we made it) to gather the beautiful Devonshire apples, or to ferret rabbits in the sand-hills by the golf-links, and saloon-pistols were forbidden because boys got to fighting-parties with dust-shot, and were careless about guarding their eyes.

Nor were we encouraged to lower each other over the cliffs with a box-rope and take the young hawks and jackdaws from their nests above the sea. Once a rope broke, or else the boys above grew tired of holding it, and a boy dropped thirty feet on to the boulders below. But as he fell on his head nothing happened, except punishment at the other end for all concerned.

In summer there was almost unlimited bathing from the Pebble-ridge, a whale-backed bank four miles long of rounded grey boulders, where you were taught to ride on the rollers as they came in, to avoid the under-tow and to watch your time for getting back to the beach.

There was a big sea bath, too, in which all boys had to qualify for open bathing by swimming a quarter of a mile, at least; and it was a matter of honour among the schoolhouses not to let the summer end with a single boy who could not "do his quarter," at any rate.

Boating was impossible off that coast, but sometimes a fishing-boat would be wrecked on Braunton Bar, and we could see the lifeboat and the rocket at work; and once just after chapel there was a cry that the herring were in. The School ran down to the beach in their Sunday clothes and fished them out with umbrellas. They were cooked by hand afterwards in all the studies and form-rooms till you could have smelt us at Exeter.

But the game of the School, setting aside golf, which everyone could play if he had patience, was foot-ball. Both cricket and foot-ball were compulsory. That is to say, unless a boy could show a doctor's certificate that he was physically unfit to stand up to the wicket or go into the scrimmage, he had to play a certain number of afternoons at the game of the season. If he had engagements elsewhere—we called it "shirking"—he was reasonably sure of three cuts with a ground-ash, from the Captain of the Games delivered cold in the evening. A good player, of course, could get leave off on any fair excuse, but it was a beautiful rule for fat boys and loafers. The only unfairness was that a Master could load you with an imposition to be shown up at a certain hour, which, of course, prevented you from playing and so secured you a licking in addition to the imposition. But the Head always told us that there was not much justice in the world, and that we had better accustom ourselves to the lack of it early.

Curiously enough, the one thing that the School did not understand was an attempt to drill it in companies with rifles, by way of making a volunteer cadet corps. We took our lickings for not attending *that* cheerfully, because we considered it "playing at soldiers," and boys reading for the Army are apt to be very particular on these points.

We were weak in cricket, but our foot-ball team (Rugby Union) at its best devastated the country from Blundell's—we always respected Blundell's because "Great John Ridd" had been educated there—to Exeter, whose team were grown men. Yet we, who had been taught to play together, once drove them back over the November mud, back to their own goal-posts, till the ball was hacked through and touched down, and you could hear the long-drawn yell of "Schoo-*ool!* Schoo-*ool!*" as far as Appledore.

When the enemy would not come to us our team went to the enemy, and if victorious, would return late at night in a three-horse brake, chanting:

> *It's a way we have in the Army,*
> *It's a way we have in the Navy,*
> *It's a way we have in the Public Schools,*
> *Which nobody can deny!*

Then the boys would flock to the dormitory windows, and wave towels and join in the "Hip-hip-hip-hurrah!" of the chorus, and the winning team would swagger through the dormitories and show the beautiful blue marks on their shins, and the little boys would be allowed to get sponges and hot water.

Very few things that the world can offer make up for having missed a place in the First Fifteen, with its black jersey and white—snow-white—knickerbockers, and the velvet skull-cap with the gold tassel—the cap that you leave out in the rain and accidentally step upon to make it look as old as if you had been in the First Fifteen for years.

The other outward sign of the First Fifteen that the happy boy generally wore through a hard season was the "jersey-mark"—a raw, red scrape on ear and jawbone where the skin had been fretted by the rough jerseys in either side in the steady drive of many scrimmages. We were trained to put our heads down, pack in the shape of a wedge and shove, and it was in that shape that the First Fifteen stood up to a team of trained men for two and twenty counted minutes. We got the ball through in the end.

At the close of the winter term, when there were no more foot-ball teams to squander and the Christmas holidays were coming, the School set itself to the regular yearly theatricals —a farce and a three-act play all complete. Sometimes it was "The Rivals," or sometimes an attempt at a Shakespearean play; but the farces were the most popular.

All ended with the School-Saga, the *"Vive la Compagnie!"* in which the Senior boy of the School chanted the story of the School for the past twelve months. It was very long and very difficult to make up, though all the poets of all the forms had been at work on it for weeks; and the School gave the chorus at the top of its voice.

On the last Sunday of the term the last hymn in chapel was "Onward, Christian Soldiers." We did not know what it meant then, and we did not care, but we stood up and sang it till the music was swamped in the rush. The big verse, like the "tug-of-war" verse in Mrs. Ewing's "Story of a Short Life," was:

We are not divided,
All one body we,
One in faith and doctrine,
One in charity.

Then the organ would give a hurricane of joyful roars, and try to get us in hand before the refrain. Later on, meeting our men all the world over, the meaning of that hymn became much too plain.

Except for this outbreak we were not very pious. There was a boy who had to tell stories night after night in the Dormitory, and when his stock ran out he fell back on a book called "Eric, or Little by Little," as comic literature, and read it till the gas was turned off. The boys laughed abominably, and there was some attempt to give selections from it at the meeting of the Reading Society. That was quashed by authority because it was against discipline.

There were no public-houses near us except tap-rooms that sold cider; and raw Devonshire cider can only be drunk after a long and very hot paper-chase. We hardly ever saw, and certainly never spoke to, anything in the nature of a woman from one year's end to the other; for our masters were all unmarried. Later on, a little colony of mothers came down to live near the School, but their sons were day-boys who couldn't do this and mustn't do that, and there was a great deal too much dressing up on week-days and going out to tea, and things of that kind, which, whatever people say nowadays, are not helpful for boys at work.

Our masters, luckily, were never gushing. They did not call us Dickie or Johnnie or Tommy, but Smith or Thompson; and when we were undoubtedly bad we were actually and painfully beaten with an indubitable cane on a veritable back till we wept unfeigned tears. Nobody seemed to think that it brutalized our finer feelings, but everybody was relieved when the trouble was over.

Canes, especially when they are brought down with a drawing stroke, sting like hornets; but they are a sound cure for certain offences; and a cut or two, given with no malice, but as a reminder, can correct and keep corrected a false quantity or a wandering mind, more completely than any amount of explanation.

There was one boy, however, to whom every Latin quantity was an arbitrary mystery, and he wound up his crimes by suggesting that he could do better if Latin verse rhymed as decent verse should. He was given an afternoon's reflection to purge himself of his contempt; and feeling certain that he was in for something rather warm, he turned "*Donec gratus eram*" into pure Devonshire dialect, rhymed, and showed it up as his contribution to the study of Horace.

He was let off, and his master gave him the run of a big library, where he found as much verse and prose as he wanted; but that ruined his Latin verses and made him write verses of his own. There he found all the English poets from Chaucer to Matthew Arnold, and a book called "Imaginary Conversations" which he did not understand, but it seemed to be a good thing to imitate. So he imitated and was handed up to the Head, who said that he had better learn Russian under his own eye, so that if ever he were sent to Siberia for lampooning the authorities he might be able to ask for things.

That meant the run of another library—English Dramatists this time; hundreds of old plays; as well as thick brown books of voyages told in language like the ringing of bells. And the Head would sometimes tell him about the manners and customs of the Russians, and sometimes about his own early days at college, when several people who afterwards became great, were all young, and the Head was young with them, and they wrote wonderful things in college magazines.

It was beautiful and cheap—dirt cheap, at the price of a permanent load of impositions, for neglecting mathematics and algebra.

The School started a Natural History Society, which took the birds and plants of North Devon under its charge, reporting first flowerings and first arrivals and new discoveries to learned societies in London, and naturally attracting to itself every boy in the School who had the poaching instinct.

Some of us made membership an excuse for stealing apples and pheasant eggs and geese from farmers' orchards and gentlemen's estates, and we were turned out with disgrace. So we spoke scornfully of the Society ever afterwards. None the less, some of us had our first introduction to gunpowder in the shape of a charge of salt which stings like bees, fired at our legs by angry game-keepers.

The institution that caused some more excitement was the School paper. Three of the boys, who had moved up the School side by side for four years and were allies in all things, started the notion as soon as they came to the dignity of a study of their own with a door that would lock. The other two told the third boy what to write, and held the staircase against invaders.

It was a real printed paper of eight pages, and at first the printer was more thoroughly ignorant of type-setting, and the Editor was more completely ignorant of proof-reading, than any printer and any Editor that ever was. It was printed off by a gas engine; and even the engine despised its work, for one day it fell through the floor of the shop, and crashed—still working furiously—into the cellar.

The paper came out at odd times and seasons, but every time it came out there was sure to be trouble, because the Editor was learning for the first time how sweet and good and profitable it is—and how nice it looks on the page—to make fun of people in actual print.

For instance, there was friction among the study-fags once, and the Editor wrote a descriptive account of the Lower School,—the classes whence the fags were drawn,—their manners and customs, their ways of cooking half-plucked sparrows and imperfectly cleaned blackbirds at the gas-jets on a rusty nib, and their fights over sloe-jam made in a gallipot. It was an absolutely truthful article, but the Lower School knew nothing about truth, and would not even consider it as literature.

It is less safe to write a study of an entire class than to discuss individuals one by one; but apart from the fact that boys throw books and inkpots with a straighter eye, there is very little difference between the language of grown-up people and that of children.

In those days the Editor had not learned this; so when the study below the Editorial study threw coal at the Editorial legs and kicked in the panels of the door, because of personal paragraphs in the last number, the Editorial Staff—and there never was so loyal and hard-fighting a staff—fried fat bacon till there was half an inch of grease in the pan, and let the greasy chunks down at the end of a string to bob against and defile the lower study windows.

When that lower study—and there never was a public so low and unsympathetic as that lower study—looked out to see what was frosting their window-panes, the Editorial Staff emptied the hot fat on their heads, and it stayed in their hair for days and days, wearing shiny to the very last.

The boy who suggested this sort of warfare was then reading a sort of magazine, called *Fors Clavigera,* which he did not in the least understand,—it was not exactly a boy's paper, —and when the lower study had scraped some of the fat off their heads and were thundering with knobby pokers on the door-lock, this boy began to chant pieces of the *Fors* as a war-song, and to show that his mind was free from low distractions. He was an extraordinary person, and the only boy in the School who had a genuine contempt for his masters. There was no affectation in his quiet insolence. He honestly *did* despise them; and threats that made us all wince only caused him to put his head a little on one side and watch the master as a sort of natural curiosity.

The worst of this was that his allies had to take their share of his punishments, for they lived as communists and socialists hope to live one day, when everybody is good. They were bad, as bad as they dared to be, but their possessions were in common, absolutely. And when "the Study" was out of funds they took the most respectable clothes in possession of the Syndicate, and leaving the owner one Sunday and one week-day suit, sold the rest in Bideford town. Later, when there was another crisis, it was *not* the respectable one's watch that was taken by force for the good of the Study and pawned, and never redeemed.

Later still, money came into the Syndicate honestly, for a London paper that did not know with whom it was dealing, published and paid a whole guinea for some verses that one of the boys had written and sent up under a nom-de-plume, and the Study caroused on chocolate and condensed milk and pilchards and Devonshire cream, and voted poetry a much sounder business than it looks.

So things went on very happily till the three were seriously warned that they must work in earnest, and stop giving amateur performances of "Aladdin" and writing librettos of comic operas which never came off, and worrying their house-masters into grey hairs.

Then they all grew very good, and one of them got into the Army; and another—the Irish one—became an engineer, and the third one found himself on a daily paper half a world away from the Pebble-ridge and the sea-beach. The three swore eternal friendship before they parted, and from time to time they met boys of their year in India, and magnified the honour of the old School.

The boys are scattered all over the world, one to each degree of land east and west, as their fathers were before them, doing much the same kind of work; and it is curious to notice how little the character of the man differs from that of the boy of sixteen or seventeen.

The general and commander-in-chief of the Study, he who suggested selling the clothes, never lost his head even when he and his friends were hemmed round by the enemy—the Drill Sergeant—far out of bounds and learning to smoke under a hedge. He was sick and dizzy, but he rose to the occasion, took command of his forces, and by strategic manœuvres along dry ditches and crawlings through tall grass, outflanked the enemy and got into safe ground without losing one man of the three.

A little later, when he was a subaltern in India, he was bitten by a mad dog, went to France to be treated by Pasteur, and came out again in the heat of the hot weather to find himself almost alone in charge of six hundred soldiers, and his Drill Sergeant dead and his office clerk run away, leaving the Regimental books in the most ghastly confusion. Then we happened to meet; and as he was telling his story there was just the same happy look on his face as when he steered us down the lanes with the certainty of a superior thrashing if we were caught.

And there were others who went abroad with their men, and when they got into tight places behaved very much as they had behaved at foot-ball.

The boy who used to take flying jumps on to the ball and roll over and over with it, because he was big and fat and could not run, took a flying jump onto a Burmese dacoit whom he had surprised by night in a stockade; but he forgot that he was much heavier than he had been at School, and by the time he rolled off his victim the little dacoit was stone dead.

And there was a boy who was always being led astray by bad advice, and begging off punishment on that account. He got into some little scrape when he grew up, and we who knew him knew, before he was reprimanded by his commanding officer, exactly what his excuse would be. It came out almost word for word as he was used to whimper it at School. He was cured, though by being sent off on a small expedition where he alone would be responsible for any advice that was going, as well as for fifty soldiers.

And the best boy of all—he was really good, not book good—was shot in the thigh as he was leading his men up the ramp of a fortress. All he said was, "Put me up against that tree and take my men on"; and when the men came back he was dead.

Ages and ages ago, when Queen Victoria was shot at by a man in the street, the School paper made some verses about it that ended like this:

One school of many, made to make
Men who shall hold it dearest right
To battle for their ruler's sake,
And stake their being in the fight,

Sends greeting, humble and sincere,
Though verse be rude and poor and mean,
To you, the greatest as most dear,
Victoria, by God's Grace, our Queen!

Such greetings as should come from those
Whose fathers faced the Sepoy hordes,
Or served you in the Russian snows
And dying, left their sons their swords.

For we are bred to do your will
By land and sea, wherever flies
The Flag to fight and follow still,
And work your empire's destinies.

Once more we greet you, though unseen
Our greetings be, and coming slow.
Trust us, if need arise, O Queen!
We shall not tarry with the blow.

And there are one or two places in the world that can bear witness how the School kept its word.

UNTIMELY
1926

NOTHING in life has been made by man for man's using
But it was shown long since to man in ages
Lost as the name of the maker of it,

Who received oppression and shame for his wages—
Hate, avoidance, and scorn in his daily dealings—
Until he perished, wholly confounded.
More to be pitied than he are the wise
Souls which foresaw the evil of losing
Knowledge or Art before time, and aborted
Noble devices and deep-wrought healings,
Lest offence should arise.

Heaven delivers on earth the Hour that cannot be thwarted,
Neither advanced, at the price of a world or a soul, and its
    Prophet
Comes through the blood of the vanguards who dreamed—
    too soon—it had sounded.

THE EYE OF ALLAH
1926

THE Cantor of St. Illod's being far too enthusiastic a musician to concern himself with its Library, the Sub-Cantor, who idolized every detail of the work, was tidying up, after two hours' writing and dictation in the Scriptorium. The copying-monks handed him in their sheets—it was a plain Four Gospels ordered by an Abbot at Evesham—and filed out to vespers. John Otho, better known as John of Burgos, took no heed. He was burnishing a tiny boss of gold in his miniature of the Annunciation for his Gospel of St. Luke, which it was hoped that Cardinal Falcodi, the Papal Legate, might later be pleased to accept.

"Break off, John," said the Sub-Cantor in an undertone.

"Eh? Gone, have they? I never heard. Hold a minute, Clement."

The Sub-Cantor waited patiently. He had known John more than a dozen years, coming and going at St. Illod's, to which monastery John, when abroad, always said he belonged. The claim was gladly allowed for, more even than other Fitz Otho's, he seemed to carry all the Arts under his hand, and most of their practical receipts under his hood.

The Sub-Cantor looked over his shoulder at the pinned-down sheet where the first words of the Magnificat were built up in gold washed with red-lac for a background to the Virgin's hardly yet fired halo. She was shown, hands joined in wonder, at a lattice of infinitely intricate arabesque, round the edges of which sprays of orange-bloom seemed to load the blue hot air that carried back over the minute parched landscape in the middle distance.

"You've made her all Jewess," said the Sub-Cantor, studying the olive-flushed cheek and the eyes charged with foreknowledge.

"What else was Our Lady?" John slipped out the pins. "Listen, Clement. If I do not come back, this goes into my Great Luke, whoever finishes it." He slid the drawing between its guard-papers.

"Then you're for Burgos again—as I heard?"

"In two days. The new Cathedral yonder—but they're slower than the Wrath of God, those masons—is good for the soul."

"Thy soul?" The Sub-Cantor seemed doubtful.

"Even mine, by your permission. And down south—on the

edge of the Conquered Countries—Granada way—there's some Moorish diaper-work that's wholesome. It allays vain thought and draws it toward the picture—as you felt, just now, in my Annunciation."

"She—it was very beautiful. No wonder you go. But you'll not forget your absolution, John?"

"Surely." This was a precaution John no more omitted on the eve of his travels than he did the recutting of the tonsure which he had provided himself with in his youth, somewhere near Ghent. The mark gave him privilege of clergy at a pinch, and a certain consideration on the road always.

"You'll not forget, either, what we need in the Scriptorium. There's no more true ultramarine in this world now. They mix it with that German blue. And as for vermilion——"

"I'll do my best always."

"And Brother Thomas (this was the Infirmarian in charge of the monastery hospital) he needs——"

"He'll do his own asking. I'll go over his side now, and get me re-tonsured."

John went down the stairs to the lane that divides the hospital and cook-house from the back-cloisters. While he was being barbered, Brother Thomas (St. Illod's meek but deadly persistent Infirmarian) gave him a list of drugs that he was to bring back from Spain by hook, crook, or lawful purchase. Here they were surprised by the lame, dark Abbot Stephen, in his fur-lined night-boots. Not that Stephen de Sautré was any spy; but as a young man he had shared an unlucky Crusade, which had ended, after a battle at Mansura, in two years' captivity among the Saracens at Cairo where men learn to walk softly. A fair huntsman and hawker, a reasonable disciplinarian but a man of science above all, and a Doctor of Medicine under one Ranulphus, Canon of St. Paul's, his heart was more in the monastery's hospital work than its religious. He checked their list interestedly, adding items of his own. After the Infirmarian had withdrawn he gave John generous absolution, to cover lapses by the way; for he did not hold with chance-bought Indulgences.

"And what seek you *this* journey?" he demanded, sitting

on the bench beside the mortar and scales in the little warm cell for stored drugs.

"Devils, mostly," said John, grinning.

"In Spain? Are not Abana and Pharphar——?"

John, to whom men were but matter for drawings, and well-born to boot (since he was a de Sanford on his mother's side), looked the Abbot full in the face and—"Did *you* find it so?" said he.

"No. They were in Cairo too. But what's your special need of 'em?"

"For my Great Luke. He's the master-hand of all Four when it comes to devils."

"No wonder. He was a physician. You're not."

"Heaven forbid! But I'm weary of our Church-pattern devils. They're only apes and goats and poultry conjoined. 'Good enough for plain red-and-black Hells and Judgment Days—but not for me."

"What makes you so choice in them?"

"Because it stands to reason and Art that there are all musters of devils in Hell's dealings. Those Seven, for example, that were haled out of the Magdalene. They'd be she-devils—no kin at all to the beaked and horned and bearded devils-general."

The Abbot laughed.

"And see again! The devil that came out of the dumb man. What use is snout or bill to *him?* He'd be faceless as a leper. Above all—God send I live to do it!—the devils that entered the Gadarene swine. They'd be—they'd be—I know not yet what they'd be, but they'd be surpassing devils. I'd have 'em diverse as the Saints themselves. But now, they're all one pattern, for wall, window, or picture-work."

"Go on, John. You're deeper in this mystery than I."

"Heaven forbid! But I say there's respect due to devils, damned tho' they be."

"Dangerous doctrine."

"My meaning is that if the shape of anything be worth man's thought to picture to man, it's worth his best thought."

"That's safer. But I'm glad I've given you Absolution."

"There's less risk for a craftsman who deals with the outside shapes of things—for Mother Church's glory."

"Maybe so, but John"—the Abbot's hand almost touched John's sleeve—"tell me, now, is—is she Moorish or—or Hebrew?"

"She's mine," John returned.

"Is that enough?"

"I have found it so."

"Well—ah well! It's out of my jurisdiction but—how do they look at it down yonder?"

"Oh, they drive nothing to a head in Spain—neither Church nor King, bless them! There's too many Moors and Jews to kill them all, and if they chased 'em away there'd be no trade nor farming. Trust me, in the Conquered Countries, from Seville to Granada, we live lovingly enough together—Spaniard, Moor, and Jew. Ye see, *we* ask no questions."

"Yes—yes," Stephen sighed. "And always there's the hope, she may be converted."

"Oh yes, there's always hope."

The Abbot went on into the hospital. It was an easy age before Rome tightened the screw as to clerical connections. If the lady were not too forward, or the son too much his father's beneficiary in ecclesiastical preferments and levies, a good deal was overlooked. But, as the Abbot had reason to recall, unions between Christian and Infidel led to sorrow. None the less, when John with mule, mails, and man, clattered off down the lane for Southampton and the sea, Stephen envied him.

. . . .

He was back, twenty months later, in good hard case, and loaded down with fairings. A lump of richest lazuli, a bar of orange-hearted vermilion, and a small packet of dried beetles which make most glorious scarlet, for the Sub-Cantor. Besides that, a few cubes of milky marble, with yet a pink flush in them, which could be slaked and ground down to incomparable background-stuff. There were quite half the drugs that the Abbot and Thomas had demanded, and there was a long deep-red cornelian necklace for the Abbot's Lady—Anne of Norton. She received it graciously, and asked where John had come by it.

"Near Granada," he said.

"You left all well there?" Anne asked. (Maybe the Abbot had told her something of John's confession.)

"I left all in the hands of God."

"Ah me! How long since?"

"Four months less eleven days."

"Were you—with her?"

"In my arms. Childbed."

"And?"

"The boy too. There is nothing now."

Anne of Norton caught her breath.

"I think you'll be glad of that," she said after a while.

"Give me time, and maybe I'll compass it. But not now."

"You have your handwork and your art and—John—remember there's no jealousy in the grave."

"Ye-es! I have my Art, and Heaven knows I'm jealous of none."

"Thank God for that at least," said Anne of Norton, the always ailing woman who followed the Abbot with her sunk eyes. "And be sure I shall treasure this," she touched the beads, "as long as I shall live."

"I brought—trusted—it to you for that," he replied, and took leave. When she told the Abbot how she had come by it, he said nothing, but as he and Thomas were storing the drugs that John handed over in the cell which backs on to the hospital kitchen-chimney, he observed, of a cake of dried poppy-juice: "This has power to cut off all pain from a man's body."

"I have seen it," said John.

"But for pain of the soul there is, outside God's Grace, but one drug; and that is a man's craft, learning, or other helpful motion of his own mind."

"That is coming to me, too," was the answer.

John spent the next fair May day out in the woods with the monastery swineherd and all the porkers; and returned loaded with flowers and sprays of spring, to his own carefully kept place in the north bay of the Scriptorium. There with his travelling sketch-books under his left elbow, he sunk himself past all recollections in his Great Luke.

Brother Martin, Senior Copyist (who spoke about once a fortnight) ventured to ask, later, how the work was going.

"All here!" John tapped his forehead with his pencil. "It has been only waiting these months to—ah God!—be born. Are ye free of your plain-copying, Martin?"

Brother Martin nodded. It was his pride that John of Burgos turned to him, in spite of his seventy years, for really good page-work.

"Then see!" John laid out a new vellum—thin but flawless. "There's no better than this sheet from here to Paris. Yes! Smell it if you choose. Wherefore—give me the compasses and I'll set it out for you—if ye make one letter lighter or darker than its next, I'll stick ye like a pig."

"Never, John!" the old man beamed happily.

"But I will! Now, follow! Here and here, as I prick, and in script of just this height to the hair's-breadth, ye'll scribe the thirty-first and thirty-second verses of Eighth Luke."

"Yes, the Gadarene Swine! *'And they besought him that he would not command them to go out into the abyss. And there was a herd of many swine'* "——Brother Martin naturally knew all the Gospels by heart.

"Just so! Down to *'and he suffered them.'* Take your time to it. My Magdalene has to come off my heart first."

Brother Martin achieved the work so perfectly that John stole some soft sweetmeats from the Abbot's kitchen for his reward. The old man ate them; then repented; then confessed and insisted on penance. At which the Abbot, knowing there was but one way to reach the real sinner, set him a book called *De Virtutibus Herbarum* to fair-copy. St. Illod's had borrowed it from the gloomy Cistercians, who do not hold with pretty things, and the crabbed text kept Martin busy just when John wanted him for some rather specially spaced letterings.

"See now," said the Sub-Cantor reprovingly. "You should

not do such things, John. Here's Brother Martin on penance for your sake——"

"No—for my Great Luke. But I've paid the Abbot's cook. I've drawn him till his own scullions cannot keep straight-faced. *He*'ll not tell again."

"Unkindly done! And you're out of favour with the Abbot too. He's made no sign to you since you came back—never asked you to high table."

"I've been busy. Having eyes in his head, Stephen knew it. Clement, there's no Librarian from Durham to Torre fit to clean up after you."

The Sub-Cantor stood on guard; he knew where John's compliments generally ended.

"But outside the Scriptorium——"

"Where I never go." The Sub-Cantor had been excused even digging in the garden, lest it should mar his wonderful book-binding hands.

"In all things outside the Scriptorium you are the master-fool of Christendie. Take it from me, Clement. I've met many."

"I take everything from you," Clement smiled benignly. "You use me worse than a singing-boy."

They could hear one of that suffering breed in the cloister below, squalling as the Cantor pulled his hair.

"God love you! So I do! But have you ever thought how I lie and steal daily on my travels—yes, and for aught you know, murder—to fetch you colours and earths?"

"True," said just and conscience-stricken Clement. "I have often thought that were I in the world—which God forbid!—I might be a strong thief in some matters."

Even Brother Martin, bent above his loathed *De Virtutibus*, laughed.

. . . .

But about mid-summer, Thomas the Infirmarian conveyed to John the Abbot's invitation to supper in his house that night, with the request that he would bring with him anything that he had done for his Great Luke.

"What's toward?" said John, who had been wholly shut up in his work.

"Only one of his 'wisdom' dinners. You've sat at a few since you were a man."

"True: and mostly good. How would Stephen have us——?"

"Gown and hood over all. There will be a doctor from Salerno—one Roger, an Italian. Wise and famous with the knife on the body. He's been in the Infirmary some ten days, helping me—even me!"

" 'Never heard the name. But our Stephen's *physicus* before *sacerdos,* always."

"And his Lady has a sickness of some time. Roger came hither in chief because of her."

"Did he? Now I think of it, I have not seen the Lady Anne for a while."

"Ye've seen nothing for a long while. She has been housed near a month—they have to carry her abroad now."

"So bad as that, then?"

"Roger of Salerno will not yet say what he thinks. But——"

"God pity Stephen! . . . Who else at table, beside thee?"

"An Oxford friar. Roger is his name also. A learned and famous philosopher. And he holds his liquor too, valiantly."

"Three doctors—counting Stephen. I've always found that means two atheists."

Thomas looked uneasily down his nose. "That's a wicked proverb," he stammered. "You should not use it."

"Hoh! Never come you the monk over me, Thomas! You've been Infirmarian at St. Illod's eleven years—and a lay-brother still. Why have you never taken orders, all this while?"

"I—I am not worthy."

"Ten times worthier than that new fat swine—Henry Who's-his-name—that takes the Infirmary Masses. He bullocks in with the Viaticum, under your nose, when a sick man's only faint from being bled. So the man dies—of pure fear. Ye know it! I've watched your face at such times. Take Orders,

Didymus. You'll have a little more medicine and a little less Mass with your sick then; and they'll live longer."

"I am unworthy—unworthy," Thomas repeated pitifully.

"Not you—but—to your own master you stand or fall. And now that my work releases me for a while, I'll drink with any philosopher out of any school. And Thomas," he coaxed, "a hot bath for me in the Infirmary before vespers."

. . . .

When the Abbot's perfectly cooked and served meal had ended, and the deep-fringed naperies were removed, and the Prior had sent in the keys with word that all was fast in the Monastery, and the keys had been duly returned with the word: "Make it so till Prime," the Abbot and his guests went out to cool themselves in an upper cloister that took them, by way of the leads, to the South Choir side of the Triforium. The summer sun was still strong, for it was barely six o'clock, but the Abbey Church, of course, lay in her wonted darkness. Lights were being lit for choir-practice thirty feet below.

"Our Cantor gives them no rest," the Abbot whispered. "Stand by this pillar and we'll hear what he's driving them at now."

"Remember all!" the Cantor's hard voice came up. "This is the soul of Bernard himself, attacking our evil world. Take it quicker than yesterday, and throw all your words clean-bitten from you. In the loft there! Begin!"

The organ broke out for an instant, alone and raging. Then the voices crashed together into that first fierce line of the *"De Contemptu Mundi."*[1]

"Hora novissima—tempora pessima"—a dead pause till, the assenting *sunt* broke, like a sob, out of the darkness, and one boy's voice, clearer than silver trumpets, returned the long-drawn *vigilemus.*

"Ecce minaciter, imminet Arbiter" (organ and voices were leashed together in terror and warning, breaking away liquidly to the *"ille supremus"*). Then the tone-colours shifted for the prelude to—*"Imminet, imminet, ut mala terminet——"*

[1]Hymn No. 226, A. and M., "The world is very evil."

"Stop! Again!" cried the Cantor; and gave his reasons a little more roundly than was natural at choir-practice.

"Ah! Pity o' man's vanity! He's guessed we are here. Come away!" said the Abbot. Anne of Norton, in her carried chair, had been listening too, further along the dark Triforium, with Roger of Salerno. John heard her sob. On the way back, he asked Thomas how her health stood. Before Thomas could reply the sharp-featured Italian doctor pushed between them. "Following on our talk together, I judged it best to tell her," said he to Thomas.

"What?" John asked simply enough.

"What she knew already." Roger of Salerno launched into a Greek quotation to the effect that every woman knows all about everything.

"I have no Greek," said John stiffly. Roger of Salerno had been giving them a good deal of it, at dinner.

"Then I'll come to you in Latin. Ovid hath it neatly. *'Utque malum late solet immedicabile cancer——'* but doubtless you know the rest, worthy Sir."

"Alas! My school-Latin's but what I've gathered by the way from fools professing to heal sick women. *'Hocus-pocus——'* but doubtless you know the rest, worthy Sir."

Roger of Salerno was quite quiet till they regained the dining-room, where the fire had been comforted and the dates, raisins, ginger, figs, and cinnamon-scented sweetmeats set out, with the choicer wines, on the after-table. The Abbot seated himself, drew off his ring, dropped it, that all might hear the tinkle, into an empty silver cup, stretched his feet towards the hearth, and looked at the great gilt and carved rose in the barrel-roof. The silence that keeps from Compline to Matins had closed on their world. The bull-necked Friar watched a ray of sunlight split itself into colours on the rim of a crystal salt-cellar; Roger of Salerno had re-opened some discussion with Brother Thomas on a type of spotted fever that was baffling them both in England and abroad; John took note of the keen profile, and—it might serve as a note for the Great Luke—his hand moved to his bosom. The Abbot saw, and nodded permission. John whipped out silver-point and sketch-book.

"Nay—modesty is good enough—but deliver your own opinion," the Italian was urging the Infirmarian. Out of courtesy to the foreigner nearly all the talk was in table-Latin; more formal and more copious than monk's patter. Thomas began with his meek stammer.

"I confess myself at a loss for the cause of the fever unless—as Varro saith in his *De Re Rustica*—certain small animals which the eye cannot follow enter the body by the nose and mouth, and set up grave diseases. On the other hand, this is not in Scripture."

Roger of Salerno hunched head and shoulders like an angry cat. "Always *that!*" he said, and John snatched down the twist of the thin lips.

"Never at rest, John," the Abbot smiled at the artist. "You should break off every two hours for prayers, as we do. St. Benedict was no fool. Two hours is all that a man can carry the edge of his eye or hand."

"For copyists—yes. Brother Martin is not sure after one hour. But when a man's work takes him, he must go on till it lets him go."

"Yes, that is the Demon of Socrates," the Friar from Oxford rumbled above his cup.

"The doctrine leans toward presumption," said the Abbot. "Remember, 'Shall mortal man be more just than his Maker?' "

"There is no danger of justice"; the Friar spoke bitterly. "But at least Man might be suffered to go forward in his Art or his thought. Yet if Mother Church sees or hears him move anyward, what says she? 'No!' Always 'No.' "

"But if the little animals of Varro be invisible"—this was Roger of Salerno to Thomas—"how are we any nearer to a cure?"

"By experiment"—the Friar wheeled round on them suddenly. "By reason and experiment. The one is useless without the other. But Mother Church——"

"Ay!" Roger de Salerno dashed at the fresh bait like a

pike. "Listen, Sirs. Her bishops—our Princes—strew our roads in Italy with carcasses that they make for their pleasure or wrath. Beautiful corpses! Yet if I—if we doctors—so much as raise the skin of one of them to look at God's fabric beneath, what says Mother Church? 'Sacrilege! Stick to your pigs and dogs, or you burn!' "

"And not Mother Church only!" the Friar chimed in. "*Every* way we are barred—barred by the words of some man, dead a thousand years, which are held final. Who is any son of Adam that his one say-so should close a door towards truth? I would not except even Peter Peregrinus, my own great teacher."

"Nor I Paul of Aegina," Roger of Salerno cried. "Listen Sirs! Here is a case to the very point. Apuleius affirmeth, if a man eat fasting of the juice of the cut-leaved buttercup—*sceleratus* we call it, which means 'rascally' "—this with a condescending nod towards John—"his soul will leave his body laughing. Now this is the lie more dangerous than truth, since truth of a sort is in it."

"He's away!" whispered the Abbot despairingly.

"For the juice of that herb, I know by experiment, burns, blisters, and wries the mouth. I know also the *rictus,* or pseudo-laughter on the face of such as have perished by the strong poisons of herbs allied to this ranunculus. Certainly that spasm resembles laughter. It seems then, in my judgment, that Apuleius, having seen the body of one thus poisoned, went off at score and wrote that the man died laughing."

"Neither staying to observe, nor to confirm observation by experiment," added the Friar, frowning.

Stephen the Abbot cocked an eyebrow toward John.

"How think *you?*" said he.

"I'm no doctor," John returned, "but I'd say Apuleius in all these years might have been betrayed by his copyists. They take shortcuts to save 'emselves trouble. Put case that Apuleius wrote the soul *seems to* leave the body laughing, after this poison. There's not three copyists in five (*my* judgment) would not leave out the 'seems to.' For who'd question Apuleius? If it seemed so to him, so it must be. Otherwise any child knows cut-leaved buttercup."

"Have you knowledge of herbs?" Roger of Salerno asked curtly.

"Only, that when I was a boy in convent, I've made tetters round my mouth and on my neck with buttercup-juice, to save going to prayer o' cold nights."

"Ah!" said Roger. "I profess no knowledge of tricks." He turned aside, stiffly.

"No matter! Now for your own tricks, John," the tactful Abbot broke in. "You shall show the doctors your Magdalene and your Gadarene Swine and the devils."

"Devils? Devils? *I* have produced devils by means of drugs; and have abolished them by the same means. Whether devils be external to mankind or immanent, I have not yet pronounced." Roger of Salerno was still angry.

"Ye dare not," snapped the Friar from Oxford. "Mother Church makes Her own devils."

"Not wholly! Our John has come back from Spain with brand-new ones." Abbot Stephen took the vellum handed to him, and laid it tenderly on the table. They gathered to look. The Magdalene was drawn in palest, almost transparent, grisaille, against a raging, swaying background of woman-faced devils, each broke to and by her special sin, and each, one could see, frenziedly straining against the Power that compelled her.

"I've never seen the like of this grey shadow-work," said the Abbot. "How came you by it?"

"*Non nobis!* It came to me," said John, not knowing he was a generation or so ahead of his time in the use of that medium.

"Why is she so pale?" the Friar demanded.

"Evil has all come out of her—she'd take any colour now."

"Ay, like light through glass. *I* see."

Roger of Salerno was looking in silence—his nose nearer and nearer the page. "It is so," he pronounced finally. "Thus it is in epilepsy—mouth, eyes, and forehead—even to the droop of her wrist there. Every sign of it! She will need restoratives, that woman, and, afterwards, sleep natural. No poppy-juice, or she will vomit on her waking. And thereafter —but I am not in my Schools." He drew himself up. "Sir," said he, "you should be of Our calling. For, by the Snakes of Aesculapius, you *see!*"

The two struck hands as equals.

"And how think you of the Seven Devils?" the Abbot went on.

These melted into convoluted flower- or flame-like bodies, ranging in colour from phosphorescent green to the black purple of outworn iniquity, whose hearts could be traced beating through their substance. But, for sign of hope and the sane workings of life, to be regained, the deep border was of conventionalized spring flowers and birds, all crowned by a kingfisher in haste, atilt through a clump of yellow iris.

Roger of Salerno identified the herbs and spoke largely of their virtues.

"And now, the Gadarene Swine," said Stephen. John laid the picture on the table.

Here were devils dishoused, in dread of being abolished to the Void, huddling and hurtling together to force lodgment by every opening into the brute bodies offered. Some of the swine fought the invasion, foaming and jerking; some were surrendering to it, sleepily, as to a luxurious back-scratching; others, wholly possessed, whirled off in bucking droves for the lake beneath. In one corner the freed man stretched out his limbs all restored to his control, and Our Lord, seated, looked at him as questioning what he would make of his deliverance.

"Devils indeed!" was the Friar's comment. "But wholly a new sort."

Some devils were mere lumps, with lobes and protuberances—a hint of a fiend's face peering through jelly-like walls. And there was a family of impatient, globular devillings who had burst open the belly of their smirking parent, and were revolving desperately towards their prey. Others patterned themselves into rods, chains and ladders, single or conjoined, round the throat and jaws of a shrieking sow, from whose ear emerged the lashing, glassy tail of a devil that had made good his refuge. And there were granulated and conglomerate devils, mixed up with the foam and slaver where the attack was fiercest. Thence the eye carried on to the insanely active backs of the downward-racing swine, the swineherd's aghast face, and his dog's terror.

Said Roger of Salerno, "I pronounce that these were begotten of drugs. They stand outside the rational mind."

"Not these," said Thomas the Infirmarian, who as a servant of the Monastery should have asked his Abbot's leave to speak. "Not *these*—look!—in the bordure."

The border to the picture was a diaper of irregular but balanced compartments or cellules, where sat, swam, or weltered, devils in blank, so to say—things as yet uninspired by Evil—indifferent, but lawlessly outside imagination. Their shapes resembled, again, ladders, chains, scourges, diamonds, aborted buds, or gravid phosphorescent globes—some well-nigh star-like.

Roger of Salerno compared them to the obsessions of a Churchman's mind.

"Malignant?" the Friar from Oxford questioned.

" 'Count everything unknown for horrible,' " Roger quoted with scorn.

"Not I. But they are marvellous—marvellous. I think——"

The Friar drew back. Thomas edged in to see better, and half opened his mouth.

"Speak," said Stephen, who had been watching him. "We are all in a sort doctors here."

"I would say then"—Thomas rushed at it as one putting out his life's belief at the stake—"that these lower shapes in the bordure may not be so much hellish and malignant as models and patterns upon which John has tricked out and embellished his proper devils among the swine above there!"

"And that would signify?" said Roger of Salerno sharply.

"In my poor judgment, that he may have seen such shapes —without help of drugs."

"Now who—*who*"—said John of Burgos, after a round and

unregarded oath—"has made thee so wise of a sudden, my Doubter?"

"I wise? God forbid! Only John, remember—one winter six years ago—the snowflakes melting on your sleeve at the cookhouse-door. You showed me them through a little crystal, that made small things larger."

"Yes. The Moors call such a glass the Eye of Allah," John confirmed.

"You showed me them melting—six-sided. You called them, then, your patterns."

"True. Snow-flakes melt six-sided. I have used them for diaper-work often."

"Melting snow-flakes as seen through a glass? By art optical?" the Friar asked.

"Art optical? *I* have never heard!" Roger of Salerno cried.

"John," said the Abbot of St. Illod's commandingly, "was it—is it so?"

"In some sort," John replied, "Thomas has the right of it. Those shapes in the bordure were my workshop-patterns for the devils above. In *my* craft, Salerno, we dare not drug. It kills hand and eye. My shapes are to be seen honestly, in nature."

The Abbot drew a bowl of rose-water towards him. "When I was prisoner with—with the Saracens after Mansura," he began, turning up the fold of his long sleeve, "there were certain magicians—physicians—who could show—" he dipped his third finger delicately in the water—"all the firmament of Hell, as it were, in—" he shook off one drop from his polished nail on to the polished table—"even such a supernaculum as this."

"But it must be foul water—not clean," said John.

"Show us then—all—all," said Stephen. "I would make sure —once more." The Abbot's voice was official.

John drew from his bosom a stamped leather box, some six or eight inches long, wherein, bedded on faded velvet, lay what looked like silver-bound compasses of old box-wood, with a screw at the head which opened or closed the legs to minute fractions. The legs terminated, not in points, but spoonshapedly, one spatula pierced with a metal-lined hole less than a quarter of an inch across, the other with a half-inch hole. Into this latter John, after carefully wiping with a silk rag, slipped a metal cylinder that carried glass or crystal, it seemed, at each end.

"Ah! Art optic!" said the Friar. "But what is that beneath it?"

It was a small swivelling sheet of polished silver no bigger than a florin, which caught the light and concentrated it on the lesser hole. John adjusted it without the Friar's proffered help.

"And now to find a drop of water," said he, picking up a small brush.

"Come to my upper cloister. The sun is on the leads still," said the Abbot, rising.

They followed him there. Half way along, a drip from a gutter had made a greenish puddle in a worn stone. Very carefully, John dropped a drop of it into the smaller hole of the compass-leg, and, steadying the apparatus on a coping, worked the screw in the compass-joint, screwed the cylinder, and swung the swivel of the mirror till he was satisfied.

"Good!" He peered through the thing. "My Shapes are all here. Now look, Father! If they do not meet your eye at first, turn this nicked edge here, left or right-handed."

"I have not forgotten," said the Abbot, taking his place. "Yes! They are here—as they were in my time—my time past. There is no end to them, I was told. . . . There *is* no end!"

"The light will go. Oh, let me look! Suffer me to see, also!" the Friar pleaded, almost shouldering Stephen from the eye-piece. The Abbot gave way. His eyes were on time past. But the Friar, instead of looking, turned the apparatus in his capable hands.

"Nay, nay," John interrupted, for the man was already fiddling at the screws. "Let the Doctor see."

Roger of Salerno looked, minute after minute. John saw his blue-veined cheek-bones turn white. He stepped back at last, as though stricken.

"It is a new world—a new world and—Oh, God Unjust!—I am old!"

"And now Thomas," Stephen ordered.

John manipulated the tube for the Infirmarian, whose hands shook, and he too looked long. "It is Life," he said presently in a breaking voice. "No Hell! Life created and rejoicing—the work of the Creator. They live, even as I have dreamed. Then it was no sin for me to dream. No sin—O God—no sin!"

He flung himself on his knees and began hysterically the *Benedicite omnia Opera.*

"And now I will see how it is actuated," said the Friar from Oxford, thrusting forward again.

"Bring it within. The place is all eyes and ears," said Stephen.

They walked quietly back along the leads, three English counties laid out in evening sunshine around them; church upon church, monastery upon monastery, cell after cell, and the bulk of a vast cathedral moored on the edge of the banked shoals of sunset.

When they were at the after-table once more they sat down, all except the Friar who went to the window and huddled bat-like over the thing. "I see! I see!" he was repeating to himself.

"He'll not hurt it," said John. But the Abbot, staring in front of him, like Roger of Salerno, did not hear. The Infirmarian's head was on the table between his shaking arms.

John reached for a cup of wine.

"It was shown to me," the Abbot was speaking to himself, "in Cairo, that man stands ever between two Infinities—of greatness and littleness. Therefore, there is no end—either to life—or——"

"And *I* stand on the edge of the grave," snarled Roger of Salerno. "Who pities *me?*"

"Hush!" said Thomas the Infirmarian. "The little creatures shall be sanctified—sanctified to the service of His sick."

"What need?" John of Burgos wiped his lips. "It shows no more than the shapes of things. It gives good pictures. I had it at Granada. It was brought from the East, they told me."

Roger of Salerno laughed with an old man's malice. "What of Mother Church? Most Holy Mother Church? If it comes to Her ears that we have spied into Her Hell without Her leave, where do we stand?"

"At the stake," said the Abbot of St. Illod's, and, raising his voice a trifle. "You hear that? Roger Bacon, heard you that?"

The Friar turned from the window, clutching the compasses tighter.

"No, no!" he appealed. "Not with Falcodi—not with our English-hearted Foulkes made Pope. He's wise—he's learned. He reads what I have put forth. Foulkes would never suffer it."

"'Holy Pope is one thing, Holy Church another,'" Roger quoted.

"But I—*I* can bear witness it is no Art Magic," the Friar went on. "Nothing is it, except Art optical—wisdom after trial and experiment, mark you. I can prove it, and—my name weighs with men who dare think."

"Find them!" croaked Roger of Salerno. "Five or six in all the world. That makes less than fifty pounds by weight of ashes at the stake. I have watched such men—reduced."

"I will not give this up!" The Friar's voice cracked in passion and despair. "It would be to sin against the Light."

"No, no! Let us—let us sanctify the little animals of Varro," said Thomas.

Stephen leaned forward, fished his ring out of the cup, and slipped it on his finger. "My sons," said he, "we have seen what we have seen."

"That it is no magic but simple Art," the Friar persisted.

"'Avails nothing. In the eyes of Mother Church we have seen more than is permitted to man."

"But it was Life—created and rejoicing," said Thomas.

"To look into Hell as we shall be judged—as we shall be proved—to have looked, is for priests only."

"Or green-sick virgins on the road to sainthood who, for cause any mid-wife could give you——"

The Abbot's half-lifted hand checked Roger of Salerno's outpouring.

"Nor may even priests see more in Hell than Church knows to be there. John, there is respect due to Church as well as to Devils."

"My trade's the outside of things," said John quietly. "I have my patterns."

"But you may need to look again for more," the Friar said.

"In my craft, a thing done is done with. We go on to new shapes after that."

"And if we trespass beyond bounds, even in thought, we lie open to the judgment of the Church," the Abbot continued.

"But thou knowest—*knowest!*" Roger of Salerno had returned to the attack. "Here's all the world in darkness concerning the causes of things—from the fever across the lane to thy Lady's—thine own Lady's—eating malady. Think!"

"I have thought upon it, Salerno! I have thought indeed."

Thomas the Infirmarian lifted his head again; and this time he did not stammer at all. "As in the water, so in the blood must they rage and war with each other! I have dreamed these ten years—I thought it was a sin—but my dreams and Varro's are true! Think on it again! Here's the Light under our very hand!"

"Quench it! You'd no more stand to roasting than—any other. I'll give you the case as Church—as I myself—would frame it. Our John here returns from the Moors, and shows us a hell of devils contending in the compass of one drop of water. Magic past clearance! You can hear the faggots crackle."

"But thou knowest! Thou hast seen it all before! For man's poor sake! For old friendship's sake—Stephen!" The Friar was trying to stuff the compasses into his bosom as he appealed.

"What Stephen de Sautré knows, you his friends know also. I would have you, now, obey the Abbot of St. Illod's. Give to me!" He held out his ringed hand.

"May I—may John here—not even make a drawing of one—one screw?" said the broken Friar, in spite of himself.

"Nowise!" Stephen took it over. "Your dagger, John. Sheathed will serve."

He unscrewed the metal cylinder, laid it on the table, and with the dagger's hilt smashed some crystal to sparkling dust which he swept into a scooped hand and cast behind the hearth.

"It would seem," said he, "the choice lies between two sins. To deny the world a Light which is under our hand, or to enlighten the world before her time. What you have seen, I saw long since among the physicians at Cairo. And I know what doctrine they drew from it. Hast *thou* dreamed, Thomas? I also—with fuller knowledge. But this birth, my sons, is untimely. It will be but the mother of more death, more torture, more division, and greater darkness in this dark age. Therefore I, who know both my world and the Church, take this Choice on my conscience. Go! It is finished."

He thrust the wooden part of the compasses deep among the beech logs till all was burned.

THE CHURCH THAT WAS AT ANTIOCH

1929

"But when Peter was come to Antioch, I withstood him to the face, because he was to be blamed."

—ST. PAUL'S EPISTLE TO THE GALATIANS, ii. II.

HIS mother, a devout and well-born Roman widow, decided that he was doing himself no good in an Eastern Legion so near to free-thinking Constantinople, and got him seconded for civil duty in Antioch, where his uncle, Lucius Sergius, was head of the urban Police. Valens obeyed as a son and as a young man keen to see life, and, presently, cast up at his uncle's door.

"That sister-in-law of mine," said the elder, "never remembers me till she wants something. What have you been doing?"

"Nothing, Uncle."

"Meaning everything?"

"That's what Mother thinks. But I haven't."

"We shall see. Your quarters are across the inner courtyard. Your—er—baggage is there already. . . . Oh, I shan't interfere with your private arrangements! I'm not the uncle with the rough tongue. Get your bath. We'll talk at supper."

But before that hour "Father Serga," as the Prefect of Police was called, learned from the Treasury that his nephew had marched overland from Constantinople in charge of a treasure-convoy which, after a brush with brigands in the pass outside Tarsus, he had duly delivered.

"Why didn't you tell me about it?" his uncle asked at the meal.

"I had to report to the Treasury first," was the answer.

Serga looked at him. "Gods! You *are* like your father," said he. "Cilicia is scandalously policed."

"So I noticed. They ambushed us not five miles from Tarsus town. Are we given to that sort of thing here?"

"You make yourself at home early. No. *We* are not, but Syria is a Non-regulation Province—under the Emperor—not the Senate. We've the entire unaccountable East to one side; the scum of the Mediterranean on the other; and all hellicat Judæa southward. Anything can happen in Syria. D'you like the prospect?"

"I shall—under you."

"It's in the blood. The same with men as horses. Now what have you done that distresses your mother so?"

"She's a little behind the times, sir. She follows the old school, of course—the home-worships, and the strict Latin Trinity. I don't think she recognizes any Gods outside Jupiter, Juno, and Minerva."

"I don't either—officially."

"Nor I, as an officer, sir. But one wants more than that, and—and—what I learned in Byzant squared with what I saw with the Fifteenth."

"You needn't go on. All Eastern Legions are alike. You mean you follow Mithras—eh?"

The young man bowed his head slightly.

"No harm, boy. It's a soldier's religion, even if it comes from outside."

"So I thought. But Mother heard of it. She didn't approve and—I suppose that's why I'm here."

"Off the trident and into the net! Just like a woman! All Syria is stuffed with Mithraism. *My* objection to fancy religions is that they mostly meet after dark, and that means more work for the Police. We've a College here of stiff-necked Hebrews who call themselves Christians."

"I've heard of them," said Valens. "There isn't a ceremony or symbol they haven't stolen from the Mithras ritual."

" 'No news to *me!* Religions are part of my office-work; and they'll be part of yours. Our Synagogue Jews are fighting like Scythians over this new faith."

"Does that matter much?"

"So long as they fight each other, we've only to keep the ring. Divide and rule—especially with Hebrews. Even these Christians are divided now. You see—one part of their worship is to eat together."

"Another theft! The Supper is the essential Symbol with us," Valens interrupted.

"With *us,* it's the essential symbol of trouble for your uncle, my dear. Anyone can become a Christian. A Jew may; but he still lives by his Law of Moses (I've had to master that cursed code, too), and it regulates all his doings. Then he sits down at a Christian love-feast beside a Greek or Westerner, who doesn't kill mutton or pig—No! No! Jews don't touch pork —as the Jewish Law lays down. Then the tables are broken up—but not by laughter—No! No! Riot!"

"That's childish," said Valens.

" 'Wish it were. But my lictors are called in to keep order, and I have to take the depositions of Synagogue Jews, denouncing Christians as traitors to Caesar. If I chose to act on half the stuff their Rabbis swear to, I'd have respectable little Jew shop-keepers up every week for conspiracy. *Never* decide on the evidence, when you're dealing with Hebrews! Oh, you'll get your bellyful of it! You're for Market-duty tomorrow in the Little Circus ward, all among 'em. And now, sleep you well! I've been on this frontier as far back as anyone remembers—that's why they call me the Father of Syria—and oh—it's good to see a sample of the old stock again!"

Next morning, and for many weeks after, Valens found himself on Market-inspection duty with a fat Aedile, who flew into rages because the stalls were not flushed down at the proper hour. A couple of his uncle's men were told off to him, and, of course, introduced him to the thieves' and prostitutes' quarters, to the leading gladiators, and so forth.

One day, behind the Little Circus, near Singon Street, he ran into a mob, where a race-course gang were trying to collect, or evade, some bets on recent chariot-races. The Aedile said it was none of his affair and turned back. The lictors closed up behind Valens, but left the situation in his charge. Then a small hard man with eyebrows was punted on to his chest, amid howls from all around that he was the ringleader of a conspiracy. "Yes," said Valens, "that was an old trick in Byzant; but I think we'll take *you,* my friend." Turning the small man loose, he gathered in the loudest of his accusers to appear before his uncle.

"You were quite right," said Serga next day. "That gentleman was put up to the job—by someone else. I ordered him one Roman dozen. Did you get the name of the man they were trying to push off on you?"

"Yes. Gaius Julius Paulus. Why?"

"I guessed as much. He's an old acquaintance of mine, a Cilician from Tarsus. Well-born—a citizen by descent, and well-educated, but his people have disowned him. So he works for his living."

"He spoke like a well-born. He's in splendid training, too. 'Felt him. All muscle."

"Small wonder. He can outmarch a camel. He is really the Prefect of this new sect. He travels all over our Eastern Provinces starting their Colleges and keeping them up to the mark. That's why the Synagogue Jews are hunting him. If they could run him in on the political charge, it would finish him."

"Is he seditious, then?"

"Not in the least. Even if he were, I wouldn't feed him to the Jews just because they wanted it. One of our Governors tried that game down-coast—for the sake of peace—some years ago. He didn't get it. Do you like your Market-work, my boy?"

"It's interesting. D'you know, Uncle, I think the Synagogue Jews are better at their slaughter-house arrangements than we."

"They are. That's what makes 'em so tough. A dozen stripes are nothing to Apella, though he'll howl the yard down while he's getting 'em. You've the Christians' College in your quarter. How do they strike you?"

"'Quiet enough. They're worrying a bit over what they ought to eat at their love-feasts."

"I know it. Oh, I meant to tell you—we mustn't try 'em too high just now, Valens. My office reports that Paulus, your small friend, is going down-country for a few days to meet another priest of the College, and bring him back to help smooth over their difficulties about their victuals. That means their congregation will be at loose ends till they return. Mass without mind always comes a cropper. So, *now* is when the Synagogue Jews will try to compromise them. I don't want the poor devils stampeded into what can be made to look like political crime. Understand?"

Valens nodded. Between his uncle's discursive evening talks, studded with kitchen-Greek and out-of-date Roman society-verses; his morning tours with the puffing Aedile; and the confidences of his lictors at all hours; he fancied he understood Antioch.

So he kept an eye on the rooms in the colonnade behind the Little Circus, where the new faith gathered. One of the many Jew butchers told him that Paulus had left affairs in the hands of some man called Barnabas, but that he would come back with one, Petrus—evidently a well-known character—who would settle all the food-differences between Greek and Hebrew Christians. The butcher had no spite against Greek Christians as such, if they would only kill their meat like decent Jews.

Serga laughed at this talk, but lent Valens an extra man or two, and said that this lion would be his to tackle, before long.

The boy found himself rushed into the arena one hot dusk, when word had come that this was to be a night of trouble. He posted his lictors in an alley within signal, and entered the common-room of the College, where the love-feasts were held. Everyone seemed as friendly as a Christian—to use the slang of the quarter—and Barnabas, a smiling, stately man by the door, specially so.

"I am glad to meet you," he said. "You helped our Paulus in that scuffle the other day. We can't afford to lose *him*. I wish he were back!"

He looked nervously down the hall, as it filled with people, of middle and low degree, setting out their evening meal on the bare tables, and greeting each other with a special gesture.

"I assure you," he went on, his eyes still astray, "*we've* no intention of offending any of the brethren. Our differences can be settled if only——"

As though on a signal, clamour rose from half a dozen tables at once, with cries of "Pollution! Defilement! Heathen! The Law! The Law! Let Caesar know!" As Valens backed against the wall, the crowd pelted each other with broken meats and crockery, till at last stones appeared from nowhere.

"It's a put-up affair," said Valens to Barnabas.

"Yes. They come in with stones in their breasts. Be careful! They're throwing your way," Barnabas replied. The crowd was well-embroiled now. A section of it bore down to where they stood, yelling for the Justice of Rome. His two lictors slid in behind Valens, and a man leaped at him with a knife.

Valens struck up the hand, and the lictors had the man helpless as the weapon fell on the floor. The clash of it stilled the tumult a little. Valens caught the lull, speaking slowly: "Oh, citizens," he called, "*must* you begin your love-feasts with battle? Our tripe-sellers' burial-club has better manners."

A little laughter relieved the tension.

"The Synagogue has arranged this," Barnabas muttered. "The responsibility will be laid on me."

"Who is the Head of your College?" Valens called to the crowd.

The cries rose against each other.

"Paulus! Saul! *He* knows the world—— No! No! Petrus! Our Rock! *He* won't betray us. Petrus, the Living Rock."

"When do they come back?" Valens asked. Several dates were given, sworn to, and denied.

"Wait to fight till they return. I'm not a priest; but if you don't tidy up these rooms, our Aedile (Valens gave him his gross nick-name in the quarter) will fine the sandals off your feet. And you mustn't trample good food either. When you've finished, I'll lock up after you. Be quick. *I* know our Prefect if you don't."

They toiled, like children rebuked. As they passed out with baskets of rubbish, Valens smiled. The matter would not be pressed further.

"Here is our key," said Barnabas at the end. "The Synagogue will swear I hired this man to kill you."

"Will they? Let's look at him."

The lictors pushed their prisoner forward.

"Ill-fortune!" said the man. "I owed you for my brother's death in Tarsus Pass."

"Your brother tried to kill me," Valens retorted.

The fellow nodded.

"Then we'll call it even-throws." Valens signed to the lictors, who loosed hold. "Unless you *really* want to see my uncle?"

The man vanished like a trout in the dusk. Valens returned the key to Barnabas, and said:

"If I were you, I shouldn't let your people in again till your leaders come back. You don't know Antioch as I do."

He went home, the grinning lictors behind him, and they told his uncle, who grinned also, but said that he had done the right thing—even to patronizing Barnabas.

"Of course, *I* don't know Antioch as you do; but, seriously, my dear, I think you've saved their Church for the Christians this time. I've had three depositions already that your Cilician friend was a Christian hired by Barnabas. 'Just as well for Barnabas that you let the brute go."

"You told me you didn't want them stampeded into trouble. Besides, it was fair-throws. I may have killed his brother after all. We had to kill two of 'em."

"Good! You keep a level head in a tight corner. You'll need it. There's no lying about in secluded parks for *us!* I've got to see Paulus and Petrus when they come back, and find out what they've decided about their infernal feasts. Why can't they all get decently drunk and be done with it?"

"They talk of them both down-town as though they were

Gods. By the way, Uncle, all the riot was worked up by Synagogue Jews sent from Jerusalem—not by our lot at all."

"You *don't* say so? Now, perhaps, you understand why I put you on market-duty with old Sow-Belly! You'll make a Police-officer yet."

Valens met the scared, mixed congregation round the fountains and stalls as he went about his quarter. They were rather relieved at being locked out of their rooms for the time; as well as by the news that Paulus and Petrus would report to the Prefect of Police before addressing them on the great food-question.

Valens was not present at the first part of that interview, which was official. The second, in the cool, awning-covered courtyard, with drinks and *hors-d'œuvres,* all set out beneath the vast lemon and lavender sunset, was much less formal.

"You have met, I think," said Serga to the little lean Paulus as Valens entered.

"Indeed, yes. Under God, we are twice your debtors," was the quick reply.

"Oh, that was part of my duty. I hope you found our roads good on your journey," said Valens.

"Why, yes. I think they were." Paulus spoke as if he had not noticed them.

"We should have done better to come by boat," said his companion, Petrus, a large fleshy man, with eyes that seemed to see nothing, and a half-palsied right hand that lay idle in his lap.

"Valens came overland from Byzant," said his uncle. "He rather fancies his legs."

"He ought to at his age. What was your best day's march on the Via Sebaste?" Paulus asked interestedly, and, before he knew, Valens was reeling off his mileage on mountain-roads every step of which Paulus seemed to have trod.

"That's good," was the comment. "And I expect you march in heavier order than I."

"What would you call your best day's work?" Valens asked in turn.

"I have covered . . ." Paulus checked himself. "And yet

not I but the God," he muttered. "It's hard to cure oneself of boasting."

A spasm wrenched Petrus' face.

"Hard indeed," said he. Then he addressed himself to Paulus as though none other were present. "It is true I have eaten with Gentiles and as the Gentiles ate. Yet, at the time, I doubted if it were wise."

"That is behind us now," said Paulus gently. "The decision has been taken for the Church—that little Church which you saved, my son." He turned on Valens with a smile that half-captured the boy's heart. "Now—as a Roman and a Police-officer—what think you of us Christians?"

"That I have to keep order in my own ward."

"Good! Caesar must be served. But—as a servant of Mithras, shall we say—how think you about our food-disputes?"

Valens hesitated. His uncle encouraged him with a nod. "As a servant of Mithras I eat with any initiate, so long as the food is clean," said Valens.

"But," said Petrus, "*that* is the crux."

"Mithras also tells us," Valens went on, "to share a bone covered with dirt, if better cannot be found."

"You observe no difference, then, between peoples at your feasts?" Paulus demanded.

"How dare we? We are all His children. Men make laws. Not Gods," Valens quoted from the old Ritual.

"Say that again, child!"

"Gods do not make laws. They change men's hearts. The rest is the Spirit."

"You heard it, Petrus? You heard that? It is the utter Doctrine itself!" Paulus insisted to his dumb companion.

Valens, a little ashamed of having spoken of his faith, went on:

"They tell me the Jew butchers here want the monopoly of killing for your people. Trade feeling's at the bottom of most of it."

"A little more than that perhaps," said Paulus. "Listen a minute." He threw himself into a curious tale about the God of the Christians, Who, he said, had taken the shape of a Man, and Whom the Jerusalem Jews, years ago, had got the authorities to deal with as a conspirator. He said that he himself, at that time a right Jew, quite agreed with the sentence, and had denounced all who followed the new God. But one day the Light and the Voice of the God broke over him, and he experienced a rending change of heart—precisely as in the Mithras creed. Then he met, and had been initiated by, some men who had walked and talked and, more particularly, had eaten, with the new God before He was killed, and who had seen Him after, like Mithras, He had risen from His grave. Paulus and those others—Petrus was one of them—had next tried to preach Him to the Jews, but that was no success; and, one thing leading to another, Paulus had gone back to his home at Tarsus, where his people disowned him for a renegade. There he had broken down with overwork and despair. Till then, he said, it had never occurred to any of them to show the new religion to any except right Jews; for their God had been born in the shape of a Jew. Paulus himself only came to realize the possibilities of outside work, little by little. He said he had all the foreign preaching in his charge now, and was going to change the whole world by it.

Then he made Petrus finish the tale, who explained, speaking very slowly, that he had, some years ago, received orders from the God to preach to a Roman officer of Irregulars down-country; after which that officer and most of his people wanted to become Christians. So Petrus had initiated them the same night, although none of them were Hebrews. "And," Petrus ended, "I saw there is nothing under heaven that we dare call unclean."

Paulus turned on him like a flash and cried:

"You admit it! Out of your own mouth it is evident." Petrus shook like a leaf and his right hand almost lifted.

"Do *you* too twit me with my accent?" he began, but his face worked and he choked.

"Nay! God forbid! And God once more forgive *me!*" Paulus seemed as distressed as he, while Valens stared at the extraordinary outbreak.

"Talking of clean and unclean," his uncle said tactfully, "there's that ugly song come up again in the City. They were singing it on the city-front yesterday, Valens. Did you notice?"

He looked at his nephew, who took the hint.

"If it was 'Pickled Fish,' sir, they were. Will it make trouble?"

"As surely as these fish"—a jar of them stood on the table —"make one thirsty. How does it go? Oh yes." Serga hummed:

"Oie-eaah!
'From the Shark and the Sardine—the clean and the unclean—
To the Pickled Fish of Galilee, said Petrus, shall be mine."

He twanged it off to the proper gutter-drawl.

"(Ha-ow?)
In the nets or on the line,
Till the Gods Themselves decline.
(Whe-en?)
When the Pickled Fish of Galilee ascend the Esquiline!

That'll be something of a flood—worse than live fish in trees! Hey?"

"It will happen one day," said Paulus.

He turned from Petrus, whom he had been soothing tenderly, and resumed in his natural, hardish voice:

"Yes. We owe a good deal to that Centurion being converted when he was. It taught us that the whole world could receive the God; and it showed *me* my next work. I came over from Tarsus to teach here for a while. And I shan't forget how good the Prefect of Police was to us then."

"For one thing, Cornelius was an early colleague," Serga smiled largely above his strong cup. " 'Prime companion'—how does it go?—'we drank the long, long Eastern day out together,' and so on. For another, I know a good workman when I see him. That camel-kit you made for my desert-tours, Paul, is as sound as ever. And for a third—which to a man of my habits is most important—that Greek doctor you recommended me is the only one who understands my tumid liver."

He passed a cup of all but unmixed wine, which Paulus handed to Petrus, whose lips were flaky white at the corners.

"But your trouble," the Prefect went on, "will come from your own people. Jerusalem never forgives. They'll get you run in on the charge of *laesa majestatis* soon or late."

"Who knows better than I?" said Petrus. "And the decision we *all* have taken about our love-feasts may unite Hebrew and Greek against us. As I told you, Prefect, we are asking Christian Greeks not to make the feasts difficult for Christian Hebrews by eating meat that has not been lawfully killed. (Our way is much more wholesome, anyhow.) Still, we may get round that. But there's *one* vital point. Some of our Greek Christians bring food to the love-feasts that they've bought from your priests, after your sacrifices have been offered. That we can't allow."

Paulus turned to Valens imperiously.

"You mean they buy Altar-scraps," the boy said. "But only the very poor do it; and it's chiefly block-trimmings. The sale's a perquisite of the Altar-butchers. They wouldn't like its being stopped."

"Permit separate tables for Hebrew and Greek, as I once said," Petrus spoke suddenly.

"That would end in separate churches. There shall be but *one* Church," Paulus spoke over his shoulder, and the words fell like rods. "You think there may be trouble, Valens?"

"My uncle——" Valens began.

"No, no!" the Prefect laughed. "Singon Street Markets are your Syria. Let's hear what our Legate thinks of his Province."

Valens flushed and tried to pull his wits together.

"Primarily," he said, "it's pig, I suppose. Hebrews hate pork."

"Quite right, too. Catch *me* eating pig east of the Adriatic! *I* don't want to die of worms. Give me a young Sabine tush-ripe boar! I have spoken!"

Serga mixed himself another raw cup and took some pickled Lake fish to bring out the flavour.

"But, still," Petrus leaned forward like a deaf man, "if we admitted Hebrew and Greek Christians to separate tables we should escape——"

"Nothing, except salvation," said Paulus. "We have broken with the whole Law of Moses. We live in and through and by our God only. Else we are nothing. What is the sense of harking back to the Law at meal-times? Whom do we deceive? Jerusalem? Rome? The God? You yourself have eaten with Gentiles! You yourself have said——"

"One says more than one means when one is carried away," Petrus answered, and his face worked again.

"This time you will say precisely what is meant," Paulus spoke between his teeth. "We will keep the Churches *one*—in and through the Lord. You dare not deny this?"

"I dare nothing—the God knows! But I have denied Him. . . . I denied Him. . . . And He said—He said I was the Rock on which His Church should stand."

"*I* will see that it stands, and yet not I——" Paulus' voice dropped again. "To-morrow you will speak to the one Church of the one Table the world over."

"That's *your* business," said the Prefect. "But I warn you again, it's your own people who will make you trouble."

Paulus rose to say farewell, but in the act he staggered, put his hand to his forehead and, as Valens steered him to a divan, collapsed in the grip of that deadly Syrian malaria which strikes like a snake. Valens, having suffered, called to his rooms for his heavy travelling-fur. His girl, whom he had bought in Constantinople a few months before, fetched it. Petrus tucked it awkwardly round the shivering little figure; the Prefect ordered lime-juice and hot water, and Paulus thanked them and apologized, while his teeth rattled on the cup.

"Better to-day than to-morrow," said the Prefect. "Drink—sweat—and sleep here the night. Shall I send for my doctor?"

But Paulus said that the fit would pass naturally, and as soon as he could stand he insisted on going away with Petrus, late though it was, to prepare their announcement to the Church.

"Who was that big, clumsy man?" his girl asked Valens as she took up the fur. "He made more noise than the small one, who was really suffering."

"He's a priest of the new College by the Little Circus, dear. He believes, Uncle told me, that he once denied his God, Who, he says, died for him."

She halted in the moonlight, the glossy jackal skins over her arm.

"Does he? *My* God bought me from the dealers like a horse. Too much, too, he paid. Didn't he? 'Fess, thou?"

"No, thee!" emphatically.

"But I wouldn't deny *my* God—living or dead! . . . Oh—but *not* dead! My God's going to live—for me. Live—live Thou, my heart's blood, for ever!"

It would have been better had Paulus and Petrus not left the Prefect's house so late; for the rumour in the city, as the Prefect knew, and as the long conference seemed to confirm, was that Caesar's own Secretary of State in Rome was, through Paulus, arranging for a general defilement of the Hebrew with the Greek Christians, and that after this had been effected, by promiscuous eating of unlawful foods, all Jews would be lumped together as Christians—members, that is, of a mere free-thinking sect instead of the very particular and troublesome "Nation of Jews within the Empire." Eventually, the story went, they would lose their rights as Roman citizens, and could then be sold on any slave-stand.

"Of course," Serga explained to Valens next day, "that has been put about by the Jerusalem Synagogue. Our Antioch Jews aren't clever enough. Do you see their game? Petrus is a defiler of the Hebrew nation. If he is cut down to-night by some properly primed young zealot so much the better."

"He won't be," said Valens. "I'm looking after him."

" 'Hope so. But, if he isn't knifed," Serga went on, "they'll try to work up city riots on the grounds that, when all the Jews have lost their civil rights, he'll set up as a sort of King of the Christians."

"At Antioch? In the present year of Rome? That's crazy, Uncle."

"Every crowd is crazy. What else do we draw pay for? But, listen. Post a Mounted Police patrol at the back of the Little Circus. Use 'em to keep the people moving when the congregation comes out. Post two of your men in the Porch of their College itself. Tell Paulus and Petrus to wait there with them, till the streets are clear. Then fetch 'em both over here. Don't hit till you have to. Hit hard *before* the stones fly. Don't get my little horses knocked about more than you can help, and—look out for 'Pickled Fish'!"

Knowing his own quarter, it seemed to Valens as he went on duty that evening, that his uncle's precautions had been excessive. The Christian Church, of course, was full, and a large crowd waited outside for word of the decision about the feasts. Most of them seemed to be Christians of sorts, but there was an element of gesticulating Antiochene loafers, and like all crowds they amused themselves with popular songs while they waited. Things went smoothly, till a group of Christians raised a rather explosive hymn, which ran:

"Enthroned above Caesar and Judge of the Earth!
We wait on Thy coming—oh tarry not long!
As the Kings of the Sunrise
Drew sword at Thy Birth,
So we arm in this midnight of insult and wrong!"

"Yes—and if one of their fish-stalls is bumped over by a camel—it's *my* fault!" said Valens. "Now they've started it!"

Sure enough, voices on the outskirts broke into "Pickled Fish," but before Valens could speak, they were suppressed by someone crying:

"Quiet there, or you'll get your pickle before your fish."

It was close on twilight when a cry rose from within the packed Church, and its congregation breasted out into the crowd. They all talked about the new orders for their love-feasts, most of them agreeing that they were sensible and easy. They agreed, too, that Petrus (Paulus did not seem to have taken much part in the debate) had spoken like one inspired, and they were all extremely proud of being Christians. Some of them began to link arms across the alley, and strike into the "Enthroned above Caesar" chorus.

"And this, I *think,*" Valens called to the young Commandant of the Mounted Patrol, "is where we'll begin to steer 'em home. Oh! And 'Let night also have her well-earned hymn,' as Uncle 'ud say."

There filed out from behind the Little Circus four blaring trumpets, a standard, and a dozen Mounted Police. Their wise little grey Arabs sidled, passaged, shouldered, and nosed softly into the mob, as though they wanted petting, while the trumpets deafened the narrow street. An open square, near by, eased the pressure before long. Here the Patrol broke into fours, and gridironed it, saluting the images of the Gods at each corner and in the centre. People stopped, as usual, to watch how cleverly the incense was cast down over the withers into the spouting cressets; children reached up to pat horses which they said they knew; family groups re-found each other in the smoky dusk; hawkers offered cooked suppers; and soon the crowd melted into the main traffic avenues. Valens went over to the Church porch, where Petrus and Paulus waited between his lictors.

"That was well done," Paulus began.

"How's the fever?" Valens asked.

"I was spared for to-day. I think, too, that by The Blessing we have carried our point."

"Good hearing! My uncle bids me say you are welcome at his house."

"That is always a command," said Paulus, with a quick down-country gesture. "Now that this day's burden is lifted, it will be a delight."

Petrus joined up like a weary ox. Valens greeted him, but he did not answer.

"Leave him alone," Paulus whispered. "The virtue has gone out of me—him—for the while." His own face looked pale and drawn.

The street was empty, and Valens took a short cut through

an alley, where light ladies leaned out of windows and laughed. The three strolled easily together, the lictors behind them, and far off they heard the trumpets of the Night Horse saluting some statue of a Caesar, which marked the end of their round. Paulus was telling Valens how the whole Roman Empire would be changed by what the Christians had agreed to about their love-feasts, when an impudent little Jew boy stole up behind them, playing "Pickled Fish" on some sort of desert bag-pipe.

"Can't you stop that young pest, one of you?" Valens asked laughing. "You shan't be mocked on this great night of yours, Paulus."

The lictors turned back a few paces, and shook a torch at the brat, but he retreated and drew them on. Then they heard Paulus shout, and when they hurried back, found Valens prostrate and coughing—his blood on the fringe of the kneeling Paulus' robe. Petrus stooped, waving a helpless hand above them.

"Someone ran out from behind that well-head. He stabbed him as he ran, and ran on. Listen!" said Paulus.

But there was not even the echo of a footfall for clue, and the Jew boy had vanished like a bat. Said Valens from the ground:

"Home! Quick! I have it!"

They tore a shutter out of a shop-front, lifted and carried him, while Paulus walked beside. They set him down in the lighted inner courtyard of the Prefect's house, and a lictor hurried for the Prefect's physician.

Paulus watched the boy's face, and, as Valens shivered a little, called to the girl to fetch last night's fur rug. She brought it, laid the head on her breast, and cast herself beside Valens.

"It isn't bad. It doesn't bleed much. So it *can't* be bad—can it?" she repeated. Valens' smile reassured her, till the Prefect came and recognized the deadly upward thrust under the ribs. He turned on the Hebrews.

"To-morrow you will look for where your Church stood," said he.

Valens lifted the hand that the girl was not kissing.

"No—no!" he gasped. "The Cilician did it! For his brother! He said it."

"The Cilician you let go to save these Christians because I——?" Valens signed to his uncle that it was so, while the girl begged him to steal strength from her till the doctor should come.

"Forgive me," said Serga to Paulus. "None the less I wish your God in Hades once for all. . . . But what am I to write his mother? Can't either of you two talking creatures tell me what I'm to tell his mother?"

"What has *she* to do with him?" the slave-girl cried. "He is mine—mine! I testify before all Gods that he bought me! I am his. He is mine."

"We can deal with the Cilician and his friends later," said one of the lictors. "But what now?"

For some reason, the man, though used to butcher-work, looked at Petrus.

"Give him drink and wait," said Petrus. "I have—seen such a wound." Valens drank and a shade of colour came to him. He motioned the Prefect to stoop.

"What is it? Dearest of lives, what troubles?"

"The Cilician and his friends. . . . Don't be hard on them. . . . They get worked up. . . . They don't know what they are doing. . . . Promise!"

"This is not I, child. It is the Law."

"'No odds. You're Father's brother. . . . Men make laws—not Gods. . . . Promise! . . . It's finished with me."

Valens' head eased back on its yearning pillow.

Petrus stood like one in a trance. The tremor left his face as he repeated:

"'Forgive them, for they know not what they do.' Heard you *that,* Paulus? He, a heathen and an idolator, said it!"

"I heard. What hinders now that we should baptize him?" Paulus answered promptly.

Petrus stared at him as though he had come up out of the sea.

"Yes," he said at last. "It is the little maker of tents. . . . And what does he *now*—command?"

Paulus repeated the suggestion.

Painfully, that other raised the palsied hand that he had once held up in a hall to deny a charge.

"Quiet!" said he. "Think you that one who has spoken Those Words needs such as *we* are to certify him to any God?"

Paulus cowered before the unknown colleague, vast and commanding, revealed after all these years.

"As you please—as you please," he stammered, overlooking the blasphemy. "Moreover there is the concubine."

The girl did not heed, for the brow beneath her lips was chilling, even as she called on her God who had bought her at a price that he should not die but live.

From A Book of Words *1906*

ENGLAND AND THE ENGLISH

Royal Society of St. George: April 1920

I THINK this is an occasion on which it behoves us all to walk rather circumspectly. If you will let me, I will try and tell you why. About sixteen hundred years ago, when Rome was mistress of the world and the Picts and the Scots lived on the other side of the Wall that ran from Newcastle to Carlisle, the story goes that Rome allowed all those peoples one night in the year in which they could say aloud exactly what they thought of Rome, without fear of the consequences. So then, on that one night of the year, they would creep out of the heather in droves and light their little wandering fires and criticize their Libyan Generals and their Roman Pontiffs and the Eastern camp followers, who looked down on them from the top of the great high unbreakable Roman Wall sixteen hundred years ago.

To-day, Imperial Rome is dead. The Wall is down and the Picts and the Scots are on this side of it, but thanks to our Royal Society of St. George, there still remains one night in the year when the English can creep out of their hiding-places and whisper to each other exactly what we think about ourselves. No, it is not quite safe to criticize our masters—our masters who tax us and educate us, and try us, and minister so abundantly to what they instruct us our wants ought to be. Since these masters of ours have not yet quite the old untroubled assurance of power and knowledge that made Rome so tolerant in the days when the Picts and the Scots lived on the other side of the Wall, we will confine ourselves to our own popular and widely recognized defects.

Some of our severest critics, who, of course, are of our

own household, have said that there never was such a thing as the English Race—that it is at best the intolerably insolent outcome of ancient invasions and immigrations, freshened with more recent Continental gaol-deliveries. Far be it from me to traverse such statements. I give them on no less authority than that of the late Mr. Daniel Defoe, Liveryman of the City of London, author of *Robinson Crusoe* and of a pamphlet called *The True-born Englishman.* He deals very faithfully with the English. So faithfully that, in deference to the susceptibilities of some races, I will not give his version of the Englishman's pedigree, but in his summing up of the true-born Englishman, Defoe says:

A true-born Englishman's a contradiction,
In speech an irony, in fact a fiction,
A metaphor intended to express
A man akin to all the Universe.

In that last line it seems to me that Defoe slips into a blessing where he meant to curse, because a man "akin to all the Universe" cannot be wholly lost. He must have some points of contact with humanity. And the Englishman has had several.

The Phoenicians taught him the rudiments of shopkeeping; the Romans taught him love of sport by hiring him to fight wild beasts in their arenas. Under the Heptarchy he studied Social Reform, which in those unenlightened days consisted of raising levies on capital in order to buy off the Heathen of the North from taking direct action against English industries. He next took a three-hundred-years' course of colloquial and Law French under eminent Norman teachers. He did not learn that language then or since, but it left him with a profound respect, based on experience, for his neighbours across the Channel, and a conviction, which time has deepened, that they were the only other people in the world who mattered.

For five hundred years his affairs, domestic and foreign, were controlled by French, Italian, Spanish, with occasional Austrian, politico-ecclesiastical authorities, who tried to teach him that "this realm of England" was but part of a vast international organization destined to embrace, protect, and instruct all mankind. He escaped from those embraces only to find himself subjected to the full rigours of the Puritan Conscience, which at that time was largely directed by gentlemen from Geneva, Leyden, Amsterdam, and the Low Countries. While thus engaged he was, under pretext of union, finally and fatally subjugated by the Scot. A few years later he embarked on the swelling tide of party politics in all their attendant purity; since which he has seldom been allowed to look back, and never forward.

I submit that such a nightmare of national experiences would have driven an unmixed race to the edge of lunacy. But the Englishman is like a built-up gun barrel, all one temper though welded of many different materials, and he has strong powers of resistance. Roman, Dane, Norman, Papist, Cromwellian, Stuart, Hollander, Hanoverian, Upper Class, Middle Class, Democracy, each in turn through a thousand years experimented on him and tried to make him to their own liking. He met them each in turn with a large silent toleration, which each in turn mistook for native stupidity. He gave them each in turn a fair trial and, when he had finished with them, an equally fair dismissal. As an additional safeguard he devised for himself a social system in watertight compartments, so arranged that neither the waters of popular emotion nor the fires of private revenge could sweep his ship of State from end to end. If, in spite of this, the domestic situation became too much for him he could always take a ship and go to sea, and there seek or impose the peace which the Papal Legate, or the Mediaeval Trade Union, or a profligate Chancellor of the Exchequer denied to him at home. And thus, gentlemen—*not* in a fit of absence of mind—was the Empire born. It was the outcome of the relaxations of persecuted specialists—men who for one cause or another were unfit for the rough and tumble of life at home. They did it for change and rest, exactly as we used to take our summer holidays, and, like ourselves, they took their national habits with them. For example, they did not often gather together with harps and rebecks to celebrate their national glories, or to hymn their national heroes. When they did not take them both for granted, they, like ourselves, generally denied the one and did their best to impeach the other. But, by some mysterious rule-of-thumb magic, they *did* establish and maintain reasonable security and peace among simple folk in very many parts of the world, and that, too, without overmuch murder, robbery, oppression, or torture.

One secret of the success of the English was, perhaps, their imperturbable tolerance. A race that has been persecuted, or —what comes to the same thing—bored by every persecuted refugee to whom they have ever given an asylum, naturally learns to tolerate anything. Their immensely mixed origin, too, made the English in a very real sense "akin to all the universe", and sympathetic in their dumb way with remote Gods and strange people. Above all, their long insular experience of imported brain-storms had taught them that men should not try to do better than good for fear lest worse than bad might follow. And there has been enough of worse than bad in the world for the last few years. Our national weakness for keeping to the easiest road to the latest possible minute sooner than inconvenience ourselves or our neighbours has been visited upon us full tale. After ninety-nine years of peace the English were given ninety-six hours in which to choose whether they would buy a little longer peace from the Heathen of the North, as some of their ancestors had done, or whether they would make peace with them as our King Alfred made it with the Danes. It was a race that had almost forgotten how to say "No" to anybody who said "Yes" in a sufficiently loud voice. It seemed as if it had quite forgotten that it had broken a Church, killed a King, closed a Protectorate and exiled another King, sooner than be driven where it did not want to go. But when its hour came, once again it decided to go its own way, and once again by instinct. For it had prepared nothing —it had foreseen nothing. It had been assured that not only was there no need for preparation against war, but that the mere thought of preparation against war was absurd where it was not criminal. Therefore, through the first two years of the war, it was necessary to throw up a barricade of the dead bodies of the nation's youth behind which the most elementary preparations could be begun.

There has been no such slaughter of the English in English history, but the actual war was no more than a large-scale repetition of previous national experiences. If an Elizabethan Statesman (or adventurer) could have returned to England during the war he would, I think, in a very short time have been able to pick up his office work almost where he dropped it. His reports and his maps would have been a little more detailed, but he would have been surprisingly abreast of the whole situation.

Where the old English influence had struck deep all the world over, he would have seen help and comfort hurried up to all the fronts from all the world over without count or tale, without word or bond to limit or confirm it. Where the old alien influences that he knew so well had persisted, or where the new influences directed by the old were at work, he would have seen, as he would have expected, all help for the war denied, withheld, or doled out grudgingly, piecemeal at a high price. He would have recognized that what held firm in the days of the Armada held firm at Armageddon: that what had broken beneath his hand then was rotten in our hand now. Bar a few minor differences of equipment, he would have felt just like any sailor or soldier returning to some bitterly familiar job of sea-patrol or trench life between '14 and '18. Like those men he would have taken for granted a great deal upon which other nations might have wasted valuable thought and attention. Our stories of Coronel and Zeebrugge, of the English county battalions not one year old that died to the last man as a matter of routine on the fronts that they were ordered to hold, would have moved him no more and no less than the little affair of Sir Richard Grenville off Flores, in the *Revenge*. That troopers of County Yeomanry in Mesopotamia, picked almost at random, could, single-handed, and by sheer force of character, control and conciliate in a few days a turbulent Arab village, would have amazed him no more and no less than any tale of Panama, or of our first venture across the world, told him by Sir Francis Drake or any forgotten captain of the same age. Being of the breed he would have known the breed and would have taken the work of the breed for granted.

And herein, as I see it, lies the strength of the English—that they have behind them this continuity of immensely varied race-experience and race-memory, running equally through all classes back to the very dawn of our dawn. This imposes on them unconsciously, even while they deny or deride it, standards of achievement and comparison, hard perhaps, and perhaps a little unsympathetic, but not low—not low—and, as all earth is witness, not easily to be lowered. And that is the reason why in the things nearest our hearts we praise so little and criticize so lavishly. It is the only compliment which an Englishman dare pay to his country.

As you know, our standards of achievement and comparison do not appear on the surface; nor are they much in men's mouths. When they are, they are mostly translated into terms of sport or the slang of our various games. But whenever the English deal in earnest with each other, or with the outside world, those standards are taken for granted. And it is by the things that we take for granted without word that we live. It was taken for granted during the war that every day was St. George's Day, on one or other of our seven fronts.

And now, we and our kin, after these great years, are sick, dizzy, and shaken—like all convalescents, a little inclined to pity ourselves, a little inclined to stay as long as possible on a diet of invalid slops, and a little more than inclined to mistake the hysteria of convalescence for the symptoms of returning life and thought. Here also instinct tells us that the weight, the range, and the evenly spread richness of our national past should ballast us sufficiently to navigate through whatever storms—or brain-storms—there may be ahead. And we are threatened with several.

One school of thought, Muscovite in origin, holds, as the Danes held twelve hundred years ago, that rapine and scientific torture will elevate our ideals, which up to the present have merely taught us to try to do our duty to our God and our neighbour. Others are content to work for the organized bankruptcy of whatsoever is of good repute, including the systematic betrayal of our friends, very much on the same lines as some people used to panic after every Crusade and every visitation of the plague. We are further promised an unparalleled outbreak of education, guaranteed to produce a standardized State-aided mind. The Church evolved almost a parallel system in the Middle Ages, which, much to her surprise, produced the Reformation.

Lastly, lest we should ever again lapse into our "pathetic contentment," the breed which organized at a week's notice to achieve the impossible and achieved it—by earth, sea, and air achieved it—is now, as a reward, to be ruthlessly reorganized in every detail of its life, walk, and conduct. That great work was begun by William the Conqueror, Anno Domini 1066, and has been before Committee or Commission ever since.

Norman, Papist, Cromwellian, Stuart, Hollander, Hanoverian, Upper Class, Middle Class, Democracy, have each in turn tried their fleeting hand on the "man akin to all the Universe." From each in turn he has taken what he wanted; to each in turn he has given a fair trial; and when he has quite finished, an equally fair dismissal.

What will he do in the future? We are too near to the dust of the main battle to see clearly. We know that England is crippled by the loss and wastage of a whole generation, and that her position, from the civil point of view to-day, is the position of our armies in the darkest days of the war. That is to say, all leave is stopped for any man who can manage to stand up to his job, no matter how sick or stale he may feel himself to be, and there is undreamed-of promotion for untried men who, simply because they are not dead, will now have to face heavier responsibility, longer hours, and criticism that certainly will not grow milder as the years pass. But no miracles have occurred.

This world of ours, which some of us in their zeal to do better than good have helped to create, but which we must all inherit, is not a new world, but the old world grown harder. The wheel has come full circle. The whole weight of the world at the present moment lies again, as it used to lie in the time of our fathers, on the necks of two nations, England and France. The sole force under God's good Providence that can meet this turn of our fate, is not temperament, not opportunism, nor any effort to do better than good, but character and again character—such mere ingrained, common-sense, hand-hammered, loyal strength of character as one humbly dares to hope that fifteen hundred years of equality of experience have given us.

If this hope be true—and because we know the breed in our hearts we know that it is true—if this hope be justified, our children's children, looking back through the luminous years to where we here stumble and falter, will say to themselves: "Was it possible—was it possible that the English of that age did not know, could not see, dared not even guess, to what height of strength, wisdom, and enduring honour they had lifted their land?"

But we will be circumspect! My lords, ladies and gentlemen—for what there is of it—for such as it is—and for what it may be worth—will you drink to England and the English?

VERSE
1885–1932

The arrangement of verse, not always chronological, follows that in "Inclusive Verse, 1885–1932."

THE OVERLAND MAIL

(*Foot-service to the Hills*)

1886

IN THE name of the Empress of India, make way,
  O Lords of the Jungle, wherever you roam,
The woods are astir at the close of the day—
  We exiles are waiting for letters from Home.
Let the robber retreat—let the tiger turn tail—
In the Name of the Empress, the Overland Mail!

With the jingle of bells as the dusk gathers in,
  He turns to the footpath that heads up the hill—
The bags on his back and a cloth round his chin,
  And, tucked in his waistbelt, the Post Office bill;—
"Despatched on this date, as received by the rail,
"*Per* runner, two bags of the Overland Mail."

Is the torrent in spate? He must ford it or swim.
  Has the rain wrecked the road? He must climb by the cliff.
Does the tempest cry halt? What are tempests to him?
  The service admits not a "but" or an "if."
While the breath's in his mouth, he must bear without fail,
In the Name of the Empress, the Overland Mail.

From aloe to rose-oak, from rose-oak to fir,
  From level to upland, from upland to crest,
From rice-field to rock-ridge, from rock-ridge to spur,
  Fly the soft-sandalled feet, strains the brawny, brown chest.
From rail to ravine—to the peak from the vale—
Up, up through the night goes the Overland Mail.

There's a speck on the hillside, a dot on the road—
  A jingle of bells on the footpath below—
There's a scuffle above in the monkey's abode—
  The world is awake and the clouds are aglow.
For the great Sun himself must attend to the hail:—
In the Name of the Empress, the Overland Mail.

THE GALLEY-SLAVE

1890

OH GALLANT was our galley from her carven steering-wheel
To her figurehead of silver and her bead of hammered steel.
The leg-bar chafed the angle and we gasped for cooler air,
But no galley on the waters with our galley could compare!

Our bulkheads bulged with cotton and our masts were stepped
    in gold—
We ran a mighty merchandise of niggers in the hold;
The white foam spun behind us, and the black shark swam
    below,
As we gripped the kicking sweep-head and we made the galley
    go.

It was merry in the galley, for we revelled now and then—
If they wore us down like cattle, faith, we fought and loved
    like men!

As we snatched her through the water, so we snatched a minute's bliss,
And the mutter of the dying never spoiled the lover's kiss.

Our women and our children toiled beside us in the dark—
They died, we filed their fetters, and we heaved them to the shark—
We heaved them to the fishes, but so fast the galley sped
We had only time to envy, for we could not mourn our dead.

Bear witness, once my comrades, what a hard-bit gang were we—
The servants of the sweep-head, but the masters of the sea!
By the hands that drove her forward as she plunged and yawed and sheered,
Woman, Man, or God or Devil, was there anything we feared?

Was it storm? Our fathers faced it and a wilder never blew.
Earth that waited for the wreckage watched the galley struggle through.
Burning noon or choking midnight, Sickness, Sorrow, Parting, Death?
Nay, our very babes would mock you had they time for idle breath.

But to-day I leave the galley and another takes my place;
There's my name upon the deck-beam—let it stand a little space.
I am free—to watch my messmates beating out to open main,
Free of all that Life can offer—save to handle sweep again.

By the brand upon my shoulder, by the gall of clinging steel,
By the welt the whips have left me, by the scars that never heal;
By eyes grown old with staring through the sunwash on the brine,
I am paid in full for service. Would that service still were mine!

Yet they talk of times and seasons and of woe the years bring forth,
Of our galley swamped and shattered in the rollers of the North;
When the niggers break the hatches and the decks are gay with gore,
And a craven-hearted pilot crams her crashing on the shore.

She will need no half-mast signal, minute-gun, or rocket-flare.
When the cry for help goes seaward, she will find her servants there.
Battered chain-gangs of the orlop, grizzled drafts of years gone by,
To the bench that broke their manhood, they shall lash themselves and die.

Hale and crippled, young and aged, paid, deserted, shipped away—
Palace, cot, and lazaretto shall make up the tale that day,
When the skies are black above them, and the decks ablaze beneath,
And the top-men clear the raffle with their clasp-knives in their teeth.

It may be that Fate will give me life and leave to row once more—
Set some strong man free for fighting as I take awhile his oar.
But to-day I leave the galley. Shall I curse her service then?
God be thanked! Whate'er comes after, I have lived and toiled with men!

L'ENVOI

(*Departmental Ditties*)

1886

THE smoke upon your Altar dies,
  The flowers decay,
The Goddess of your sacrifice
  Has flown away.
What profit then to sing or slay
The sacrifice from day to day?

"We know the Shrine is void," they said,
  "The Goddess flown—
"Yet wreaths are on the altar laid—
  "The Altar-Stone
"Is black with fumes of sacrifice,
"Albeit She has fled our eyes.

"For, it may be, if still we sing
  "And tend the Shrine,
"Some Deity on wandering wing
  "May there incline;
"And, finding all in order meet,
"Stay while we worship at Her feet."

THE FIRES

(*Prelude to Collected Verse*)

1907

Men make them fires on the hearth
  Each under his roof-tree,
And the Four Winds that rule the earth
  They blow the smoke to me.

Across the high hills and the sea
And all the changeful skies,
The Four Winds blow the smoke to me
Till the tears are in my eyes.

Until the tears are in my eyes
And my heart is wellnigh broke
For thinking on old memories
That gather in the smoke.

With every shift of every wind
The homesick memories come,
From every quarter of mankind
Where I have made me a home.

Four times a fire against the cold
And a roof against the rain—
Sorrow fourfold and joy fourfold
The Four Winds bring again!

How can I answer which is best
Of all the fires that burn?
I have been too often host or guest
At every fire in turn.

How can I turn from any fire,
On any man's hearthstone?
I know the wonder and desire
That went to build my own!

How can I doubt man's joy or woe
Where'er his house-fires shine,
Since all that man must undergo
Will visit me at mine?

Oh, you Four Winds that blow so strong
And know that this is true,
Stoop for a little and carry my song
To all the men I knew!

Where there are fires against the cold,
Or roofs against the rain—
With love fourfold and joy fourfold,
Take them my songs again!

THE EXPLORER

Written 1898, Published 1903

"THERE'S no sense of going further—it's the edge of cultivation,"
So they said, and I believed it—broke my land and sowed my crop—
Built my barns and strung my fences in the little border station
Tucked away below the foothills where the trails run out and stop:

Till a voice, as bad as Conscience, rang interminable changes
On one everlasting Whisper day and night repeated—so:
"Something hidden. Go and find it. Go and look behind the Ranges—
"Something lost behind the Ranges. Lost and waiting for you. Go!"

So I went, worn out of patience; never told my nearest neighbours—
Stole away with pack and ponies—left 'em drinking in the town;

And the faith that moveth mountains didn't seem to help my labours
As I faced the sheer main-ranges, whipping up and leading down.

March by march I puzzled through 'em, turning flanks and dodging shoulders,
Hurried on in hope of water, headed back for lack of grass;
Till I camped above the tree-line—drifted snow and naked boulders—
Felt free air astir to windward—knew I'd stumbled on the Pass.

'Thought to name it for the finder: but that night the Norther found me—
Froze and killed the plains-bred ponies; so I called the camp Despair
(It's the Railway Gap to-day, though). Then my Whisper waked to hound me:—
"Something lost behind the Ranges. Over yonder! Go you there!"

Then I knew, the while I doubted—knew His Hand was certain o'er me.
Still—it might be self-delusion—scores of better men had died—
I could reach the township living, but . . . He knows what terror tore me . . .
But I didn't . . . but I didn't. I went down the other side,

Till the snow ran out in flowers, and the flowers turned to aloes,
And the aloes sprung to thickets and a brimming stream ran by;
But the thickets dwined to thorn-scrub, and the water drained to shallows,
And I dropped again on desert—blasted earth, and blasting sky. . . .

I remember lighting fires; I remember sitting by 'em;
  I remember seeing faces, hearing voices, through the smoke;
I remember they were fancy—for I threw a stone to try 'em.
  "Something lost behind the Ranges" was the only word they spoke.

I remember going crazy. I remember that I knew it
  When I heard myself hallooing to the funny folk I saw.
'Very full of dreams that desert, but my two legs took me through it . . .
  And I used to watch 'em moving with the toes all black and raw.

But at last the country altered—White Man's country past disputing—
  Rolling grass and open timber, with a hint of hills behind—
There I found me food and water, and I lay a week recruiting.
  Got my strength and lost my nightmares. Then I entered on my find.

Thence I ran my first rough survey—chose my trees and blazed and ringed 'em—
  Week by week I pried and sampled—week by week my findings grew.
Saul he went to look for donkeys, and by God he found a kingdom!
  But by God, who sent His Whisper, I had struck the worth of two!

Up along the hostile mountains, where the hair-poised snow-slide shivers—
  Down and through the big fat marshes that the virgin ore-bed stains,
Till I heard the mile-wide mutterings of unimagined rivers,
  And beyond the nameless timber saw illimitable plains!

'Plotted sites of future cities, traced the easy grades between 'em;
Watched unharnessed rapids wasting fifty thousand head an hour;
Counted leagues of water-frontage through the axe-ripe woods that screen 'em—
Saw the plant to feed a people—up and waiting for the power!

Well I know who'll take the credit—all the clever chaps that followed—
Came, a dozen men together—never knew my desert-fears;
Tracked me by the camps I'd quitted, used the water-holes I'd hollowed.
They'll go back and do the talking. *They'll* be called the Pioneers!

They will find my sites of townships—not the cities that I set there.
They will rediscover rivers—not my rivers heard at night.
By my own old marks and bearings they will show me how to get there,
By the lonely cairns I builded they will guide my feet aright.

Have I named one single river? Have I claimed one single acre?
Have I kept one single nugget—(barring samples)? No, not I!
Because my price was paid me ten times over by my Maker.
But you wouldn't understand it. You go up and occupy.

Ores you'll find there; wood and cattle; water-transit sure and steady
(That should keep the railway-rates down), coal and iron at your doors.

God took care to hide that country till He judged His people ready,
Then He chose me for His Whisper, and I've found it, and it's yours!

Yes, your "Never-never country"—yes, your "edge of cultivation"
And "no sense in going further"—till I crossed the range to see.
God forgive me! No, *I* didn't. It's God's present to our nation.
Anybody might have found it but—His Whisper came to Me!

M'ANDREW'S HYMN
1893

LORD, Thou hast made this world below the shadow of a dream,
An', taught by time, I tak' it so—exceptin' always Steam.
From coupler-flange to spindle-guide I see Thy Hand, O God—
Predestination in the stride o' yon connectin'-rod.
John Calvin might ha' forged the same—enorrmous, certain, slow—
Ay, wrought it in the furnace-flame—*my* "Institutio."
I cannot get my sleep to-night; old bones are hard to please;
I'll stand the middle watch up here—alone wi' God an' these
My engines, after ninety days o' race an' rack an' strain
Through all the seas of all Thy world, slam-bangin' home again.
Slam-bang too much—they knock a wee—the crosshead-gibs are loose,
But thirty thousand mile o' sea has gied them fair excuse. . . .

Fine, clear an' dark—a full-draught breeze, wi' Ushant out
o' sight,
An' Ferguson relievin' Hay. Old girl, ye'll walk to-night!
His wife's at Plymouth. . . . Seventy—One—Two—Three
since he began—
Three turns for Mistress Ferguson . . . and who's to blame
the man?
There's none at any port for me, by drivin' fast or slow,
Since Elsie Campbell went to Thee, Lord, thirty years ago.
(The year the *Sarah Sands* was burned. Oh roads we used to
tread,
Fra' Maryhill to Pollokshaws—fra' Govan to Parkhead!)
Not but they're ceevil on the Board. Ye'll hear Sir Kenneth
say:
"Good morrn, McAndrew! Back again? An' how's your bilge
to-day?"
Miscallin' technicalities but handin' me my chair
To drink Madeira wi' three Earls—the auld Fleet Engineer
That started as a boiler-whelp—when steam and he were low.
I mind the time we used to serve a broken pipe wi' tow!
Ten pound was all the pressure then—Eh! Eh!—a man wad
drive;
An' here, our workin' gauges give one hunder sixty-five!
We're creepin' on wi' each new rig—less weight an' larger
power;
There'll be the loco-boiler next an' thirty miles an hour!
Thirty an' more. What I ha' seen since ocean-steam began
Leaves me na doot for the machine: but what about the man?
The man that counts, wi' all his runs, one million mile o' sea:
Four time the span from earth to moon. . . . How far,
O Lord, from Thee
That wast beside him night an' day? Ye mind my first
typhoon?
It scoughed the skipper on his way to jock wi' the saloon.
Three feet were on the stokehold-floor—just slappin' to an'
fro—
An' cast me on a furnace-door. I have the marks to show.

Marks! I ha' marks o' more than burns—deep in my soul an' black,
An' times like this, when things go smooth, my wickudness comes back.
The sins o' four an' forty years, all up an' down the seas.
Clack an' repeat like valves half-fed. . . . Forgie's our trespasses!
Nights when I'd come on deck to mark, wi' envy in my gaze,
The couples kittlin' in the dark between the funnel-stays;
Years when I raked the Ports wi' pride to fill my cup o' wrong—
Judge not, O Lord, my steps aside at Gay Street in Hong-Kong!
Blot out the wastrel hours of mine in sin when I abode—
Jane Harrigan's an' Number Nine, The Reddick an' Grant Road!
An' waur than all—my crownin' sin—rank blasphemy an' wild.
I was not four and twenty then—Ye wadna judge a child?
I'd seen the Tropics first that run—new fruit, new smells, new air—
How could I tell—blind-fou wi' sun—the Deil was lurkin' there?
By day like playhouse-scenes the shore slid past our sleepy eyes;
By night those soft, lasceevious stars leered from those velvet skies,
In port (we used no cargo-steam) I'd daunder down the streets—
An ijjit grinnin' in a dream—for shells an' parrakeets,
An' walkin'-sticks o' carved bamboo an' blowfish stuffed an' dried—
Fillin' my bunk wi' rubbishry the Chief put overside.
Till, off Sambawa Head, Ye mind, I heard a land-breeze ca',
Milk-warm wi' breath o' spice an' bloom: "McAndrew, come awa'!"

Firm, clear an' low—no haste, no hate—the ghostly whisper went,
Just statin' eevidential facts beyon' all argument:
"Your mither's God's a graspin' deil, the shadow o' yoursel',
"Got out o' books by meenisters clean daft on Heaven an' Hell.
"They mak' him in the Broomielaw, o' Glasgie cold an' dirt,
"A jealous, pridefu' fetich, lad, that's only strong to hurt.
"Ye'll not go back to Him again an' kiss His red-hot rod,
"But come wi' Us" (Now, who were *They?*) "an' know the Leevin' God,
"That does not kipper souls for sport or break a life in jest,
"But swells the ripenin' cocoanuts an' ripes the woman's breast."
An' there it stopped: cut off: no more; that quiet, certain voice—
For me, six months o' twenty-four, to leave or take at choice.
'Twas on me like a thunderclap—it racked me through an' through—
Temptation past the show o' speech, unnameable an' new—
The Sin against the Holy Ghost? . . . An' under all, our screw.

That storm blew by but left behind her anchor-shiftin' swell.
Thou knowest all my heart an' mind, Thou knowest, Lord, I fell—
Third on the *Mary Gloster* then, and first that night in Hell!
Yet was Thy Hand beneath my head, about my feet Thy Care—
Fra' Deli clear to Torres Strait, the trial o' despair,
But when we touched the Barrier Reef Thy answer to my prayer! . . .
We wared na run that sea by night but lay an' held our fire,
An' I was drowsin' on the hatch—sick—sick wi' doubt an tire:
"Better the sight of eyes that see than wanderin' o' desire!"
Ye mind that word? Clear as our gongs—again, an' once again,

When rippin' down through coral-trash ran out our moorin'-
chain:
An', by Thy Grace, I had the Light to see my duty plain.
Light on the engine-room—no more—bright as our carbons
burn.
I've lost it since a thousand times, but never past return!

. . . .

Obsairve! Per annum we'll have here two thousand souls
aboard—
Think not I dare to justify myself before the Lord,
But—average fifteen hunder souls safe-borne fra' port to
port—
I *am* o' service to my kind. Ye wadna blame the thought?
Maybe they steam from Grace to Wrath—to sin by folly
led—
It isna mine to judge their path—their lives are on my head.
Mine at the last—when all is done it all comes back to me,
The fault that leaves six thousand ton a log upon the sea.
We'll tak' one stretch—three weeks an' odd by ony road ye
steer—
Fra' Cape Town east to Wellington—ye need an engineer.
Fail there—ye've time to weld your shaft—ay, eat it, ere ye're
spoke;
Or make Kerguelen under sail—three jiggers burned wi'
smoke!
An' home again—the Rio run: it's no child's play to go
Steamin' to bell for fourteen days o' snow an' floe an' blow.
The bergs like kelpies overside that girn an' turn an' shift
Whaur, grindin' like the Mills o' God, goes by the big South
drift.
(Hail, Snow and Ice that praise the Lord. I've met them at
their work,
An' wished we had anither route or they anither kirk.)
Yon's strain, hard strain, o' head an' hand, for though Thy
Power brings
All skill to naught, Ye'll understand a man must think o'
things.

Then, at the last, we'll get to port an' hoist their baggage clear—
The passengers, wi' gloves an' canes—an' this is what I'll hear:
"Well, thank ye for a pleasant voyage. The tender's comin' now."
While I go testin' follower-bolts an' watch the skipper bow.
They've words for every one but me—shake hands wi' half the crew,
Except the dour Scots engineer, the man they never knew.
An' yet I like the wark for all we've dam' few pickin's here—
No pension, an' the most we'll earn's four hunder pound a year.
Better myself abroad? Maybe. *I'd* sooner starve than sail
Wi' such as call a snifter-rod *ross.* . . . French for nightingale.
Commeesion on my stores? Some do; but I cannot afford
To lie like stewards wi' patty-pans. I'm older than the Board.
A bonus on the coal I save? Ou ay, the Scots are close,
But when I grudge the strength Ye gave I'll grudge their food to *those.*
(There's bricks that I might recommend—an' clink the firebars cruel.
No! Welsh—Wangarti at the worst—an' damn all patent fuel!)
Inventions? Ye must stay in port to mak' a patent pay.
My Deeferential Valve-Gear taught me how that business lay.
I blame no chaps wi' clearer heads for aught they make or sell.
I found that I could not invent an' look to these as well.
So, wrestled wi' Apollyon—Nah!—fretted like a bairn—
But burned the workin'-plans last run, wi' all I hoped to earn.
Ye know how hard an Idol dies, an' what that meant to me—
E'en tak' it for a sacrifice acceptable to Thee. . . .
Below there! Oiler! What's your wark? Ye find it runnin' hard?
Ye needn't swill the cup wi' oil—this isn't the Cunard!
Ye thought? Ye are not paid to think. Go, sweat that off again!

Tck! Tck! It's deeficult to sweer nor tak' The Name in vain!
Men, ay an' women, call me stern. Wi' these to oversee,
Ye'll note I've little time to burn on social repartee.
The bairns see what their elders miss; they'll hunt me to an' fro,
Till for the sake of—well, a kiss—I tak' 'em down below.
That minds me of our Viscount loon—Sir Kenneth's kin—the chap
Wi' Russia leather tennis-shoon an' spar-decked yachtin'-cap.
I showed him round last week, o'er all—an' at the last says he:
"Mister McAndrew, don't you think steam spoils romance at sea?"
Damned ijjit! I'd been doon that morn to see what ailed the throws,
Manholin', on my back—the cranks three inches off my nose.
Romance! Those first-class passengers they like it very well,
Printed an' bound in little books; but why don't poets tell?
I'm sick of all their quirks an' turns—the loves an' doves they dream—
Lord, send a man like Robbie Burns to sing the Song o' Steam!
To match wi' Scotia's noblest speech yon orchestra sublime
Whaurto—uplifted like the Just—the tail-rods mark the time.
The crank-throws give the double-bass, the feed-pump sobs an' heaves,
An' now the main eccentrics start their quarrel on the sheaves:
Her time, her own appointed time, the rocking link-head bides,
Till—hear that note?—the rod's return whings glimmerin' through the guides.
They're all awa'! True beat, full power, the clangin' chorus goes
Clear to the tunnel where they sit, my purrin' dynamos.
Interdependence absolute, foreseen, ordained, decreed,
To work, Ye'll note, at ony tilt an' every rate o' speed.
Fra' skylight-lift to furnace-bars, backed, bolted, braced an' stayed.
An' singin' like the Mornin' Stars for joy that they are made;

While, out o' touch o' vanity, the sweatin' thrust-block says:
"Not unto us the praise, or man—not unto us the praise!"
Now, a' together, hear them lift their lesson—theirs an' mine:
"Law, Orrder, Duty an' Restraint, Obedience, Discipline!"
Mill, forge an' try-pit taught them that when roarin' they arose,
An' whiles I wonder if a soul was gied them wi' the blows.
Oh for a man to weld it then, in one trip-hammer strain,
Till even first-class passengers could tell the meanin' plain!
But no one cares except mysel' that serve an' understand
My seven thousand horse-power here. Eh, Lord! They're grand—they're grand!
Uplift am I? When first in store the new-made beasties stood,
Were Ye cast down that breathed the Word declarin' all things good?
Not so! O' that warld-liftin' joy no after-fall could vex,
Ye've left a glimmer still to cheer the Man—the Arrtifex!
That holds, in spite o' knock and scale, o' friction, waste an' slip,
An' by that light—now, mark my word—we'll build the Perfect Ship.
I'll never last to judge her lines or take her curve—not I.
But I ha' lived an' I ha' worked. Be thanks to Thee, Most High!
An' I ha' done what I ha' done—judge Thou if ill or well—
Always Thy Grace preventin' me. . . .
Losh! Yon's the "Stand-by" bell.
Pilot so soon? His flare it is. The mornin'-watch is set.
Well, God be thanked, as I was sayin', I'm no Pelagian yet.
Now I'll tak' on. . . .
'Morrn, Ferguson. Man, have ye ever thought
What your good leddy costs in coal? . . . I'll burn 'em down to port.

THE "MARY GLOSTER"
1894

I'VE paid for your sickest fancies; I've humoured your crackedest whim—
Dick, it's your daddy, dying; you've got to listen to him!
Good for a fortnight, am I? The doctor told you? He lied.
I shall go under by morning, and—— Put that nurse outside.
'Never seen death yet, Dickie? Well, now is your time to learn,
And you'll wish you held my record before it comes to your turn.
Not counting the Line and the Foundry, the Yards and the village, too,
I've made myself and a million; but I'm damned if I made you.
Master at two-and-twenty, and married at twenty-three—
Ten thousand men on the pay-roll, and forty freighters at sea!
Fifty years between 'em, and every year of it fight,
And now I'm Sir Anthony Gloster, dying, a baronite:
For I lunched with his Royal 'Ighness—what was it the papers had?
"Not least of our merchant-princes." Dickie, that's me, your dad!
I didn't begin with askings. *I* took my job and I stuck;
I took the chances they wouldn't, an' now they're calling it luck.
Lord, what boats I've handled—rotten and leaky and old—
Ran 'em, or—opened the bilge-cock, precisely as I was told.
Grub that 'ud bind you crazy, and crews that 'ud turn you grey,
And a big fat lump of insurance to cover the risk on the way.

The others they dursn't do it; they said they valued their life
(They've served me since as skippers). *I* went, and I took my
wife.
Over the world I drove 'em, married at twenty-three,
And your mother saving the money and making a man of me.
I was content to be master, but she said there was better
behind;
She took the chances I wouldn't, and I followed your mother
blind.
She egged me to borrow the money, an' she helped me to
clear the loan,
When we bought half-shares in a cheap 'un and hoisted a flag
of our own.
Patching and coaling on credit, and living the Lord knew how,
We started the Red Ox freighters—we've eight-and-thirty
now.
And those were the days of clippers, and the freights were
clipper-freights,
And we knew we were making our fortune, but she died in
Macassar Straits—
By the Little Paternosters, as you come to the Union Bank—
And we dropped her in fourteen fathom: I pricked it off
where she sank.
Owners we were, full owners, and the boat was christened for
her,
And she died in the *Mary Gloster*. My heart, how young we
were!
So I went on a spree round Java and well-nigh ran her ashore,
But your mother came and warned me and I wouldn't liquor
no more:
Strict I stuck to my business, afraid to stop or I'd think,
Saving the money (she warned me), and letting the other men
drink.
And I met M'Cullough in London (I'd saved five 'undred
then),
And 'tween us we started the Foundry—three forges and
twenty men.

Cheap repairs for the cheap 'uns. It paid, and the business grew;
For I bought me a steam-lathe patent, and that was a gold mine too.
"Cheaper to build 'em than buy 'em," *I* said, but M'Cullough he shied,
And we wasted a year in talking before we moved to the Clyde.
And the Lines were all beginning, and we all of us started fair,
Building our engines like houses and staying the boilers square.
But M'Cullough 'e wanted cabins with marble and maple and all,
And Brussels an' Utrecht velvet, and baths and a Social Hall,
And pipes for closets all over, and cutting the frames too light,
But M'Cullough he died in the Sixties, and—— Well, I'm dying to-night. . . .
I knew—*I* knew what was coming, when we bid on the *Byfleet's* keel—
They piddled and piffled with iron. I'd given my orders for steel!
Steel and the first expansions. It paid, I tell you, it paid,
When we came with our nine-knot freighters and collared the long-run trade!
And they asked me how I did it, and I gave 'em the Scripture text,
"You keep your light so shining a little in front o' the next!"
They copied all they could follow, but they couldn't copy my mind,
And I left 'em sweating and stealing a year and a half behind.
Then came the armour-contracts, but that was M'Cullough's side;
He was always best in the Foundry, but better, perhaps, he died.
I went through his private papers; the notes was plainer than print;
And I'm no fool to finish if a man'll give me a hint.
(I remember his widow was angry.) So I saw what his drawings meant,
And I started the six-inch rollers, and it paid me sixty per cent.

Sixty per cent *with* failures, and more than twice we could do,
And a quarter-million to credit, and I saved it all for you!
I thought—it doesn't matter—you seemed to favour your ma,
But you're nearer forty than thirty, and I know the kind you
 are.
Harrer an' Trinity College! I ought to ha' sent you to sea—
But I stood you an education, an' what have you done for me?
The things I knew was proper you wouldn't thank me to give,
And the things I knew was rotten you said was the way to
 live.
For you muddled with books and pictures, an' china an'
 eatchin's an' fans,
And your rooms at college was beastly—more like a whore's
 than a man's;
Till you married that thin-flanked woman, as white and as
 stale as a bone,
An' she gave you your social nonsense; but where's that kid
 o' your own?
I've seen your carriages blocking the half o' the Cromwell
 Road,
But never the doctor's brougham to help the missus unload.
(So there isn't even a grandchild, an' the Gloster family's
 done.)
Not like your mother, she isn't. *She* carried her freight each
 run.
But they died, the pore little beggars! At sea she had 'em—
 they died.
Only you, an' you stood it. You haven't stood much beside.
Weak, a liar, and idle, and mean as a collier's whelp
Nosing for scraps in the galley. No help—my son was no
 help!
So he gets three 'undred thousand, in trust and the interest
 paid.
I wouldn't give it you, Dickie—you see, I made it in trade.
You're saved from soiling your fingers, and if you have no
 child,
It all comes back to the business. 'Gad, won't your wife be
 wild!

'Calls and calls in her carriage, her 'andkerchief up to 'er eye:
"Daddy! dear daddy's dyin!" and doing her best to cry.
Grateful? Oh, yes, I'm grateful, but keep her away from here.
Your mother 'ud never ha' stood 'er, and, anyhow, women
are queer. . . .
There's women will say I've married a second time. Not quite!
But give pore Aggie a hundred, and tell her your lawyers'll
fight.
She was the best o' the boiling—you'll meet her before it ends.
I'm in for a row with the mother—I'll leave you settle my
friends.
For a man he must go with a woman, which women don't
understand—
Or the sort that say they can see it they aren't the marrying
brand.
But I wanted to speak o' your mother that's Lady Gloster
still;
I'm going to up and see her, without its hurting the will.
Here! Take your hand off the bell-pull. Five thousand's wait-
ing for you,
If you'll only listen a minute, and do as I bid you do.
They'll try to prove me crazy, and, if you bungle, they can;
And I've only you to trust to! (O God, why ain't it a man?)
There's some waste money on marbles, the same as M'Cul-
lough tried—
Marbles and mausoleums—but I call that sinful pride.
There's some ship bodies for burial—we've carried 'em,
soldered and packed;
Down in their wills they wrote it, and nobody called *them*
cracked.
But me—I've too much money, and people might . . . All
my fault:
It come o' hoping for grandsons and buying that Wokin'
vault. . . .
I'm sick o' the 'ole dam' business. I'm going back where I
came.
Dick, you're the son o' my body, and you'll take charge o'
the same!

I want to lie by your mother, ten thousand mile away,
And they'll want to send me to Woking; and that's where you'll earn your pay.
I've thought it out on the quiet, the same as it ought to be done—
Quiet, and decent, and proper—an' here's your orders, my son.
You know the Line? You don't, though. You write to the Board, and tell
Your father's death has upset you an' you're goin' to cruise for a spell,
An' you'd like the *Mary Gloster*—I've held her ready for this—
They'll put her in working order and you'll take her out as she is.
Yes, it was money idle when I patched her and laid her aside
(Thank God, I can pay for my fancies!)—the boat where your mother died,
By the Little Paternosters, as you came to the Union Bank,
We dropped her—I think I told you—and I pricked it off where she sank.
['Tiny she looked on the grating—that oily, treacly sea—]
'Hundred and Eighteen East, remember, and South just Three.
Easy bearings to carry—Three South—Three to the dot;
But I gave McAndrew a copy in case of dying—or not.
And so you'll write to McAndrew, he's Chief of the Maori Line;
They'll give him leave, if you ask 'em and say it's business o' mine.
I built three boats for the Maoris, an' very well pleased they were,
An' I've known Mac since the Fifties, and Mac knew me—and her.
After the first stroke warned me I sent him the money to keep
Against the time you'd claim it, committin' your dad to the deep;

For you are the son o' my body, and Mac was my oldest
friend,
I've never asked 'im to dinner, but he'll see it out to the end.
Stiff-necked Glasgow beggar! I've heard he's prayed for my
soul,
But he couldn't lie if you paid him, and he'd starve before he
stole.
He'll take the *Mary* in ballast—you'll find her a lively ship;
And you'll take Sir Anthony Gloster, that goes on 'is wedding-
trip,
Lashed in our old deck-cabin with all three port-holes wide,
The kick o' the screw beneath him and the round blue seas
outside!
Sir Anthony Gloster's carriage—our 'ouse-flag flyin' free—
Ten thousand men on the pay-roll and forty freighters at sea!
He made himself and a million, but this world is a fleetin'
show,
And he'll go to the wife of 'is bosom the same as he ought to
go—
By the heel of the Paternosters—there isn't a chance to mis-
take—
And Mac'll pay you the money as soon as the bubbles break!
Five thousand for six weeks' cruising, the staunchest freighter
afloat,
And Mac he'll give you your bonus the minute I'm out o' the
boat!
He'll take you round to Macassar, and you'll come back
alone;
He knows what I want o' the *Mary*. . . . I'll do what I
please with my own.
Your mother 'ud call it wasteful, but I've seven-and-thirty
more;
I'll come in my private carriage and bid it wait at the
door. . . .
For my son 'e was never a credit: 'e muddled with books and
art,
And 'e lived on Sir Anthony's money and 'e broke Sir
Anthony's heart.

There isn't even a grandchild, and the Gloster family's done—
The only one you left me—O mother, the only one!
Harrer and Trinity College—me slavin' early an' late—
An' he thinks I'm dying crazy, and you're in Macassar Strait!
Flesh o' my flesh, my dearie, for ever an' ever amen,
That first stroke come for a warning. I ought to ha' gone to
you then.
But—cheap repairs for a cheap 'un—the doctors said I'd
do.
Mary, why didn't *you* warn me? I've allus heeded to you,
Excep'—I know—about women; but you are a spirit now;
An', wife, they was only women, and I was a man. That's
how.
An' a man 'e must go with a woman, as you *could* not under-
stand;
But I never talked 'em secrets. I paid 'em out o' hand.
Thank Gawd, I can pay for my fancies! Now what's five
thousand to me,
For a berth off the Paternosters in the haven where I would
be?
I believe in the Resurrection, if I read my Bible plain,
But I wouldn't trust 'em at Wokin'; we're safer at sea again.
For the heart it shall go with the treasure—go down to the sea
in ships.
I'm sick of the hired women. I'll kiss my girl on her lips!
I'll be content with my fountain. I'll drink from my own well,
And the wife of my youth shall charm me—an' the rest can
go to Hell!
(Dickie, *he* will, that's certain.) I'll lie in our standin'-bed,
An' Mac'll take her in ballast—an' she trims best by the
head. . . .
Down by the head an' sinkin', her fires are drawn and cold,
And the water's splashin' hollow on the skin of the empty
hold—
Churning an' choking and chuckling, quiet and scummy and
dark—
Full to her lower hatches and risin' steady. Hark!

That was the after-bulkhead. . . . She's flooded from stem
to stern. . . .
'Never seen death yet, Dickie? . . . Well, now is your time
to learn!

THE LINER SHE'S A LADY

1894

THE Liner she's a lady, an' she never looks nor 'eeds—
The Man-o'-War's 'er 'usband, an' 'e gives 'er all she needs;
But, oh, the little cargo-boats, that sail the wet seas roun'.
They're just the same as you an' me a-plyin' up an' down!

Plyin' up an' down, Jenny, 'angin' round the Yard,
All the way by Fratton tram down to Portsmouth 'Ard;
Anythin' for business, an' we're growin' old—
Plyin' up an' down, Jenny, waitin' in the cold!

The Liner she's a lady by the paint upon 'er face,
An' if she meets an accident they count it sore disgrace.
The Man-o'-War's 'er 'usband, and 'e's always 'andy by,
But, oh, the little cargo-boats, they've got to load or die!

The Liner she's a lady, and 'er route is cut an' dried;
The Man-o'-War's 'er 'usband, an' 'e always keeps beside;
But, oh, the little cargo-boats that 'aven't any man,
They've got to do their business first, and make the most they
can!

The Liner she's a lady, and if a war should come,
The Man-o'-War's 'er 'usband, and 'e'd bid 'er stay at home;
But, oh, the little cargo-boats that fill with every tide!
'E'd 'ave to up an' fight for them for they are England's pride.

The Liner she's a lady, but if she wasn't made,
There still would be the cargo-boats for 'ome an' foreign
trade.

The Man-o'-War's 'er 'usband, but if we wasn't 'ere,
'E wouldn't have to fight at all for 'ome an' friends so dear.

'Ome an' friends so dear, Jenny, 'angin' round the Yard,
All the way by Fratton tram down to Portsmouth 'Ard;
Anythin' for business, an' we're growin' old—
'Ome an' friends so dear, Jenny, waitin' in the cold!

THE LONG TRAIL

1891

THERE'S a whisper down the field where the year has shot her yield,
And the ricks stand grey to the sun,
Singing: "Over then, come over, for the bee has quit the clover,
"And your English summer's done."

You have heard the beat of the off-shore wind,
And the thresh of the deep-sea rain;
You have heard the song—how long? how long?
Pull out on the trail again!
Ha' done with the Tents of Shem, dear lass,
We've seen the seasons through,
And it's time to turn on the old trail, our own trail, the out trail,
Pull out, pull out, on the Long Trail—the trail that is always new!

It's North you may run to the rime-ringed sun
Or South to the blind Horn's hate;
Or East all the way into Mississippi Bay,
Or West to the Golden Gate—

Where the blindest bluffs hold good, dear lass,
And the wildest tales are true,
And the men bulk big on the old trail, our own trail,
the out trail,
And life runs large on the Long Trail—the trail that
is always new.

The days are sick and cold, and the skies are grey and old,
And the twice-breathed airs blow damp;
And I'd sell my tired soul for the bucking beam-sea roll
Of a black Bilbao tramp,
With her load-line over her hatch, dear lass,
And a drunken Dago crew,
And her nose held down on the old trail, our own trail,
the out trail
From Cadiz south on the Long Trail—the trail that
is always new.

There be triple ways to take, of the eagle or the snake,
Or the way of a man with a maid;
But the sweetest way to me is a ship's upon the sea
In the heel of the North-East Trade.
Can you hear the crash on her bows, dear lass,
And the drum of the racing screw,
As she ships it green on the old trail, our own trail,
the out trail,
As she lifts and 'scends on the Long Trail—the trail
that is always new?

See the shaking funnels roar, with the Peter at the fore,
And the fenders grind and heave,
And the derricks clack and grate, as the tackle hooks the
crate,
And the fall-rope whines through the sheave;
It's "Gang-plank up and in," dear lass,
It's "Hawsers warp her through!"

And it's "All clear aft" on the old trail, our own trail, the out trail,
We're backing down on the Long Trail—the trail that is always new.

O the mutter overside, when the port-fog holds us tied,
And the sirens hoot their dread,
When foot by foot we creep o'er the hueless viewless deep
To the sob of the questing lead!
It's down by the Lower Hope, dear lass,
With the Gunfleet Sands in view,
Till the Mouse swings green on the old trail, our own trail, the out trail,
And the Gull Light lifts on the Long Trail—the trail that is always new.

O the blazing tropic night, when the wake's a welt of light
That holds the hot sky tame,
And the steady fore-foot snores through the planet-powdered floors
Where the scared whale flukes in flame!
Her plates are flaked by the sun, dear lass,
And her ropes are taut with the dew,
For we're booming down on the old trail, our own trail, the out trail,
We're sagging south on the Long Trail—the trail that is always new.

Then home, get her home, where the drunken rollers comb,
And the shouting seas drive by,
And the engines stamp and ring, and the wet bows reel and swing,
And the Southern Cross rides high!
Yes, the old lost stars wheel back, dear lass,
That blaze in the velvet blue.
They're all old friends on the old trail, our own trail, the out trail,
They're God's own guide on the Long Trail—the trail that is always new.

Fly forward, O my heart, from the Foreland to the Start—
We're steaming all too slow,
And it's twenty thousand mile to our little lazy isle
Where the trumpet-orchids blow!
You have heard the call of the off-shore wind
And the voice of the deep-sea rain;
You have heard the song. How long—how long?
Pull out on the trail again!

The Lord knows what we may find, dear lass,
And The Deuce knows what we may do—
But we're back once more on the old trail, our own trail, the out trail,
We're down, hull-down, on the Long Trail—the trail that is always new!

WHEN EARTH'S LAST PICTURE IS PAINTED

1892

WHEN Earth's last picture is painted and the tubes are twisted and dried,
When the oldest colours have faded, and the youngest critic has died,
We shall rest, and, faith, we shall need it—lie down for an æon or two,
Till the Master of All Good Workmen shall put us to work anew.

And those that were good shall be happy: they shall sit in a golden chair;
They shall splash at a ten-league canvas with brushes of comets' hair.

They shall find real saints to draw from—Magdalene, Peter, and Paul;
They shall work for an age at a sitting and never be tired at all!

And only The Master shall praise us, and only The Master shall blame;
And no one shall work for money, and no one shall work for fame,
But each for the joy of the working, and each, in his separate star,
Shall draw the Thing as he sees It for the God of Things as They are!

THE BALLAD OF EAST AND WEST

1889

Oh, East is East, and West is West, and never the twain shall meet,
Till Earth and Sky stand presently at God's great Judgment Seat;
But there is neither East nor West, Border, nor Breed, nor Birth,
When two strong men stand face to face, though they come from the ends of the earth!

Kamal is out with twenty men to raise the Border side,
And he has lifted the Colonel's mare that is the Colonel's pride.
He has lifted her out of the stable-door between the dawn and the day,
And turned the calkins upon her feet, and ridden her far away.
Then up and spoke the Colonel's son that led a troop of the Guides:
"Is there never a man of all my men can say where Kamal hides?"

Then up and spoke Mohammed Khan, the son of the Ressaldar:
"If ye know the track of the morning-mist, ye know where his pickets are.
"At dusk he harries the Abazai—at dawn he is into Bonair,
"But he must go by Fort Bukloh to his own place to fare.
"So if ye gallop to Fort Bukloh as fast as a bird can fly,
"By the favour of God ye may cut him off ere he win to the Tongue of Jagai.
"But if he be past the Tongue of Jagai, right swiftly turn ye then,
"For the length and the breadth of that grisly plain is sown with Kamal's men.
"There is rock to the left, and rock to the right, and low lean thorn between,
"And ye may hear a breech-bolt snick where never a man is seen."
The Colonel's son has taken horse, and a raw rough dun was he,
With the mouth of a bell and the heart of Hell and the head of a gallows-tree.
The Colonel's son to the Fort has won, they bid him stay to eat—
Who rides at the tail of a Border thief, he sits not long at his meat.
He's up and away from Fort Bukloh as fast as he can fly,
Till he was aware of his father's mare in the gut of the Tongue of Jagai,
Till he was aware of his father's mare with Kamal upon her back,
And when he could spy the white of her eye, he made the pistol crack.
He has fired once, he has fired twice, but the whistling ball went wide.
"Ye shoot like a soldier," Kamal said. "Show now if ye can ride!"
It's up and over the Tongue of Jagai, as blown dust-devils go,
The dun he fled like a stag of ten, but the mare like a barren doe.

The dun he leaned against the bit and slugged his head above,
But the red mare played with the snaffle-bars, as a maiden plays with a glove.
There was rock to the left and rock to the right, and low lean thorn between,
And thrice he heard a breech-bolt snick tho' never a man was seen.
They have ridden the low moon out of the sky, their hoofs drum up the dawn,
The dun he went like a wounded bull, but the mare like a new-roused fawn.
The dun he fell at a water-course—in a woeful heap fell he,
And Kamal has turned the red mare back, and pulled the rider free.
He has knocked the pistol out of his hand—small room was there to strive,
" 'Twas only by favour of mine," quoth he, "ye rode so long alive:
"There was not a rock for twenty mile, there was not a clump of tree,
"But covered a man of my own men with his rifle cocked on his knee.
"If I had raised my bridle-hand, as I have held it low,
"The little jackals that flee so fast were feasting all in a row.
"If I had bowed my head on my breast, as I have held it high,
"The kite that whistles above us now were gorged till she could not fly."
Lightly answered the Colonel's son: "Do good to bird and beast,
"But count who come for the broken meats before thou makest a feast.
"If there should follow a thousand swords to carry my bones away,
"Belike the price of a jackal's meal were more than a thief could pay.
"They will feed their horse on the standing crop, their men on the garnered grain.

"The thatch of the byres will serve their fires when all the cattle are slain.
"But if thou thinkest the price be fair,—thy brethren wait to sup,
"The hound is kin to the jackal-spawn,—howl, dog, and call them up!
"And if thou thinkest the price be high, in steer and gear and stack,
"Give me my father's mare again, and I'll fight my own way back!"
Kamal has gripped him by the hand and set him upon his feet.
"No talk shall be of dogs," said he, "when wolf and grey wolf meet.
"May I eat dirt if thou hast hurt of me in deed or breath;
"What dam of lances brought thee forth to jest at the dawn with Death?"
Lightly answered the Colonel's son: "I hold by the blood of my clan:
"Take up the mare for my father's gift—by God, she has carried a man!"
The red mare ran to the Colonel's son, and nuzzled against his breast;
"We be two strong men," said Kamal then, "but she loveth the younger best.
"So she shall go with a lifter's dower, my turquoise-studded rein,
"My 'broidered saddle and saddle-cloth, and silver stirrups twain."
The Colonel's son a pistol drew, and held it muzzle-end,
"Ye have taken the one from a foe," said he. "Will ye take the mate from a friend?"
"A gift for a gift," said Kamal straight; "a limb for the risk of a limb.
"Thy father has sent his son to me, I'll send my son to him!"
With that he whistled his only son, that dropped from a mountain-crest—
He trod the ling like a buck in spring, and he looked like a lance in rest.

"Now here is thy master," Kamal said, "who leads a troop of the Guides,
"And thou must ride at his left side as shield on shoulder rides.
"Till Death or I cut loose the tie, at camp and board and bed,
"Thy life is his—thy fate it is to guard him with thy head.
"So, thou must eat the White Queen's meat, and all her foes are thine,
"And thou must harry thy father's hold for the peace of the Border-line.
"And thou must make a trooper tough and hack thy way to power—
"Belike they will raise thee to Ressaldar when I am hanged in Peshawur!"

They have looked each other between the eyes, and there they found no fault.
They have taken the Oath of the Brother-in-Blood on leavened bread and salt:
They have taken the Oath of the Brother-in-Blood on fire and fresh-cut sod,
On the hilt and the haft of the Khyber knife, and the Wondrous Names of God.
The Colonel's son he rides the mare and Kamal's boy the dun,
And two have come back to Fort Bukloh where there went forth but one.
And when they drew to the Quarter-Guard, full twenty swords flew clear—
There was not a man but carried his feud with the blood of the mountaineer.
"Ha' done! ha' done!" said the Colonel's son. "Put up the steel at your sides!
"Last night ye had struck at a Border thief—to-night 't is a man of the Guides!"

Oh, East is East, and West is West, and never the twain shall meet,
Till Earth and Sky stand presently at God's great Judgment Seat;

But there is neither East nor West, Border, nor Breed, nor Birth,
When two strong men stand face to face, though they come from the ends of the earth!

THE FEET OF THE YOUNG MEN
1897

Now the Four-way Lodge is opened, now the Hunting Winds are loose—
Now the Smokes of Spring go up to clear the brain;
Now the Young Men's hearts are troubled for the whisper of the Trues,
Now the Red Gods make their medicine again!
Who hath seen the beaver busied? Who hath watched the black-tail mating?
Who hath lain alone to hear the wild-goose cry?
Who hath worked the chosen water where the ouananiche is waiting,
Or the sea-trout's jumping-crazy for the fly?

He must go—go—go away from here!
On the other side the world he's overdue.
'Send your road is clear before you when the old Spring-fret comes o'er you,
And the Red Gods call for you!

So for one the wet sail arching through the rainbow round the bow,
And for one the creak of snow-shoes on the crust;
And for one the lakeside lilies where the bull-moose waits the cow,
And for one the mule-train coughing in the dust.
Who hath smelt wood-smoke at twilight? Who hath heard the birch-log burning?

Who is quick to read the noises of the night?
Let him follow with the others, for the Young Men's feet are turning
To the camps of proved desire and known delight!

Let him go—go, etc.

I

Do you know the blackened timber—do you know that racing stream
With the raw, right-angled log-jam at the end;
And the bar of sun-warmed shingle where a man may bask and dream
To the click of shod canoe-poles round the bend?
It is there that we are going with our rods and reels and traces,
To a silent, smoky Indian that we know—
To a couch of new-pulled hemlock, with the starlight on our faces,
For the Red Gods call us out and we must go!
They must go—go, etc.

II

Do you know the shallow Baltic where the seas are steep and short,
Where the bluff, lee-boarded fishing-luggers ride?
Do you know the joy of threshing leagues to leeward of your port
On a coast you've lost the chart of overside?
It is there that I am going, with an extra hand to bale her—
Just one able 'long-shore loafer that I know.
He can take his chance of drowning, while I sail and sail and sail her,
For the Red Gods call me out and I must go!
He must go—go, etc.

III

Do you know the pile-built village where the sago-dealers trade—
Do you know the reek of fish and wet bamboo?
Do you know the steaming stillness of the orchid-scented glade
When the blazoned, bird-winged butterflies flap through?
It is there that I am going with my camphor, net, and boxes,
To a gentle, yellow pirate that I know—
To my little wailing lemurs, to my palms and flying foxes,
For the Red Gods call me out and I must go!

He must go—go, etc.

IV

Do you know the world's white roof-tree—do you know that windy rift
Where the baffling mountain-eddies chop and change?
Do you know the long day's patience, belly-down on frozen drift,
While the head of heads is feeding out of range?
It is there that I am going, where the boulders and the snow lie,
With a trusty, nimble tracker that I know.
I have sworn an oath, to keep it on the Horns of Ovis Poli,
And the Red Gods call me out and I must go!

He must go—go, etc.

Now the Four-way Lodge is opened—now the Smokes of Council rise—
Pleasant smokes, ere yet 'twixt trail and trail they choose—
Now the girths and ropes are tested: now they pack their last supplies:
Now our Young Men go to dance before the Trues!
Who shall meet them at those altars—who shall light them to that shrine?

Velvet-footed, who shall guide them to their goal?
Unto each the voice and vision: unto each his spoor and sign—
Lonely mountain in the Northland, misty sweat-bath 'neath the Line—
And to each a man that knows his naked soul!

White or yellow, black or copper, he is waiting, as a lover,
Smoke of funnel, dust of hooves, or beat of train—
Where the high grass hides the horseman or the glaring flats discover—
Where the steamer hails the landing, or the surf-boat brings the rover—
Where the rails run out in sand-drift . . . Quick! ah, heave the camp-kit over,
For the Red Gods make their medicine again!

And we go—go—go away from here!
On the other side the world we're overdue!
'Send the road is clear before you when the old Spring-fret comes o'er you,
And the Red Gods call for you!

"THE CITY OF BRASS"
1909

"Here was a people whom after their works thou shalt see wept over for their lost dominion: and in this palace is the last information respecting lords collected in the dust."

—THE ARABIAN NIGHTS

In a land that the sand overlays—the ways to her gates are untrod—
A multitude ended their days whose fates were made splendid by God,
Till they grew drunk and were smitten with madness and went to their fall,
And of these is a story written: but Allah Alone knoweth all!

When the wine stirred in their heart their bosoms dilated.
They rose to suppose themselves kings over all things created—
To decree a new earth at a birth without labour or sorrow—
To declare: "We prepare it to-day and inherit to-morrow."
They chose themselves prophets and priests of minute understanding,
Men swift to see done, and outrun, their extremest commanding—
Of the tribe which describe with a jibe the perversions of Justice—
Panders avowed to the crowd whatsoever its lust is.

Swiftly these pulled down the walls that their fathers had made them—
The impregnable ramparts of old, they razed and relaid them
As playgrounds of pleasure and leisure, with limitless entries,
And havens of rest for the wastrels where once walked the sentries;
And because there was need of more pay for the shouters and marchers,
They disbanded in face of their foemen their yeomen and archers.

They replied to their well-wishers' fears—to their enemies' laughter,
Saying: "Peace! We have fashioned a God Which shall save us hereafter.
We ascribe all dominion to man in his factions conferring,
And have given to numbers the Name of the Wisdom unerring."

They said: "Who has hate in his soul? Who has envied his neighbour?
Let him arise and control both that man and his labour."
They said: "Who is eaten by sloth? Whose unthrift has destroyed him?

He shall levy a tribute from all because none have employed
him."
They said: "Who hath toiled, who hath striven, and gathered
possession?
Let him be spoiled. He hath given full proof of transgres-
sion."

They said: "Who is irked by the Law? *Though we may not
remove it,*
If he lend us his aid in this raid, we will set him above it!"
So the robber did judgment again upon such as displeased
him,
The slayer, too, boasted his slain, and the judges released him.

As for their kinsmen far off, on the skirts of the nation,
They harried all earth to make sure none escaped reprobation.
They awakened unrest for a jest in their newly-won borders,
And jeered at the blood of their brethren betrayed by their
orders.
They instructed the ruled to rebel, their rulers to aid them;
And, since such as obeyed them not fell, their Viceroys obeyed
them.
When the riotous set them at naught they said: "Praise the
upheaval!
For the show and the word and the thought of Dominion is
evil!"
They unwound and flung from them with rage, as a rag that
defiled them
The imperial gains of the age which their forefathers piled
them.
They ran panting in haste to lay waste and embitter for ever
The wellsprings of Wisdom and Strength which are Faith and
Endeavour.
They nosed out and digged up and dragged forth and exposed
to derision
All doctrine of purpose and worth and restraint and prevision:

And it ceased, and God granted them all things for which they
had striven,
And the heart of a beast in the place of a man's heart was
given. . . .

. . . .

When they were fullest of wine and most flagrant in error,
Out of the sea rose a sign—out of Heaven a terror.
Then they saw, then they heard, then they knew—for none
troubled to hide it,
An host had prepared their destruction, but still they denied it.
They denied what they dared not abide if it came to the trial;
But the Sword that was forged while they lied did not heed
their denial.
It drove home, and no time was allowed to the crowd that
was driven.
The preposterous-minded were cowed—they thought time
would be given.
There was no need of a steed nor a lance to pursue them;
It was decreed their own deed, and not chance, should undo
them.
The tares they had laughingly sown were ripe to the reaping.
The trust they had leagued to disown was removed from their
keeping.
The eaters of other men's bread, the exempted from hardship,
The excusers of impotence fled, abdicating their wardship,
For the hate they had taught through the State brought the
State no defender,
And it passed from the roll of the Nations in headlong sur-
render!

THE WHITE MAN'S BURDEN
1899

TAKE up the White Man's burden—
  Send forth the best ye breed—
Go bind your sons to exile
  To serve your captives' need;
To wait in heavy harness,
  On fluttered folk and wild—
Your new-caught, sullen peoples,
  Half-devil and half-child.

Take up the White Man's burden—
  In patience to abide,
To veil the threat of terror
  And check the show of pride;
By open speech and simple,
  An hundred times made plain,
To seek another's profit,
  And work another's gain.

Take up the White Man's burden—
  The savage wars of peace—
Fill full the mouth of Famine
  And bid the sickness cease;
And when your goal is nearest
  The end for others sought,
Watch Sloth and heathen Folly
  Bring all your hope to nought.

Take up the White Man's burden—
  No tawdry rule of kings,
But toil of serf and sweeper—
  The tale of common things.

The ports ye shall not enter,
   The roads ye shall not tread,
Go make them with your living,
   And mark them with your dead.

Take up the White Man's burden—
   And reap his old reward:
The blame of those ye better,
   The hate of those ye guard—
The cry of hosts ye humour
   (Ah, slowly!) toward the light:—
"Why brought ye us from bondage,
   "Our loved Egyptian night?"

Take up the White Man's burden—
   Ye dare not stoop to less—
Nor call too loud on Freedom
   To cloak your weariness;
By all ye cry or whisper,
   By all ye leave or do,
The silent, sullen peoples
   Shall weigh your Gods and you.

Take up the White Man's burden—
   Have done with childish days—
The lightly proffered laurel,
   The easy, ungrudged praise.
Comes now, to search your manhood
   Through all the thankless years,
Cold, edged with dear-bought wisdom,
   The judgment of your peers!

RECESSIONAL
1897

God of our fathers, known of old,
Lord of our far-flung battle-line,
Beneath whose awful Hand we hold
Dominion over palm and pine—
Lord God of Hosts, be with us yet,
Lest we forget—lest we forget!

The tumult and the shouting dies;
The Captains and the Kings depart:
Still stands Thine ancient sacrifice,
An humble and a contrite heart.
Lord God of Hosts, be with us yet,
Lest we forget—lest we forget!

Far-called, our navies melt away;
On dune and headland sinks the fire:
Lo, all our pomp of yesterday
Is one with Nineveh and Tyre!
Judge of the Nations, spare us yet,
Lest we forget—lest we forget!

If, drunk with sight of power, we loose
Wild tongues that have not Thee in awe,
Such boastings as the Gentiles use,
Or lesser breeds without the Law—
Lord God of Hosts, be with us yet,
Lest we forget—lest we forget!

For heathen heart that puts her trust
In reeking tube and iron shard,
All valiant dust that builds on dust,
And guarding, calls not Thee to guard,
For frantic boast and foolish word—
Thy mercy on Thy people, Lord!

"WHEN 'OMER SMOTE 'IS BLOOMIN' LYRE"

1896

When 'Omer smote 'is bloomin' lyre,
He'd 'eard men sing by land an' sea;
An' what 'e thought 'e might require,
'E went an' took—the same as me!

The market-girls an' fishermen,
The shepherds an' the sailors, too,
They 'eard old songs turn up again,
But kep' it quiet—same as you!

They knew 'e stole; 'e knew they knowed.
They didn't tell, nor make a fuss,
But winked at 'Omer down the road,
An' 'e winked back—the same as us!

TOMLINSON

1891

Now Tomlinson gave up the ghost at his house in Berkeley Square,
And a Spirit came to his bedside and gripped him by the hair—
A Spirit gripped him by the hair and carried him far away,
Till he heard as the roar of a rain-fed ford the roar of the Milky Way:
Till he heard the roar of the Milky Way die down and drone and cease,
And they came to the Gate within the Wall where Peter holds the keys.

"Stand up, stand up now, Tomlinson, and answer loud and high
"The good that ye did for the sake of men or ever ye came to die—
"The good that ye did for the sake of men on little earth so lone!"
And the naked soul of Tomlinson grew white as a rain-washed bone.

"O I have a friend on earth," he said, "that was my priest and guide,
"And well would he answer all for me if he were at my side."
—"For that ye strove in neighbour-love it shall be written fair,
"But now ye wait at Heaven's Gate and not in Berkeley Square:
"Though we called your friend from his bed this night, he could not speak for you,
"For the race is run by one and one and never by two and two."
Then Tomlinson looked up and down, and little gain was there,
For the naked stars grinned overhead, and he saw that his soul was bare.
The Wind that blows between the Worlds, it cut him like a knife,
And Tomlinson took up the tale and spoke of his good in life.
"O this I have read in a book," he said, "and that was told to me,
"And this I have thought that another man thought of a Prince in Muscovy."
The good souls flocked like homing doves and bade him clear the path,
And Peter twirled the jangling Keys in weariness and wrath.
"Ye have read, ye have heard, ye have thought," he said, "and the tale is yet to run:
"By the worth of the body that once ye had, give answer—what ha' ye done?"

Then Tomlinson looked back and forth, and little good it bore,
For the darkness stayed at his shoulder-blade and Heaven's Gate before:—
"O this I have felt, and this I have guessed, and this I have heard men say,
"And this they wrote that another man wrote of a carl in Norroway."
"Ye have read, ye have felt, ye have guessed, good lack! Ye have hampered Heaven's Gate;
"There's little room between the stars in idleness to prate!
"O none may reach by hired speech of neighbour, priest, and kin
"Through borrowed deed to God's good meed that lies so fair within;
"Get hence, get hence to the Lord of Wrong, for the doom has yet to run,
"And . . . the faith that ye share with Berkeley Square uphold you, Tomlinson!"

. . . .

The Spirit gripped him by the hair, and sun by sun they fell
Till they came to the belt of Naughty Stars that rim the mouth of Hell.
The first are red with pride and wrath, the next are white with pain,
But the third are black with clinkered sins that cannot burn again:
They may hold their path, they may leave their path, with never a soul to mark,
They may burn or freeze, but they must not cease in the Scorn of the Outer Dark.
The Wind that blows between the Worlds, it nipped him to the bone,
And he yearned to the flare of Hell-gate there as the light of his own hearth-stone.

The Devil he sat behind the bars, where the desperate legions drew,
But he caught the hasting Tomlinson and would not let him through.
"Wot ye the price of good pit-coal that I must pay?" said he,
"That ye rank yoursel' so fit for Hell and ask no leave of me?
"I am all o'er-sib to Adam's breed that ye should give me scorn,
"For I strove with God for your First Father the day that he was born.
"Sit down, sit down upon the slag, and answer loud and high
"The harm that ye did to the Sons of Men or ever you came to die."
And Tomlinson looked up and up, and saw against the night
The belly of a tortured star blood-red in Hell-Mouth light;
And Tomlinson looked down and down, and saw beneath his feet
The frontlet of a tortured star milk-white in Hell-Mouth heat.
"O I had a love on earth," said he, "that kissed me to my fall;
"And if ye would call my love to me I know she would answer all."
—"All that ye did in love forbid it shall be written fair,
"But now ye wait at Hell-Mouth Gate and not in Berkeley Square:
"Though we whistled your love from her bed to-night, I trow she would not run,
"For the sin ye do by two and two ye must pay for one by one!"
The Wind that blows between the Worlds, it cut him like a knife,
And Tomlinson took up the tale and spoke of his sins in life:—
"Once I ha' laughed at the power of Love and twice at the grip of the Grave,
"And thrice I ha' patted my God on the head that men might call me brave."
The Devil he blew on a brandered soul and set it aside to cool:—

"Do ye think I would waste my good pit-coal on the hide of a brain-sick fool?"
"I see no worth in the hobnailed mirth or the jolthead jest ye did
"That I should waken my gentlemen that are sleeping three on a grid."
Then Tomlinson looked back and forth, and there was little grace.
For Hell-Gate filled the houseless soul with the Fear of Naked Space.
"Nay, this I ha' heard," quo' Tomlinson, "and this was noised abroad,
"And this I ha' got from a Belgian book on the word of a dead French lord."
—"Ye ha' heard, ye ha' read, ye ha' got, good lack! and the tale begins afresh—
"Have ye sinned one sin for the pride o' the eye or the sinful lust of the flesh?"
Then Tomlinson he gripped the bars and yammered, "Let me in—
"For I mind that I borrowed my neighbour's wife to sin the deadly sin."
The Devil he grinned behind the bars, and banked the fires high:
"Did ye read of that sin in a book?" said he; and Tomlinson said, "Ay!"
The Devil he blew upon his nails, and the little devils ran,
And he said: "Go husk this whimpering thief that comes in the guise of a man:
"Winnow him out 'twixt star and star, and sieve his proper worth:
"There's sore decline in Adam's line if this be spawn of earth."
Empusa's crew, so naked-new they may not face the fire,
But weep that they bin too small to sin to the height of their desire,
Over the coal they chased the Soul, and racked it all abroad,
As children rifle a caddis-case or the raven's foolish hoard.

And back they came with the tattered Thing, as children after play,
And they said: "The soul that he got from God he has bartered clean away.
"We have threshed a stook of print and book, and winnowed a chattering wind,
"And many a soul wherefrom he stole, but his we cannot find.
"We have handled him, we have dandled him, we have seared him to the bone,
"And Sire, if tooth and nail show truth he has no soul of his own."
The Devil he bowed his head on his breast and rumbled deep and low:—
"I'm all o'ersib to Adam's breed that I should bid him go.
"Yet close we lie, and deep we lie, and if I gave him place,
"My gentlemen that are so proud would flout me to my face;
"They'd call my house a common stews and me a careless host,
"And—I would not anger my gentlemen for the sake of a shiftless ghost."
The Devil he looked at the mangled Soul that prayed to feel the flame,
And he thought of Holy Charity, but he thought of his own good name:—
"Now ye could haste my coal to waste, and sit ye down to fry.
"Did ye think of that theft for yourself?" said he; and Tomlinson said, "Ay!"
The Devil he blew an outward breath, for his heart was free from care:—
"Ye have scarce the soul of a louse," he said, "but the roots of sin are there.
"And for that sin should ye come in were I the lord alone.
"But sinful pride has rule inside—ay, mightier than my own.
"Honour and Wit, fore-damned they sit, to each his Priest and Whore;
"Nay, scarce I dare myself go there, and you they'd torture sore.

"Ye are neither spirit nor spirk," he said; "ye are neither book nor brute
"Go, get ye back to the flesh again for the sake of Man's repute.
"I'm all o'er-sib to Adam's breed that I should mock your pain,
"But look that ye win to worthier sin ere ye come back again.
"Get hence, the hearse is at your door—the grim black stallions wait—
"They bear your clay to place to-day. Speed, lest ye come too late!
"Go back to Earth with a lip unsealed—go back with an open eye,
"And carry my word to the Sons of Men or ever ye come to die:
"That the sin they do by two and two they must pay for one by one,
"And . . . the God that you took from a printed book be with you, Tomlinson!"

EN-DOR
1914-19—

1919

"Behold there is a woman that hath a familiar spirit at En-dor."

—I SAMUEL xxviii. 7.

THE road to En-dor is easy to tread
For Mother or yearning Wife.
There, it is sure, we shall meet our Dead
As they were even in life.
Earth has not dreamed of the blessing in store
For desolate hearts on the road to En-dor.

Whispers shall comfort us out of the dark—
Hands—ah God!—that we knew!
Visions and voices—look and hark!—
Shall prove that the tale is true,
And that those who have passed to the further shore
May be hailed—at a price—on the road to En-dor.

But they are so deep in their new eclipse
Nothing they say can reach,
Unless it be uttered by alien lips
And framed in a stranger's speech.
The son must send word to the mother that bore,
Through an hireling's mouth. 'Tis the rule of En-dor.

And not for nothing these gifts are shown
By such as delight our dead.
They must twitch and stiffen and slaver and groan
Ere the eyes are set in the head,
And the voice from the belly begins. Therefore,
We pay them a wage where they ply at En-dor.

Even so, we have need of faith
  And patience to follow the clue.
Often, at first, what the dear one saith
  Is babble, or jest, or untrue.
(Lying spirits perplex us sore
Till our loves—and their lives—are well known at En-
  dor). . . .

Oh the road to En-dor is the oldest road
  And the craziest road of all!
Straight it runs to the Witch's abode,
  As it did in the days of Saul,
And nothing has changed of the sorrow in store
For such as go down on the road to En-dor!

THE FEMALE OF THE SPECIES
1911

WHEN the Himalayan peasant meets the he-bear in his pride,
He shouts to scare the monster, who will often turn aside.
But the she-bear thus accosted rends the peasant tooth and
  nail.
For the female of the species is more deadly than the male.

When Nag the basking cobra hears the careless foot of man,
He will sometimes wriggle sideways and avoid it if he can.
But his mate makes no such motion where she camps beside
  the trail.
For the female of the species is more deadly than the male.

When the early Jesuit fathers preached to Hurons and Choc-
  taws,
They prayed to be delivered from the vengeance of the
  squaws.
'Twas the women, not the warriors, turned those stark en-
  thusiasts pale.
For the female of the species is more deadly than the male.

Man's timid heart is bursting with the things he must not say,
For the Woman that God gave him isn't his to give away;
But when hunter meets with husband, each confirms the
other's tale—
The female of the species is more deadly than the male.

Man, a bear in most relations—worm and savage other-
wise,—
Man propounds negotiations, Man accepts the compromise.
Very rarely will he squarely push the logic of a fact
To its ultimate conclusion in unmitigated act.

Fear, or foolishness, impels him, ere he lay the wicked low,
To concede some form of trial even to his fiercest foe.
Mirth obscene diverts his anger—Doubt and Pity oft perplex
Him in dealing with an issue—to the scandal of The Sex!

But the Woman that God gave him, every fibre of her frame
Proves her launched for one sole issue, armed and engined for
the same;
And to serve that single issue, lest the generations fail,
The female of the species must be deadlier than the male.

She who faces Death by torture for each life beneath her
breast
May not deal in doubt or pity—must not swerve for fact or
jest.
These be purely male diversions—not in these her honour
dwells.
She the Other Law we live by, is that Law and nothing else.

She can bring no more to living than the powers that make
her great
As the Mother of the Infant and the Mistress of the Mate.
And when Babe and Man are lacking and she strides un-
claimed to claim
Her right as femme (and baron), her equipment is the same.

She is wedded to convictions—in default of grosser ties:
Her contentions are her children, Heaven help him who
denies!—
He will meet no suave discussion, but the instant, white-hot,
wild,
Wakened female of the species warring as for spouse and
child.

Unprovoked and awful charges—even so the she-bear fights,
Speech that drips, corrodes, and poisons—even so the cobra
bites,
Scientific vivisection of one nerve till it is raw
And the victim writhes in anguish—like the Jesuit with the
squaw!

So it comes that Man, the coward, when he gathers to confer
With his fellow-braves in council, dare not leave a place for
her
Where, at war with Life and Conscience, he uplifts his erring
hands
To some God of Abstract Justice—which no woman understands.

And Man knows it! Knows, moreover, that the Woman that
God gave him
Must command but may not govern—shall enthral but not
enslave him.
And *She* knows, because She warns him, and Her instincts
never fail,
That the Female of Her Species is more deadly than the
Male.

THE KING

1894

"FAREWELL, Romance!" the Cave-men said;
 "With bone well carved he went away.
"Flint arms the ignoble arrowhead,
 "And jasper tips the spear to-day.
"Changed are the Gods of Hunt and Dance,
"And He with these. Farewell, Romance!"

"Farewell, Romance!" the Lake-folk sighed;
 "We lift the weight of flatling years;
"The caverns of the mountain-side
 "Hold Him who scorns our hutted piers.
"Lost hills whereby we dare not dwell,
"Guard ye His rest. Romance, Farewell!"

"Farewell, Romance!" the Soldier spoke;
 "By sleight of sword we may not win,
"But scuffle 'mid uncleanly smoke
 "Of arquebus and culverin.
"Honour is lost, and none may tell
"Who paid good blows. Romance, farewell!"

"Farewell, Romance!" the Traders cried;
 "Our keels have lain with every sea.
"The dull-returning wind and tide
 "Heave up the wharf where we would be;
"The known and noted breezes swell
"Our trudging sails. Romance, farewell!"

"Good-bye, Romance!" the Skipper said;
 "He vanished with the coal we burn.
"Our dial marks full-steam ahead,
 "Our speed is timed to half a turn.
"Sure as the ferried barge we ply
" 'Twixt port and port. Romance, good-bye!"

"Romance!" the season-tickets mourn,
  "*He* never ran to catch his train,
"But passed with coach and guard and horn—
  "And left the local—late again!"
Confound Romance! . . . And all unseen
Romance brought up the nine-fifteen.

His hand was on the lever laid,
  His oil-can soothed the worrying cranks,
His whistle waked the snowbound grade,
  His fog-horn cut the reeking Banks;
By dock and deep and mine and mill
The Boy-god reckless laboured still!

Robed, crowned and throned, He wove his spell,
  Where heart-blood beat or hearth-smoke curled,
With unconsidered miracle,
  Hedged in a backward-gazing world:
Then taught his chosen bard to say:
"Our King was with us—yesterday!"

TO THOMAS ATKINS

(*Prelude to Barrack-Room Ballads*)

1892

I HAVE made for you a song,
And it may be right or wrong,
But only you can tell me if it's true.
I have tried for to explain
Both your pleasure and your pain,
And, Thomas, here's my best respects to you!

O there'll surely come a day
When they'll give you all your pay,
And treat you as a Christian ought to do;
So, until that day comes round,
Heaven keep you safe and sound,
And, Thomas, here's my best respects to you!

DANNY DEEVER

1890

"WHAT are the bugles blowin' for?" said Files-on-Parade.
"To turn you out, to turn you out," the Colour-Sergeant said.
"What makes you look so white, so white?" said Files-on-Parade.
"I'm dreadin' what I've got to watch," the Colour-Sergeant said.
For they're hangin' Danny Deever, you can hear the Dead March play,
The regiment's in 'ollow square—they're hangin' him to-day;
They've taken of his buttons off an' cut his stripes away,
An' they're hangin' Danny Deever in the mornin'.

"What makes the rear-rank breathe so 'ard?" said Files-on-Parade.
"It's bitter cold, it's bitter cold," the Colour-Sergeant said.
"What makes that front-rank man fall down?" said Files-on-Parade.
"A touch o' sun, a touch o' sun," the Colour-Sergeant said.
They are hangin' Danny Deever, they are marchin' of 'im round,
They 'ave 'alted Danny Deever by 'is coffin on the ground;
An' 'e'll swing in 'arf a minute for a sneakin' shootin' hound—
O they're hangin' Danny Deever in the mornin'!

" 'Is cot was right-'and cot to mine," said Files-on-Parade.
" 'E's sleepin' out an' far to-night," the Colour-Sergeant said.
"I've drunk 'is beer a score o' times," said Files-on-Parade.
" 'E's drinkin' bitter beer alone," the Colour-Sergeant said.
They are hangin' Danny Deever, you must mark 'im to 'is place,
For 'e shot a comrade sleepin'—you must look 'im in the face;
Nine 'undred of 'is county an' the Regiment's disgrace,
While they're hangin' Danny Deever in the mornin'.

"What's that so black agin the sun?" said Files-on-Parade.
"It's Danny fightin' 'ard for life," the Colour-Sergeant said.
"What's that that whimpers over'ead?" said Files-on-Parade.
"It's Danny's soul that's passin' now," the Colour-Sergeant said.
For they're done with Danny Deever, you can 'ear the quickstep play,
The regiment's in column, an' they're marchin' us away;
Ho! the young recruits are shakin', an' they'll want their beer to-day,
After hangin' Danny Deever in the mornin'!

"FUZZY-WUZZY"

(Soudan Expeditionary Force)

1890

WE'VE fought with many men acrost the seas,
An' some of 'em was brave an' some was not:
The Paythan an' the Zulu an' Burmese;
But the Fuzzy was the finest o' the lot.
We never got a ha'porth's change of 'im:
'E squatted in the scrub an' 'ocked our 'orses,
'E cut our sentries up at Sua*kim*,
An' 'e played the cat an' banjo with our forces.
So 'ere's *to* you, Fuzzy-Wuzzy, at your 'ome in the Soudan;
You're a pore benighted 'eathen but a first-class fightin' man;
We gives you your certificate, an' if you want it signed
We'll come an' 'ave a romp with you whenever you're inclined.

We took our chanst among the Kyber 'ills,
The Boers knocked us silly at a mile,
The Burman give us Irriwaddy chills,
An' a Zulu *impi* dished us up in style:
But all we ever got from such as they
Was pop to what the Fuzzy made us swaller;
We 'eld our bloomin' own, the papers say,
But man for man the Fuzzy knocked us 'oller.
Then 'ere's *to* you, Fuzzy-Wuzzy, an' the missis and the kid;
Our orders was to break you, an' of course we went an' did.
We sloshed you with Martinis, an' it wasn't 'ardly fair;
But for all the odds agin' you, Fuzzy-Wuz, you broke the square.

'E 'asn't got no papers of 'is own,
  'E 'asn't got no medals nor rewards,
So *we* must certify the skill 'e's shown,
  In usin' of 'is long two-'anded swords:
When 'e's 'oppin' in an' out among the bush
  With 'is coffin-'eaded shield an' shovel-spear,
An 'appy day with Fuzzy on the rush
  Will last an 'ealthy Tommy for a year.
    So 'ere's *to* you, Fuzzy-Wuzzy, an' your friends which are no more,
    If we 'adn't lost some messmates we would 'elp you to deplore.
    But give an' take's the gospel, an' we'll call the bargain fair,
    For if you 'ave lost more than us, you crumpled up the square!

'E rushes at the smoke when we let drive,
  An', before we know, 'e's 'ackin' at our 'ead;
'E's all 'ot sand an' ginger when alive,
  An' 'e's generally shammin' when 'e's dead.
'E's a daisy, 'e's a ducky, 'e's a lamb!
  'E's a injia-rubber idiot on the spree,
'E's the on'y thing that doesn't give a damn
  For a Regiment o' British Infantree!
    So 'ere's *to* you, Fuzzy-Wuzzy, at your 'ome in the Soudan;
    You're a pore benighted 'eathen but a first-class fightin' man;
    An' 'ere's *to* you, Fuzzy-Wuzzy, with your 'ayrick 'ead of 'air—
    You big black boundin' beggar—for you broke a British square!

GUNGA DIN

1890

You may talk o' gin and beer
When you're quartered safe out 'ere,
An' you're sent to penny-fights an' Aldershot it;
But when it comes to slaughter
You will do your work on water,
An' you'll lick the bloomin' boots of 'im that's got it.
Now in Injia's sunny clime,
Where I used to spend my time
A-servin' of 'Er Majesty the Queen,
Of all them black-faced crew
The finest man I knew
Was our regimental bhisti, Gunga Din.
He was "Din! Din! Din!
"You limpin' lump o' brick-dust, Gunga Din!
"Hi! Slippy *hitherao!*
"Water, get it! *Panee lao*[1]
"You squidgy-nosed old idol, Gunga Din."

The uniform 'e wore
Was nothin' much before,
An' rather less than 'arf o' that be'ind,
For a piece o' twisty rag
An' a goatskin water-bag
Was all the field-equipment 'e could find.
When the sweatin' troop-train lay
In a sidin' through the day,
Where the 'eat would make your bloomin' eyebrows crawl,
We shouted "Harry By!"[2]
Till our throats were bricky-dry,
Then we wopped 'im 'cause 'e couldn't serve us all.
It was "Din! Din! Din!

[1]Bring water swiftly. [2]O Brother.

"You 'eathen, where the mischief 'ave you been?
"You put some *juldee*[1] in it
"Or I'll *marrow*[2] you this minute
"If you don't fill up my helmet, Gunga Din!"

'E would dot an' carry one
Till the longest day was done;
An' 'e didn't seem to know the use o' fear.
If we charged or broke or cut,
You could bet your bloomin' nut,
'E'd be waitin' fifty paces right flank rear.
With 'is mussick[3] on 'is back,
'E would skip with our attack,
An' watch us till the bugles made "Retire"
An' for all 'is dirty 'ide
'E was white, clear white, inside
When 'e went to tend the wounded under fire!
It was "Din! Din! Din!"
With the bullets kickin' dust-spots on the green
When the cartridges ran out,
You could hear the front-ranks shout,
"Hi! ammunition-mules an' Gunga Din!"

I sha'n't forgit the night
When I dropped be'ind the fight
With a bullet where my belt-plate should 'a' been.
I was chokin' mad with thirst,
An' the man that spied me first
Was our good old grinnin', gruntin' Gunga Din.
'E lifted up my 'ead,
An' he plugged me where I bled,
An' 'e guv me 'arf-a-pint o' water green.
It was crawlin' and it stunk,
But of all the drinks I've drunk,
I'm gratefullest to one from Gunga Din.
It was "Din! Din! Din!

[1]Be quick. [2]Hit you. [3]Water-skin.

"'Ere's a beggar with a bullet through 'is spleen;
"'E's chawin' up the ground,
"An' 'e's kickin' all around:
"For Gawd's sake git the water, Gunga Din!"

'E carried me away
To where a dooli lay,
An' a bullet come an' drilled the beggar clean.
'E put me safe inside,
An' just before 'e died,
"I 'ope you liked your drink," sez Gunga Din.
So I'll meet 'im later on
At the place where 'e is gone—
Where it's always double drill and no canteen.
'E'll be squattin' on the coals
Givin' drink to poor damned souls,
An' I'll get a swig in hell from Gunga Din!
Yes, Din! Din! Din!
You Lazarushian-leather Gunga Din!
Though I've belted you and flayed you,
By the livin' Gawd that made you,
You're a better man than I am, Gunga Din!

THE WIDOW AT WINDSOR

1890

'AVE you 'eard o' the Widow at Windsor
With a hairy gold crown on 'er 'ead?
She 'as ships on the foam—she 'as millions at 'ome,
An' she pays us poor beggars in red.
(Ow, poor beggars in red!)

There's 'er nick on the cavalry 'orses,
There's 'er mark on the medical stores—
An' 'er troopers you'll find with a fair wind be'ind
That takes us to various wars.

(Poor beggars!—barbarious wars!)
Then 'ere's to the Widow at Windsor,
An' 'ere's to the stores an' the guns,
The men an' the 'orses what makes up the forces
O' Missis Victorier's sons.
(Poor beggars! Victorier's sons!)

Walk wide o' the Widow at Windsor,
For 'alf o' Creation she owns:
We 'ave bought 'er the same with the sword an' the flame,
An' we've salted it down with our bones.
(Poor beggars!—it's blue with our bones!)
Hands off o' the sons o' the widow,
Hands off o' the goods in 'er shop,
For the Kings must come down an' the Emperors frown
When the Widow at Windsor says "Stop!"
(Poor beggars!—we're sent to say "Stop!")
Then 'ere's to the Lodge o' the Widow,
From the Pole to the Tropics it runs—
To the Lodge that we tile with the rank an' the file,
An' open in form with the guns.
(Poor beggars!—it's always they guns!)

We 'ave 'eard o' the Widow at Windsor,
It's safest to leave 'er alone:
For 'er sentries we stand by the sea an' the land
Wherever the bugles are blown.
(Poor beggars!—an' don't we get blown!)
Take 'old o' the Wings o' the Mornin',
An' flop round the earth till you're dead;
But you won't get away from the tune that they play
To the bloomin' old rag over'ead.
(Poor beggars!—it's 'ot over'ead!)
Then 'ere's to the Sons o' the Widow,
Wherever, 'owever they roam.
'Ere's all they desire, an' if they require
A speedy return to their 'ome.
(Poor beggars!—they'll never see 'ome!)

MANDALAY

1890

BY THE old Moulmein Pagoda, lookin' lazy at the sea,
There's a Burma girl a-settin', and I know she thinks o' me;
For the wind is in the palm-trees, and the temple-bells they say:
"Come you back, you British soldier; come you back to Mandalay!"
Come you back to Mandalay,
Where the old Flotilla lay:
Can't you 'ear their paddles chunkin' from Rangoon to Mandalay?
On the road to Mandalay,
Where the flyin'-fishes play,
An' the dawn comes up like thunder outer China 'crost the Bay!

'Er petticoat was yaller an' 'er little cap was green,
An' 'er name was Supi-yaw-lat—jes' the same as Theebaw's Queen,
An' I seed her first a-smokin' of a whackin' white cheroot,
An' a-wastin' Christian kisses on an 'eathen idol's foot:
Bloomin' idol made o' mud—
Wot they called the Great Gawd Budd—
Plucky lot she cared for idols when I kissed 'er where she stud!
On the road to Mandalay . . .

When the mist was on the rice-fields an' the sun was droppin' slow,
She'd git 'er little banjo an' she'd sing *"Kulla-lo-lo!"*
With 'er arm upon my shoulder an' 'er cheek agin my cheek

We useter watch the steamers an' the *hathis* pilin' teak.
Elephints a-pilin' teak
In the sludgy, squdgy creek,
Where the silence 'ung that 'eavy you was 'arf afraid to speak!
On the road to Mandalay . . .

But that's all shove be'ind me—long ago an' fur away,
An' there ain't no 'busses runnin' from the Bank to Mandalay;
An' I'm learnin' 'ere in London what the ten-year soldier tells:
"If you've 'eard the East a-callin', you won't never 'eed naught else."
No! you won't 'eed nothin' else
But them spicy garlic smells,
An' the sunshine an' the palm-trees an' the tinkly temple-bells;
On the road to Mandalay . . .

I am sick o' wastin' leather on these gritty pavin'-stones,
An' the blasted English drizzle wakes the fever in my bones;
Tho' I walks with fifty 'ousemaids outer Chelsea to the Strand,
An' they talks a lot o' lovin', but wot do they understand?
Beefy face an' grubby 'and—
Law! wot do they understand?
I've a neater, sweeter maiden in a cleaner, greener land!
On the road to Mandalay . . .

Ship me somewheres east of Suez, where the best is like the worst,
Where there aren't no Ten Commandments an' a man can raise a thirst;
For the temple-bells are callin', an' it's there that I would be—

By the old Moulmein Pagoda, looking lazy at the sea;
On the road to Mandalay,
Where the old Flotilla lay,
With our sick beneath the awnings when we went to Mandalay!
O the road to Mandalay,
Where the flyin'-fishes play,
An' the dawn comes up like thunder outer China 'crost the Bay!

THE LADIES
1896

I'VE taken my fun where I've found it;
I've rogued an' I've ranged in my time;
I've 'ad my pickin' o' sweethearts,
An' four o' the lot was prime.
One was an 'arf-caste widow,
One was a woman at Prome,
One was the wife of a *jemadar-sais*,[1]
An' one is a girl at 'ome.

Now I aren't no 'and with the ladies,
For, takin' 'em all along,
You never can say till you've tried 'em,
An' then you are like to be wrong.
There's times when you'll think that you mightn't,
There's times when you'll know that you might;
But the things you will learn from the Yellow an' Brown,
They'll 'elp you a lot with the White!

I was a young un at 'Oogli,
Shy as a girl to begin;
Aggie de Castrer she made me,
An' Aggie was clever as sin;

[1]Head-groom.

Older than me, but my first un—
  More like a mother she were—
Showed me the way to promotion an' pay,
  An' I learned about women from 'er!

Then I was ordered to Burma,
  Actin' in charge o' Bazar,
An' I got me a tiddy live 'eathen
  Through buyin' supplies off 'er pa.
Funny an' yellow an' faithful—
  Doll in a teacup she were—
But we lived on the square, like a true-married pair,
  An' I learned about women from 'er!

Then we was shifted to Neemuch
  (Or I might ha' been keepin' 'er now),
An' I took with a shiny she-devil,
  The wife of a nigger at Mhow;
'Taught me the gipsy-folks' *bolee;*[1]
  Kind o' volcano she were,
For she knifed me one night 'cause I wished she was white,
  And I learned about women from 'er!

Then I come 'ome in a trooper,
  'Long of a kid o' sixteen—
'Girl from a convent at Meerut,
  The straightest I ever 'ave seen.
Love at first sight was 'er trouble,
  She didn't know what it were;
An' I wouldn't do such, 'cause I liked 'er too much,
  But—I learned about women from 'er!

I've taken my fun where I've found it,
  An' now I must pay for my fun,
For the more you 'ave known o' the others
  The less will you settle to one;

[1]Slang.

An' the end of it's sittin' and thinkin',
  An' dreamin' Hell-fires to see;
So be warned by my lot (which I know you will not),
  An' learn about women from me!

What did the Colonel's Lady think?
  Nobody never knew.
Somebody asked the Sergeant's Wife,
  An' *she told 'em true!*
When you get to a man in the case,
  They're like as a row of pins—
For the Colonel's Lady an' Judy O'Grady
  Are sisters under their skins!

"FOLLOW ME 'OME"

1894

THERE was no one like 'im, 'Orse or Foot,
  Nor any o' the Guns I knew;
An' because it was so, why, o' course 'e went an' died,
  Which is just what the best men do.

So it's knock out your pipes an' follow me!
An' it's finish up your swipes an' follow me!
  Oh, 'ark to the big drum callin',
    Follow me—follow me 'ome!

'Is mare she neighs the 'ole day long,
  She paws the 'ole night through,
An' she won't take 'er feed 'cause o' waitin' for 'is step,
  Which is just what a beast would do.

'Is girl she goes with a bombardier
  Before 'er month is through;
An' the banns are up in church, for she's got the beggar hooked,
  Which is just what a girl would do.

We fought 'bout a dog—last week it were—
No more than a round or two;
But I strook 'im cruel 'ard, an' I wish I 'adn't now,
Which is just what a man can't do.

'E was all that I 'ad in the way of a friend,
An' I've 'ad to find one new;
But I'd give my pay an' stripe for to get the beggar back,
Which it's just too late to do!

So it's knock out your pipes an' follow me!
An' it's finish up your swipes an' follow me!
Oh, 'ark to the fifes a-crawlin'!
Follow me—follow me 'ome!

Take 'im away! 'E's gone where the best men go.
Take 'im away! An' the gun-wheels turnin' slow.
Take 'im away! There's more from the place 'e come.
Take 'im away, with the limber an' the drum.

For it's "Three rounds blank" an' follow me,
An' it's "Thirteen rank" an' follow me;
Oh, passin' the love o' women,
Follow me—follow me 'ome!

"MARY, PITY WOMEN!"
1896

YOU call yourself a man,
For all you used to swear,
An' leave me, as you can,
My certain shame to bear?
I 'ear! You do not care—
You done the worst you know.
I 'ate you, grinnin' there. . . .
Aw, Gawd, I love you so!

Nice while it lasted, an' now it is over—
Tear out your 'eart an' good-bye to your lover!
What's the use o' grievin', when the mother that bore you
(Mary, pity women!) knew it all before you?

It aren't no false alarm,
The finish to your fun;
You—you 'ave brung the 'arm,
An' I'm the ruined one!
An' now you'll off an' run
With some new fool in tow.
Your 'eart? You 'aven't none. . . .
Ah, Gawd, I love you so!

When a man is tired there is naught will bind 'im;
All 'e solemn promised 'e will shove be'ind 'im.
What's the good o' prayin' for The Wrath to strike 'im
(Mary, pity women!), when the rest are like 'im?

What 'ope for me or—it?
What's left for us to do?
I've walked with men a bit,
But this—but this is you.
So 'elp me, Christ, it's true!
Where can I 'ide or go?
You coward through and through! . . .
Ah, Gawd, I love you so!

All the more you give 'em the less are they for givin'—
Love lies dead, an' you cannot kiss 'im livin'.
Down the road 'e led you there is no returnin'
(Mary, pity women!), but you're late in learnin'!

You'd like to treat me fair?
You can't, because we're pore?
We'd starve? What do I care!
We might, but *this* is shore!
I want the name—no more—

The name, an' lines to show,
An' not to be an 'ore. . . .
Ah, Gawd, I love you so!

What's the good o' pleadin', when the mother that bore you
(Mary, pity women!) knew it all before you?
Sleep on 'is promises an' wake to your sorrow
(Mary, pity women!), for we sail to-morrow!

"FOR TO ADMIRE"
1894

THE Injian Ocean sets an' smiles
So sof', so bright, so bloomin' blue;
There aren't a wave for miles an' miles
Excep' the jiggle from the screw.
The ship is swep', the day is done,
The bugle's gone for smoke and play;
An' black ag'in the settin' sun
The Lascar sings, "*Hum deckty hai!*"[1]

For to admire an' for to see,
For to be'old this world so wide—
It never done no good to me,
But I can't drop it if I tried!

I see the sergeants pitchin' quoits,
I 'ear the women laugh an' talk,
I spy upon the quarter-deck
The orficers an' lydies walk.
I thinks about the things that was,
An' leans and looks acrost the sea,
Till, spite of all the crowded ship,
There's no one lef' alive but me.

[1]I'm looking out.

The things that was which I 'ave seen,
  In barrick, camp, an' action too,
I tells them over by myself,
  An' sometimes wonders if they're true;
For they was odd—most awful odd—
  But all the same now they are o'er,
There must be 'eaps o' plenty such,
  An' if I wait I'll see some more.

Oh, I 'ave come upon the books,
  An' frequent broke a barrick-rule,
An' stood beside an' watched myself
  Be'avin' like a bloomin' fool.
I paid my price for findin' out,
  Nor never grutched the price I paid,
But sat in Clink without my boots,
  Admirin' 'ow the world was made.

Be'old a cloud upon the beam,
  An' 'umped above the sea appears
Old Aden, like a barrick-stove
  That no one's lit for years an' years.
I passed by that when I began,
  An' I go 'ome the road I came,
A time-expired soldier-man
  With six years' service to 'is name.

My girl she said, "Oh, stay with me!"
  My mother 'eld me to 'er breast.
They've never written none, an' so
  They must 'ave gone with all the rest—
With all the rest which I 'ave seen
  An' found an' known an' met along.
I cannot say the things I feel,
  And so I sing my evenin' song:

For to admire an' for to see,
For to be'old this world so wide—
It never done no good to me,
But I can't drop it if I tried!

BOOTS

(Infantry Columns)

1903

We're foot—slog—slog—slog—sloggin' over Africa
Foot—foot—foot—foot—sloggin' over Africa—
(Boots—boots—boots—boots—movin' up and down again!)
There's no discharge in the war!

Seven—six—eleven—five—nine-an'-twenty mile to-day—
Four—eleven—seventeen—thirty-two the day before—
(Boots—boots—boots—boots—movin' up and down again!)
There's no discharge in the war!

Don't—don't—don't—don't—look at what's in front of you.
(Boots—boots—boots—boots—movin' up an' down again);
Men—men—men—men—men go mad with watchin' 'em,
An' there's no discharge in the war!

Try—try—try—try—to think o' something different—
Oh—my—God—keep—me from goin' lunatic!
(Boots—boots—boots—boots—movin' up an' down again!)
There's no discharge in the war!

Count—count—count—count—the bullets in the bandoliers.
If—your—eyes—drop—they will get atop o' you!
(Boots—boots—boots—boots—movin' up an' down again)—
There's no discharge in the war!

We—can—stick—out—'unger, thirst, an' weariness,
But—not—not—not—not the chronic sight of 'em—
Boots—boots—boots—boots—movin' up an' down again,
An' there's no discharge in the war!

'Tain't—so—bad—by—day because o' company,
But night—brings—long—strings—o' forty thousand million
Boots—boots—boots—boots—movin' up an' down again.
There's no discharge in the war!

I—'ave—marched—six—weeks in 'Ell an' certify
It—is—not—fire—devils, dark, or anything,
But boots—boots—boots—boots—movin' up an' down again,
An' there's no discharge in the war!

THE CHILDREN'S SONG
1906

LAND of our Birth, we pledge to thee
Our love and toil in the years to be;
When we are grown and take our place,
As men and women with our race.

Father in Heaven who lovest all,
Oh help Thy children when they call;
That they may build from age to age,
An undefiled heritage.

Teach us to bear the yoke in youth,
With steadfastness and careful truth;
That, in our time, Thy Grace may give
The Truth whereby the Nations live.

Teach us to rule ourselves alway,
Controlled and cleanly night and day;
That we may bring, if need arise,
No maimed or worthless sacrifice.

Teach us to look in all our ends,
On Thee for judge, and not our friends;
That we, with Thee, may walk uncowed
By fear or favour of the crowd.

Teach us the Strength that cannot seek,
By deed or thought, to hurt the weak;
That, under Thee, we may possess
Man's strength to comfort man's distress.

Teach us Delight in simple things,
And Mirth that has no bitter springs;
Forgiveness free of evil done,
And Love to all men 'neath the sun!

Land of our Birth, our faith, our pride,
For whose dear sake our fathers died;
Oh Motherland, we pledge to thee,
Head, heart, and hand through the years to be!

THE PRODIGAL SON

(*Western Version*)

1901

HERE come I to my own again,
Fed, forgiven and known again,
Claimed by bone of my bone again
And cheered by flesh of my flesh.
The fatted calf is dressed for me,
But the husks have greater zest for me.
I think my pigs will be best for me,
So I'm off to the Yards afresh.

I never was very refined, you see,
(And it weighs on my brother's mind, you see)
But there's no reproach among swine, d'you see,
For being a bit of a swine.
So I'm off with wallet and staff to eat
The bread that is three parts chaff to wheat,
But glory be!—there's a laugh to it,
Which isn't the case when we dine.

My father glooms and advises me,
My brother sulks and despises me,
And Mother catechizes me
Till I want to go out and swear.
And, in spite of the butler's gravity,
I know that the servants have it I
Am a monster of moral depravity,
And I'm damned if I think it's fair!

I wasted my substance, I know I did,
On riotous living, so I did,
But there's nothing on record to show I did
More than my betters have done.
They talk of the money I spent out there—
They hint at the pace that I went out there—
But they all forget I was sent out there
Alone as a rich man's son.

So I was a mark for plunder at once,
And lost my cash (can you wonder?) at once,
But I didn't give up and knock under at once.
I worked in the Yards, for a spell,
Where I spent my nights and my days with hogs
And shared their milk and maize with hogs,
Till, I guess, I have learned what pays with hogs
And—I have that knowledge to sell!

So back I go to my job again,
Not so easy to rob again,
Or quite so ready to sob again
On any neck that's around.
I'm leaving, Pater. Good-bye to you!
God bless you, Mater! I'll write to you. . . .
I wouldn't be impolite to you,
But, Brother, you *are* a hound!

MOTHER O' MINE
1891

IF I WERE hanged on the highest hill,
Mother o' mine, O mother o' mine!
I know whose love would follow me still,
Mother o' mine, O mother o' mine!

If I were drowned in the deepest sea,
Mother o' mine, O mother o' mine!
I know whose tears would come down to me,
Mother o' mine, O mother o' mine!

If I were damned of body and soul,
I know whose prayers would make me whole,
Mother o' mine, O mother o' mine!

THE GLORY OF THE GARDEN
1911

OUR England is a garden that is full of stately views,
Of borders, beds and shrubberies and lawns and avenues,
With statues on the terraces and peacocks strutting by;
But the Glory of the Garden lies in more than meets the eye.

For where the old thick laurels grow, along the thin red wall,
You find the tool- and potting-sheds which are the heart of all;
The cold-frames and the hot-houses, the dungpits and the tanks,
The rollers, carts and drain-pipes, with the barrows and the planks.

And there you'll see the gardeners, the men and 'prentice boys
Told off to do as they are bid and do it without noise;
For, except when seeds are planted and we shout to scare the birds,
The Glory of the Garden it abideth not in words.

And some can pot begonias and some can bud a rose,
And some are hardly fit to trust with anything that grows;
But they can roll and trim the lawns and sift the sand and loam,
For the Glory of the Garden occupieth all who come.

Our England is a garden, and such gardens are not made
By singing:—"Oh, how beautiful!" and sitting in the shade,
While better men than we go out and start their working lives
At grubbing weeds from gravel-paths with broken dinner-knives.

There's not a pair of legs so thin, there's not a head so thick,
There's not a hand so weak and white, nor yet a heart so sick,
But it can find some job that's crying to be done,
For the Glory of the Garden glorifieth every one.

Then seek your job with thankfulness and work till further orders,
If it's only netting strawberries or killing slugs on borders;
And when your back stops aching and your hands begin to harden,
You will find yourself a partner in the Glory of the Garden.

Oh, Adam was a gardener, and God who made him sees
That half a proper gardener's work is done upon his knees,
So when your work is finished, you can wash your hands and pray
For the Glory of the Garden, that it may not pass away!
And the glory of the Garden it shall never pass away!

THE GODS OF THE COPYBOOK HEADINGS
1919

As I PASS through my incarnations in every age and race,
I make my proper prostrations to the Gods of the Market Place.
Peering through reverent fingers I watch them flourish and fall,
And the Gods of the Copybook Headings, I notice, outlast them all.

We were living in trees when they met us. They showed us each in turn
That Water would certainly wet us, as Fire would certainly burn:
But we found them lacking in Uplift, Vision and Breadth of Mind,
So we left them to teach the Gorillas while we followed the March of Mankind.

We moved as the Spirit listed. *They* never altered their pace,
Being neither cloud nor wind-borne like the Gods of the Market Place,
But they always caught up with our progress, and presently word would come
That a tribe had been wiped off its icefield, or the lights had gone out in Rome.

With the Hopes that our World is built on they were utterly
out of touch,
They denied that the Moon was Stilton; they denied she was
even Dutch;
They denied that Wishes were Horses; they denied that a Pig
had Wings;
So we worshipped the Gods of the Market Who promised
these beautiful things.

When the Cambrian measures were forming, They promised
perpetual peace.
They swore, if we gave them our weapons, that the wars of
the tribes would cease.
And when we disarmed They sold us and delivered us bound
to our foe,
And the Gods of the Copybook Headings said: *"Stick to the
Devil you know."*

On the first Feminian Sandstones we were promised the Fuller
Life
(Which started by loving our neighbour and ended by loving
his wife)
Till our women had no more children and the men lost reason
and faith,
And the Gods of the Copybook Headings said: *"The Wages
of Sin is Death."*

In the Carboniferous Epoch we were promised abundance for
all,
By robbing selected Peter to pay for collective Paul;
But, though we had plenty of money, there was nothing our
money could buy,
And the Gods of the Copybook Headings said: *"If you don't
work you die."*

Then the Gods of the Market tumbled, and their smooth-
tongued wizards withdrew,

And the hearts of the meanest were humbled and began to believe it was true
That All is not Gold that Glitters, and Two and Two make Four—
And the Gods of the Copybook Headings limped up to explain it once more.

. . . .

As it will be in the future, it was at the birth of Man—
There are only four things certain since Social Progress began:—
That the Dog returns to his Vomit and the Sow returns to her Mire,
And the burnt Fool's bandaged finger goes wabbling back to the Fire;

And that after this is accomplished, and the brave new world begins
When all men are paid for existing and no man must pay for his sins,
As surely as Water will wet us, as surely as Fire will burn,
The Gods of the Copybook Headings with terror and slaughter return!

THE SCHOLARS
1919

"Some hundreds of the younger naval officers whose education was interrupted by the War are now to be sent to various colleges at Cambridge to continue their studies. The experiment will be watched with great interest."—DAILY PAPERS.

"Oh, show me how a rose can shut and be a bud again!"
Nay, watch my Lords of the Admiralty, for they have the work in train.
They have taken the men that were careless lads at Dartmouth in 'Fourteen
And entered them in the landward schools as though no war had been.
They have piped the children off all the seas from the Falklands to the Bight,
And quartered them on the Colleges to learn to read and write!

Their books were rain and sleet and fog—the dry gale and the snow,
Their teachers were the hornèd mines and the hump-backed Death below.
Their schools were walled by the walking mist and roofed by the waiting skies,
When they conned their task in a new-sown field with the Moonlight Sacrifice.
They were not rated too young to teach, nor reckoned unfit to guide
When they formed their class on Helle's beach at the bows of the "River Clyde."

Their eyes are sunk by endless watch, their faces roughed by the spray,

Their feet are drawn by the wet sea-boots they changed not night or day
When they guarded the six-knot convoy's flank on the road to Norroway.
Their ears are stuffed with the week-long roar of the West-Atlantic gale
When the sloops were watching the Irish Shore from Galway to Kinsale.
Their hands are scored where the life-lines cut or the dripping funnel-stays
When they followed their leader at thirty knot between the Skaw and The Naze.
Their mouths are filled with the magic words they learned at the collier's hatch
When they coaled in the foul December dawns and sailed in the forenoon-watch;
Or measured the weight of a Pentland tide and the wind off Ronaldshay,
Till the target mastered the breathless tug and the hawser carried away.
They know the price to be paid for a fault—for a gauge-clock wrongly read,
Or a picket-boat to the gangway brought bows-on and full-ahead,
Or the drowsy second's lack of thought that costs a dozen dead.

They have touched a knowledge outreaching speech—as when the cutters were sent
To harvest the dreadful mile of beach after the "Vanguard" went.
They have learned great faith and little fear and a high heart in distress,
And how to suffer each sodden year of heaped-up weariness.
They have borne the bridle upon their lips and the yoke upon their neck,

Since they went down to the sea in ships to save the world from wreck—
Since the chests were slung down the College stair at Dartmouth in 'Fourteen,
And now they are quit of the sea-affair as though no war had been.
Far have they steamed and much have they known, and most would they fain forget;
But now they are come to their joyous own with all the world in their debt.

. . . .

Soft—blow soft on them, little East Wind! Be smooth for them, mighty stream!
Though the cams they use are not of your kind, and they bump, for choice, by steam.
Lightly dance with them, Newnham maid—but none too lightly believe.
They are hot from the fifty-month blockade, and they carry their hearts on their sleeve.
Tenderly, Proctor, let them down, if they do not walk as they should:
For, by God, if they owe you half a crown, you owe 'em your four years' food!

. . . .

Hallowed River, most gracious Trees, Chapel beyond compare,
Here be gentlemen tired of the seas—take them into your care.
Far have they come, much have they braved. Give them their hour of play,
While the hidden things their hands have saved work for them day by day:
Till the grateful Past their youth redeemed return them their youth once more,
And the Soul of the Child at last lets fall the unjust load that it bore!

SUPPLICATION OF THE BLACK ABERDEEN

1928

I PRAY! My little body and whole span
Of years is Thine, my Owner and my Man.
For Thou hast made me—unto Thee I owe
This dim, distressed half-soul that hurts me so,
Compact of every crime, but, none the less,
Broken by knowledge of its naughtiness.
Put me not from Thy Life—'tis all I know.
If Thou forsake me, whither shall I go?

Thine is the Voice with which my Day begins:
Thy Foot my refuge, even in my sins.
Thine Honour hurls me forth to testify
Against the Unclean and Wicked passing by.
(But when Thou callest they are of Thy Friends,
Who readier than I to make amends?)
I was Thy Deputy with high and low—
If Thou dismiss me, whither shall I go?

I have been driven forth on gross offence
That took no reckoning of my penitence.
And, in my desolation—faithless me!—
Have crept for comfort to a woman's knee!
Now I return, self-drawn, to meet the just
Reward of Riot, Theft and Breach of Trust.
Put me not from Thy Life—though this is so.
If Thou forsake me, whither shall I go?

Into The Presence, flattening while I crawl—
From head to tail, I do confess it all.
Mine was the fault—deal me the stripes—but spare
The Pointed Finger which I cannot bear!
The Dreadful Tone in which my Name is named.
That sends me 'neath the sofa-frill ashamed!
(Yet, to be near Thee, I would face that woe.)
If Thou reject me, whither shall I go?

Can a gift turn Thee? I will bring mine all—
My Secret Bone, my Throwing-Stick, my Ball.
Or wouldst Thou sport? Then watch me hunt awhile,
Chasing, not after conies, but Thy Smile,
Content, as breathless on the turf I sit,
Thou shouldst deride my little legs and wit—
Ah! Keep me in Thy Life for a fool's show!
If Thou deny me, whither shall I go? . . .

Is the Dark gone? The Light of Eyes restored?
The Countenance turned meward, O my Lord?
The Paw accepted, and—for all to see—
The Abject Sinner throned upon the Knee?
The Ears bewrung, and Muzzle scratched because
He is forgiven, and All is as It was? . . .
Now am I in Thy Life, and since 'tis so—
That Cat awaits the Judgment. May I go?

Made in the USA
Middletown, DE
30 December 2020

Tips

Cruces

This book was typeset using the amazing LaTeX typesetting system and the wonderful `memoir` book-making package. A heartfelt thank you to the legions of programmers who have contributed to this powerful tool over the many years of its development.

All of the graphs and figures in the book were generated using a Python-based version of `zplot`, a simple and useful tool developed by R. Arpaci-Dusseau to generate graphs in PostScript. The `zplot` tool arose after many years of frustration with existing graphing tools such as `gnuplot` (which was limited) and `ploticus` (which was overly complex though admittedly quite awesome). As a result, R. A-D finally put his years of study of PostScript to good use and developed `zplot`.